英 语 大 书 虫
世界文学名著文库

鲁滨逊漂流记

（英）笛福　著

英语学习大书虫研究室　译

伊犁人民出版社·YILI PEOPLE'S PRESS

责任编辑:韩新帮

图书在版编目(CIP)数据
世界文学名著英汉对照全译精选/王惠君,王惠玲译
奎屯:伊犁人民出版社,2001.3
ISBN 7 - 5425 - 0570 - X

Ⅰ.世… Ⅱ.①王… ② 王… Ⅲ.英语——对照读物,
小说—英、汉 Ⅳ.H319.4;Ⅰ

中国版本图书馆 CIP 数据核字(2001)第 15738 号

英语大书虫世界文学名著文库
——世界文学名著英汉对照全译精选
王惠君,王惠玲 译

伊犁人民出版社出版发行
(奎屯北京西路 28 号 邮编 833200)
各地新华书店经销 中牟胶印厂印刷
880×1230 毫米 32 开 450 印张 10000 千字
2001 年 4 月第 1 版 2001 年 4 月第 1 次印刷
印数:1—3000 套

ISBN 7 - 5425 - 0570 - X/Ⅰ·230
定价:588.80 元

如有印装问题,请直接同承印厂调换

英语大书虫世界文学名著文库翻译委员会

导　读

　　《鲁滨逊漂流记》的作者丹尼尔·笛福一六六〇年出生于伦敦一个商人家庭。他的长篇小说都是在晚年写的,他的作品《鲁滨逊漂流记》、《摩尔·弗兰德斯》等对英国及欧洲小说的发展起了巨大的作用,被誉为"英国与欧洲的小说之父"。他在写《鲁滨逊漂流记》以前也许从来没想当个文学家,他是一个事业家,一个活动家。他经营商业,从事过内衣业,烟酒贸易,还开过砖瓦厂,经历过破产,但屡次失败,屡次开始,直到老年还未死心。在经营商业的同时,他还从事政治活动,往返于伦敦与爱丁堡的路上。因为言论关系,几次被捕。他参加过的报刊不下四五种,仅那些已判明确是他写的文章,就已达到惊人的数量。他的精力是极端旺盛的。他的一切经历都给《鲁滨逊漂流记》准备下了思想和技巧的条件,这部书的成功决不是偶然的。据说,除了《圣经》之外,《鲁滨逊漂流记》是再版最多的一本书。今天,该书被誉为英国文学史上的第一部长篇小说,成了世界文学宝库中一部不朽的名著。

　　《鲁滨逊漂流记》是笛福受一个真实故事的启发而写成的。十八世纪一个英国船上的苏格兰水手,名叫亚历山大·塞尔柯克,在航行中和船长发生冲突,被遗弃在一个距智利海岸约五百海里,周围约三十六海里的荒岛上,此岛被称作安·菲南德岛。他在那里与世完全隔绝,独自生活了四年零四个月,才被有名的航海家渥地士·罗吉斯发现,并于一七一一年将他带回英国。这件事在当时引起社会上很大的兴趣。从未写过什么文学作品,年近六旬的笛福,从这件事得到了很大的启发,从而创作了《鲁滨逊漂流记》这部不朽的杰作。这个苏格兰水手在荒岛上并没有什么值得称道的事迹,只不过做了一些为了生存必须做的事。整个说来,他在岛上的行为是消极的而不是进取的。但笛福塑造的鲁滨逊却是一个新兴资产阶级的代表人物,一个理想化的英雄。他宣传的不是知足常乐,而是要发展,要劳动、要占有。在这个人物身上体现了西方海洋文明的传统,充满向外发展的好奇心、征服欲和冒险精神,歌颂了人的坚毅品质和劳动精神。这部小说开辟了英国现实主义小说的道路。

《鲁滨逊漂流记》的故事梗概大致如下:

鲁滨逊·克鲁索出生于英国约克郡一个中产阶级家庭。由于他一心想遨游四海、了解世界。终于不听父亲的劝告而离家去做船员。他在非洲沿岸遭海盗袭击成了奴隶,由于生活难以忍受他趁机乘坐一条小船逃跑了。一艘葡萄牙货船搭救了他,并把他平安地运到了巴西。在巴西他经营种植业并发了财。当有人向他建议一起出海到非洲贩运黑奴时,他又一次屈服于自己的向往,踏上了去非洲的航海之途。途中突遇风暴,船上只有他一人幸免于难,漂流到一个荒岛上得救。他从遇难船上运出粮食、衣物、工具等物,开始了在岛上的独立生活。《圣经》成为他的精神支柱,凭着惊人的毅力和顽强不息的劳动,他盖起了房子,收获谷物,驯养山羊,用兽皮制作皮物。后来他搭救了一个野人,把他收做仆人,为他取名星期五。其间又经历了无数的风风雨雨,一直到第二十八个年头一艘英国船来到该岛附近,鲁滨逊帮助船长制服了叛乱的水手,才返回英国。这时,他的父母已辞别人世。鲁滨逊收回他在巴西的种植园的全部收益,并把其中的一部分赠给那些帮助过他的人们。

英国一位批评家说:"人们如果要重新抓住年轻的、革命的上升时期的旺盛而自信的精神,那么最好的引导莫过于笛福与《鲁滨逊漂流记》。"的确,作为新时代的典型的冒险家、实干家、殖民者,鲁滨逊在启蒙主义文学史上,在世界古典名著史上永远占有一席之地。

译　者

二〇〇一年二月

Part 1

I was born in the Year 1632, in the City of York, of a good Family, tho' not ofthat Country, my Father being a Foreigner of Bremen, who settled first at Hull: He got a good Estate by Merchandise, and leaving off his Trade, lived afterward at York, from whence he had married my Mother, Relations were named Robinson, a very good Family at Country, and from whom I was called Robinson Keutznaer; but by the usual Corruption of Words in England, we are now called, nay we call our Selves, and writer Name Crusoe, and so my Companions always call'd me.

I had two elder Brothers, one of which was Lieutenant Collonel to an English Regiment of Foot in Flanders, formerly commanded by the famous Coll. Lockhart, and was killed at the Battle near Dunkirk against the Spaniards: What became of my second Brother I never knew any more than Father or Mother did know what was become of me.

Being the third Son of the Family, and not bred to any Trade, my Head began to be fill'd very early with rambling Thoughts: My Father, who was very ancient, had given me competent Share of Learning, as far as House-Education, and a Country Free-School generally goes, and design'd for the Law; but I would be satisfied with nothing but go to Sea, and my inclination to this led me so strongly against the Will, nay the Commands of my Father, and against all the Entreaties and Perswasions of my Mother and other Friends, that there seem'd to be something fatal in Propension of Nature tending directly to the Life of Misery

第 一 部

一六三二年,我出生于约克城一个上流社会家庭。我们不是本地人,我父亲是来自不来梅市的外国人,他先是住在赫尔市,经商发家后金盆洗手,定居到约克城。在那儿,他娶了我母亲。母亲娘家姓鲁滨逊,是该城的名门望族,于是我便取名鲁滨逊·克罗伊茨内;可是由于英国人一读"克罗伊茨内"这个词就走样,变成了"克鲁索",所以我们就这么叫,这么写了,我的朋友们也都这样称呼我。

我有两个哥哥,一个哥哥是驻佛兰德斯的英国步兵团的中校,他的部队早先曾被著名的罗加特上校率领过。后来这个哥哥因为跟西班牙人打仗,在但刻尔克附近阵亡。至于我第二个哥哥的下落如何,我至今还毫无所知,正像我父亲和母亲后来不知道我的下落一样。

我是家里的小儿子,父母亲没让我学谋生的手艺,因此我从小只是喜欢胡思乱想,一心想出洋远游。当时,我父亲年事已高,但他还是让我受了相当不错的教育。他曾送我去寄宿学校就读,还让我上免费学校接受乡村义务教育,一心一意想要我将来学法律。但我对一切都没有兴趣,只是想航海。这一愿望,不仅使我坚决地抵制父亲的意愿,甚至违抗父命,也使我对母亲和一

which was to befal me.

My Father, a wise and grave Man, gave me serious excellent Counsel against what he foresaw was my Design. He call'd me one Morning into his Chamber, where he confined by the Gout, and expostulated very warmly me upon this Subject: He ask'd me what Reasons more a meer wandring inclination I had for leaving my Father House and my native Country, where I might be well introduced, and had a Prospect of raising my Fortunes Application and Industry, with a Life of Ease and Pleasure He told me it was for Men of desperate Fortunes on one Hand, or of aspiring, Superior Fortunes on the other, who went abroad upon Adventures, to rise by Enterprize, and make themselves famous in Undertakings of a Nature out of the common Road; that these things were all either too far above me, or too far below me; that mine was the middle State, or what might be called the upper Station of Low Life, which he had found by long Experience was the best State in the World, the most suited to human Happiness, not exposed to the Miseries and Hardships, the Labour and Sufferings of the mechanick Part of Mankind, and not embarass'd with the Pride, Luxury, Ambition and Envy of the upper Part of Mankind. He told me, I might judge of the Happiness of this State, by this one thing, viz. That this was the State of Life which all other People envied, that Kings have frequently lamented the miserable Consequences of being born to great things, and wish'd they had been placed in the Middle of the two Extremes, between Mean and the Great; that the wise Man gave his Testimony to this as the just Standard of true Felicity, when he pray to have neither Poverty or Riches.

He bid me observe it, and I should always find,

切亲友的央求和规劝充耳不闻;看来,这种一意孤行的脾气实在糟糕透顶,结果就直接酿成了我后来的不幸生活。

我那睿智而严肃的父亲充分预料到我的梦想将会给我带来的不幸,对我进行了一番认真的、苦口婆心的劝告。一天早上,他把我叫到他的房间,倍受痛风折磨而不能出门的父亲和蔼地对我说,他想知道,除了天性好游荡之外,我究竟为什么非要离开自己的家和家乡。在这里,我不愁没人引荐,靠实干和勤奋,能得到一个美好的前程,过上快乐而舒适的日子。他告诉我,那些到海外去冒险、去创业,或是想以此扬名的人,一种是穷途末路之人,另一种便是充满野心之人。这两种情况,对我来说,是高不就低不成。他说我的社会地位居于两者之间,也可称作中间阶层。以他长期的社会经验,他认为这恰是世界上最理想的阶层,最能予人以幸福。这不同于那些体力劳动者那样吃苦受累,也不像那些上层阔人那样,被骄奢、野心、猜忌所充斥而感到烦恼。

他叫我应时刻注意到,生

that the Calamitles of Life were shared among the upper and lower Part of Mankind; but that the middle Station had the fewest Disasters, and was not expos'd to so many Vicisitudes as the higher or lower Part of Mankind; nay, they were not subjected to so many Distempers and Uneasiness either of Body or Mind, as those were who, by vicious Living, Luxury and Extravagancies on one Hand, or by hard Labour, Want of Necessaries, and mean or insufficient Diet on the other Hand, bring Distempers upon themselves by the natural Consequences of their Way of Living; That the middle Station of Life was calculated for, all kind of Vertues and all kinds of Enjoyments; that Peace and Plenty were the Hand-maids of a middle Fortune; that Temperance, Moderation, Quietness, Health, Society, all agreeable Diversions, and all desirable Pleasures, were the Blessings attending the middle Station of Life; that this Way Men went silently and smoothly thro' the World, and comfortably out of it, not embarass'd with the Labours of the Hands or of the Head, not sold to the Life of Slavery for daily Bread, or harrast with perplex'd Circumstances, which rob the Soul of Peace, and the Body of Rest; not enrag'd with the Passion of Envy, or secret burning Lust of Ambition for great things; but in easy Circumstances sliding gently thro' the World, and sensibly tasting the Sweets of living, without the bitter, feeling that they are happy, and learning by every Day's Experience to know it more sensibly.

After this, he press'd me earnestly, and in the most affectionate manner, not to play the young Man, not to precipitate my self into Miseries which Nature and the Station of Life I was born in, seem'd to have provided against; that I was under no Necessity of seeking my Bread; that he would do well for me, and endeavour to enter me fairly into the Station of Life which he had been just recommending to me; and that if I was not

活中的苦恼和不幸老是发生在上层与下层中;而处于中间阶层生活状态的人,他们却几乎不会遇上灾难,也不会像处于高层和低层的人那样,经受那么多的冷暖变更。进一步地说,处于中间阶层的人们,不必像上层人士那样,因罪恶奢华、挥霍无度的生活而身心失衡,也不会像下层庶民那样,因终日劳累、少吃少穿而愁苦不堪。又说,只有中间阶层才有福气享受一切美德和安乐;安定和富裕可以说是中产之家的随身侍女。他说,遇事不过分,中庸克己,宁静健康,愉快的交游,各种令人欢喜的消遣,各种称心如意的乐趣,所有这些幸福都属于中间阶层的人;在这种环境里,人人都可以悠然自适地过一辈子,既用不着劳力劳心,为每日的面包去过奴隶生活,困难不堪,弄得身心没有片刻的安宁;也用不着被欲望和发大财、成大名的野心所苦,心劳日拙;只不过舒舒服服地过日子,品尝着生活的甜美滋味,而且愈来愈能体会到自己的幸福。

接着,他态度诚挚、充满慈爱地劝我不要孩子气,不要急于自讨苦吃;因为,不论从人之常情来说,还是从我的家庭出身而言,都不会让我吃苦。他说,我不必为每日生计去操劳,他会为我作好一切安排,并将尽力让我过上前面所说的中间阶层的生活。如果

very easy and happy in the World, it must be my meer, Fate or Fault that must hinder it, and that he should have nothing to answer for, having thus discharg'd his Duty in warning me against Measures which he knew would be to my Hurt: In a word, that as he would do very kind things for me if I would stay and settle at Home as he directed, so he would not have so much Hand in my Misfortunes, as to give me any Encouragement to go away: And to close all, he told me I had my elder Brother for an Example, to whom he had used the same earnest Perswasions to keep him from going into the Low Country Wars, but could not prevail, his young Desires prompting him to run into the Army where he was kill'd; and tho' he said he would not cease to pray for me, yet he would venture to say to me, that if I did take this foolish Step, God would not bless me, and I would have Leisure hereafter to reflect upon having neglected his Counsel when there might be none to assist in my Recovery.

I observed in this last Part of his Discourse, which was truly Prophetick, tho' I suppose my Father did not know it to be so himself; I say, I observed the Tears run down his Face very plentifully, and especially when he spoke of my Brother who was kill'd; and that when he spoke of my having Leisure to repent, and none to assist me, he was so mov'd, 0that he broke off the Discourse, and told me, his Heart was so full he could say no more to me.

I was sincerely affected with this Discourse, as indeed who could be otherwise? and I resolv'd not to think of going abroad any more, but to settle at home according to my Father's Desire. But alas! a few Days wore it all off; and in short, to prevent

我不能在世上过上安逸幸福的生活,那完全是我的命运或我自己的过错所致,而他已尽了自己的责任。因为他已看出我的打算会给我带来的伤害,早就告诫过我,对我尽了责任。总而言之,只要我听从他的话,不要外出,在本乡本土成家立业,那么他就会百般地帮助我;同样的道理,他决不会对我离家的打算给予任何鼓励,免得日后我的倒霉事中有他的份。最后,他叫我从哥哥的事例中汲取教训,说是他也屡屡规劝我哥哥,要他别去那个低地国家打仗,但毫无效果,到头来,凭着年轻人那种一意孤行的意气,他还是投身军旅,枉送了性命;他还说,他一方面仍将继续为我祈祷,另一方面他断定如果我非要愚蠢地走这一步,上帝也不会保佑我,当我走投无路时我有的是时间去后悔当初不听从他的忠告。

后来想起他的最后这段话,我觉得确实很有预见性,尽管我确信当时我父亲自己并不知道。尤其是当他谈到我那丢掉性命的哥哥时已是泪流满面。当他说到我日后"有的是时间去后悔"、"无人相助"时,他伤感得说不下去了,他对我说,他心里非常难过,不能跟我再多说了。

这番话深深地感动了我,说句良心话,谁能不被感动呢?于是,我决定不再胡思乱想去闯荡天下,而是听从父亲的意愿,留在家中。可是,唉!

any of my Father's farther Importunities, in a few Weeks after, I resolv'd to run quite away from him. However, I did not act so hastily neither as my first Heat of Resolution prompted, but I took my Mother, at a time when I thought her a little pleasanter than ordinary, and told her, that my Thoughts were so entirely bent upon seeing the World, that I should never settle to any thing with Resolution enough to go through with it, and my Father had better give me his Consent than force me to go without it; that I was now Eighteen Years old, which was too late to go Apprentice to a Trade, or Clerk to an Attorney; that I was sure if I did, I should never serve out my time, and I should certainly run away from my Master before my Time was out, and go to Sea; and if she would speak to my Father to let me go but one Voyage abroad, if I came home again and did not like it, I would go no more, and I would promise by a double Diligence to recover that Time I had lost.

This put my Mother into a great Passion: She told me, she knew it would be to no Purpose to speak to my Father upon any such Subject; that he knew too well what was my Interest to give his Consent to any thing so much for my Hurt, and that she wondered how I could think of any such thing after such a Discourse as I had had with my Father, and such kind and tender Expressions as she knew my Father had us'd to me; and that in short, if I would ruine my self there was no Help for me; but I might depend I should never have their Consent to it: That for her Part she would not have so much Hand in my Destruction; and I should never have it to say, that my Mother was willing when my Father was not.

Tho' my Mother refused to move it to my Father, yet as I have heard afterwards, she reported all the Discourse to him. , and that my Father, after shewing a great Concern at it, said to her with a Sigh, That Boy might be happy if he would stay

过了几天,我又忘乎所以了。简单地说,几个礼拜后,为了避免他再来苦心哀求,我决定跑得离他远远的。但是我并没有一冲动就走掉。有一天我觉得母亲比往日高兴些,就告诉她我决心看看海外的世界,除此之外无论什么事我都不想干,父亲最好尊重我的想法,不要阻止我。我说我已经十八岁了,年龄太大,无论去当学徒或是做律师的助手都迟了。我说,我敢保证如果让我去做这些我不喜欢做的事,那我一定会在中途逃走,到海外去。如果母亲能说服父亲给我一次机会,回来后,我再也不会外出了,并且会以双倍的勤奋挽回我损失的时间。

母亲听完后情绪非常激动:她告诉我,和父亲再谈此事已毫无意义,他太知道什么对我有利,决不会同意我去做于己不利的事。她不懂为何父亲和我长谈之后我依旧执迷不悟。她说,总而言之,假如我自寻绝路,谁也不会来帮助我;所以我就不用妄想他们会答应我这件事。至于她自己,她更不愿意帮助我自取灭亡,免得我以后说,当时我父亲不愿意,而我母亲却愿意。

虽然我母亲在表面上不肯把我的话向我父亲传达,可是我后来却听说,她把我们的全部谈话都告诉他了,我父亲听了之后,非常忧虑,对她叹

at home, but if he goes abroad he will be the miserablest Wretch that was ever born: I can give no Consent to it.

It was not till almost a Year after this that I broke loose, tho' in the mean time I continued obstinately deaf to all Proposals of settling to Business, and frequently expostulating with my Father and Mother, about their being so positively determin'd against what they knew my Inclinations prompted me to. But being one Day at Hull, where I went casually, and without any Purpose of making an Elopement that time; but I say, being there, and one of my Companions being going by Sea to London, in his Father's Ship, and prompting me to go with them, with the common Allurement of Seafaring Men, viz That it should cost me nothing for my Passage, I consulted neither Father or Mother any more, nor so much as sent them Word of it; but leaving them to hear of it as they might, without asking God's Blessing, or my Father's, without any Consideration of Circumstances or Consequences, and in an ill Hour, God knows. On the first of September 1651 I went on Board a Ship bound for London; never any young Adventurer's Misfortunes, I believe, began sooner, or continued longer than mine. The Ship was no sooner gotten out of the Humber, but the Wind began to blow, and the Winds' to rise in a most frightful manner; and as I had never been at Sea before, I was most inexpressibly sick in Body, and terrify'd in my Mind: I began now seriously to reflect upon what I had done, and how justly I was overtaken by the Judgment of Heaven for my wicked leaving my Father's House, and abandoning my Duty; all the good Counsel of my Parents, my Father's Tears and my Mother's Entreaties came now fresh into my Mind, and my Conscience, which was not yet come to the Pitch of

息道："这孩子苦守在家里，一定可以幸福；可是如果一定要出洋去，他就会成为世界上最苦命的人。因此，我说什么也不能答应他。"

事过了一年光景，我终于离家出走了，而在这一年里，尽管家里人多次建议我去干点正经事，但我就是冥顽不化，一概不听，反而老是与父母亲纠缠，要他们不要那样反对自己孩子的心愿。有一天，我偶然来到赫尔市。当时，我还没有私自出走的念头。但在那里，我碰到了一个朋友。他说他将乘他父亲的船去伦敦，并怂恿我与他们一起去。他用水手们常用的诱人航海的办法对我说，我不必付船费。我不再征询父母的意见，连个口信也没带给他们（他们能不能听到我的消息，只能听其自然了），也并不祈求上帝或父亲的祝福，根本就没考虑各种情况和后果，便在一六五一年九月一日的一个只有上帝才知道的恶时辰登上了那艘去伦敦的船。我相信，从来没有一个年轻的冒险家，其不幸的生涯开始得比我早，持续的时间比我长。那艘船刚驶出亨伯湾的湾口，便碰上了大风和惊涛骇浪。我过去从没出过海，这时只感到浑身有说不出的难受，心里则非常害怕。我开始郑重其事地反省自己的行为，上帝对我离开父亲、放弃责任的劣迹的惩罚是多么公正。双亲的谆谆教诲，父亲的眼泪，母亲的哀求这时

Hardness to which it has been since, reproach'd me with the Contempt of Advice, and the Breach of my Duty to God and my Father.

All this while the Storm encreas'd, and the Sea, which I had never been upon before, went very high, tho' nothing like what I have seen many times since; no, nor like what I saw a few Days after: But it was enough to affect me then, who was but a young Sailor, and had never known any thing of the matter. I expected every Wave would have swallowed us up, and that every time the Ship fell down, as I thought, in the Trough or Hollow of the Sea, we should never rise more; and in this Agony of Mind, I made many Vows and Resolutions, that if it would please God here to spare my Life this one Voyage, if ever I got once my Foot upon dry Land again, I would go directly home to my Father, and never set it into a Ship again while I liv'd; that I would take his Advice, and never run my self into such Miseries as these any more. Now I saw plainly the Goodness of his Observations about the middle Station of Life, how easy, how comfortably he had liv'd all his Days, and never had been expos'd to Tempests at Sea, or Troubles on Shore; and I resolv'd that I would, like a true repenting Prodigal, go home to my Father.

These wise and sober Thoughts continued all the while the Storm continued, and indeed some time after; but the next Day the Wind was abated and the Sea calmer, and I began to be a little inur'd to it: However I was very grave for all that Day, being also a little Sea sick still; but towards Night the Weather clear'd up, the Wind was quite over, and a charming fine Evening follow'd; the Sun went down perfectly clear and rose so the next

都突然浮现在我的脑海,我的良心(当时还不似后来那般顽固不化)开始责备自己当初轻视别人的劝告,逃避对上帝和父亲的责任。

这时,狂虐的风愈刮愈大,波涛一浪高过一浪,虽然不像我后来几次以及过了几天后所遭遇的那样厉害,但也足以使我心惊肉跳了,由于此刻我是初次上船,对海上的事一点儿也不了解。我觉得每一个浪花好像就能把我们吞下去;我们的船每次跌入浪心时,我总以为将会永远沉下去。在这种极度痛苦的心情下,我多次发誓并下决心,假如上帝愿意在这次航海中留给我生命,假如我能再一次踏上干硬的陆地,我将径直回到我父亲身边,在今后的日子里将再不去坐船,我将听从父亲的劝告,再也不会自寻这类苦恼。现在,我终于茅塞顿开,明白了他所说的关于中间状态生活的真谛;想起来,他这一生活得多么悠闲,多么舒服啊,从没经受过海上的风暴,以及陆上的苦恼;所以,我决心回到家中,回到父亲身边,做个名符其实的回头浪子。

这些明智而清醒的想法,在暴风雨发作着的当儿,甚至在它停止以后的某一短时间内,一直盘踞在我的脑海里。但到了第二天,风也停了,浪也静了,我就开始对海上生活习以为常了。不过那天我还是整天无精打采,因为我还有点晕船。到了傍晚,天气完全

Morning; and having little or no Wind and a smooth Sea, the Sun shining upon it, the Sight was, as I thought, the most delightful that ever I saw.

I had slept well in the Night, and was now no more Sea sick: but very chearful, looking with Wonder upon the Sea that was so rough and terrible the Day before, and could be so calm and so pleasant in so little time after. And now least my good Resolutions should continue, my Companion, who had indeed entic'd me away, comes to me, Well Bob, says he, clapping me on the Shoulder, How do you do after it? I warrant you were frighted, wa'n't you, last Night, when it blew but a Cap full of Wind? A Cap full d'you call it? said I, 'twas a terrible Storm: A Storm, you Fool you, replies he, do you call that a Storm, why it was nothing at all; give us but a good Ship and Sea Room, and we think nothing of such a Squal of Wind as that; but you're but a fresh Water Sailor, Bob; come let us make a Bowl of Punch and we'll forget all that, d'ye see what charming Weather 'tis now. To make short this sad Part of my Story, we went the old way of all Sailors, the Punch was made, and I was made drunk with it, and in that one Night's Wickedness I drowned all my Repentance, all my Reflections upon my past Conduct, and all my Resolutions for my future. In a word, as the Sea was returned to its Smoothness of Surface and settled Calmness by the Abatement of that Storm, so the Hurry of my Thoughts being over, my Fears and Apprehensions of being swallow'd up by the Sea being forgotten, and the Current of my former Desires return'd, I entirely forgot the Vows and Promises that I made in my Distress. I found indeed some Intervals of Reflection, and the serious Thoughts did, as it were en-

晴了，风也完全止了，继之而来的是一个美丽可爱的黄昏。当晚的落日和第二天早晨的日出都非常清朗。此时风平浪静，太阳的光线照在上面，那种景致，真是我从来没见过的。

那天晚上我睡得很香，所以第二天也不再晕船了，精神也为之一爽。望着前天还奔腾咆哮的大海，一下子竟这么平静柔和，真是令人感到不可思议。那位引诱我上船的朋友唯恐我真的下定决心不再航海，就过来看我。"喂，鲍勃，"他拍拍我的肩膀说，"你现在觉得怎样？我说，那天晚上吹起一点微风，一定把你吓坏了吧？""你说那是一点微风？"我说，"那是一场可怕的风暴啊！""风暴？你这傻瓜，"他回答"这样的风，你就叫它风暴啦？嗨，这根本算不上什么。只要船好海面宽，我们才不把这么点小风放在心上呢；不过你老弟还没上过海船，也难怪。好吧，咱们去喝一碗潘趣酒，把这事丢在脑后吧；现在，你瞧这天光水色多迷人！"对于我那一番不妙经历这里就不必多谈了，反正我们采取了所有海员的那个老办法，把潘趣酒调制好以后，我就灌得酩酊大醉；那一夜，我实在荒唐：先前的悔恨，对自己所作所为的反省，对未来的种种打算，竟然全都一扫而空。不用说，随着大海的安宁，我的脑子里不再思绪万千、汹涌澎湃。那种害怕被大海吞没的恐惧感

deavour to return again sometimes, but I shook them off, and rouz'd my self from them as it were from a Distemper, and applying my self to Drink and Company, Soon master'd the Return of those Fits, for so I call'd them, and I had in five or six Days got as compleat a Victory over Conscience as any young Fellow that resolv'd not to be troubled with it, could desire: But I was to have another Trial for it still; and Providence, as in such Cases generally it does, resolv'd to leave me entirely without Excuse. For if I would not take this for a Deliverance, the next was to be such a one as the worst and most harden'd Wretch among us would confess both the Danger and the Mercy.

The sixth Day of our being at Sea we came into Yarmouth Roads; the Wind having been contrary, and the Weather calm, we had made but little Way since the Storm. Here we were obliged to come to an Anchor, and here we lay, the Wind continuing contrary, viz. at South-west, for seven or eight Days, during which time a great many Ships from Newcastle came into the same Roads, as the common Harbour where the Ships might wait for a Wind for the River.

We had not however rid here so long, but should have Tided it up the River, but that the Wind blew too fresh; and after we had lain four or five Days, blew very hard. However, the Roads being reckoned as good as a Harbour, the Anchorage good, and our Ground-Tackle very strong, our Men were unconcerned, and not in the least apprehensive of Danger, but spent the Time in Rest and Mirth, after the manner of the Sea; but the eighth Day in the Morning, the Wind increased,

消失得无影无踪，要去冒险的念头又上来了，曾在痛苦中发出的誓言和作出的郑重许诺早就抛到了脑后。偶尔我会有一阵迷惘，一阵悚然，那些严肃的人生思考竭力想钻进我的脑海，但我努力去摆脱它们，喝酒、聊天，一切都不复存在，而在五、六天之内，就像所有的年轻人所希望的那样，我彻底丧失了良知。可能正是如此，我就注定要再受一次灾难；造物主看我撞死南墙不回头，只好变本加利地来惩治我了。因为我这次既然不肯悔改，下一次大祸肯定会更加厉害，就连世界上最凶恶顽固的人遇见了，也会恐惧得连连求饶。

航行后第六天，我们抵达雅木斯港口；由于逆风的缘故，风暴过后我们走的路程实在不多。我们不得不在这里抛锚停泊。之后的七八天，一直是自西南方吹来的逆风。这期间，许多从新堡过来的船都驶入港口。因为这里是一个船只往来必经的港口，船只都在这里等顺风了再驶入泰晤士河。

我们本来不应该在这里停这么长时间的，本应趁着潮汐开进泰晤士河口，无奈风刮得太急。在这里停泊了四五天，风一直刮得特凶。不过，这里常常被视为泊船的理想港口，况且我们的锚也下得好，缆索又很结实，所以船上的人都掉以轻心，丝毫不担心会有什么危险，而是以水手们的通

and we had all Hands at Work to strike our Top-Masts, and make every thing snug and close, that the Ship might ride as easy as possible. By Noon the Sea went very high indeed, and our Ship rid Forecastle in, shipp'd several Seas, and we thought once or twice our Anchor had come home; upon which our Master order'd out the Sheet Anchor; so that we rode with two Anchors a-Head, and the Cables vered out to the better End.

By this Time it blew a terrible Storm indeed, and now I began to see Terror and Amazement in the Faces even of the Seamen themselves. The Master, tho' vigilant to the Business of preserving the Ship, yet as he went in and out of his Cabbin by me, I could hear him softly to himself say several times, Lord be merciful to us, we shall be all lost, we shall be all undone; and the like. During these first Hurries, I was stupid, lying still in my Cabbin, which was in the Steerage, and cannot describe my Temper: I could ill reassume the first Penitence, which I had so apparently trampled upon, and harden'd my self against: I thought the Bitterness of Death had been past, and that this would be nothing too like the first. But when the Master himself came by me as I said just now, and said we should be all lost, I dreadfully frighted: I got up out of my Cabbin, and look'd out; but such a dismal Sight I never saw: The Sea went Mountains high, and broke upon us every three or four Minutes: When I could look about, I could see nothing but Distress round us: Two Ships that rid near us we found had cut their Masts by the Board, being deep loaden; and our Men cry'd out, that a Ship which rid about a Mile a-Head of us was foundered. Two more Ships being driven from their Anchors, were run out of the Roads to Sea at

常方式休息或嬉戏。到了第八天的早上，风力增强了，我们便一起动手放下中桅，并将所有的货物捆扎妥帖、牢靠，这样，船便可以在潮水中伸缩自如。到了中午，海浪卷得更高了，我们的船头有好几次钻入水中，打进来很多水；有一两次我们甚至以为我们的锚要脱了。于是我们的船主便下令把大锚放下去，结果我们船头下了两根锚，并且把锚索放到最长的限度。

这时风暴来势大得可怕，连水手们的脸上都开始带出恐怖和惊奇的神情。船主虽然极力小心指挥，维护船只的安全，可当他出入自己的舱房而从我的舱房边经过时，我好几次听到他低声自语，"上帝啊，可怜我们吧！我们都活不了啦！我们都要完蛋了！"他说了不少诸如此类的话。在最初的一阵纷乱中，我不知所措，只是一动不动地躺在自己的船舱里。我的舱房在船头，我无法形容我当时的心情。最初，我没有像第一次那样忏悔，而是变得麻木不仁了。我原以为死亡的痛苦已经过去，这次的风暴与上次一样也会过去。但我前面说过，当船长从我舱房边经过，并说我们都要完蛋了时，可把我吓坏了。我从铺上一跃而起，跑到舱外去看。我从未见到过如此险恶的景象，只见巨浪排山倒海而来，每隔三四分钟就有一排浪兜头朝我们打来。我四下张望，在目力所及的范围里，

all Adventures, and that was not a Mast standing. The light Ships fared the best; as not so much labouring in the Sea; but two or three of them drove, and came close by us, running away with only their Sprit-sail out before the Wind.

Towards Evening the Mate and Boat-Swain begg'd the Master of our Ship to let them cut away the Foremast, which he was very unwilling to: But the Boat-Swain protesting to him, that if he did not, the Ship would founder, he consented; and when they had cut away the Foremast, the Main-Mast stood so loose, and shook the Ship so much, they were obliged to cut her away also, and make a clear Deck.

Any one may judge what a Condition I must be in at all his; who was but a young Sailor, and who had been in such Fright before at but a little. But if I can express at this Distance the Thoughts I had about me at that time, I was in tenfold more Horror of Mind upon Account of my former Convictions, and the having returned from them to the Resolutions I had wickedly taken at first, than I was at Death it self; and these added to the Terror of the Storm, put me into such a Condition, that I can by no Words describe it. But the worst was not come yet, the Storm continued with such Fury, that the Seamen themselves acknowledged they had never known a worse. We had a good Ship, but she was deep loaden, and wallowed in the Sea, that the Seamen every now and then

见到的只是一片惨状。离我们不远的地方，一直有两艘船泊着，由于货载得多而吃水很深，这时已砍掉了桅杆；接着，又听见我们船上的人大叫起来，原来是一艘泊在我们前面一英里处的船被浪头打翻了。还有两艘船由于锚已失去作用，完全失控地离开了锚地，朝外海漂去，而船上的桅杆一根也不见了。轻型船的情况最好，不像其他船那样苦苦挣扎，可也有两三艘轻船与我们擦肩而过，飘向大海，船上只剩斜杠帆吃风。

临近黄昏，大副和水手长求船主允许他们砍掉前桅杆，船主犹豫不决，水手长争辩道，如果船主不这么干，船很快就会沉没。船主只好同意。砍掉前桅杆之后，主桅杆摇摇欲坠，船也随之颠簸不止，他们不得不把主桅杆也砍掉，只留下一个光秃秃的甲板。

对于我这个没有经验的水手来说，以前遇到一点风浪还要吓得半死，在这种处境之下，心情也就可想而知了。现在回想起来，当时我对于自己那种忏悔以后又重生恶念的恐惧，比对死亡还要恐怖十倍。再加上对风暴的恐怖，使我陷入了一种难以描述的境地。但这并不是最糟糕的，更糟的是风暴越刮越猛，就是水手们也承认这是他们从未见到过的。我们的船质地非常好，可惜的是它载货太多，吃水很深，正向海中间滑去，水手们不时大叫：它快要沉底

cried out, she would founder. It was my Advantage in one respect, that I did not know what they meant by Founder, till I enquir'd. However, the Storm was so violent, that I saw what is not often seen, the Master, the Boat-Swain, and some others more sensible than the rest, at their Prayers, and expecting every Moment when the Ship would go to the Bottom. In the Middle of the Night, and under all the rest of our Distresses, one of the Men that had been down on Purpose to see, cried out we had sprung a Leak; another said there was four Foot Water in the Hold. Then all Hands were called to the Pump. At that very Word my Heart, as I thought, died within me, and I fell backwards upon the Side of my Bed where I sat, into the Cabbin. However, the Men roused me, and told me, that I that was able to do nothing before, was as well able to pump as another; at which I stirr'd up, and went to the Pump and work'd very heartily. While this was doing, the Master seeing some light Colliers, who not able to ride out the Storm, were oblig'd to slip and run away to Sea, and would come near us, ordered to fire a Gun as a Signal of Distress. I who knew nothing what that meant, was so surprised, that I thought the Ship had broke, or some dreadful thing had happen'd. In a word, I was so surprised, that I fell down in a Swoon. As this was a time when every Body had his own Life to think of, no body minded me, or what was become of me; but another Man stept up the Pump, and thrusting me aside with his Foot, let me lye, thinking I had been dead; and it was a great while before I came to my self.

We work'd on, but the Water encreasing in the Hold, it was apparent that the Ship would founder, and tho' the Storm began to abate a little, yet as it was not possible she could swim till we might run into a Port, so the Master continued firing Guns for Help; and a light Ship who had rid

了！可幸的是,在我向他们请教之前,我不知道"沉底"就是"下沉"的意思。然而,这时风力已强劲到极点,我看到了一片罕见的场面,只见船主、水手长,以及那些头脑较为清醒的水手们,都在向上帝祈祷,以为船随时都会沉底。半夜时分,我们在痛苦中煎熬的心情又火上加油:其中一个在船底察看情况的水手喊了起来,说船裂了一条缝;另外一个水手上来说,舱底已经有了四英尺深的水。于是全部的人都被喊去抽水。一听到这两句话,我的心脏好像停止了跳动,身子倒在床上。这时别人却把我唤了起来,对我说:现在你可以去抽抽水。于是我拼命在抽水机旁工作。正工作的时候,船长发现有几只运煤船,由于抵不住风浪的袭击,不得不向大海飞去,正从我们的船边驶过,就发令放一枪求救。我因为不知道鸣枪的意思,大吃一惊,以为失去了所有的希望,马上倒在地上,晕了过去。这时人们连自己的生命都无暇顾及,当然没有人来管我;于是另外一个人走过来,接着我抽水,把我一脚踢开,由我躺在那里,以为我已经死了。我过了好久才苏醒过来。

我们继续操作下去。但舱底的水愈进愈深,船显然很快就要沉了。虽然这时风暴已经小了一些,可是要希望我们的船能开到一个港口,那大概是万难的事。因此船主便

it out just a Head of us ventured a Boat out to help us. It was with the utmost Hazard the Boat came near us, but it was impossible for us to get on Board, or for the Boat to lie near the Ship Side, till at last the Men rowing very heartily, and venturing their Lives to save ours, our Men cast them a Rope over the Stern with a Buoy to it, and then vered it out a great Length, which they after great Labour and Hazard took hold of and we hall'd them close under our Stern and got all into their Boat. It was to no Purpose for or us after we were in the Boat to think of reaching to own Ship, so all agreed to let her drive and only to pull her in towards Shore as much as we could, and our Master promised them, That if the Boat was stav'd upon Shore he would make it good to their Master, so partly rowing and partly driving our Boat went away to the Norward sloaping wards the Shore almost as far as Winterton Ness.

We were not much more than a quarter of an Hour out four Ship but we saw her sink, and then I understood for the first time what was meant by a Ship foundering in the Sea; I must acknowledge I had hardly Eyes to look up when he Seamen told me she was sinking; for from that Moment hey rather put me into the Boat than that I might be said to go in, my Heart was as it were dead within me, partly with Fright, partly with Horror of Mind and the Thoughts of what was yet before me.

While we were in this Condition, the Men yet labouring the Oar to bring the Boat near the Shore, we could see, hen our Boat mounting the Waves, we were able to see the Shore, a great

继续鸣枪求救。有一艘轻量级的船顺风从我们前面飘过，就冒险放下一只小艇来救我们。小艇上的人冒着极大的危险才划近我们的大船，但我们无法下到他们的小艇，他们也无法靠拢我们的大船。最后，小艇上的人拼命划桨，舍死相救；我们则从船尾抛下一根带有浮筒的绳子，并尽量把绳子放长。小艇上的人几经努力，终于抓住了绳子。我们就慢慢把小艇拖近船尾，全体船员才得以下了小艇。此时此刻，我们已无法再回到他们的船上去了，大家一致同意任凭小艇随波漂流，并努力向岸边划去。我们的船主许下诺言，如果这小艇在岸边撞坏的话，他会向他们的船主作出赔偿；就这样，我们半漂半划地朝北去了好长一段路，渐渐靠近了温特顿岬角。

我们离开大船不过才刻把钟左右，就看见它沉没了；这时我方才明白，船在大海中灭顶是什么意思；我得承认，当他们告诉我说船正在下沉时，我可以说是顾不上抬头看它一眼；因为就在那个当口，与其说我是自己下到小艇上，倒不如说是被弄到小艇上的；当时我一来受了惊吓，二来为以后的遭遇而担忧，所以精神极度紧张，以致于心脏竟像停止了跳动。

我们向岸边费力划去的时候，看到(小艇被送上浪尖时能瞧见海岸)许多人沿沙滩跑着，准备在我们靠岸时帮一

many People running along the Shore to assist us when we should come near, but we made but slow way towards the Shore, nor were we able to reach the Shore, till being past the Light-House at Winterton, the Shore falls off to the Westward towards Cromer, and so the Land broke off a little the Violence of the Wind: Here we got in, and tho' not without much Difficulty got all safe on Shore and walk'd afterwards on Foot to Yarmouth, where, as unfortunate Men, we were used with great Humanity as well by the Magistrates of the Town, who assign'd us good Quarters, as by particular Merchants and Owners of Ships, and had Money given us sufficient to carry us either to London or back to Hull, as we thought fit.

Had I now had the Sense to have gone back to Hull, and have gone home, I had been happy, and my Father, an Emblem of our Blessed Saviour's Parable, had even kill'd the fatted Calf for me; for hearing the Ship I went away in was cast away in Yarmouth Road, it was a great while before he had any Assurance that I was not drown'd.

But my ill Fate push'd me on now with an Obstinacy that nothing could resist; and tho' I had several times loud Calls from my Reason and my more composed Judgment to go home, yet I had no Power to do it. I know not what to call this, nor will I urge, that it is a secret over-ruling Decree that hurries us on to be the Instruments of our own Destruction, even tho' it be before us, and that we rush upon it with our Eyes open. Certainly nothing but some such decreed unavoidable Misery attending, and which it was impossible for me to escape, could have push'd me forward against the calm Reasonings and Perswasions of my most retired Thoughts, and against two such visible Instructions as I had met with in my first Attempt.

把。我们缓慢艰难地向岸边靠,直到过了温特顿灯塔才成功。这一带海岸突然朝西拐向克罗马,低陷的陆地稍稍阻挡了一点强劲的风势。我们花了吃奶的劲才靠上岸,大家终于毫发未损地登上了陆地,步行去雅斯。在雅木斯,我们这些天涯沦落人受到了热情的接待。地方长官为我们安排了住处,一些商人和船主慷慨解囊,赠给我们足够去伦敦或赫尔的钱。

如果我当时有点头脑,返回赫尔市,回到家中,我肯定会很幸福的。我的父亲,肯定会像耶稣在《圣经》中所讲的那样,为我的归来宰杀肥牛;因为自从他听说我搭乘的那只船在雅木斯海口失事后,过了很长一段时间,才知道我并没有淹死。

可是,我那不幸的命运却将我进一步推向苦难,令我无力反抗;虽然我的理智也好几回向我大声疾呼,我那清醒的头脑也在催促我,要我回家,可我就是无力做到。我说不清这究竟是什么缘故,也不想让自己明白。其实,这正是那神秘的、不可逆转的天意在将我逼上自我毁灭,尽管那毁灭就在眼前,可我竟睁着眼睛冲了上去。说真的,不是别的,肯定是这种不可逃避的命数在从中作梗,使我在劫难逃,让我不顾冷静的理智和内心深

My Comrade, who had help'd to harden me before, and who was the Master's Son, was now less forward than I; the first time he spoke to me after we were at Yarmouth, which was not till two or three Days, for we were separated in the Town to several Quarters; I say, the first time he saw me, it appear'd his Tone was alter'd, and looking very melancholy and shaking his Head, ask'd me how I did, and telling his Father who I was, and how I had come this Voyage only for a Trial in order to go farther abroad; his Father turning to me with a very grave and concern'd Tone, Young Man, says he, you ought never to go to Sea any more, you ought to take his for a plain and visible Token that you are not to be a Seafaring Man. Why, Sir, said I, will you go to Sea no more? That is another Case, said he, it is my Calling, and therefore my Duty; but as you made this Voyage for a Trial, you see what a Taste Heaven has given you of what you are to expect if you persist; perhaps this is all befallen us on your Account, like Jonah in the Ship of Tarshish. Pray, continues he, what are you? and on what Account did you go to Sea? Upon that I told him some of my Story; at the End of which he burst out with a strange kind of Passion, What had I done, says he, that such an unhappy Wretch should come into my Ship? I would not set my Foot in the same Ship with thee again for a Thousand Pounds. This indeed was, as I said, an Excursion of his Spirits which were yet agitated by the Sense of his Loss, and was farther than he could have Authority to go. However he afterwards talk'd very gravely to me, exhorted me to go back to my Father, and not tempt Providence to my Ruine; told me I might see a visible Hand of Heaven against me, And young Man, said he, depend upon it, if you do not go back,

处的劝告,不顾上次航行时所留给我的活生生的教训,而接着走向毁灭。

　　我的朋友,船主的儿子,原来曾怂恿我,现在比我还胆怯。到了雅木斯之后,我们被分别安置在好几个地方住宿。所以两三天之后他才碰到我。我刚才说了,这是我们上岸分开的第一次见面。当我和他谈话时,我忽然觉得他的态度变化很大;他的神情忧郁,连连摇头,问我最近怎样,接着又把我引荐给他父亲,告诉他我这次仅仅是尝试,准备以后到更远的地方去。他父亲语重心长地对我说:"年轻人,你不应该再航行了;很明显这次遭遇证明你不能做航海家。"我说:"怎么,先生,你也不再出海了吗?"他说:"那又是一回事。这是我的行业,也是我的责任。但是你这次航行,完全是一种尝试,这是老天爷有意给你点滋味尝尝,让你知道再坚持下去会有什么结果。我们这次遭遇也许就是由于你的缘故,就像在他施船里的约拿一样。请问你到底是个什么人,到底为什么要出海呢?"于是我便向他谈了谈我的身世。不料他听完之后,忽然大发脾气说:"我怎么会让你这样一个倒霉鬼上了我的船?以后哪怕你给我一千英镑的报酬,我也不和你上一条船。"我觉得他没有权利对我这样发脾气,显然是由于自己遭了损失,借此泄愤。可是,后来他又郑重其事地与我谈了一番,

where-ever you go, you will meet with nothing but Disasters and Disappointments till your Father's Words are fulfilled upon you.

We parted soon after; for I made him little Answer, and I saw him no more; which way he went, I know not. As for me, having some Money in my Pocket, I travelled to London by Land; and there, as well as on the Road, had many Struggles with my self, what Course of Life I should take, and whether I should go Home, or go to Sea.

As to going Home, Shame opposed the best Motions that offered to my Thoughts; and it immediately occurr'd to me how I should be laugh'd at among the Neighbours, and should be asham'd to see, not my Father and Mother only, but even every Body else; from whence I have since often observed, how incongruous and irrational the common Temper of Mankind is, especially of Youth, to that Reason which ought to guide them in such Cases, viz. That they are not asham'd to sin, and yet are asham'd to repent; not asham'd of the Action for which they ought justly to be esteem'd Fools, but are asham'd of the returning, which only can make them be esteem'd wise Men.

In this of Life howeyer I remained some time, uncertain what Measures to take, and what Course of Life to lead. An irresistible Reluctance continu'd to going Home; and as I stay'd a while, the Remembrance of the Distress I had been in

敦促我回到父亲身边，不要再惹怒老天爷来毁掉自己。他说，我应该看到，老天爷是不会放过我的。"年轻人，"他说，"相信我的话，你若不回家，不论你上哪儿，你只会受难和失望。到那时，你父亲的话就会在你身上应验了。"

我对他的话不置可否，很快就跟他分手了。从此再也没有见到过他，对他的下落也一无所知。至于我自己，口袋里有了点钱，就从陆路去伦敦。在赴伦敦途中，以及到了伦敦以后，我一直在作激烈的思想斗争，不知道该选择什么样的生活道路：是回家呢还是去航海？

要说回家吧，我虽然心中也有这样的念头和冲动，但总被羞辱感所抵消；因为我马上会想到自己将遭到邻里们的笑话，不仅无颜见父母，甚至也无颜见其他人；从那时起，我也就时常注意到这样一种情况：在需要理性来指点迷途的时候，人们对理性的态度，尤其是年轻人对理性的态度，却是矛盾的，非理性的，也就是说，他们不以违背情理为耻，不以自己的愚蠢行径为耻，倒以悔过自新为耻；而他们要不被看成十足的愚妄之徒，要被看作明智之人，唯有悔过自新一途。

我就这样百无聊赖地打发着日子，不知道干什么好，也不知道该走什么样的人生道路。我仍旧不愿意回家，自己也说不出为什么。滞留时

wore off; and as that abated, the little Motion I had in my Desires to a Return wore off with it, till at last I quite lay'd aside the Thoughts of it, and lookt out for a Voyage.

That evil Influence which carried me first away from my Father's House, that hurried me into the wild and indigested Notion of raising my Fortune; and that imprest those Conceits so forcibly upon me, as to make me deaf to all good Advice, and to the Entreaties and even Command of my Father: I say the same Influence, whatever it was, presented the most unfortunate of all Enterprises to my View; and I went on board a Vessel bound to the Coast of Africa; or, as our Sailors vulgarly call it, a Voyage to Guinea.

It was my great Misfortune that in all these Adventures I did not ship my self as a Sailor; whereby, tho' I might indeed have work'd a little harder than ordinary, yet at the same time I had learn'd the Duty and Office of a Fore-mast Man; and in might have qualified my self for a Mate or Lieutenant, ifs a Master: But as it was always my Fate to choose for the worse, so I did here; for having Money in my Pocket, and good Cloaths upon my Back, I would always go on board in the Habit of a Gentleman; and so I neither had any Business Ship, or learn'd to do any.

It was my Lot first of all to fall into pretty good Company in London which does not always happen to such loose and unguided young Fellows as I then was; the Devil generally not omitting to lay some Snare for them very early: But it was not as with me, I first fell acquainted with the Master of a Ship who had been on the Coast of Guinea; and who having had very good Success there, was resolved to go again; and who taking a Fancy to my

间一久，我渐渐淡忘了那段痛苦经历。随着忘却，一丝想回家的残念也烟消云散，最后我干脆把这个想法抛弃至脑后，一心寻找新的出海机会。

那股邪恶的力量，曾使我离开父亲，促使我外出碰运气，使我异想天开以致听不进一切忠告，甚至是我父亲的恳求和命令。现在，这股力量又像以前那样，把航海这种最不幸的职业摆在了我面前，我又上了一只开往非洲海岸的船。用水手们常说的话来说，到几内亚去了。

在我一生的多次冒险中，我从来没有以水手身份搭乘过船，这是我最大的不幸；假如是那样，我或许会比通常情况下辛苦一点，但同时也能学会管理船桅之类的职责，即使做不了船主至少也会当个大副什么的。可惜的是，我这人运气太坏，总是选择最坏的，在这方面也是一样。由于口袋里有几个钱，身上又穿着漂亮的衣服，所以我老是以绅士的派头去搭船，所以我在船上既无事可做，也不肯学着去做。

命运使我在伦敦首次碰到了好人：对于像我这样狂妄无知、放荡不羁的年轻人来说，这实在是十分稀奇的事。魔鬼对于这种人照例是一有机会就要下手的，但是对我却恰恰相反。我认识了一个过去曾经到过几内亚的船主，他在那边发过一次财，决定再去

Conversation, which was not at all disagreeable at that time, hearing me say I had a mind to see the World, told me if I wou'd go the, Voyage with him I should be at no Expence; I should be his Mess-mate and his Companion, and if I could carry any thing with me, I should have all the Advantage of it that the Trade would admit; and perhaps I might meet with some Encouragement.

I embrac'd the Offer, and entring into a strict Friendship with this Captain, who was an honest and plain-dealing Man, I went the Voyage with him, and carried a small Adventure with me, which by the disinterested Honesty of my Friend the Captain, I increased very considerably; for I carried about 40 l. in such Toys and Trifles as the Captain directed me to buy. This 40 l. I had mustered together by the Assistance of some of my Relations whom I corresponded with, and who, I believe, got my Father, or at least my Mother, to contribute so much as that to my first Adventure.

This was the only Voyage which I may say was successful in all my Adventures, and which I owe to the Integrity and Honesty of my Friend the Captain, under whom also I got a competent Knowledge of the Mathematicks and the Rules of Navigation, learn'd how to keep an Account of the Ship's Course, take an Observation; and in short, to understand some things that were needful to be understood by a Sailor: For, as he took Delight to introduce me, I took Delight to learn; and, in a word, this Voyage made me both a Sailor and a Merchant: for I brought Home L. 5. 9 Ounces of Gold Dust for my Adventure, which yielded me in London at my Return, almost 300 l. and this fill'd me with those aspiring Thoughts which have since so compleated my Ruin.

Yet even in this Voyage I had my Misfortunes

一趟。我俩谈得十分投机,他听我说要到海外去闯一闯,就对我说,如果我和他同去,他不要我的钱,我将是他的伙伴;如果我想带一点货,他可以给我提供最大的方便;说不定还可以发一大笔财。

我立刻接受了他的盛意,并且和这位船长作了亲密的朋友,这位船长是一个正直而诚实的人。我便带了一点货物,同他一船走了。由于这位船长朋友的正直无私,我赚了不少钱,因为我按照船主的指示,带了一批玩物和其他零碎货物,大约值四十英镑。这四十英镑是我用通信的方式靠几位亲戚的帮助筹划出来的,我想他们送我的钱,大概是从我父亲或者我母亲那里弄来的,送给我作第一次出门的资本。

可以说,这是我一生冒险活动中唯一成功的一次航行。这完全应归功于我那船长朋友的正直无私。在他的指导下,我还学会了一些航海的数学知识和方法,学会了记航海日志和观察天文。一句话,懂得了一些做水手的基本知识。他乐于教我,我也乐于跟他学。总之,这次航行使我既成了水手,又成了商人。这次航行,我带回了五磅零九盎司金沙;回到伦敦后,我换回了约三百英镑,赚了不少钱。这更使我踌躇满志,因而也由此断送了我的一生。

但即使在这次航行里,我

too; particularly, that I was continually sick, being thrown into a violent Calenture by the excessive Heat of the Climate; our principal Trading being upon the Coast, from the Latitude of 15 Degrees, North even to the Line it self.

I was now set up for a Guiney Trader; and my Friend, to my great Misfortune, dying soon after his Arrival, I resolved to go the same Voyage again, and I embark'd in the same Vessel with one who was his Mate in the former Voyage, and had now got the Command of the Ship. This was the unhappiest Voyage that ever Man made; for tho' I did not carry quite 100 l. of my new gain'd Wealth, so that I had 200 left, and which I lodg'd with my Friend's Widow, who was very just to me, yet I fell into terrible Misfortunes in this Voyage; and the first was this, viz. Our Ship making her Course towards the Canary Islands, or rather between those Islands and the African Shore, was surprised in the Grey of the Morning, by a Turkish Rover of Sallee, who gave Chase to us with all the Sail she could make. We crowded also as much Canvas as our Yards would spread, or our Masts carry, to have got clear; but finding the Pirate gain'd upon us, and would certainly come up with us in a few Hours, we prepar'd to fight; our Ship having 12 Guns, and the Rogue 18. About three in the Afternoon he came up with us, and bringing to by Mistake, just athwart our Quarter, instead of athwart our Stern, as he intended, we brought 8 of our Guns to bear on that Side, and pour'd in a Broadside upon him, which made him sheer off again, after returning our Fire, and pouring in also his small Shot from near 200 Men which he had on Board. However, we had not a Man touch'd, all our Men keeping close. He prepar'd to attack us again, and we to defend our selves; but laying us on Board the next time upon our other Quarter, he

照样也有倒霉的地方;特别是由于我们做交易的地方,主要在北纬十五度附近的非洲西海岸,有时甚至到达赤道一带,天气的酷热使我得了发高烧的热病,所以身体一直不好。

这时,我已准备再去几内亚做生意;倒霉的是,我那朋友回国不久便去世了;我既然决定照样再去跑一趟,就仍旧上了原先的那条船,只是上次航行中的大副现在成了船长。在人们的航海经历中,得数这一次最为不幸;还好,我只从刚赚的钱中拿出不到一百英镑带在身上,剩下的二百英镑我存在朋友的遗孀那里,她是一个很公正的人。然而我终究未能逃出这次旅行带来的厄运。第一次不幸是我们的船在驶向加纳利群岛,或者说这些群岛和非洲海岸之间的海域时,遭到一艘从萨利来的摩尔人海盗船的袭击。这艘船穿过濛濛晨雾,高速向我们追来。我们也尽力把船帆扯满,全速前进,希望能够逃脱它的追赶。但我们发现海盗船对我们穷追不舍,而且肯定会在几小时之内追上我们,我们只好准备战斗。我们船上有十二尊炮,而海盗船上却有十八尊。到下午三点钟的时候,它还是追上了我们。它本打算要横冲过来撞击我们的船尾,由于出了差错,却冲到我们的后舷上。但是,我们把八门炮搬到这边,朝那艘船的正面开火,迫使它往后退。海

entred 60 Men upon our Decks, who immediately fell to cutting and hacking the Decks and Rigging. We ply'd them with Small-shot, Half-Pikes, Powder-Chests, and such like, and clear'd our Deck of them twice. However, to cut short this melancholly Part of our Story, our Ship being disabled, and three of our Men kill'd, and eight wounded, we were obliged to yield, and were carry'd all Prisoners into Sallee, a Port belonging to the Moors.

The Usage I had there was not so dreadful as at first I apprehended, nor was I carried up the Country to the Emperor's Court, as the rest of our Men were, but was kept by the Captain of the Rover, as his proper Prize, and made is Slave, being young and nimble, and fit for his Business. At this surprising Change of my Circumstances from a Merchant to a miserable Slave, I was perfectly overwhelmed; and now I look'd back upon my Father's prophetick Disourse to me, that I should be miserable, and have none to relieve me, which I thought was now so effectually brought pass, that it could not be worse; that now the Hand of Heaven had overtaken me, and I was undone without Redemption. But alas! this was but a Taste of the Misery I was to go thro', as will appear in the Sequel of this Story.

As my new Patron or Master had taken me Home to his House, so I was in hopes that he

盗船上的将近两百人也用火枪朝我们还击。但我们的人没有一个伤着,因为我们都掩蔽得很好。接着,他们又准备进攻我们,我们也作好了自卫的准备。但是,他们这回是从我们船另一侧的后舷进攻我们的,有六十个海盗上了我们的甲板,他们一上船就乱劈乱砍甲板与缆索。我们则用火枪、长矛,以及火药桶之类的武器和他们殊死搏斗,先后两回把他们赶下了船。但是,我现在不忍再细说这段可悲的故事,总之,在死三人、伤八人的情况下,我们只好投降成了俘虏,他们把剩余的我们这帮人带到萨利的摩尔人港口去了。

我在那里所受的待遇,并没有我起初预料到的那样可怕,因为我并没像别的人一样,被带到皇帝的宫里去,而是被留在海盗船的船长室里,做了他的战利品,成了他的奴隶,因为我年轻伶俐,很合他的需要。由于这种环境的突然变化,由一个商人一下子变成了可怜的奴隶,我完全灰心丧气了。我回想到我父亲的预言,说我一定要受罪,谁也救不了我,觉得他的话果然应验,现在我的处境实在再糟也没有了,因为我已经受到了天谴,永无出头之日了。可是,唉! 这不过是我的苦难的一个开头罢了,诸位读到下文,自然就会知道。

我的新主人把我带回他家中,我满以为他出海时会带

would take me with him hen he went to Sea a-
gain, believing that it would some time or other be
his Fate to be taken by a Spanish or Portugal an of
War; and that then I should be set at Liberty. But
his Hope of mine was soon taken away; for when
he went to Sea, he left me on Shoar to look after
his little Garden, and do the common Drudgery of
Slaves about his House; and when he came home
again from his Cruise, he order'd me to lye in the
Cabbin to look after the Ship.

Here I meditated nothing but my Escape; and
what Method I might take to effect it, but found
no Way that had the least Probability in it: Nothing presented to make the Supposition of it rational; for I had no Body to communicate it to, that
would embark with me; no Fellow-Slave, no Englishman, Irishman, or Scotsman there but my
self; so that for two Years, tho' I often pleased
my self with the Imaginaion, yet I never had the
least encouraging Prospect of putting it in Practice.

After about two Years an odd Circumstance presented it self which put the old Thought of making
some Attempt for my Liberty, again in my Head:
My Patron lying at Home longer than usual, without fitting out his Ship, which, as I heard, was
for want of Money; he used constantly, once or
twice a Week, sometimes oftner, if the Weather
was fair, to take the Ship's Pinnace, and go Out
into the Road a-fishing; and as he always took me
and a young Maresco with him to row the Boat,
we made him very merry, and I prov'd very dexterous in catching Fish; insomuch that sometimes
he would send me with a Moor, one of his Kins-
men, and the Youth the Maresco, as they call'd
him, to catch a Dish of Fish for him.

It happen'd one time, that going a fishing in a

上我。如果这样,我想,他迟早
会被西班牙或葡萄牙的战舰
俘获,那时我就可以恢复自由
了。但我的这个希望很快就
破灭了。他每次出海时,总把
我留在岸上照看他那座小花
园,并在家里做各种奴隶干的
苦活。当他从海上航行回来
时,又叫我睡到船舱里替他看
船。

在这里,我头脑里整天盘
算着如何逃跑,但怎么也想不
出稍有希望的办法。从当时
的情况来看,我根本没有条件
逃跑。因为我根本就没有一
个可以商量的人,没有一个想
同我一起出逃的伙伴,那儿就
我一个人,没有别的家奴,没
有英格兰人,没有爱尔兰人,
也没有苏格兰人;所以,有两
年工夫,我虽然常常以空想逃
跑来自我安慰,却从来没有一
点点令人鼓舞的迹象,使我可
把这空想付诸实施。

过了约摸两年的时间,居
然出现了意想不到的情况,使
我脑子里重萌旧念,想设法恢
复自由。我的主人在家逗留
的时间愈来愈长,不大做海上
买卖,据说是因为缺钱的缘
故。天气晴朗的话,他一个星
期有一两次甚至更多地驾舢
板出去钓鱼,总是带上我和年
幼的莫瑞斯柯替他摇船。我
们很讨他的欢心,尤其是我,
在钓鱼方面颇有一手,因此他
常派我和他的一个摩尔亲戚
还有莫瑞斯柯替他捕鱼下酒。

一天早晨,微风轻拂,波

stark calm Morning, a Fog rose so thick, that tho'
we were not half a League from the Shoar we lost
Sight of it; and rowing we knew not whither or
which way, we labour'd all Day and all the next
Night, and when the Morning came we found we
had pull'd off to Sea instead of pulling in for the
Shoar; and that we were at least two Leagues
from the Shoar: However we got well in again,
tho' with a great deal of Labour, and some Danger; for the Wind began to blow pretty fresh in
the Morning; but particularly we were all very
hungry.

But our Patron warn'd by this Disaster, resolved
to take more Care of himself for the future; and
having lying by him the Long-boat of our English
Ship we had taken, he resolved he would not go a
fishing any more without a Compass and some
Provision; so he ordered the Carpenter of his
Ship, who also was an English Slave, to build a
little State-room or Cabin in the middle of the
Long Boat, like that of a Barge, with a Place to
stand behind it to steer and hale home the Main-
sheet; and Room before for a hand or two to stand
and work the Sails; she sail'd with that we call a
Shoulder of Mutton Sail; and the Boom gib'd over
the Top of the Cabbin, which lay very snug and
low, and had in it Room for him to lye, with a
Slave or two, and a Table to eat on, with some
small Lockers to put in some Bottles of such Liquor
as he thought fit to drink in; particularly his
Bread, Rice and Coffee.

We went frequently out with this Boat a fishing, and as I was most dextrous to catch fish for
him, he never went without me: It happen'd that
he had appointed to go out in this Boat, either for
Pleasure or for Fish, with two or three Moors of
some Distinction in that Place, and for whom he

浪平静,我们出去打鱼。突然
间,海上起了大雾,尽管离海
岸还不到一海里,却无法看到
海岸。我们无法辨清方向和
路途,划了整整一天一夜,直
到第二天早晨,才发现我们不
但没有靠近海岸,反而划到深
海里了,我们远离岸边至少有
两海里。最后,我们费了些劲,
冒了很大的风险,才划到岸
边。那是由于那天早晨的风
很硬,我们又饿得要命。

这次灾难让我们的主人
受惊不轻,他觉得他自己以后
也应当小心些。正好他那里
有一只从我们英国大船上夺
来的小长船,他计划以后出去
打鱼一定要带上罗盘和粮食。
于是,他便吩咐他大船上的木
工(也是一个英籍奴隶),在小
长船的中部造一船舱或卧舱
(像驳船上的那样),人可以站
在船后操纵船舵,调拉帆缆;
舱前面要有供一两个人站的
地方,以便操纵船帆。这只舢
板所用的帆即我们所说的三
角帆。舱顶上用桁条搭着。船
舱虽小但特别舒服,除了供他
一个人睡觉之外,还能睡进一
两个奴隶;里面可以放张桌子
吃饭,上面有一些小抽屉,可
以放几瓶他所喜欢的酒,特别
是,可以贮存他的面包、米与
咖啡。

我们乘坐这只舢板钓鱼,
主人因为我擅长垂钓,每次都
带我同去的。有一次,他邀请
了两、三个当地知名的摩尔
人,打算乘这只舢板去钓鱼游
乐,他为他们准备了大量供吃

had provided extraordinarily; and had therefore sent on board the Boat over Night, a larger Store of Provisions than ordinary; and had order'd me to get ready three Fuzees with Powder and Shot, which were on board his Ship; for that they design'd some Sport of Fowling as well as Fishing.

I got all things ready as he had directed, and waited the next Morning with the Boat, washed clean, her Antient and Pendants out, and every thing to accomodate his Guests; when by and by my Patroon came on board alone, and told me his Guests had put off going, upon some Business that fell out, and order'd me with the Man and Boy, as usual, to go out with the Boat and catch them some Fish, for that his friends were to sup at his House; and commanded that as soon as I had got some Fish I should bring it home to his House; all which I prepar'd to do.

This Moment my former Notions of Deliverance darted into my Thoughts, for now I found I was like to have a little Ship at my Command; and my Master being gone, I prepar'd to furnish my self, not for a fishing Business but for a Voyage; tho' I knew not, neither did I so much as consider whither I should steer; for any where to get out of that Place was my Way.

My first Contrivance was to make a Pretence to speak to this Moor, to get something for our Subsistance on board; for I told him we must not presume to eat of our Patroon's Bread, he said that was true; so he brought a large Basket of Rusk or Bisket of their kind, and three Jarrs with fresh Water into the Boat; I knew where my Patroon's Case of Bottles stood, which it was evident by the make were taken out of some English Prize; and I convey'd them into the Boat while the Moor was

喝的东西，前夜提前先送到船上去；还让我把船上的三枝短枪和火药、子弹准备好，打算另外射射鸟。

我按照吩咐，把一切都安排妥当了。第二天早晨，船也洗干净了，船旗也挂上了，我就在船上等候客人的到来。可是过了一会儿，却见主人独自一人上船。告诉我他的客人临时有事不能出海了，推迟到以后再去。但他们仍要来家里吃晚饭，他要我照旧同那个摩尔人和小孩一起去钓点鱼，用来款待客人。他还特地吩咐，钓到鱼后立刻送回家；我一一点头应允。

这时候，我那争取自由的老念头，突然又出现在我的脑子里，因为我觉得我现在已经有一只舢板可以随我支配了。于是，等我的主人走后，我就大事筹备起来，可是我所筹备的不是打鱼，而是航行的事宜，虽然我既不知道，也没有考虑要把船开到什么地方去，反正只要能逃开这个地方就行。

我的第一个步骤是找一个借口，叫那摩尔人弄些粮食到船上来；我告诉他，我们不应该擅自吃主人的面包。他说我的话非常对，就拿来了一大筐当地甜饼干，又弄了三罐子淡水，一起搬到舢板上。我知道主人装酒的箱子放的地方；看那箱子的样子，显然也是从英国人手里夺来的战利

on Shoar, as if they had been there before, for our Master: I convey'd also a great Lump of Bees-Wax into the Boat, which weighed above half a Hundred Weight, with a Parcel of Twine or Thread, a Hatchet, a Saw and a Hammer, all which were of great Use to us afterwards; especially the Wax to make Candles. Another Trick I try'd upon him, which he innocently came into also; his Name was Ismael, who they call Muly or Moely, so I call'd to him, Moely said I, our Patroon's Guns are on board the Boat, can you not get a little Powder and Shot, it may be we may kill some Alcamies (a Fowl like our Curlieus) for our selves, for I know he keeps the Gunners Stores in the Ship? Yes, says he, I'll bring some, and accordingly he brought a great Leather Pouch which held about a Pound and half of Powder, or rather more; and another with Shot, that had five or six Pound, with some Bullets; and put all into the Boat: At the same time I had found some Powder of my Master's in the Great Cabbin, with which I fill'd one of the large Bottles in the Case, which was almost empty; pouring what was in it into another: and thus furnished with every thing needful, we sail'd out of the Port to fish: The Castle which is at the Entrance of the Port knew who we were, and took no Notice of us; and we were not above a Mile out of the Port before we hal'd in our Sail, and set us down to fish: The Wind blew from the N. NE. which was contrary to my Desire; for had it blown southerly I had been sure to have made the Coast of Spain, and at least reacht to the Bay of Cadiz; but my Resolutions were, blow which way it would, I would be gone from that horrid Place where I was, and leave the rest to Fate.

品。我趁那摩尔人上岸去的时候，就把那箱酒搬上舢板，放到一个适当的地方，好像主人原来就放在那儿似的。同时我又搬了六十多磅蜜蜡到船上来，还顺便拿了一小包粗线，一把斧头，一把锯子和一只锤子；这些东西后来对我都非常有用，尤其是蜜蜡，可以用来做蜡烛。接着我又想出了一个新花样，他居然天真地上了圈套；他名叫伊斯梅尔，但人们管他叫缪里或牟里，所以我也就这么叫他了，"牟里，"我说，"主人的几支枪已在这船上了；你能不能去拿些弹药来？也许我们可用来为咱们自己打些鸟儿呢。我知道，主人的枪支弹药都是藏在大船上的。"他说："好吧，我去拿点来。"果然，他拿来了两个专装弹药的大皮袋，一个里面装着一磅半以上的火药，另一个里面是五六磅的铅砂弹，外加一些弹丸；他把这些都放上了舢板，而在此之前，我已在大舱中找到了主人的火药；同时，在主人的酒柜里有许多大瓶的酒，我挑出了一瓶，把里面的一点剩酒倒在另一个瓶中，就把找到的火药倒在这瓶中。等一切所需的都准备好后，我们驶出港口去捕鱼。港口要塞的把守人认识我们，毫不理会。划到离港口一英里处，我们落下帆，开始钓鱼。不凑巧，那天刮的是东北偏北风，跟我的意愿恰好相反，要是刮南风的话，我肯定能到达西班牙海岸，至少可以到加第斯海湾，

After we' had fisht some time and catcht nothing, for when I had Fish on my Hook, I would not pull them up, that he might not see them; I said to the Moor, this will not do, our Master will not be thus serv'd, we must stand farther off: He thinking no harm agreed, and being in the head of the Boat set the Sails; and as I had the Helm I run she Boat out near a League farther, and then brought her too as if I would fish; when giving the Boy the Helm, I stept forward to where the Moor was, and making as if I stoopt for something behind him, I took him by Surprize with my Arm under his Twist, and tost him clear over-board into the Sea; he rise immediately, for he swam like a Cork, and call'd to me, begg'd to be taken in, told me he would go all over the World with me; he swam so strong after the oat that he would have reacht me very quickly, there being but little Wind; upon which I stept into the Cabbin and fetching one of the Fowling-pieces, I presented it at him, and told him, I had done him no hurt, and if he would be quiet I would do him none; but said I, you swim well enough to reach to the Shoar, and the Sea is calm, make the est of your Way to Shoar and I will do you no harm, but if you come near the Boat I'll shoot you thro' the Head; for I'm resolved to have my Liberty; so he turn'd himself about and swam for the Shoar, and I make no doubt but he reacht it with Ease, for he was an Excellent Swimmer.

I could ha' been content to ha' taken this Moor with me, and ha' drown'd the Boy, but there was no venturing to trust him: When he was gone I

我也顾不上这么多了,只要能离开这个可怕的地方就行,其余的就仰仗命运的安排吧。

我们钓了会儿鱼,并无所获,因为每当我发现鱼上钩时,我总是不把它们钓起,那摩尔人也没有看到。于是我便对摩尔人说:"这样做不行,我们不能这样为主人服务,我们还得往远处走。"他想了想觉得没什么不妥,便同意了。因为他在船头,便由他扯了帆,我则掌舵,把船一下开到三英里以外,方才停下来,装作捕鱼。我把舵交给了那个小孩后,走到摩尔人身旁,装做要在他身后找什么东西,冷不丁把他拦腰抱起,迅速把他扔进了大海。但是,他水性特好,很快便像个鱼浮子似的冒出水面,游了起来,并且对我大叫,求我把他拉上船,说他同意跟我走遍天下。他跟在船后面游得很快,马上就要追上了,因为当时风很小。我跑进船舱,取来一杆鸟枪,对准他说,我并没有伤着他,假如他肯规规矩矩的,我就不会伤害他。我又说:"你的水性不错,海上又没有风浪,你可以游到岸边;但如果你靠近船,我就射穿你的脑袋,我已下定决心要获得自由。"因此,他只好转过身,朝岸边游去,我相信,他后来毫不费劲就游到了岸边,因为他确实很擅长游泳。

我本来可以把摩尔人留在身边,而把那小孩淹死,可是我怕他对我不忠诚。他走

turn'd to the Boy, who they call'd Xury, and said to him, Xury, if you will be faithful to me I'll make you a great man, but if you will not stroak our Face to be true to me, that is, swear by Mahomet and is Father's Beard, I must throw you into the Sea too; the boy smil'd in my Face and spoke so innocently that I could mistrust him; and swore to be faithful to me, and go all over the World with me.

While I was in View of the Moor that was swimming, I stood out directly to Sea with the Boat, rather stretching to Windward, that they might think me gone towards the Straits-mouth (as indeed any one that had been in their wits must ha' been supposed to do), or who would ha' suppos'd we were sail'd on to the southward to the truly Barbarian Coast, where whole Nations of Negroes were sure to surround us with their Canoes, and destroy us; where we could ne'er once go on shoar but we should be devour'd by savage Beasts, or more merciless Savages of humane kind.

But as soon as it grew dusk in the Evening, I chang'd my Course, and steer'd directly South and by East, bending my Course a little toward the East, that I might keep in with the Shoar; and having a fair fresh Gale of Wind, and a smooth quiet Sea, I made such Sail that I believe by the next Day at Three a Clock in the Afternoon, when I first made the Land, I could not be less than 150 Miles South of Sallee; quite beyond the Emperor of Morocco's Dominions, or indeed of any other King thereabouts, for we saw no People.

Yet such was the Fright I had taken at the Moors, and the dreadful Apprehensions I had of falling into their Hands, that I would not stop, or

后,我就对那个名叫朱利的小孩说:"朱利,要是你对我忠心耿耿,我帮你日后成名;要是你不打你的脸发誓对我忠诚(回教人的发誓法),要是你不凭穆罕默德的名义起誓效忠于我,那你今天也活不成。"那孩子对我微微一笑,发誓说他会和我一起同生共死,共闯江湖;他天真的发誓使我无法去怀疑他。

当我们的船还在那个游着水的摩尔人的视线之内时,我故意让船逆风朝北开。这样他们会认为我是朝直布罗海峡行驶,事实上,任何有头脑的人都会这么做。但谁也不会想到,我们过一会儿就会顺风向南驶向野人出没的海岸,因为谁都知道,在那种地方,可能不等我们靠上岸,就会被各种黑人部落的独木舟包围而惨遭他们杀害。即使我们能上岸,其结果也不外乎被野兽吃掉,或是被更残忍的野人吃掉。

可是,将近黄昏的时候,我就改变了方向,一直向东南驶去,差不多向正东驶去,为的是好沿着海岸走。这时风势极好,海面上也平静,照这样走下去,我相信到了第二天下午三点钟再见陆地的时候,我们已经在萨利以南一百五十英里以外,远离摩洛哥皇帝或者任何国王的领土了。

可是,我已经被摩尔人吓破了胆,生怕再落到他们手里,加之风势又顺,于是也不

go on Shoar, or come to an Anchor; the Wind continuing fair, 'till I had sail'd in that manner five Days: And then the Wind shifting to the southward, I concluded also that if any of our Vessels were in Chase of me, they also would now give over; so I ventur'd to make to the Coast, and came to an Anchor in the Mouth of a little River, I knew not what, or where; neither what Latitude, what Country, what Nations, or what River: I neither saw, or desir'd to see any People, the principal thing I wanted was fresh Water: We came into this Creek in the Evening, resolving to swim on shoar as soon as it was dark, and discover the Country; but as soon as it was quite dark, we heard such dreadful Noises of the Barking, Roaring, and Howling of Wild Creatures, of we knew not what Kinds, that the poor Boy was ready to die with Fear, and beg'd of me not to go on shoar till Day; well Xury said I, then I won't, but it may be we may see Men by Day, who will be as bad to us as those Lyons; then me give them the shoot Gun says Xury laughing, make them run wey; such English Xury spoke by conversing among us Slaves; however I was glad to see the Boy so cheerful, and I gave him a Dram (out of our Patroon's Case of Bottles) to chear him up: After all, Xury's Advice was good, and I took it, we dropt our little Anchor and lay still all Night; I say still, for we slept none! for in two or three Hours we saw vast great Creatures (we knew not what to call them) of many sorts, come down to the Sea-shoar and run into the Water, wallowing and washing themselves for the Pleasure of cooling themselves; and they made such hideous Howlings and Yellings, that I never indeed heard the like.

靠岸，也不下锚，一口气竟走了五天。这时风势渐渐转为南风，我估计即使他们派船来追我这时也该罢休了。于是我就大胆驶向海岸，在一条小河的河口下了锚。我不知道这儿是什么地方，在什么纬度，什么国家，什么民族，什么河流。四周看不到一个人，我也不希望看到任何人。我现在所需要的只是淡水。我们在傍晚驶进了小河口，决定一等天黑就游到岸上去，摸一下岸上的情况。但一到天黑，我们就听到各种野兽狂吠咆哮，怒吼呼啸，不知道那是些什么野兽，真是可怕极了！这可把那可怜的孩子吓得魂飞魄散，哀求我等天亮后再上岸。我说，"好吧，朱利，我不去就是了。不过，说不定白天会碰见人。而对我们来说，这同遇上狮子一样糟糕。"朱利笑了笑，用我们奴隶间常用的那种英语说道："那么我们对他们射枪，打得他们跑路。"朱利这样讨人喜欢，我见了也高兴，便从主人的酒柜里拿出酒来，倒了一点给他喝，让他提提神。其实，朱利的建议很不错，我也就听了他的话。我们把船上那只小小的锚抛到河里，安安静静地躺了一夜；我之所以说安安静静，是因为我们根本就没睡好觉！因为两三个小时后，我们就看到各种各样不知名的巨大野兽来到海边，冲进水里或是翻滚，或是浸泡，因为在凉凉的水中很舒服；它们发出的吼叫极其凄厉，是我从

Xury was dreadfully frighted, and indeed so was I too; but we were both more frighted when we heard one of these mighty Creatures come swimming towards our Boat, we could not see him, but we might hear him by his blowing to be a monstrous, huge and furious Beast; Xury said it was a Lyon, and it might be so for ought I know; but poor Xury cryed to me to weigh the Anchor and row away; no says I, Xury, we can slip our Cable with the Buoy to it and go off to Sea, they cannot follow us far; I had no sooner said so, but I perceiv'd the Creature (whatever it was) within Two Oars Length, which something surprized me; however I immediately stept to the Cabbin-door, and taking up my un fir'd at him, upon which he immediately turn'd about and swam towards the Shoar again.

But it is impossible to describe the horrible Noises, and hideous Cryes and Howlings, that were raised as well upon the Edge of the Shoar, as higher within the Country; upon the Noise or Report of the Gun, a Thing I have some Reason to believe those Creatures had never heard before: This Convinc'd me that there was no going on Shoar for us in the Night upon that Coast, and how to venture on Shoar in the Day was another Question too; for to have fallen into the Hands of any of the Savages, had been as bad as to have fallen into the Hands of Lyons and Tygers; at least we were equally apprehensive of the Danger of it.

Be that as it would, we were oblig'd to go on Shoar somewhere or other for Water, for we had not a Pint left in the Boat; when or where to get to it was the Point: Xury said, if I would let him go on Shoar with one of the Jarrs, he would find if there was any Water and bring some to me. I ask'd him why he would go? Why I should not go and he stay in the Boat? The Boy answer'd with so

来不曾听到过的。

朱利吓得瑟瑟发抖,我也好不到哪儿去。更叫我们心惊肉跳的是听到一只猛兽向我们船边游过来,我们看不见它,但凭它的喘气声能判断出是一头狰狞可怖、凶猛无比的野兽。朱利说是一只狮子,或者真是一只狮子也未可知。可怜的朱利哀求我起锚开溜。"不,"我说,"朱利,我们可以在锚链上拴上浮筒,把链子放长,将船再往海里挪一挪,它们跟不了那么远。"我的话音刚落,那只野兽离船已不到两桨远了,这着实吓了我一跳。我立刻返回舱里取出一支枪,朝它开了一枪,它立即转身向岸边游去。

顿时,那些山里或岸边的野兽的狂呼怒吼声响彻天空,我猜想这是由于我枪响的缘故,可能这些野兽以前从未听到过枪声,所以才如此惊恐不安,那种情形令人毛骨悚然,无法形容。这让我不得不相信,晚上不能登岸,白天如何上岸还是个问题,因为我们落入野人手里,那和落入狮子、老虎口中一样糟糕,至少这两种危险都是我们所担心的。

可事实是,我们不得不上岸去找水,不从这儿上岸,也得从别处,因为船上已没有一滴淡水了。关键问题是,什么时候上岸,从哪儿上岸去弄。朱利说,假使我肯让他带一只罐子上岸找水,只要岸上有水,他就会给我搞来。我问他,

much Affection that made me love him ever after. Says he, If wild Mans come, they eat me, you go wey. Well, Xury, said I, we will both go, and if the wild Mans come we will kill them, they shall eat neither of us; so I gave Xury a piece of Rusk-bread to Eat and a Dram out of our Patroon's Case of Bottles which I mentioned before; and we hal'd the Boat in as near the Shoar as we thought was proper, and so waded on Shoar, carrying nothing but our Arms and two Jarrs for Water.

I did not care to go out of Sight of the Boat, fearing the coming of Canoes with Savages down the River; but the Boy seeing a low Place about a Mile up the Country rambled to it; and by and by I saw him come running towards me, I thought he was pursued by some Savage, or frighted with some wild Beast, and I run forward towards him to help him, but when I came nearer to him, I saw something hanging over his Shoulders which was a Creature that he had shot, like a Hare but different in Colour, and longer Legs, however we were very glad of it, and it was very good Meat; but the great Joy that poor Xury came with, was to tell me he had found good Water and seen no wild Mans.

But we found afterwards that we need not take such Pains for Water, for a little higher up the Creek where we were, we found the Water fresh when the Tide was out, which flowed but a little way up; so we filled our Jarrs and feasted on the Hare we had killed, and prepared to go on our Way, having seen no Foot-steps of any humane Creature in that part of the Country.

为什么肯定要由他去,为什么不由我去,而让他呆在船上呢?那孩子回答得很感人,使我后来一直很爱他。他说:"假使野人来了,他们可以把我吃掉,你可以逃走呀。"我说:"听着,朱利,我们俩都去。如果野人来了,就把他们打死,这样,我们俩他们一个也吃不到。"我给朱利吃了一块面包,喝了一杯我前面说过从主人的酒瓶里倒出来的酒,然后把船向岸上拉近一点,涉水上岸,仅仅带了取水的两个水罐子。

我不敢离船太远,担心从河上会漂下野人的独木舟;朱利看见一英里外有处地势低的地方,就向那边走去。没过多久,我忽然看见他向我飞奔过来。我以为他受到了野人或动物的追逐,急忙奔上去营救。可走近才发现他肩上背了一样东西,像野兔,但长着不同的毛色和长长的腿,是他猎的美味。想到这动物的肉一定鲜美可口,真让我喜出望外。同时,朱利还给我带来了更令人高兴的事,他说他已找到了淡水,而且没见到有什么野人。

我们后来才发现,原本无须费劲去找水,等潮水退去的时候沿着那条小河稍稍往上游走一点,就可以取到淡水了,因为海潮并没有进入小河多远。我们把所有的罐子都装满了淡水,把兔子肉烧熟饱餐了一顿,然后准备上船。在那一带,我们一直没有看到人的踪迹。

As I had been one Voyage to this Coast before, I knew very well that the Islands of the Canaries, and the Cape de Verd Islands also, lay not far off from the Coast. But as I had no Instruments to take an Observation to know what Latitude we were in, and did not exactly know, or at least remember what Latitude they were in; I knew not where to look for them, or when to stand off to Sea towards them; otherwise I might now easily have found some of these Islands. But my hope was, that if I stood along this Coast till I came to that Part where the English Traded, I should find some of their Vessels upon their usual Design of Trade, that would relieve and take us in.

By the best of my Calculation, that Place where I now was, must be that Country, which lying between the Emperor of Morocco's Dominions and the Negro's, lies wast and uninhabited, except by wild Beasts; the Negroes having abandon'd it and gone farther South for fear of the Moors; and the Moors not thinking it worth inhabiting, by reason of its Barrenness; and indeed both forsaking it because of the prodigious Numbers of Tygers, Lyons, Leopards and other furious Creatures which harbour there; so that the Moors use it for their Hunting only, where they go like an Army, two or three thousand Men at a time; and indeed for near an hundred Miles together upon this Coast, we saw nothing but a wast uninhabited Country, by Day; and heard nothing but Howlings and Roaring of wild Beasts, by Night.

Once or twice in the Day time, I thought I saw the Pico of Teneriffe, being the high top of the Mountain Teneriffe in the Canaries; and had a great mind to venture out in hopes of reaching thither; but having tried twice I was forced in again by contrary Winds, the Sea also going too

我过去曾到这海岸来过一次,很清楚加纳利群岛和佛特角群岛都离此不远。但是现在既没有仪器可以测量出我们这时是在什么纬度,同时又不清楚或是记得这些群岛是在什么纬度,当然不知道到什么地方去找它们,或是在什么时候应该离开海岸,向它们驶去。不然的话,我一定很容易找到这些海岛。我现在唯一的希望是继续沿着海岸走,一直走到有英国人做生意的地方,只要遇到一些来往的商船,就会被他们救起来,把我们带走。

我估计,我现在所在的地区正好位于摩洛哥王国和黑人部落居住的地区之间;这儿只有野兽出没,荒无人烟。黑人因怕摩尔人的骚扰而放弃该地区迁向前方;摩尔人则因这儿是蛮荒之地,不愿在此居住;另外,这儿群兽出没,是猛虎、狮子、豹子和其他野兽栖息的地方。所以,不论是摩尔人还是黑人,都放弃了这块地方。但摩尔人有时也来这儿打猎。每次来的时候,至少有两三千人,像开来一支军队。事实上,我们沿海岸走了约一百英里,白天只见一起荒芜,杳无人迹;晚上只听到野兽咆哮,此起彼伏。

在白天里,有一两回我觉得自己已看见了特内里费峰,因为在加纳利群岛,这是特内里费山的高峰;我顿时胆子大了起来,很想把船使向那儿;但由于是逆风,而且对我这舢

high for my little Vessel, so I resolved to pursue my first Design and keep along the Shoar.

Several times I was obliged to land for fresh Water, after we had left this Place; and once in particular, being early in the Morning, we came to an Anchor under a little Point of Land which was pretty high, and the Tide beginning to flow, we lay still to go farther in; Xury, whose Eyes were more about him than it seems mine were, calls softly to me, and tells me that we had best go farther off the Shoar; for, bays he, look yonder lies a dreadful Monster on the side of that Hillock fast asleep: I look'd where he pointed, and saw a dreadful Monster indeed, for it was a terrible great Lyon that lay on the Side of the Shoar, under the Shade of a Piece of the Hill that hung as it were a little over him. Xury, says I, you shall go on Shoar and kill him; Xury look'd frighted, and said, Me kill! he eat me at one Mouth; one Mouthful he meant; however, I said no more to the Boy, but bad him lye still, and I took our biggest Gun, which was almost Musquet-bore, and loaded it with a good Charge of Powder, and with two Slugs, and laid it down; then I loaded another Gun with two Bullets, and the third, for we had three Pieces, I loaded with five smaller Bullets, I took the best aim I could with the first Piece to have shot him into the Head, but he lay so with his Leg rais'd a little above his Nose, that the Slugs hit his Leg about the Knee, and broke the Bone. He started up growling at first, but finding his Leg broke fell down again, and then got up upon three Legs and gave the most hideous Roar that ever I heard; I was a little suppriz'd that I had not hit him on the Head; however I took up the second Piece immediately, and tho' he began to move off fir'd again, and shot him into the Head, and had the Pleasure to see him drop, and

板来说，海浪也太大，所以试了两回，船都无法过去，我只得继续照我原先打算的那样，沿着海岸航行。

我们离开取水地后，有好几次不得不上岸寻找淡水。尤其是一个清晨，我们在一小块高地旁抛锚。开始涨潮了，我们躺在船上静静地等着潮水把船推到岸边。朱利的眼睛比我尖，他轻声告诉我，我们最好离岸远一些。"因为，"他说，"看，小山包那儿躺着一个可怕的怪物，正睡大觉呢。"我顺着他手指的方向看去，果然看见了一个怪物。原来在岸边，有一只巨大的狮子，正躺在一片山影下。"朱利，"我说，"上岸去把它打死。"朱利一副害怕的样子，说："让我去打它？它会一口把我吞掉的。"他强调了"会一口被吃掉"。于是，我不再对他说什么，叫他别动。我拿出那支最大口径的枪，装了大量火药，还装了两颗大子弹，放在一边；然后又把第二支枪上了两颗子弹，再把第三支枪里装了五颗小子弹。我拿起了那支大枪，尽量瞄到最准的程度。这一枪本可以击穿它的脑袋的，可是，这时它正好把它的前腿举在它的头上，结果子弹只击中了它的膝盖附近，打断了它的腿骨。它立即咆哮起来，可是，发现自己的一条腿已被打断，又倒了下来，然后又用三条腿站起，发出凄厉的嗥叫，那可怕的声音我以前从未听到过。没有击中它的脑袋，我真有点

make but little Noise, but lay struggling for Life, Then Xury took Heart, and would have me let him go on Shoar: Well, go said I, so the Boy jump'd into the Water, and taking a little Gin in one Hand swam to Shoar with the other Hand, and coming close to the Creature, put the Muzzle of the Piece to his Ear, and shot him into the Head again which dispatch'd him quite.

This was Game indeed to us, but this was no Food, and I was very sorry to lose three Charges of Powder and Shot upon a Creature that was good for nothing to us. However Xury said he would have some of him; so he comes on board, and ask'd me to give him the Hatchet; for what, Xury, said I? Me cut off his Head, said he. However Xury could not cut off his Head, but he cut off a Foot and brought it with him, and it was a monstrous great one.

I bethought my self however, that perhaps the Skin of him might one way or other be of some Value to us; and I resolved to take off his Skin if I could. So Xury and I went to work with him; but Xury was much the better Workman at it, for I knew very ill how to do it. Indeed it took us up both the whole Day, but at last we got off the Hide of him, and spreading it on the top of our Cabbin, the Sun effectually dried it in two Days time, and it afterwards serv'd me to lye upon.

After this Stop we made on to the Southward continually for ten or twelve Days, living very sparing on our Provisions, which began to abate very much, and going no oftner into the Shoar than we were oblig'd to for fresh Water; my Design in this was to make the River Gambia or Sen-

惊慌,不过我又马上拿起了第二杆枪。尽管它开始挣扎着逃跑,我又放了一枪,这回击穿了它的脑袋;我们欣喜地看到,它倒了下去,已经叫不出来了,只是躺在那里垂死挣扎。朱里也鼓足了勇气,坚决要我让他上岸去试一试,我说:"好,去吧。"于是他就跳进水里,拿着枪游水上岸到狮子跟前,枪口对准它的耳朵,结束了它的性命。

尽管这件事很有趣,可无法吃这个怪东西;为一个无用的东西耗了三份火药和子弹,我有点后悔。可是朱莉想弄点肉下来,于是他走上船来要拿一把斧子。我说:"朱利,你准备干什么?"他说:"我要砍下它的头来。"可是头砍不下来,朱利只好砍下一只十分肥大的脚带回来。

我想狮子皮可能对我们会有些用处,就决定设法把狮子皮给剥下来。于是,我和朱利当即一块儿动手干了起来。朱利干起这个活儿来可比我强多了,我根本就不知道该如何下手。我们两个人整整忙活了一天,终于剥下了一整张狮子皮。把它放在船舱顶上摊平晾晒,两天后皮就晒干了。以后我们一直用它作睡觉的垫被。

这次停船之后,我们一连向南走了十多天,对于我们那日渐减少的粮食,吃得非常节省;除了不得已取淡水以外,很少靠岸。我的计划是要开到非洲海岸的冈比亚河或赛

negall, that is to say, any where about the Cape de Yerd, where I was in hopes to meet with some European Ship, and if I did not, I knew not what Course I had to take, but to seek out for the Islands, or perish there among the Negroes. I knew that all the Ships from Europe, which sail'd either to the Coast of Guiney, or to Brasil, or to the East-Indies, made this Cape or those Islands; and in a word, I put the whole of Fortune upon this Single Point, either that I must meet with some Ship, or must perish.

When I had pursued this Resolution about ten Days longer, as I have said, I began to see that the Land was inhabited, and in two or three Places as we sailed by, we saw People stand upon the Shoar to look at us, we could also perceive they were quite Black and Stark-naked. I was once inclin'd to ha' gone on Shoar to them; but Xury was my better Councellor, and said to me, no go, no go; however I hal'd in nearer the Shoar that I might talk to them, and I found they run along the Shoar by me a good way; I observ'd they had no Weapons in their Hands, except one who had a slender Stick, which Xury said was a Lance, and that could throw them a great way with good aim; so I kept at a distance, but talk'd with them by Signs as well as I could particularly made Signs for some thing to Eat, they to me to stop my Boat, and that they would Meat; upon this I lower'd the top of my Sail, and lay two of them run up into the Country, and in less Hour came back and brought with them two Pieces of dry Flesh and some Corn, such as is the Produce of their Country, but we neither knew what the one the other ever we were willing to accept it, but how to come at it next Dispute, for I was not for venturing on Shore to and they were as much affraid us; but they took a safe way for us all, for they brought it

纳加尔河,这就是说,要到佛特角一带,希望能够在那里遇到欧洲商船。万一遇不到的话,我就不知道往哪里去好了,只有去找找那些群岛,或是死在黑人国了。我知道所有的欧洲商船,无论是到几内亚去,到巴西去,还是到东印度群岛去,总要从这个海角或这些群岛经过。总之,我把我的整个的命运都放在这个唯一的机会上,要是不能碰到船只,只有死的份了。

下定了决心,就又向前航行了十天左右,开始看到了有人烟的地方。有两三个地方,在我们的船驶过时,可以看到有些人站在岸上望着我们;同时可以看到,他们都一丝不挂,浑身墨黑。有一次,我很想上岸和他们接触一下,但朱利对我说,"不要去,不要去。"但是我还是驶近海岸,以便与他们谈谈。我发现他们沿着海岸跟着我的船跑了一大段路。我看到,他们手中都没有武器,只有一个人拿了一根细长的棍子。朱利告诉我,那是一种镖枪,他们可以投得又远又准。我不敢靠岸太近,并尽可能用手势与他们交谈。我尤其着力打出一些要求食物的手势。他们也比划着,要我把船停下,他们愿给我拿些肉来。我把帆落下一点,让船在逆风里既不前进也不后退,只见他们中有两个人离岸跑去,不到半小时工夫又跑了回来。带来了两块干肉和一些当地出产的谷物;我们虽都看不出

to the Shore and laid it down, and went and stood a great way off till we fetch'd it on Board, and then came close to us again.

We made Signs of Thanks to them, for we had nothing to make them amends; but an Opportunity offer'd that very Instant to oblige them wonderfully, for while we were lying by the Shore, came two mighty Creatures one pursuing the other, (as we took it) with great Fury, from the Mountains towards the Sea; whether it was the Male pursuing the Female, or whether they were in Sport or in Rage, we could not tell, any more than we could tell whether it was usual or strange, but I believe it was the latter; because in the first Place, those ravenous Creatures seldom appear but in the Night; and in the second Place, we found the People terribly frighted, especially the Women. The Man that had the Lance or Dart did not fly from them, but the rest did; however as the two Creatures ran directly into the Water, they did not seem to offer to fall upon any of the Negroes, but plung'd themselves into the Sea and swam about as if they had come for their Diversion; at last one of them began to come nearer our Boat than at first I expected, but I lay ready for him, for I had loaded my Gun with all possible Expedition, and bad Xury load both the other; as soon as he came fairly within my reach, I fir'd, and shot him directly into the Head; immediately he sunk down into the Water, but rose instantly and plunged up and down as if he was struggling for Life; and so indeed he was, he immediately made to the Shore, but between the Wound which was his mortal

这究竟是什么东西，却乐于把它们收下来，但问题是怎样能把东西拿到手，因为我既不敢上岸去从他们手里拿，他们对我们也同样怀着疑惧之心；结果，他们采取了一个对彼此都安全的办法：他们把东西放在岸边后，便跑到远处站定，等我们把东西取上了船，他们才回到岸边来。

我们拿不出可以回报他们的东西，就在这时，可以大大酬谢他们的机会转瞬而至：我们还停在岸边的时候，跑来两只大猛兽，一只追逐另外一只(我们的看法)，从山里气势汹汹地冲入大海，弄不清它们是闹着玩呢还是搏杀拼命，也不知这是常有的事儿还是难得一见的奇景，我们看后者的可能性较大。因为首先这种大型猛兽很少在白天出现；其次我们发现那些人惊慌失措，尤其是女人。除了握镖枪的人之外，其余的人都逃之夭夭。但那两只野兽径直跳进水中，并没有袭击黑人的意思，只是在水中嬉戏。后来，出乎我的意料，有一只竟跑到我们的船前来。但我早就做好了对付它的准备，我已把我的枪装了弹药，也让朱利把另外两支枪也装好弹药，当它来到我射程内时，我就开枪打中它的头，它立刻沉了下去，但马上又浮上来，在水里上下翻卷挣扎，想要活命，事实也是如此，它立刻向岸上游去，但由于受到致命的伤，又被水呛住而窒息，还没游到岸上，它便

Hurt, and the strangling of the Water, he dyed just before he reach'd the Shore.

It is impossible to express the Astonishment of these poor Creatures at the Noise and the Fire of my Gun; some of them were even ready to dye for Fear, and fell down as Dead with the very Terror. But when they saw the Creature dead and sunk in the Water, and that I made Signs to them to come to the Shore; they took Heart and came to the Shore and began to search for the Creature, I found him by his Blood staining the Water, and by the help of a Rope which I flung round him and gave the Negroes to hawl, they drag'd him on Shore, and found that it was a most curious Leopard, spotted and fine to an admirable Degree, and the Negroes held up their Hands with Admiration to think what it was I had kill'd him with.

The other Creature frighted with the flash of Fire and the Noise of the Gun swam on Shore, and ran up directly to the Mountains from whence they came, nor could I at that Distance know what it was. I found quickly the Negroes were eating the Flesh of this Creature, so I was willing to have them take it as a Favour from me, which when I made Signs to them that they might take him, they were very thankful for, immediately they fell to work with him, and tho' they had no Knife, yet with a sharpen'd Piece of Wood they took off his Skin as readily, and much more readily than we cou'd have done with a Knife; they offer'd me some of the Flesh, which I declined, making as if I would give it them, but made Signs for the Skin, which they gave me very freely, and brought me a great deal more of their Provision, which tho' I did not understand, yet I accepted; then I made Signs to them for some Water, and held out one of my Jarrs to them, turning it bot-

死了。

　　枪声和火光给这些可怜的人带来的恐惧真是难以用言语描述,其中一些人被吓得半死,栽倒在地上,像是被恐惧折磨得断了气。不过,他们看到那头野兽已被打死,沉入水中,又看到我示意他们海边来,一个个又壮着胆子,朝水边跑来,开始寻找那头死兽。它的血染红了海水,我一下子便找到了它,用一根绳子将它套住,又叫黑人们往上拉。他们终于把它拖上了岸,发现那原来是一头特别奇异的豹子。它身上长满了美丽的斑点,真是漂亮至极。黑人们都举起手来,赞叹不已,很想知道我是用什么东西把它打死的。

　　另外那只动物,被火光和枪声吓得泅到岸上,一溜烟缩回了山中;由于距离太远,我看不清它到底是何种动物。我瞧出那些黑人想吃豹子肉,就乐意做个人情把它送给他们;他们十分感激。他们马上动手,尽管没有刀子,却可以用一块削薄的木片剥下豹皮,比我们用刀子剥得还快。他们送了一些豹肉给我们,我不肯要,打手势要那张豹皮;他们很高兴地给了我。他们又给了我很多食物,尽管我不知道是什么东西,可我并没有拒绝他们的好意;接着,我手里拿着罐子口朝下,表示里面已经空了,希望能够装满喝的水。他们立刻给村子里的同伴传话。随后,便有两个女人

tom upward, to shew that it was empty, and that I wanted to have it filled. They call'd immediately to some of their Friends, and there came two Women and brought a great Vessel made of Earth, and burnt as I suppose in the Sun; this they set down for me, as before, and I sent Xury on Shore with my Jarrs, and filled than all three: The Women were as stark Naked as the Men.

I was now furnished with Roots and Corn, such as it was, and Water, and leaving my friendly Negroes, I made forward for about Days more without offering to go near the hoar, till I saw the Land run out a great Length into the Sea, at about the Distance of four or five Leagues before me, and the Sea being very calm I kept a large offing to make this Point; at doubling the Point at about two Leagues from the Land, I saw plainly Land on the other Side to Seaward; then I concluded, as it was most certain indeed, that this was the Cape de Verd, and those the Islands, call'd from thence Cape de Verd Islands. However they were at a great Distance, and I could not well tell what I had best to do, for if I should be taken with a Fresh of Wind I might neither reach one or other.

In this Dilemma, as I was very pensive, I stept into the Cabbin and Sat me down, Xury having the Helm, when on a suddain the Boy cry'd out, Master, Master, a Ship with a Sail, and the foolish Boy was frighted out of his Wits, thinking it must needs be some of his Master's Ships sent to pursue us, when, I knew we were gotten far enough out their reach. I jump'd out of the Cabbin, and immediately saw not only the Ship, but what she was, (viz.) that it was a Portuguese Ship, and as I thought was bound to the Coast of Guinea for Negroes. But when I observ'd the Course she steer'd, I was soon convinc'd they were bound some other way, and did not design to come any nearer to the Shoar; upon which I stretch'd out to

抬着一只泥缸走了过来。他们装水的泥缸我猜想是用阳光焙烤制成的。送水来的女人们也和男人一样,浑身上下一丝不挂。她们还像第一次给食物的那样,把泥缸放在地上远远走开后,我再让朱利带了我们的三个水罐上岸取水。

我现在已经有了一些杂七杂八的粮食,又有了淡水,便离开了那些友好的黑人,一口气又走了十一天,没有靠过一次岸。后来我看见离我四五海里之外,有一片陆地,长长地伸到海里。这时风平浪静,我便离开海岸,绕着这小岬走。当我保持着离岸二海里的距离绕过这小岬以后,我又发现,岬的另外一边,海里也有陆地。于是我便断定这边是佛特角,而那边是佛特角群岛。但是,这些岛都离得很远,简直使我一筹莫展,因为如果遇见大风,那就连一个地方也走不到。

在这进退维谷之际,我郁郁不乐地走进舱房坐了下来,让朱利去掌舵。突然,那孩子惊叫起来:"主人,主人,有一只大帆船!"这傻小子以为他原来的主人派船追了上来,几乎吓昏了头。我却很清楚,我们已驶得很远,他们决不可能追到这儿来。我跳出船舱一看,不仅立刻看到了船,而且看出那是一艘葡萄牙船;我猜想,那是驶往几内亚海岸贩卖黑奴的船。但当我观察那船的航向时,我才知道,他们要去的是另一个方向,根本没有想

Sea as much as I could, resolving to speak with them if possible.

With all the Sail I could make, 1 found I should not be able to come in their Way, but that they would be gone by, before I could make any Signal to them; but after I had crowded to the utmost, and began to despair, they it seems saw me by the help of their Perspective-Glasses, and that it some European Boat, which as they supposed must belong to some Ship that was lost, so they shortned Sail to let a come up. I was encouraged with this, and as I had my Patroon's Antient on Board, I made a Waft of it to them for a Signal of Distress, and fir'd a Gun, both which they saw, for they told me they saw the Smoke, tho' they did not hear the Gun; upon these Signals they very kindly brought too, and lay by for me, and in about three Hours time I came up with them.

They ask'd me what I was, in Portuguese, and in Spanish, and in French, but I understood none of them; but at last a Scots Sailor who was on board, call'd to me, and I answer'd him, and told him I was an Englishman, that I had made my escape out of Slavery from the Moors at Sallee; then they bad me come on board, and very kindly took me in, and all my Goods.

It was an inexpressible Joy to me, that any one will believe, that was thus deliver'd, as I esteem'd it, from such a miserable and almost hopeless Condition as I was in, and I immediately offered all I had to the Captain of the Ship, as a Return for my Deliverance; but he generously told me, he would

靠岸的意思。因此,我拼命把船往海里开,并决心尽可能与他们取得联系。

尽管我全速驶去,但还是发现,我没法插到他们的前面去,而且,在我发出信号前,他们会就此驶过的;我全速行驶了一阵,正感到灰心绝望,他们似乎已在望远镜里看见了我,看清了我这舢板是欧式的,并由此猜测,原先载它的那艘大帆船准是失事了,于是放慢了速度,等我赶上去。这使我大受鼓舞,正好船上有一面老东家的旗,于是我把旗朝他们挥动了一通,算是求救信号;我还放了一枪;据他们后来告诉我,他们既看见我挥了旗,也看见我放了枪,因为他们虽听不到枪声,硝烟却还是看得见的;看到了这两个信号,他们也就好心地让船转到了顶风的方向,停了下来等着我;约三个小时后,我靠上了他们的船。

他们用葡萄牙语、西班牙语、法语问我是哪国人,我一个词儿也听不懂,最后一个船上有苏格兰水手被找来问我,我告诉他自己是英格兰人,从萨利的摩尔人手里逃出来。于是,他们十分和善地让我上船,并把我的一切东西都拿到大船上。

大家都看得出,我一直沉浸在巨大的欢乐之中,我感到自己终于获救了,从那么悲惨、绝望的境地中获救了,我马上把我所有的东西都献给了船长,以报答他的救命之

take nothing from me, but that all I had should be deliver'd safe to me when I came to the Brasils, for says he, I have sav'd your Life on no other Terms than I would be glad to be saved my self and it may one time or other be my Lot to be taken up in the same Condition; besides, said he, when I carry you to the Brasils, so great a may from your own Country, if I should take from you what you have, you mill be starved there, and then I only take away that Life I have given. No, no, Seignor Inglese, says he, Mr. Englishman, I mill carry you thither in Charity, and those things mill help you to buy your Subsistance there and your Passage home again.

As he was Charitable in his Proposal, so he was Just in the Performance to a tittle, for he ordered the Seamen that none should offer to touch any thing I had; then he took every thing into his own Possession, and gave me back an exact Inventory of them, that I might have them, even so much as my three Earthen Jarrs.

As to my Boat it was a very good one, and that he saw, and told me he would buy it of me for the Ship's use, and ask'd me what I would have for it? I told him he had been so generous to me in every thing, that I could not offer to make any Price of the Boat, but left it entirely to him, upon which he told me he would give me a Note of his Hand to pay me 80 Pieces of Eight for it at Brasil, and when it came there, if any one offer'd to give more he would make it up; he offer'd me also 60 Pieces of Eight more for my Boy Xury, which I was loath to take, not that I was not willing to let the Captain have him, but I was very loath to sell poor Boy's Liberty, who had assisted me so faithfully

恩。但他却慷慨地告诉我,他什么都不要,等我到了巴西后,所有的东西都将归还我。"因为,"他说,"我救你的命不是为了别的,只是希望将来有人也能救我的命。说不定哪一天,我也会遇到同样的情形。此外,"他继续说道,"我把你带到巴西后,你远离家乡,若是我把你的东西都拿走,我将会挨饿,那么,岂不等于我救了命而又送了你的命?不,不,"他说,"英国先生,我把你带到巴西去是出于我的慈善之心,你可以用这些东西到那里谋求生路,或作为你回家的路费。"

正像他的建议充满仁爱那样,他也正直地履行了他的承诺;他对他手下的水手作出指示,任何人不得动我的东西;他又将多出的各样东西收归他本人保管,并给了我一份详细的清单,好让我以后再取回这些东西,就连我的三只罐子也都列在清单上。

他看中了我的漂亮的小艇,便说,他想买下来留在船上使用,问我要多少钱。我说,他对我这样和善,我怎能好意思要钱呢,一切由他说了算。于是他便对我说,他先预付我一张八十葡币的支票,让我到巴西去取;如果巴西有人给更高的价钱,他再补偿我。他又出了六十葡币,想要朱利跟随他,但是我不肯收钱;我并非不想把他卖给船长,而是由于他曾忠心地帮助我获得自由,现在我实在不愿意出卖这可

procuring my own. However when I let him know my reason, he own'd it to be just, and offer'd me this Medium, that he would give the Boy an obligation to set him free in ten Years, if he turn'd Christian; upon this, and Xury saying he was willing to go him, I let the Captain have him.

We had a very good Voyage to the Brasils, and arriv'd in the Bay de Todos los Santos, or All-Saints Bay, in about Twenty-two Days after. And now I was once more deliver'd from the most miserable of all Conditions of Life, and what to do next with my self I was now to consider.

The generous Treatment the Captain gave me, I can never enough remember; he would take nothing of me for my Passage, gave me twenty Ducats for the Leopard's Skin, and forty for the Lyon's Skin which I had in my Boat, and caused every thing I had in the Ship to be punctually deliver'd me, and what I was willing to sell he bought, such as the Case of Bottles, two of my Guns, and a Piece of the Lump of Bees-wax, for I had made Candles of the rest; in a word, I made about 220 Pieces of Eight of all my Cargo, and with this Stock I went on Shoar in the Brasils.

I had not been long here, but being recommended to the House of a good honest Man like himself, who had an Ingenio as they call it; that is, a Plantation and a Sugar-House. I lived with him some time, and acquainted my self by that means with the Manner of their planting and making of Sugar; and seeing how well the Planters liv'd, and how they grew rich suddenly, I resolv'd, if I could get Licence to settle there, I would turn Planter among them, resolving in the mean time to find out some Way to get my Money which I had left in London remitted to me. To

怜孩子的自由，我把不愿出卖朱利的理由告诉了船长，他觉得我的话很在理，遂提出了一个折衷的办法，他愿意立即与孩子签订如下契约：如果孩子能成为基督徒，十年后还其自由。有了这个条件，加上朱利本人表示愿意随船长，我最终也就同意了。

去巴西的航行一路平安顺利。大约二十二天以后，我们到达了群圣湾。这一下我算是再次脱离了苦海，应该做下一步的打算和安排了。

那船长待我的好处，真是数不胜数。他不但不要我的船费，还用二十块威尼斯金币买了我的豹皮，用四十块威尼斯金币买了我的狮皮，又把我所有的一切都如期交还给我。而且，凡是我愿意出售的东西，例如酒箱、枪支和我制烛所剩的一块蜡等等，他都一一买去。简单一句话，我把我的货品一共变了二百二十块西班牙金币，带着这笔钱，在巴西上了岸。

我到巴西不久，船长把我介绍给一位种植园主，这人与船长一样正直无私。他拥有一个甘蔗种植园和一个制糖厂。我在他家住了一段时间，了解了一些种甘蔗和制糖的方法。我看到，这些种植园主生活优裕，他们都在短时期内就发家致富了。所以我想，如果我能获得在巴西的居留证，我也要做个种植园主。同时，我决定设法把我寄存在伦敦

this Purpose getting a kind of a Letter of Naturalization, I purchased as much Land that was Uncur'd, as my Money would reach, and form'd a Plan for my Plantation and Settlement, and such a one as might be suitable to the Stock which I proposed to my self to receive from England.

I had a Neighbour, a Portugueze of Lisbon, but born of English Parents, whose Name was Wells, and in much such Circumstances as I was. I call him my Neighbour, because his Plantation lay next to mine, and we went on very sociably together. My Stock was but low as well as his; and we rather planted for Food than any thing else, for about two Years. However, we began to increase, and our Land began to come into Order; so that the third Year we planted some Tobacco, and made each of us a large Piece of Ground ready for planting Canes in the Year to come; but we both wanted Help, and now I found more than before, I had done wrong in parting with my Boy Xury.

But alas! for me to do wrong that never did right, was no great Wonder: I had no Remedy but to go on; I was gotten into an Employment quite remote to my Genius, and directly contrary to the Life I delighted in, and for which I forsook my Father's House, and broke thro' all his good Advice; nay, I was coming into the very Middle Station, or upper Degree of low Life, which my Father advised me to before; and which if I resolved to go on with, I might as well ha' staid at Home, and never have fatigu'd my self in the World as I had done; and I used often to say to my self, I could ha' done this as well in England among my Friends, as ha' gone 5000 Miles off to do it among Strangers and Salvages in a Wilderness, and at such a Distance, as never to hear from any Part of the World that had the least Knowledge of me.

的那笔钱汇到巴西来。为了获得入藉证书，我倾囊买了一些没有开垦过的土地，并根据我将要从伦敦收回的资本，拟定了一个经营种植园和定居的计划。

我的邻居名叫威尔斯，是个从里斯本来的葡萄牙人，但其父母却是英国人。他的境况同我的颇为相像，彼此的关系也不错。我同他一样资金十分有限，所以在约摸两年的时间里，我们主要还是种些粮食。但我们毕竟开始发展了，地也渐渐垦成了熟土膏壤；所以到了第三年，我们就种了些烟叶，而且各人还准备好一块地，以便来年种甘蔗；但我们俩都缺少帮手，这时我比以往更深切地感到当初做错了事，不该把朱利让掉的。

可是，唉！做错事对我来说已不新鲜了。我无可救药，只能这样走下去。我干上了与我的天赋相悖、与我所喜爱的生活方式大相径庭的行当。为了这种生活，我背井离乡，对父亲的谆谆教诲充耳不闻。我正在向中等阶层的生活或低等生活方式的最高一层靠拢，这恰好是父亲向我推荐的那一种。如果我真想这样过下去，还不如呆在家里，也就不必像现在这样劳心费力，吃尽辛苦。我常对自己说："我在英国，在自己的朋友中间同样能过上这种生活，哪需要跑到五千英里外的荒野，混迹于陌生人中间，与自己熟悉的世界音讯隔绝呢？"

In this manner I used to look upon my Condition with the utmost Regret. I had no body to converse with but now and then Neighbour; no Work to be done, but by the Labour of my Hands; and I used to say, I liv'd just like a Man cast some desolate Island, that had no body there but how just has it been, and how should all Men reflect, that when they compare their present Conditions with others that are worse, Heaven may oblige them to make the Exchange, and be convinc'd of their former Felicity by their Experience: I say, how just has it been, that the truly solitary Life I reflected on in an Island of meer Desolation should be my Lot, who had so of unjustly compar'd it with the Life which I then led, which had I continued, I had in all Probability been exceeding prosperous and rich.

I was in some Degree settled in my Measures for carrying on the Plantation, before my kind Friend the Captain of the Ship that tool: me up at Sea, went back; for the Ship remained there in providing his Loading, and preparing for his Voyage, near three Months, when telling him what little Stock I had left behind me in London, he gave me this friendly and sincere Advice, Seignior Inglese says he, for so he always called me, if you will give me Letters, band a Procuration here in Form to me, with Orders to the Person who has your Money in London, to send your Effects to Lisbon, to such Persons as I shall direct and in such Goods as are proper for this Country, I will bring you the Produce of them, God willing, at my Return; but since human Affairs are all subject to Changes and Disasters, I would have you give Orders but for One Hundred Pounds Sterl. which you say is Half your Stock, and let the Hazard be run for the

每次我这样想到自己目前处境的时候，都非常懊丧。我除了有时跟那位邻居聊聊外，没有任何人同我谈话。在这里，没有别的依靠，只有靠自己的双手劳动。我常想，我住在这里就像独自一人被丢弃在荒岛上一样。当现实生活很好时，人们总是不满足现状，总拿更糟的情况与其相比。上帝就会让他们交换环境，让他们从自身的体验中认识到以前的生活是何等幸福。这仿佛是一种报应，值得我们好好反思。比如我，倘若继续过我现在的这种生活，完全有可能发大财赚大钱，可我却不知足地把我现在的这种生活比成孤岛上的生活，致使我后来真的领受到了荒岛生活的孤独，这真是报应。

当我在开发种植园方面有了一定的进展的时候，我的那位好心的朋友——在海上将我救上大船的那位船长——又从欧洲回来了。他的船这回要在这里停留将近三个月。装载货物，准备下一趟航行。我告诉他，我还有一点资本存在伦敦，他听后给了我这样一个友好而又诚恳的忠告："英国先生，"他像往常那样叫我，"假如你给我一封信和一张正式的委托书，叫拿着你那笔款的人把钱交给我派遣的人，要他买一些在巴西能够销售得掉的货物，送到里斯本去，我从欧洲返航时就可以替你带来。可人和事有时琢磨不足，因此为保险起见你最好

first; so that if it come safe, you may order the rest the same Way; and if it miscarry, you may have the other Half to have Recourse to for your Supply.

This was so wholesom Advice, and look'd so friendly, that I could not but be convinc'd it was the best Course I could take; so I accordingly prepared Letters to the Gentle-woman with whom I had left my Money, and a Procuration to the Portuguese Captain, as he desired.

I wrote the English Captain's Widow a full Account of all my Adventures, my Slavery, Escape, and how I had met with the Portugal Captain at Sea, the Humanity of his Behaviour, and in what Condition I was now in, with all other necessary Directions for my Supply; and when this honest Captain came to Lisbon, he found means by some of the English Merchants there, to send over not the Order only, but a full Account of my Story to a Merchant at London, who represented it effectually to her; whereupon, she not only delivered the Money, but out of her own Pocket sent the Portugal Captain a very handsom Present for his Humanity and Charity to me.

The Merchant in London vesting this Hundred Pounds in English Goods, such as the Captain had writ for, sent them directly to him at Lisbon, and he brought them all safe to me to the Brasils, among which, without my Direction (for I was too young in my Business to think of them) he had taken Care to have all Sorts of Tools, Iron-Work, and Utensils necessary for my Plantation, and which were of great Use to me.

先支存款的半数——冒冒险；如果顺利到手，再取另一半也不迟；如果丢了，你也损失了一半的钱。"

船长的建议谨慎周密，而且充满了诚意，我深信这是个万全良策。于是我按葡萄牙船长的要求，给保管我存款的英国船长的遗孀写了一封信，又写了一份委托书交给船长。

在写给那位好心夫人的信中，我详细告知了我离开英国后的种种遭遇，告诉她我怎样成了奴隶，又怎样逃了出来，怎样在海上遇到葡萄牙船长，船长怎样对我慷慨仁慈等等，还顺告了我目前的情况，同时又把汇款的办法一一说明。这位正直的船长回到里斯本以后，就通过一个英国商号，把我的信和我的全部消息转给一位伦敦的商人，由那位商人妥交给她。她接到信之后，除了把钱如数交出之外，又从自己的私蓄里取出了一笔款，赠送给船长，报答他对我的恩义。

伦敦的那位商人用这笔钱——一百英镑——购买了葡萄牙船长开列的单子上的全部货物，直接运往里斯本给船长。船长又把全部货物安全运抵巴西。在这些货物中，他替我带来了各样各样的工具、铁器和用具；这些都是经营种植园非常有用的东西。船长对我可谓想得周到备至，因为我自己并未想到要带这些东西。当时，我经营种植园还是个新手呢。

When this Cargo arrived, I thought my Fortunes made, for I was surprised with the Joy of it; and my good Steward the Captain had laid out the Five Pounds which my Friend had sent him for a Present for himself, to purchase, and bring me over a Servant under Bond for six Years Service, and would not accept of any Consideration, except a little Tobacco, which I would have him accept, being of my own Produce.

Neither was this all; but my Goods being all English Manufactures, such as Cloath, Stuffs, Bays, and things particularly valuable and desirable in the Country, I found means to sell them to a very great Advantage; so that I might say, I had more than four times the Value of my first Cargo, and was now infinitely beyond my poor Neighbour, I mean in the Advancement of my Plantation; for the first thing I did, I bought me a Negro Slave, and an European Servant also; I mean another besides that which the Captain brought me from Lisbon.

But as abus'd Prosperity is oftentimes made the very Means of our greatest Adversity, so was it with me. I went on the next Year with great Success in my Plantation: I raised fifty great Rolls of Tobacco on my own Ground, more than I had disposed of for Necessaries among my Neighbours; and these fifty Rolls being each of above a 100 Wt. were well cur'd and laid by against the Return of the Fleet from Lisbon: and now increasing in Business and in Wealth, my Head began to be full of Projects and Undertakings beyond my Reach; such as are indeed often the Ruine of the best Heads in Business.

Had I continued in the Station I was now in, I had room for all the happy things to have yet be-

当这批货物运抵巴西时，我以为自己发大财了，真是喜出望外。这位船长简直成了我的好管家，他甚至拿出那位遗孀送他的五英镑钱，替我弄来一个得为我干六年活的白奴；然而，他却不肯要我的酬谢，最后我一定要他收下我自己种出来的一点烟草，他总算接受了。

事情还不止如此；由于我的这些货都是棉布、呢绒、桌面呢之类的英国产品，在巴西特别受欢迎，也特别值钱，所以我就设法把它们都卖了个好价钱；可以说，我现在的钱是当初货价的四倍多，把我那可怜的邻居远远地甩在后面，我指的是在发展各自的种植园方面；我先是买了个黑奴并弄来个白奴，这是另一个白奴，不是船长从里斯本替我带来的那个。

常言说得好，得意往往是厄运的媒介，我的情形正是这样。第二年，我的种植园非常成功。我从自己的地里收获了五十捆烟叶，除了供应附近一带人们的需要之外，还剩下很多。这五十捆烟叶每捆有一百二十多磅重，我把它们晒好了，堆在一处，专等那些商船从里斯本回来，就可以起运了。随着我的产业日益兴旺发达，我脑子里装满了荒诞不经的宏伟计划，这往往就是构成许多优秀企业家毁灭的契机。

假如我照目前这副样子过下去，不知会有多幸福多惬

fallen me, for which my Father so earnestly recommended a quiet retired Life, and of which he had so sensibly describ'd the middle Station of Life to be full of; but other things attended me, and I was still to be the wilful Agent of all my own Miseries; and particularly to encrease my Fault and double the Reflections upon my self, which in my future Sorrows I should have leisure to make; all these Miscarriages were pro by my apparent obstinate adhering to my foolish inclination of wandring abroad and pursuing that Inclination, in contradiction to the clearest Views of doing my self good in a fair and plain pursuit of those Prospects and those measures of Life, which Nature and Providence concurred to present me with, and to make my Duty.

As I had once done thus in my breaking away from my Parents, so I could not be content now, but I must go and leave the happy View I had of being a rich and thriving Man in my new Plantation, only to pursue a rash and immoderate Desire of rising faster than the Nature of the Thing admitted; and thus I cast my self down again into the deepest Gulph of human Misery that ever Man fell into, or perhaps could be consistent with Life and a State of Health in the World.

To come then by the just Degrees, to the Particulars of this Part of my Story; you may suppose, that having now lived almost four Years in the Brasils, and beginning to thrive and prosper very well upon my Plantation; I had not only learn'd the Language, but had contracted Acquaintance and Friendship among my Fellow-Planters, as well as among the Merchants at St. Salvadore, which was our Port; and that in my Discourses among them, I had frequently given them an Account of my two Voyages to the Coast of Guinea, the manner of Trading with the Negroes there, and how easy it was to purchase upon the Coast, for Trifles, such as Beads, Toys,

意,这就是父亲恳切向我推荐的一种宁静、悠闲的生活,也就是他恰如其分地称为中间阶层的生活方式。可我热衷于其他事情,总是不让自己吃足苦头就决不罢休。特别是错上加错,固执地转着去海外游历的愚蠢念头,不愿意顺其自然去追求对自己有益无害的生活方式,履行自己的职责,从而误入歧途,在痛苦生涯中倍加悔恨。

正像我当初逃离我父母那样,我现在又贪心不足起来。我本可以靠我的新种植园,使自己成为一人富裕发达的人,享受人间宁静且健康的生活。可是,我硬是不顾这种幸福的前景,固执于鲁莽且不切实际的欲望,希望自己超乎寻常地暴发起来,这使我再次坠入人类苦难深渊的最深处。

现在我详细谈谈这段经历,不难想象,我在巴西已经住了差不多四年,我的种植园已日益繁荣。我不仅学会了当地语言,而且同许多种植园主以及在当地口岸的圣萨尔瓦多商人相熟成了朋友。我经常向他们谈到我两次到几内亚海岸航行的情况,谈到怎样同黑人做生意,如何用一些小杂货诸如小珠子、玩具、小刀、剪子、斧子、玻璃器皿等诸如此类的东西,不仅能轻易地换到金沙、粮食、象牙等,而且

Knives, Scissars, Hatchets, bits of Glass, and the like; not only Gold Dust, Guinea Grains, Elephants Teeth, &c. but Negroes for the Service of the Brasils, in great Numbers.

They listened always very attentively to my Discourses on these Heads, but especially to that Part which related to the buying Negroes, which was a Trade at that time not only not far entred into, but as far as it was, had been carried on by the Assiento's, or Permission of the Kings of Spain and Portugal, and engross'd in the Publick, so that few Negroes were brought, and those excessive dear.

It happen'd, being in Company with some Merchants and Planters of my Acquaintance, and talking of those things very earnestly, three of them came to me the next Morning, and told me they had been musing very much urn what I had discoursed with them of, the last Night, and they came to make a secret Proposal to me; and after enjoining me Secrecy, they told me, that they had a mind to fit out a Ship to go to Guinea, that they had all Plantations as well as I, and were straiten'd for nothing so much as Servants; that as it was a Trade that could not be carried on, because they could not publickly sell the Negroes when they came home, so they desired to make but one Voyage, to bring the Negroes on Shoar privately, and divide them among their own Plantations; and in a Word, the Question was, whether I would go their Super-Cargo in the Ship to manage the Trading Part upon the Coast of Guinea? And they offer'd me that I should have my equal Share of the Negroes without providing any Part of the Stock.

This was a fair Proposal it must be confess'd, had it been made to one that had not had a Settlement and Plantation of his own to look after, which was in a fair way of coming to be very Con-

还可以换到在巴西经常使用的商品。

大家对我的谈话总是凝神倾听,而对我买卖黑奴的话题更显示出极大的兴趣。贩运黑奴这项贸易在当时不仅刚刚兴起,而且受到西班牙和葡萄牙皇家的严格控制。要想买卖黑奴,必须经过这两国国王的同意,还必须签署契约。因此,买入巴西的黑奴数量不多,价格也极其昂贵。

有一回,我又同几个种植园主和商人热烈地谈论起这件事。到了第二天上午,其中的三个人来找了我。他们说,把我昨天晚上的谈话认真思考了一番,现在特地前来告诉我一个秘密的计划。他们要求我目前不要说出去,告诉我说,他们想弄一只船到我所说的那个海湾去。他们说,他们都有蔗田,都十分缺少人手。他们说,他们并不想做这种危险的生意,只想去一次,把黑奴秘密运上岸来,每个人分一部分。总之,他们想让我做他们船上的管货员,到几内亚海岸去替他们经营交易方面的事情。他们答应把黑奴同样分给我一份,并不要我拿出任何资本。

必须承认,假使这个建议是向一个没有定居在这里、没有自己的种植园需要照顾的人提出来的话,那实在是个好

siderable, and with a good Stock upon it. But for me that was thus entered and established, and had nothing to do but go on as I had begun for three or four Years more, and to have sent for the other hundred Pound from England, and who in that time, and with that little Addition, could scarce ha' fail'd of being worth three or four thousand Pounds Sterling, and that encreasing too; for me to think of such a Voyage, was the most preposterous Thing that ever Man in such Circumstances could be guilty of.

But I that was born to be my own Destroyer, could no more resist the Offer than I could restrain my first rambling Designs, when my Father's good Counsel was lost upon me. In a word, I told them I would go with all my Heart, if they would undertake to look after my Plantation in my Absence, and would dispose of it to such as I should direct if I miscarry'd. This they all engag'd to do, and entred into Writings or Covenants to do so; and I made a formal Will, disposing of my Plantation and Effects, in Case of my Death, making the Captain of the Ship that had sav'd my Life as before, my universal Heir, but obliging him to dispose of my Effects as I had directed in my Will, one half of the Produce being to himself, and the other to be ship'd to England.

In short, I took all possible Caution to preserve my Effects, and keep up my Plantation; had I used half as much Prudence to have look'd into my own Intrest, and have made a Judgment of what I ought to have done, and not to have done, I had certainly never gone away from so prosperous an Undertaking, leaving all the probable Views of a thriving Circumstance, and gone upon a Voyage to Sea, attended with all its common Hazards; to say nothing of the Reasons I had to expect particular Misfortunes to my self.

机会,既有现成的资本,又有赚大钱的希望。然而,我的情况却完全不同。我的种植事业已经有了一些基础,只要再干上三四年,把伦敦那一百英镑想法子弄回来,加了下去,不愁不会挣出一个三四千英镑的家当,而且以后还要增加下去。处在我这种情况的人,再要去考虑这次航行,那简直是天下最荒谬的事了。

但我这个人真是命里注定自取灭亡,竟然抵御不了这种提议的诱惑,就像我当初一心要周游世界而不听父亲的忠告一样。一句话,我告诉他们,只要他们答应我不在的时候照料我的种植园,如果我失事遇难的话,又能按照我的嘱咐处理种植园,那我极愿同他们一同前往几内亚。对此他们都一一答应,并立下了字据。我又立了一份正式的遗嘱,安排我的种植园和财产。我立我的救命恩人船长为我的种植园和财产的全权继承人,但他应按照我在遗嘱中的指示处置我的财产:一半归他自己,一半运往英国。

简言之,我尽可能地注意保全自己的资财,维持住我的种植园,要是我能用一半的谨慎态度来考虑自己的切身利益,来判断我该做什么事、不该做什么事,那么我绝对不会撇下如此蒸蒸日上的事业,撇下大有希望的发家前景,竟去参加一次远航,而这种航行本来就艰险万端,何况我有理由相信我是尤其会大倒其霉的。

But I was hurried on, and obey'd blindly the Dictates of my Fancy rather than my Reason; and accordingly the Ship being fitted out, and the Cargo furnished, and all things done as by Agreement, by my Partners in the Voyage, I went on Board in an evil Hour, the [first] of [September], [1659], being the same Day eight Year that I went from my Father and Mother at Hull, in order to act the Rebel to their Authority, and the Fool to my own Interest.

Our Ship was about 120 Tun Burthen, carried 6 Guns, and 14 Men, besides the Master, his Boy, and my self; we had on board no large Cargo of Goods, except of such Toys as were fit for our Trade with the Negroes, such as Beads, bits of Glass, Shells, and odd Trifles, especially little Looking-Glasses, Knives, Scissars, Hatchets, and the like.

The same Day I went on board we set sail, standing away to the Northward upon our own Coast, with Design to stretch over for the African Coast, when they came about 10 or 12 Degrees of Northern Latitude, which it seems was the manner of their Course in those Days. We had very good Weather, only excessive hot, all the way upon our own Coast, till we came the Height of Cape St. Augustino, from whence keeping farther off at Sea we lost Sight of Land, and steer'd as if we was bound for the Isle Fernand de Horonha holding our Course N. E. by N. and leaving those Isles on the East; in this Course we past the Line in about 12 Days time, and were by our last Observation in 7 Degrees 22 Min. Northern Latitude, when a violent Tournado or Hurricane took us quite out of our Knowledge: it began from the South-East, came about to the North-West, and en settled into the North-East, from whence it blew in such a terrible manner, that for twelve Days together we could do

然而,我身不由己,盲目地接受了幻想而不是理智的支配。与此同时,船已备好,货已装完,所有一切都照协议和同伴的要求准备停当。我又在一个邪恶的时间登上了船,那就是一六五九年九月一日,八年前的这一天,我从在赫尔的父母身边逃开,叛逆了家庭的结束,成为不顾自己利益的傻瓜。

我们的船载重约一百二十吨,装有六门小炮,除了船主、他的小仆人和我之外,还有十四个人。我们没在船上装什么大件货物,只带了些适合与黑人交易的小玩艺,比如小珠子、玻璃片、贝壳新奇的小东西,还有望远镜、小刀子、剪子、斧子等等。

我上船的当天我们就开了船,沿着巴西海岸向北航行,计划开到北纬十至十二度之间,再横穿大洋,开向非洲海岸,这好像是当时通行的航线。一路上天气很好,只是非常炎热。我们一直沿着海岸朝前开,并到圣奥古斯丁角附近后,开始偏移大陆。陆地从我们的视野中消失了,我们好像是直朝费尔南多迪诺罗尼亚岛方向开去,但其实是朝东北偏北方向开,所以那些岛屿还在我们东面。沿着这条航线,我们用了差不多十二天时间就过了赤道。根据最后的观测,我们现在已行到了北纬七度二十三分。但就在这时,刮起了龙卷风或飓风,把我们刮得不辨东西。风暴开始的

nothing but drive, and scudding away before it, let it carry us whither ever Fate and the Fury of the Winds directed; and during these twelve Days, I aced not say, that I expected every Day to be swallowed up, nor indeed did any in the Ship expect to save their Lives.

In this Distress, we had besides the Terror of the Storm, one of our Men dyed of the Calenture, and one Man and the Boy wash'd over board; about the 12th Day the Weather abating a little, the Master made an Observation as well as he could, and found that he was in about 11 Degrees North Latitude, but that he was 22 Degrees of Longitude difference West from Cape St. Augustino; so that he found he was gotten upon the Coast of Guinea, or the North Part of Brasil, beyond the River Amozones, toward that of the River Oronoque, commonly call'd the Great River, and began to consult with me what Course he should take, for the Ship leaky and very much disabled, and he was going directly back to the Coast of Brasil.

I was positively against that, and looking over the Charts the Sea-Coast of America with him, we concluded the as no inhabited Country for us to had recourse to, till we came within the Circle of the Carribbe-Islands, and therefore resolved to stand away for Barbadoes, which by keeping off at Sea, to avoid the Indraft of the Bay or Gulph of Mexico, we night easily perform, as we hoped, in about fifteen Day Sail; whereas we could not possibly make our Voyage to the Coast of Africa without some Assistance, both to our Ship and to our selves.

时候刮的是东南风,然后转为西北风,最后变成东北风。疯狂的飓风一连猛刮了十二天,弄得我们束手无策,只能任风摆布,随浪漂泊。不用说,在这十二天中,我日日提心吊胆,时时担心着会被风浪吞没,船上的人也同样无不希冀能在这样的风暴中逃生。

在这种灭顶之灾中,我们除了承受风暴带来的恐惧外,还要接受其他的不幸。船上有一个人患了赤道热病死去,另外一个人和小仆人则被大浪卷入海中。飓风一直刮到第十二天,风力才稍有减退。船主尽了最大的努力,观测了一下,才知道我们是在北纬十一度左右,然而却在圣奥古斯丁角以西二十二经度;我们已经被刮到巴西以北的圭亚那,到了亚马孙河入海的地方,靠近那条号称"大河"的俄利诺科河了。于是船主向我请示航行方针,并主张开回巴西海岸,因为我们的船已经漏了,而且坏得很厉害。

我极力反对这个办法。我和他一起看了看美洲沿岸的航海图,得到的结论是,除非我们能够开到加勒比群岛附近去,否则就找不到有人烟的地方可以求援。因此,我们决定向巴尔巴多群岛驶去。据我们估计,只要我们能避开墨西哥湾的逆流,在大海里航行,就可在半个月之内到达。在那儿,如果我们不能把船修一下,补充食物和人员,我们就不可能到达非洲海岸。

With this Design we chang'd our Course and steer'd away N. W. by W. in order to reach some of our English Islands, where I hoped for Relief; but our Voyage was otherwise determined, for being in the Latitude of Deg. 18 Min. a second Storm came upon us, which carry'd us away with the same Impetuosity Westward, and drove us so out of the very Way of all humane Commerce, that had all our Lives been saved, as to the Sea, we were rather in Danger of being devoured by Savages than ever returning to our own Country. In this Distress, the Wind still blowing very hard, one of our Men early in the Morning, cry'd out, Land; and we had no sooner run out of the Cabbin to look out in hopes of seeing where abouts in the World we were; but the Ship struck upon a Sand, and in a moment her Motion being so stopp'd, the Sea broke over her in such a manner, that we expected we should all have perish'd immediately, and we were immediately driven into our close Quarters to shelter us the very Foam and Sprye of the Sea.

It is not easy for any one, who has not been in the like Condition, to describe or conceive the Consternation of Men in such Circumstances; we knew nothing where we were, or upon what Land it was we were driven, whether an Island or the Main, whether inhabited or not, inhabited; and as the Rage of the Wind was still great, tho rather less than at first, we could not so much as hope to have the Ship hold many Minutes without breaking in Pieces, unless the Winds by a kind of Miracle should turn immediately about. In a word, we sat looking upon one another, and expecting Death every Moment, and every Man acting accordingly, as preparing for another World, for there was little or nothing more for us to do in this; that which was our present Comfort, and all the Comfort we had, was, that contrary to our Expectation the Ship did not break yet, and that the Master said

计划一定,我们便改变航向,向西北偏西方向驶去,希望能到达一个英属海岛;在那儿我希望能获得救援;但航行方向却不由我们自己决定,因为到了北纬十二度十八分左右,飓风第二次袭来,甚至比第一次还要厉害,挟持我们向西方走,一直把我们吹离人类涉猎过的地方,在这里要么葬身鱼腹,要么成为野人的美餐。暴风依旧,情况万分危急,一天清早船上忽然有人喊道:"看到陆地了!"我们正要跑出舱去,想看看我们到了什么地方,我们的船却搁浅在沙滩上了。船停了下来,海浪又拍击得这样凶猛,我们都觉得生还没希望了。我们马上躲进了舱房,避开海浪的冲击。

一个人如果没有类似的经历,就很难描述或想象处于这种境地时的惊恐之状;我们不知道自己在什么方位,不知道撞上的地方是个岛屿还是一片陆地,甚至连这儿是否有人居住也不知道;现在风虽然比先前略为小了一点,但仍十分狂烈,看来已难以指望什么了,要不了几分钟就会船破人亡,除非出现风立刻停止的奇迹。总之,我们面面相觑地枯坐在那里,人人随时准备等死神一来,便去那另一个世界,因为我们在这种情况下,实在是无能为力了;但我们总算还有一点宽慰之处,而这也是我们唯一聊可自慰的,那就是尽

the Wind began to abate.

Now tho' we thought that the Wind did a little abate, yet the Ship having thus struck upon the Sand, and sticking too fast for us to expect her getting off, we were in a dreadful Condition indeed, and had nothing to do but to think of saving our Lives as well as we could; we had a Boat at our Stern just before the Storm, but she was first stav'd by dashing against the Ship's Rudder, and in the next Place she broke away, and either sunk or was driven off to Sea, so there was no hope from her; we had another Boat on board, but how to get her off into the Sea, was a doubtful thing; however there was no room to debate, for we fancy'd the Ship would break in Pieces every Minute, and some told us she was actually broken already.

In this Distress the Mate of our Vessel lays hold of the Boat, and with the help of the rest of the Men, they got her flung over the Ship's-side, and getting all into her, let go, and committed our selves being Eleven in Number, to God's Merry, and the wild Sea; for tho' the Storm was abated considerably, yet the Sea went dreadful high upon the Shore, and might well be call'd, Den mild Zee, as the Dutch call the Sea in a Storm.

And now our Case was very dismal indeed; for we all saw plainly, that the Sea went so high, that the Boat could not live, and that we should be inevitably drowned. As to baking Sail, we had none, nor, if we had, could we ha' done any thing with it; so we work'd at the Oar towards the Land, tho' with heavy Hearts, like Men going to Execution; for we all knew, that when the Boat came nearer the Shore, she would be dash'd in a Thousand Pieces by the Breach of the Sea. However, we committed our Souls to God in the most earnest Manner, and the Wind driving us towards

管我们本以为就要船破人亡的,但还没到这地步,而这时据船主说,风开始变小了。

虽然我们认为风变小了,但船搁浅得厉害,别指望把它从沙地里拔出来。我们处境凶险,唯一能做的就是尽可能地觅得一条逃生之路。暴风到来之前,船尾拴着一条小艇,可小艇撞到大船的舵上,撞出了个大窟窿,很快被风刮跑了,也不知是沉了还是漂走了,反正没指望。甲板上还有一条舢板,问题是如何放进大海,不过我们已没时间讨论,我们都以为大船倾刻之间就会粉身碎骨,有人说实际上它已经开始漏水了。

在这危急时刻,大副抓住那条舢板,在众人的帮助下,把它放到大船的一侧,让我们十一个人上了舢板,然后放开了它,我们将命运完全交给了上帝和大海。风势虽然小了些,但海浪仍然可怕地拍击着海岸,荷兰人形容大海为"疯狂之海",真是恰如其分。

现在的处境真的太凄惨了。我们都看得很明白,海浪简直卷到了天上,舢板肯定经受不住,我们不可避免地会被淹死。想挂船帆,我们没有,即使有也不能挂,所以只好用桨朝岸边划。大家心情都很沉重,像是些被押赴刑场的囚犯,因为我们心里都很明白,等舢板靠近了岸边,它肯定会被海浪打得粉身碎骨。然而,我们都万分虔诚地把灵魂交

the Shore, we hastened our Destruction with our own Hands, pulling as well as we could towards Land.

What the Shore was, whether Rock or Sand, whether Steep or Shoal, we knew not; the only Hope that could rationally give us the least Shadow of Expectation, was, if we might happen into some Bay or Gulph, or the Mouth of some River, where by great Chance we might have run our Boat in, or got under the Lee of the Land, and perhaps made smooth Water. But there was nothing of this appeared; but as we made nearer and nearer the Shore, the Land look'd more frightful than the Sea.

After we had row'd, or rather driven about a League and Half, as we reckon'd it, a raging Wave, Mountain-like, came rowling a-stern of us, and plainly bad us expect the Coup de Grace. In a word, it took us with such a Fury, that it overset the Boat at once; and separating us as well from the Boat, as from one another, gave us not time hardly to say, O God! for we were all swallowed up in a Moment.

Nothing can describe the Confusion of Thought which I felt when I sunk into the Water; for tho' I swam very well, yet I could not deliver my self from the Waves so as to draw Breath, till that Wave having driven me, or rather carried me a vast Way on towards the Shore, and having spent it self, went back, and left me upon the Land almost dry, but half-dead with the Water I took in. I had so much Presence of Mind as well as Breath left, that seeing my self nearer the main Land than I expected, I got upon my Feet, and endeavoured to make on towards the Land as fast as I could, before another Wave should return, and take me up again. But I soon found it was impossi-

给了上帝,任狂浪将我们推向岸边,同时我们自己也拼命用桨划着,其实,这是在用自己的双手加速自己的毁灭。

我们会到达什么样的海岸? 岩石还是沙地,陡岸还是浅滩? 对于这些我们全然不知,仅抱有一丝渺茫的希望,梦想着能侥幸划进一个海湾或是一个河口,或者碰到一个避风的陡岸,找到一片宁静的海面,可是这些在当时都只能是幻想。而且,我们越划近海岸,陆地越是显得比海上更为可怕。

我们一半摇着桨,一半被风吹赶着,大约走了一海里半的路,忽然有一个大浪,像山一样高,从我们后面滚滚而来,显然要给我们以致命的打击。说时迟,那时快,顿时把我们的舢板打得船底朝天,把我们从舢板上打翻到海里,东一个,西一个,我们还来不及喊一声"上帝啊!"就通通被汹涌的波涛吞吃下去了。

当我沉入水中时,心乱如麻,实难言表。我平日虽善泅水,但在这种惊涛骇浪之中,连浮起来呼吸一下也十分困难。最后,海浪把我冲上了岸,等浪势使尽而退时,把我留在半干的岸上。虽然海水已把我灌得半死,但我头脑尚清醒,见到自己已靠近陆地,就立即爬起来拼命向陆上奔去,以免第二个浪头打来时再把我卷入大海。可是,我立即发现,这种情境已无法逃脱,只见身后高山似的海浪汹涌而

ble to avoid it; for I saw the Sea come after me as high as a great Hill, and as furious as an Enemy which I had no Means or Strength to contend with; my Business was to hold my Breath, and raise my self upon the Water, if I could; and so by swimming to preserve my Breathing, and Pilot my self towards the Shore, if possible; my greatest Concern now being, that the Sea, as it would carry me a great Way towards the Shore when it came on, might not carry me back again with it when it gave back towards the Sea.

The Wave that came upon me again, buried me at once 20 or 30 Foot deep in its own Body; and I could feel my self carried with a mighty Force and Swiftness towards the Shore a very great Way; but I held my Breath, and assisted my self to swim still forward with all my Might. I was ready to burst with holding my Breath, when, as I felt my self rising up, so to my immediate Relief, I found my Head and Hands shoot out above the Surface of the Water; and tho' it was not two Seconds of Time that I could keep my self so, yet it reliev'd me greatly, gave me Breath and new Courage. I was covered again with Water a good while, but not so long but I held it out; and finding the Water had spent it self, and began to return, I strook forward against the Return of the Waves, and felt Ground again with my Feet. I stood still a few Moments to recover Breath, and till the Water went from me, and then took to my Heels, and run with what Strength I had farther towards the Shore. But neither would this deliver me from the Fury of the Sea, which came pouring in after me again, and twice more I was lifted up by the Waves, and carried forwards as before, Shore being very flat.

The last Time of these two had well near been fatal to me; the Sea having hurried me along as before, landed me, rather dash'd me against a

至,我根本无法抗拒,也无力抗拒。这时,我只能尽力气息浮出水面,并竭力向岸上游去。由于这排浪头打来时,会带着我朝前冲上好一段距离,所以这时我最要注意的,就是当这排浪往海里回流时,千万别让它把我也卷回海里去。

这时,那大浪已兜头打来,把我压在二三十英尺的水下;我能够感觉到,有个迅猛的力量推动着我,带着我朝岸边冲去了好长一段距离;但我屏住气,使出浑身力气仍然朝前游去。正当我屏气屏得快憋不住的时候,只觉得身子往上一浮,脑袋和双手居然都一下子露出了水面;我尽力想待在水面上,但这情况却只持续了两秒种。不过这一下已使我受益匪浅,不但使我缓过了气来,还给了我新的勇气。水又一次淹没了我,好在时间不长,我总算撑了下来,等海浪力量消退,开始后缩时,我死命逆水前进,终于双脚又触到了陆地。我静静地站了一会儿,恢复呼吸,待水退尽,立即拔腿朝岸上没命地奔去。可是我终于没有逃脱滚滚怒潮的袭击,巨浪再次从我背后汹涌而至,一连两次又像以前那样把我卷起来,推向平坦的海岸。

最后一次险些要了我的命。海浪像上次那样急速地把我推向陆地,猛地撞到了一

Piece of a Rock, and that with such Force, as it left me senseless, and indeed helpless, as my own Deliverance; for the Blow taking my Side and east, beat the Breath as it were quite out of my Body; and it returned again immediately, I must have been strangled in the Water; but I recover'd a little before the turn of the Waves, and seeing I should be cover'd again with the Water, I resolv'd to hold fast by a Piece of the Rock, and so to hold my Breath, if possible, till the Wave went back; now as the Waves were not so high as at first, being nearer Land, I held my Hold till the Wave abated, and then fetch'd another Run, which brought me so near the Shore, that the next Wave, tho' it went over me, yet did not so swallow me up as to carry me away, and the next run I took, I got to the main Land, where, to my great Comfort, I clamber'd up the Clifts of the Shore, and sat me down upon the Grass, free from Danger, and quite out of the Reach of the Water.

I was now landed, and safe on Shore, and began to look up and thank God that my Life was sav'd in a Case wherein there was some Minutes before scarce any room to hope. I believe it is impossible to express to the Life what the Extasies and Transports of the Soul are, when it is so sav'd, as I may say, out of the very Grave; and I do not wonder now at that Custom, vis. That when a Malefactor who has the Halter about his Neck, is tyed up, and just going to be turn'd off, and has a Reprieve brought to him: I say, I do not wonder that they bring a Surgeon with it, to let him Blood that very Moment they tell him of it, that the Surprise may not drive the Animal Spirits from the Heart, and overwhelm him:

块礁石上，力量之大，顿时让我失去了知觉，奄奄一息。因为正好撞到了我的胸口上，使我出不了气。如果这时再有一个浪头打来，我一定会被憋死在水里。可是，在浪头再来之前，我醒了过来，眼看自己将被海水淹没，就决心紧紧抱住一块岩石，尽可能屏住呼吸，直到海水退去。这时浪头已不像先前那么高，而且离陆地已不远，于是我紧紧抱住那块岩石，等海水退去后，我向前又是一阵猛跑，一直跑到离海岸很近的地方。所以，紧跟而来的一个海浪虽然从我的头上覆了过去，但它并没有将我吞没，或将我卷回海中。我又朝前跑了一阵，终于登上了陆地，爬上岸上的岩石，在草地上坐了下来。现在，我终于脱离了危险，海浪已在远处，淹不到我了。我心中感到莫大的欣慰。

我真的登上了陆地，真的平安脱险了！我抬起头来仰望苍天，感谢上帝的拯救。几分钟前我还没有一丝生还的希望，现在竟然死里逃生，捡回了性命。我相信，很难有人能够用语言来表述出我此时此刻因绝境逢生而产生出的那种心灵的狂喜和情绪的激荡。我现在完全理解了我们英国的那种风俗：在犯人被套进绞索，收紧绳结，即将被吊起来的时刻，突然赦免令传到。这时，与赦免令同到的往往还有外科医生，以便在宣告赦免令的同时好给犯人放血，

For sudden Joys, like Griefs, confound at first.

I walk'd about on the Shore, lifting up my Hands, and my whole Being, as I may say, wrapt up in the Contemplation of my Deliverance, making a Thousand Gestures and Motions which I cannot describe, reflecting upon all my Comerades that were drown'd, and that there should not be one Soul sav'd but my self; for, as for them, I never saw them afterwards, or any Sign of them, except three of their Hats, one Cap, and two Shoes that were not Fellows.

I cast my Eyes to the stranded Vessel, when the Breach and Froth of the Sea being so big, I could hardly see it, it lay so far off, and considered, Lord! how was it possible I could get on Shore?

After I had solac'd my Mind with the comfortable Part of my Condition, I began to look round me to see what kind of Place I was in, and what was next to be done, and I soon found my Comforts abate, and that in a word I had a dreadful Deliverance: For I was wet, had no Clothes to shift me, nor any thing either to eat or drink to comfort me, neither did I see any Prospect before me, but that of perishing with Hunger, or being devour'd by wild Beasts; and that which was particularly afflicting to me, was, that I had no Weapon either to hunt and kill any Creature for my Sustenance, or to defend my self against any other Creature that might desire to kill me for theirs: In a Word, I had nothing about me but a Knife, a Tobacco-pipe, and a little Tobacco in a Box, this was all my Provision, and this threw me into terrible Agonies of Mind, that for a while I run about like a Mad-man; Night coming upon me, I began with a heavy Heart to consider what

免得这意外之喜使犯人血气攻心,晕死过去,可谓:

突然而来的喜悦正如突然而来的忧伤一样,起初的时候,都是那么地惊心动魄。

因此我在陆地上狂奔,举起双手,用全身来体验我的幸存;我手舞足蹈,默想为何在全船所有的人中只有我这么幸运。全船的人我没碰到一个,除了几顶帽子,一顶便帽,两只不般配的鞋子之外。

我用眼去眺望那只搁了浅的大船,这时海上烟波迷漫,船又离得很远,简直看不清,我不由地想道:"上帝啊!我怎么会有可能上岸呢?"

我用自己遭遇中值得庆幸的一些事情把自己安慰了一番之后,开始环顾四周,看看我究竟到了什么地方,下一步应该怎么办。但不看则已,这一看使我的情绪立即低落下来。我虽获救,却又陷入了另一种绝境。我浑身湿透,却没有衣服可更换;我又饥又渴,却没有任何东西可充饥解渴。我看不到有任何出路,除了饿死,就是给野兽吃掉。我身上除了一把小刀、一个烟斗和一小匣烟草,别无他物。这使我忧心如焚,有好一阵子,我在岸上狂乱地跑来跑去,像疯子一样。夜色降临,我想到野兽多半在夜间出来觅食,更是愁思满腔。我想,若这儿真有猛兽出没,我的命运将会如

would be my Lot if there were any ravenous Beasts in that Country, seeing at Night they always come abroad for their Prey.

All the Remedy that offer'd to my Thoughts at that Time, was, to get up into a thick bushy Tree like a Firr, but thorny, which grew near me, and where I resolv'd to set all Night, and consider the next Day what Death I should dye, for as yet I saw no Prospect of Life; I walk'd about a Furlong from the Shore, to see if I could find any fresh Water to drink, which I did, to my great Joy; and having drank and put a little Tobacco in my Mouth to prevent Hunger, I went to the Tree, and getting up into it, endeavour'd to place my self so, as that if I should sleep I might not fall; and having cut me a short Stick, like a Truncheon, for my Defence, I took up my Lodging, and having been excessively fatigu'd, I fell fast asleep, and slept as comfortably as, I believe, few could have done in my Condition, and found my self the cost refresh'd with it, that I think I ever was on such an Occasion.

When I wak'd it was broad Day, the Weather clear, and the Storm abated, so that the Sea did not rage and swell as before: But that which surpris'd me most, was, that the Ship was lifted off in the Night from the Sand where she lay, by the Swelling of the Tyde, and was driven up almost as far as the Rock which I first mention'd, where I had been so bruis'd by the dashing me against it; this being within about a Mile from the Shore where I was, and the Ship seeming to stand upright still, I wish'd my self on board, that, at least, I might save some necessary things for my use.

When I came down from my Appartment in the

何呢？

当时，我想到的办法只有一个，就是选定近旁一棵像是枞树但长有刺的枝叶繁密的大树，准备晚上爬上去过夜，等第二天再考虑怎么个死法，因为在我看来，实在没有生存下去的可能；树选定之后，我想找淡水喝，便离开岸边走了二百来码，真找到了淡水，这使我大为高兴；我喝了水，撮了些烟草放进嘴里，免得肚子饿，随后又回到那棵树下，爬了上去，尽量把自己安顿好，免得睡着以后摔下去，我又截下一截树枝，削成一根短棍，算是防身的武器，便在树上歇下了；由于我已筋疲力尽，很快就睡着了，那股子香甜劲儿恐怕没几个像我这种处境的人能做到。一觉醒来，神清气爽，精神抖擞，以前遇到这种情况时，感觉从来没这么好过。

天大亮了，我才醒来。天空晴朗，风暴已经过去，大海变得格外宁静温柔。最叫我吃惊的是船从搁浅的沙地里拔了出来，靠涨潮的推动，已经到了我先前提到的那块岩石旁，就是那块把我撞伤的岩石，离海岸我站立的位置大约一英里左右。船看上去没翻，我希望自己能登上船，至少拿出一些物品为我所用。

我从树上的住所爬下来，

Tree, I look'd about me again, and the first thing I found was the Boat, which lay as the Wind and the Sea had toss'd her up upon the Land, about two Miles on my right Hand. I walk'd as far as I could upon the Shore to have got to her, but found a Neck or Inlet of Water between me and the Boat, which was about half a Mile broad, so I came back for the present, being more intent upon getting at the Ship, where I hop'd to find something for my present Subsistence.

A little after Noon I found the Sea very calm, and the Tyde ebb'd so far out, that I could come within a Quarter of a Mile of the Ship; and here I found a fresh renewing of my Grief, for I saw evidently, that if we had kept on board, we had been all safe, that is to say, we had all got safe on Shore, and I had not been so miserable as to be left entirely destitute of all Comfort and Company, as I now was; this forc'd Tears from my Eyes again, but as there was little Relief in that, I resolv'd, if possible, to get to the Ship, so I pull'd off my Clothes, for the Weather was hot to Extremity, and took the Water, but when I came to the Ship, my Difficulty was still greater to know how to get on board, for as she lay a ground, and high out of the Water, there was nothing within my Reach to lay hold of; I swam round her twice, and the second Time I spy'd a small Piece of a Rope, which I wonder'd I did not see at first, hang down by the Fore-Chains so low, as that with great Difficulty I got hold of it, and by the help of that Rope, got up into the Forecastle of the Ship; here I found that the Ship was bulg'd, and had a great deal of Water in her Hold, but that she lay so on the Side of a Bank of hard Sand, or rather Earth, that her Stern lay lifted up upon the Bank, and her Head low almost to the Water; by this Means all her Quarter was free, and all that was in that Part was dry; for you may be sure my first Work was to search and to see what was

放眼向四面望去,首先看到的是那只舢板,因为被风浪所吹,已被冲到沙滩上,在我右侧约两英里处。我沿着海岸朝它走去,但却看到有条小海湾横在中间,约有半英里宽。于是我便往回返,因为我目前最关心的是能够到大船上去,希望能找些度日的东西。

响午刚过一会儿,海上风平浪静,潮水已后退到很远的地方,所以我现在离那条大船不到四分之一英里了。这时,一种忧伤的情绪重新光临我的心头,因为,事实明摆着,假如我们都在大船上不下来,一个个都能活命,就是说,都能安全上岸;而我也就不会受那样的罪,落得如此孤苦伶仃的下场。想到这一点,泪水又涌出了我的眼眶。但是,悔恨又有什么用呢?我决定,只要有可能,肯定要到大船上去。由于此刻天气已热到了极点,我便脱掉了衣服,下到了水中,可是,等我游到大船旁边,我才发现,更大的困难是,该如何爬上甲板。大船因为搁浅而离水面很高,我双臂可以够到的地方,没有任何可以抓住攀援的东西。我绕着船游了两圈才突然发现一根短绳,我很诧异为何先前竟没注意到这根绳子。那条绳子从倾斜的船头桅链上垂下来。我用劲够着绳子,拽着它向上攀登进入了船的前舱。我发现,船的确已经破漏,而且船底已灌进了许多水。由于船搁浅

spoil'd and what was free; and first I found that all the Ship's Provisions were dry and untouch'd by the Water, and being very well dispos'd to eat, I went to the Bread-room and fill'd my Pockets with Bisket, and eat it as I went about other things, for I had no time to lose; I also found some Rum in the great Cabbin, of which I took a large Dram, and which I had indeed need enough of to spirit me for what was before me: Now I wanted nothing but a Boat to furnish my self with many things which I forsaw would be very necessary to me.

It was in vain to sit still and wish for what was not to be had, and this Extremity rouz'd my Application; we had several spare Yards, and two or three large sparrs of Wood, and a spare Top-mast or two in the Ship; I resolv'd to fall to work with these, and I flung as many of them over board as I could manage for their Weight, tying every one with a Rope that they might not drive away; when this was done I went down the Ship's Side, and pulling them to me, I ty'd four of them fast together at both Ends as well as I could, in the Form of a Raft, and laying two or three short Pieces of Plank upon them cross-ways, I found I could walk upon it very well, but that it was not able to bear any great Weight, the Pieces being too light; so I went to work, and with the Carpenter's Saw I cut a spare Top-mast into three Lengths, and added them to my Raft, with a great deal of Labour and Pains, but hope of furnishing my self with Necessaries, encourag'd me to go beyond what I should have been able to have done upon another Occasion.

在沙滩上时是船头吃进沙土，船尾上翘，所以水都浸在船头，船的后半截没有进水。不用说，我要做的第一件事就是查清船上哪些东西已经损坏，哪些东西依然完好。我首先发现船上的粮食干燥无恙，接着又急切地走到面包柜那去寻找吃的。我把找到的饼干塞满我的口袋，以便边吃边干别的事，因为我非得抓紧在船上的时间不可。我又在大舱里找到了一些甘蔗酒；我就喝了一大杯，因为在当前的情况下，我很需要喝点酒提提神。现在我什么都不想，只想有一只小艇，把我认为需要的东西，装到岸上去。

一个人只是呆呆地坐着，空想自己所得不到的东西，是没有用的；这个绝对的真理，使我重新振作起来。我们船上有几根多余的帆杠，还有两三块木板，还有一两根多余的第二接桅。我决定把这些东西扔在水中，做成一个像筏子一样的东西；我在上面走了走，觉得非常平稳，但由于木块太轻恐怕驮不了很多东西，于是我又用锯子把一根第二接桅锯成三段，连在筏子上；这个工作十分困难，但我因为急于要把东西载到岸上去，所以不知不觉竟能忍受常日无法忍受的辛劳。

My Raft was now strong enough to bear any reasonable Weight; my next Care was what to load it with, and how to preserve what I laid upon it from the Surf of the Sea; But I was not long considering this, I first laid all the Plank or Boards upon it that I could get, and having consider'd well what I most wanted, I first got three of the Seamens Chests, which I had broken open and empty'd, and lower'd them down upon my Raft; the first of these I fill'd with Provision, viz. Bread, Rice, three Dutch Cheeses, five Pieces of dry'd Goat's Flesh, which we liv'd much u'pon, and a little Remainder of European Corn which had been laid by for some Fowls which we brought to Sea with us, but the Fowls were kill'd; there had been some Barly and Wheat together, but, to my great Disappointment, I found afterwards that the Rats had eaten or spoil'd it all; as for Liquors, I found several Cases of Bottles belonging to our Skipper, in which some Cordial Waters, and in all about five or six Gallons of Rack, these I stow'd by themselves, there being no need to put them into the Chest, nor no room for them. While I was doing this, I found the Tyde began to flow, tho' very calm, and I had the Mortification to see my Coat, Shirt, and Wast-coat which I had left on Shore upon the Sand, swim away; as for my Breeches which were only Linnen and open knee'd, I swam on board in them and my Stockings: However this put me upon rummaging for Clothes, of which I found enough, but took no more than I wanted for present use, for I had other things which my Eye was more upon, as first Tools to work with on Shore, and it was after long searching that I found out the Carpenter's Chest, which was indeed a very useful Prize to me, and much more valuable than a Ship Loading of Gold would have been at that time; I got it down to my Raft, even whole as it was, without losing time to look into it, for I knew in general what it contain'd.

筷子做得相当牢固,也能吃得住相当的重量。接着我就考虑该装些什么东西上去,还要防止东西给海浪打湿。不久我便想出了办法。我先把船上所能找到的木板都铺在筷子上,然后考虑了一下所需要的东西。我打开三只船员用的箱子,把里面的东西倒空,再把它们一一吊到筷子上。第一只箱子里我主要装食品:粮食、面包、米、三块荷兰酪干、五块羊肉干,以及一些剩下来的欧洲麦子,这些麦子原来是喂船上的家禽的,现在家禽都已死了。船上本来还有一点大麦和小麦,但后来发现都给老鼠吃光了或搞脏了,使我大为失望。至于酒类,我也找到了几箱,那都是船长的。里面有几瓶烈性甜酒,还有五、六加仑椰子酒。箱子里既已装不下这些酒,事实上它们也没有装进箱子的必要,所以我也就要把它们堆在筷子上。正这么干着,我发现已开始涨潮,虽说涨得很慢很和缓,却让我脱在岸上的外套、背心和衬衣都漂走了;这使我非常懊丧,因为我游到这船上来时,只穿着长袜和一条长及膝盖的麻布裤子。既然如此,我不得不搜寻些衣服了,结果虽找到了不少,却只能先挑些眼下急需的,因为在我心目中还有更重要的东西,首先就是以后要在岸上用到的工具;我找了好多时间,终于看到了那木匠的工具箱,这真是我的一大收获,对我大有用处,对我来

My next Care was for some Ammunition and Arms; there were two very good Fowling-pieces in the great Cabbin, and two Pistols, these I secur'd first, with some Powder-horns, and a small Bag of Shot, and two old rusty Swords; I knew there were three Barrels of Powder in the Ship, but knew not where our Gunner had stow'd them, but with much search I found them, two of them dry and good, the third had taken Water, those two I got to my Raft, with the Arms, and now I thought my self pretty well freighted, and began to think how I should get to Shore with them, having neither Sail, Oar, or Rudder, and the least Cap full of Wind would have overset all my Navigation.

I had three Encouragements, 1. A smooth calm Sea, 2. The Tide rising and setting in to the Shore, 3. What little Wind there was blew me towards the Land; and thus, having found two or three broken Oars belonging to the Boat, and besides the Tools which were in the Chest, I found two Saws, an Axe, and a Hammer, and with this Cargo I put to Sea; For a Mile, or thereabouts, my Raft went very well, only that I found it drive a little distant from the Place where I had landed before, by which I perceiv'd that there was some Indraft of the Water, and consequently I hop'd to find some Creek or River there, which I might make use of as a Port to get to Land with my Cargo.

As I imagin'd, so it was, there appear'd before me a little opening of the Land, and I found a strong Current of the Tide set into it, so I guided my Raft as well as I could to keep in the Middle of

说,当时它比整整一船黄金更有价值;我把这整个工具箱吊到筏子上,根本没花时间打开箱子看看,因为我大致上知道箱子里有些什么。

其次,我需要枪支和弹药;在大舱里有两支性能良好的鸟枪和两把手枪。我先拿上它们,顺带拿了几支装火药的角筒,一小袋子弹和两把生锈的旧剑。我知道船上有三桶火药,就是不知道炮手把它藏在哪儿,找了半天才找到。其中有两桶完好无损,有一桶浸了水。我把枪和两桶火药搬上筏子。我感到东西装得够多的了,该考虑怎样把这些东西送上岸。我既没有帆,没有桨,也没有舵,一股小风就能把筏子掀翻。

但以下三个方面却鼓励着我:1.海面平静;2.海水正在涨潮,且要向岸边冲去;3.仅有的一点风是吹向海岸的。恰在这时,我发现了两三只大船上的断桨,而且除了箱子里的工具外,我又找到了两把锯、一把斧头、一个锤子。我便载了这些货物向岸上进发。开始的一英里路,我的筏子行驶得很好,只是漂向的地方与我昨天着陆的地方有些距离,我发现那里水面上有回流。我希望附近有条小溪或小河,可以作一个港口,把我的货物运到岸上。

正像我希望的那样,前面岸上果然有一处缺口,我看到潮水正往里直灌呢;我便小心翼翼地驾着筏子,从缺口的中

the Stream: But here I had like to have suffer'd a second Shipwreck, which, if I had, I think verily would have broke my Heart, for knowing nothing of the Coast, my Raft run a-ground at one End of it upon a Shoal, and not being a-ground at the other End, it wanted but a little that all my Cargo had slip'd off towards that End that was a-float, and so fall'n into the Water: I did my utmost by setting my Back against the Chests, to keep them in their Places, but could not thrust off the Raft with all my Strength, neither durst I stir from the Posture I was in, but holding up the Chests with all my Might, stood in that Manner near half an Hour, in which time the rising of the Water brought me a little more upon a Level, and a little after, the Water still rising, my Raft floated again, and I thrust her off with the Oar I had, into the Channel, and then driving up higher, I at length found my self in the Mouth of a little River, with Land on both Sides, and a strong Current or Tide running up, I look'd on both Sides for a proper Place to get to Shore, for I was not willing to be driven too high up the River, hoping in time to see some Ship at Sea, and therefore resolv'd to place my self as near the Coast as I could.

At length I spy'd a little Cove on the right Shore of the Creek, to which with great Pain and Difficulty I guided my Raft, and at last got so near, as that, reaching Ground with my Oar, I could thrust her directly in, but here I had like to have dipt all my Cargo in the Sea again; for that Shore lying pretty steep, that is to say sloping, there was no Place to land, but where one End of my Float, if it run on Shore, would lie so high, and the other sink lower as before, that it would en-

间往里开。可是,这回我差点儿又要遭受翻船的灾难(要是筏子真的翻倾,肯定会让我心碎)。由于我对岸边的地形一无所知,筏子一头搁上了浅滩,而另一头却在水中晃荡,只差一点儿,我所有的货物就要从没有搁浅的这一头滑下来,掉到水里去。我便使出吃奶的力气,用后背死死顶住那几只箱子,不让它们下滑。纵使我拼出全部的力气,也不能把筏子支开,再说,我这样用力顶着最终也不能支持多长时间;但是,我只能尽我全部的力量,挡住那几只箱子,就这样,坚持了半个小时。这期间,随着潮水慢慢上涨,筏子也渐渐趋于平衡,终于,上涨的海水又使筏子重新漂浮起来。于是我重新操桨撑排向那个小缺口划去。从小缺口进入了一个小河道,两边是陆地,上涨的海水直往里面涌动。我察看了一下小河两岸的地势,打算在靠近河口处找个合适的地方停泊筏子,我不想进入小河太远的地方,因为靠近海边能看到海上过往的船只。

最后我在小河右岸找到一处小湾,好不容易提心吊胆费劲力气把筏子撑到离小湾最近的一片浅滩,想用桨抵住河底,把筏子撑进湾里停泊,可又一次差点翻船。由于岸十分陡峭,没有地方可以登岸,如果筏子一头着地,另一头又下沉得厉害,货物就又要危险了。只有用桨做为锚,使

danger my Cargo again: All that I could do, was to wait 'till the Tide was at highest, keeping the Raft with my Oar like an Anchor to hold the Side of it fast to the Shore, near a flat Piece of Ground, which I expected the Water would flow over; and so it did: As soon as I found Water enough, for my Raft drew about a Foot of Water, I thrust her on upon that flat Piece of Ground, and there fasten'd or mor'd her by sticking my two broken Oars into the Ground; one on one Side near one End, and one on the other Side near the other End; and thus I lay 'till the Water ebb'd away, and left my Raft and all my Cargo safe on Shore.

My next Work was to view the Country, and seek a proper Place for my Habitation, and where to stow my Goods to secure them from whatever might happen; where I was I yet knew not, whether on the Continent or on an Island, whether inhabited or not inhabited, whether in Danger of wild Beasts or not: There was a Hill not above a Mile from me, which rose up very steep and high, and which seem'd to over-top some other Hills which lay as in a Ridge from it northward; I took out one of the fowling Pieces, and one of the Pistols, and an Horn of Powder, and thus arm'd I travell'd for Discovery up to the Top of that Hill, where after I had with great Labour and Difficulty got to the Top, I saw my Fate to my great Affliction, (viz.) that I was in an Island environ'd every Way with the Sea, no Land to be seen, except some Rocks which lay a great Way off, and two small Islands less than this, which lay about three Leagues to the West.

I found also that the Island I was in was barren, and, as I saw good Reason to believe, un-inhabited, except by wild Beasts, of whom however I saw none, yet I saw Abundance of Fowls, but

筏子不离河岸,等涨潮水再涨一些再看一看。果然当我一看见水已涨得筏子要吃一英尺多深的水——我就把筏子撑到平地上,再把两只断桨在船两头插下,把筏子系在那里。退潮后,筏子和货物就都安安稳稳的留在岸上了。

我的下一步工作就是要查看一下地势,找一个适当的地方来安置我的住所,贮藏我的东西,预防意外的事情发生。我现在还不知道自己到了一个什么地方,是在一片大陆上呢还是在一个岛上;有人烟呢还是没有人烟;有野兽呢还是没有野兽。离我不到一英里的地方,有一座又陡又高的小山,它北边还有一连串的小山,好像一道山脉,但都不及它高。我带了一支鸟枪,一把手枪,和一角筒火药,向这个山顶出发。当我费了很大的气力和艰苦,爬上山顶一看,我不禁为我的命运担忧起来,原来我是在一个海岛上,四面环海,看不见一点陆地,只有很远的地方有几块礁岩,另外就是在三海里之外,在西边,有两个比本岛还小的岛屿。

我还发现,这个海岛非常荒凉,看来荒无人烟,只有野兽出没其间,但至今我尚未遇见过任何野兽,却看到无数飞

knew not their Kinds, neither when I kill'd them could I tell what was fit for Food, and what not; at my coming back, I shot at a great Bird which I saw sitting upon a Tree on the Side of a great Wood, I believe it was the first Gun that had been fir'd there since the Creation of the World; I had no sooner fir'd, but from all the Parts of the Wood there arose an innumerable Number of Fowls of many Sorts, making a confus'd Screaming, and crying every one according to his usual Note; but not one of them of any Kind that I knew: As for the Creature I kill'd, I took it to be a Kind of a Hawk, its Colour and Beak resembling it, but had no Talons or Claws more than common, its Flesh was Carrion, and fit for nothing.

Contented with this Discovery, I came back to my Raft, and fell to Work to bring my Cargo on Shore, which took me up the rest of that Day, and what to do with my self at Night I knew not, nor indeed where to rest; for I was afraid to lie down on the Ground, not knowing but some wild Beast might devour me, tho', as I afterwards found, there was really no Need for those Fears.

However, as well as I could, I barricaded my self round with the Chests and Boards that I had brought on Shore, and me a Kind of a Hut for that Night's Lodging; as for Food, I yet saw not which Way to supply my self, except that I had seen two or three Creatures like Hares run out of the Wood where I shot the Fowl.

I now began to consider, that I might yet get a great many Things out of the Ship, which would be useful to me, and particularly some of the Rigging, and Sails, and such other Things as might come to Land, and I resolv'd to make another Voyage on Board the Vessel, if possible; and as I knew that the first Storm that blew must necessarily break her all in Pieces, I resolv'd to set all other Things apart, 'till I got every Thing out of the

禽,可都叫不出是什么飞禽,也不知道打死之后肉好不好吃。回来的路上,见一只大鸟停在大树林旁的一棵树上,我就向它开了一枪。我相信,自上帝创造世界以来,第一次有人在这个岛上开枪。枪声一响,整个森林里飞出无数的飞鸟,各种鸟鸣聒噪而起,呼号交作,乱成一片,但我却叫不出一个来。我打死的那只鸟,从毛色和嘴看,像是一种老鹰,但没有钩爪,其肉酸腐难吃,毫无用处。

我察看够了,便回到筏子上,动手把东西全搬到岸上;等做好了这事,白天已快结束,但我还不知道自己将怎么过夜,也不知道该在哪里过夜;因为我害怕席地而卧,生恐这么睡觉时会被野兽吞了,但我后来发现,在那岛上其实不用担那份心。

然而,我仍旧尽量用带上岸的箱子和木板把自己围在中间过夜。至于食品,我不知道从何处弄来,但看到过几只野兔模样的动物从我打鸟的林子里蹿出来。

我开始寻思能从船上搬来多少有用的东西,特别是索具、帆和其他一些物品。我打算如果可能的话再上一次船。我知道来一阵大风就会把船打个粉碎。我决心先丢开别的事情,从船上取出我所带回来的东西。之后我便琢磨,能否把筏子再撑回去,但这显然

Ship that I could get; then I call'd a Council, that is to say, in my Thoughts, whether I should take back the Raft, but this appear'd impracticable; so I resolv'd to go as before, when the Tide was down, and I did so, only that I stripp'd before I went from my Hut, having nothing on but a Chequer'd Shirt, and a Pair of Linnen Drawers, and a Pair of Pumps on my Feet.

I got on Board the Ship, as before, and prepar'd a second Raft, and having had Experience of the first, I neither made this so unwieldy, nor loaded it so hard, but yet I brought away several Things very useful to me; as first, in the Carpenter's Stores I found two or three Bags full of Nails and Spikes, a great Skrew-Jack, a Dozen or two of Hatchets, and above all, that most useful Thing call'd a Grindstone; all these I secur'd together, with several Things belonging to the Gunner, particularly two or three Iron Crows, and two Barrels of Musquet Bullets, seven Musquets, and another fowling Piece, with some small Quantity of Powder more; a large Bag full of small Shot, and a great Roll of Sheet Lead: But this last was so heavy, I could not hoise it up to get it over the Ship's Side.

Besides these Things, I took all the Mens Cloths that I could find, and a spare Fore-top-sail, a Hammock, and some Bedding; and with this I loaded my second Raft, and brought them all safe on Shore to my very great Comfort.

I was under some Apprehensions during my Absence from the Land, that at least my Provisions might be devour'd on Shore; but when I came back, I found no Sign of any Visitor, only there sat a Creature like a wild Cat upon one of the Chests, which when I came towards it, ran away

是不可能的。我决定等潮水退去后,像上次那样上船。我这样做了,只是当我走出我的小屋前,把衣服脱了,只穿了件衬衣、一条短裤和一双软鞋。

我像上次那样上了船,做了第二只筏子,因为有了第一次经验,我没有把它做得那么笨重,也没有让它负荷过重,但还是搬了些对我很有用处的东西。首先,我在木匠的舱里找到了满满两三袋的大小铁钉,一只大绞盘,一两把短柄斧头,最重要的是,找到了一件特别有用的东西:磨石。我把这些东西跟后来所找到的东西都放在一块,因为,我又从炮手的舱里找到了一些东西,尤其有用的是三把起货钩和两桶短枪子弹,七把短枪和一杆鸟枪,还有少量的火药,以及满满七大口袋的小子弹和一大卷铅皮。但是,铅皮太重了,我搬不动,没法将它从船舷上放下去。

除此之外,我还拿走了船上所有的男式衣服,外加一个备用樯帆、一只吊床和一些被褥。我把这些东西吊到我的第二只筏子上,并平安地运到岸上。现在我感觉宽慰多了。

离岸期间,我一直担心岸上的粮食会不会被什么动物吃掉。还好,回来后并未见到有何不速之客拜访过的痕迹,却见一只野猫似的东西站在一只箱子上面。我走近它,它

a little Distance, and then stood still; she sat very compos'd, and unconcern'd, and look'd full in my Face, as if she had a Mind to be acquainted with me, I presented my Gun at her, but as she did not understand it, she was perfectly unconcern'd at it, nor did she offer to stir away; upon which I toss'd her a Bit of Bisket, tho' by the Way I was not very free of it, for my Store was not great: However, I spar'd her a Bit, I Say, and she went to it, smell'd of it, and ate it, and look'd (as pleas'd) for more, but I thank'd her, and could spare no more; so she march'd off.

Having got my second Cargo on Shore, tho' I was fain to open the Barrels of Powder, and bring them by Parcels, for they were too heavy, being large Casks, I went to work to make me a little Tent with the Sail and some Poles which I cut for that Purpose, and into this Tent I brought every Thing that I knew would spoil, either with Rain or Sun, and I piled all the empty Chests and Casks up in a Circle round the Tent, to fortify it from any sudden Attempt, either from Man or Beast.

When I had done this I block'd up the Door of the Tent with some Boards within, and an empty Chest set up an End without, and spreading one of the Beds upon the Ground, laying my two Pistols just at my Head, and my Gun at Length by me, I went to Bed for the first Time, and slept very quietly all Night, for I was very weary and heavy, for the Night before I had slept little, and had labour'd very hard all Day, as well to fetch all those Things from the Ship, as to get them on Shore.

I had the biggest Maggazin of all Kinds now that ever were laid up, I believe, for one Man,

就跑开几步，然后又站住不动。那小东西神情安然自若，直直地瞅着我的脸，好像要和我交朋友似的。我用枪向它比了比，可是它不懂得是什么东西，还是一点也不在乎，毫无跑开的意思。于是我取了一块饼干丢给它，虽然，说句老实话，我的手头并不宽裕，因为我的存粮也不多，可是我还是分出这点给它吃。它走过去，闻了闻，把它吃下去，样子仿佛很满意，还想讨一点。可是我实在没法再分给它了，只好谢绝了它，于是它就走了。

第二批货上岸后，我很想把两桶火药打开，分成小包藏起来，因为两大桶的火药分量太重，但我得先用船上的帆布和砍好的支柱做一顶帐篷，把凡是经不起雨打日晒的东西通通搬进去；又把那些空箱子和空桶放在帐篷周围，以防人或野兽的突然袭击。

做好这件事以后，我就在帐篷里面用几块木板把帐篷的出入口堵住，又在外面顶头竖好一只空箱子，接着就在地上铺好床，头边放好两支手枪，身边又放了一支长枪，总算是上岛以来第一次在床上睡觉了；这一夜，我睡得很香，因为上一夜睡得很少，整个白天里又是上船去拿那些东西，又是把东西弄到岸上，实在是又累又困了。

我相信我现在已备有一个品种齐全的军火库，其数量

but I was not satisfy'd still; for while the Ship sat upright in that Posture, I thought I ought to get every Thing out of her that I could; so every Day at low Water I went on Board, and brought away some Thing or other: But particularly the third Time I went, I brought away as much of the Rigging as I could, as also all the small Ropes·and Rope-twine I could get, with a Piece of spare Canvass, which was to mend the Sails upon Occasion, the Barrel of wet Gun-powder: In a Word, I brought away all the Sails first and last, only that I was fain to cut them in Pieces, and bring as much at a Time as I could; for they were no more useful to be Sails, but as meer Canvass only.

But that which comforted me more still was, that at last of all, after I had made five or six such Voyages as these, and thought I had nothing more to expect from the Ship that was worth my medling with, I say, after all this, I found a great Hogshead of Bread and three large Runlets of Rum or Spirits, and a Box of Sugar, and a Barrel of fine Flower; this was surprizing to me, because I had given over expecting any more Provisions, except what was spoil'd by the Water: I soon empty'd the Hogshead of that Bread, and wrapt it up Parcel by Parcel in Pieces of the Sails, which I cut out; and in a Word, I got all this safe on Shore also.

The next Day I made another Voyage; and now having plunder'd the Ship of what was portable and fit to hand out, I began with the Cables; and cutting the great Cable into Pieces, such as I could move, I got two Cables and a Hawser on Shore, with all the Iron Work I could get; and having cut down the Spritsail-yard, and the Missen-yard, and every Thing I could to make a large Raft, I loaded it with all those heavy Goods, and came away: But my good Luck began now to leave me; for this Raft was so unwieldy, and so overloaden, that after I was enter'd the little Cove, where I had landed the rest of my Goods, not being able to guide it

足够一个人用,但我依然不满足。只要那条船没翻,我觉得自己就应该把所有能带走的东西通通带走。因此,每天潮水一退,我就上船,带些东西出来,尤其是第三次,我拿到许多能找到的索具和小绳子,一块用来修补帆的多余的帆布,一桶打湿的火药。总之,我带走了所有的帆,只是不得不把它们裁成一块一块的,每次能带多少就带多少,因为我已用不上帆,只需要帆布。

最使我感到欣慰的是,当我往船上往返了五六趟后,原以为船上再也没有什么东西值得我费劲时,我又找到了一大桶面包,三大桶甜酒,一箱食用糖,一桶上等的面粉。这真是出乎我的意料,我原以为船上除了被水浸湿的东西外,再也没有什么食物了。我把那桶面包全倒出来,用撕下来的帆布一包包地裹好,带到了岸上。

第二日我又去了一趟。大船上凡是能搬得动的物品都被我搜掠走了,现在我又来运锚缆。为了好装运,我把这些锚缆砍成了许多截。最后,我把两圈锚缆与一根钢缆,以及所能找到的铁器,全都搬了出来。我把前桅和后桅的帆桁砍了下来,再用凡是我能找到的材料做成了一块大木筏,把这些笨重的货物都装在上面,运了回来。结果这一次很不走运。由于木筏做得太笨,

so handily as I did the other, it overset, and threw me and all my Cargo into the Water; as for my self it was no great Harm, for I was near the Shore; but as to my Cargo, it was great Part of it lost, especially the Iron, which I expected would have been of great Use to me: However, when the Tide was out, I got most of the Pieces of Cable ashore, and some of the Iron, tho' with infinite Labour; for I was fain to dip for it into the Water, a Work which fatigu'd me very much: After this I went every Day on Board, and brought away what I could get.

I had been now thirteen Days on Shore, and had been eleven Times on Board the Ship; in which Time I had brought away all that one Pair of Hands could well be suppos'd capable to bring, tho' I believe verily, had the calm Weather held, I should have brought away the whole Ship Piece by Piece: But preparing the 12th Time to go on Board, I found the Wind begin to rise; however at low Water I went on Board, and tho' I thought I had rumag'd the Cabbin so effectually, as that nothing more could be found, yet I discover'd a Locker with Drawers in it, in one of which I found two or three Razors, and one Pair of large Sizzers, with some ten or a Dozen of good Knives and Forks; in another I found about Thirty six Pounds value in Money, some European Coin, some Brazil, some Pieces of Eight, some Gold, some Silver.

I smil'd to my self at the Sight of this Money, O Drug Said I aloud, what art thou good for, Thou art not worth to me, no not the taking off of the Ground, one of those Knives is worth all this

货物又太重,所以驾驭起来不如以前灵活,在驶进御货的小水湾时,一下子操纵失控,于是连人带货全都翻入了水里。我倒没受什么大伤,可是货物全淹在水里了,实在让我心痛,特别是那些铁器,还指望着能派上大用场呢!所以等到退潮后,我还是不辞劳苦地去水中打捞这些货物。我一次又一次地潜入水中,打捞出大部分锚缆和一些铁器。这可真是一项异常艰苦的工作,真把我给累惨了。这以后,我还是每天都到船上去一次,每回都要尽力带些东西上岸。

我已经到小岛上十三天,去过船上十一次。这段时间,我把我双手能搬得动的东西通通搬了下来,我相信,如果天气不变坏,我肯定能够把整只船都肢解掉,搬上岸来。第十二次我再打算往船上去时,发现开始起风,可我照旧在退潮时上了船,尽管我以为我已搜遍了全船,不可能再找到什么有用的东西了,结果还是有新发现。我找到了一个有抽屉的柜子;在一个抽屉里装着两三把剃刀,一把十分锋利大剪子,十几把刀子和叉子;在旁边另外一个抽屉里装着许多钱币,有些是欧洲的,有些是巴西的,有些是西班牙的;有金币,有银币,一共差不多值三十六英镑。

我看见这些钱,不禁失笑起来,大声说:“你这废物! 你现在还有什么用处呢? 你现在对于我连粪土都不如,那些

Heap, I have no Manner of use for thee, e'en remain where thou art, and go to the Bottom as a Creature whose Life is not worth saving. However, upon Second Thoughts, I took it away, and wrapping all this in a Piece of Canvas, I began to think of making another Raft, but while I was preparing this, I found the Sky over-cast, and the Wind began to rise, and in a Quarter of an Hour it blew a fresh Gale from the Shore; it presently occur'd to me, that it was in vain to pretend to make a Raft with the Wind off Shore, and that it was my Business to be gone before the Tide of Flood began, otherwise I might not be able to reach the Shore at all: Accordingly I let my self down into the Water, and swam cross the Channel, which lay between the Ship and the Sands, and even that with Difficulty enough, partly with the Weight of the Things I had about me, and partly the Roughness of the Water, for the Wind rose very hastily, and before it was quite high Water, it blew a Storm.

But I was gotten home to my little Tent, where I lay with all my Wealth about me very secure. It blew very hard all that Night, and in the Morning when I look'd out, behold no more Ship was to be seen; I was a little surpriz'd, but recover'd my self with this satisfactory Reflection, viz. That I had lost no time, nor abated no Diligence to get every-thing out of her that could be useful to me, and that indeed there was little left in her that I was able to bring away if I had had more Time.

I now gave over any more Thoughts of the Ship, or of any thing out of her, except what might drive on Shore from her Wreck, as indeed divers Pieces of her afterwards did; but those things were of small use to me.

刀子，一把就值得你这一大堆。我现在用不着你；你就留在老地方，像一个不值得挽救的生命，沉到海底去吧。"可是考虑了一会儿，我还是把它们拿走了。我一面把这些东西包在一块帆布里，一面开始盘算着再做一个木筏。可是，我正在做着的时候，就看见天色阴暗下来，风也刮起来了，不到一刻钟的工夫，变成了一股狂风从岸上刮来。我马上想到，风从岸上刮来，做木筏是没有用的，还不如乘着潮水还没有涨，赶快走，否则也许根本上不了岸了。于是我立刻跳下水，游过船和沙滩之间那片狭长的水湾。这一次，由于带的东西太重，再加上风势越刮越强劲，我游得很吃力。当潮水上涨不久后，海面上已刮起风暴了。

我回到了自己搭的小帐篷，这算是我的家了。我躺下来睡觉，四周是我全部的财产，心中感到安稳踏实。大风整整刮了一夜，第二天早晨，我向外一望，那只船已无影无踪！这使我感到有点意外，但回头一想，我又觉得坦然了。我没有浪费时间，也没有偷懒，把船上一切有用的东西都搬了下来，即使再多留一点时间，船上也已没有多少有用的东西好拿了。

我就此不再去想那条船或船上的东西了，要想的话，也无非是想那船毁坏后会有什么东西被冲上海滩；后来，果然有各种各样东西漂上了

My Thoughts were now wholly employ'd about securing my self against either Savages, if any should appear, or wild Beasts, if any were in the Island; and I had many Thoughts of the Method how to do this, and what kind of Dwelling to make, whether I should make me a Cave in the Earth, or a Tent upon the Earth: And, in short, I resolv'd upon both, the Manner and Description of which, it may not be improper to give an Account of.

I soon found the Place I was in was not for my Settlement, particularly because it was upon a low moorish Ground near the Sea, and I believ'd would not be wholesome, and more particularly because there was no fresh Water near it, so I resolv'd to find a more healthy and more convenient Spot of Ground.

I consulted several Things in my Situation which I found would be proper for me, 1st. Health, and fresh Water I just now mention'd, 2dly. Shelter from the Heat of the Sun, 3dly. Security from ravenous Creatures, whether Men or Beasts, 4thly. a View to the Sea, that if God sent any Ship in Sight, I might not lose any Advantage for my Deliverance, of which I was not willing to banish all my Expectation yet.

In search of a Place proper for this, I found a little Plain on the Side of a rising Hill; whose Front towards this little Plain, was steep as a House-side, so that nothing could come down upon me from the Top; on the Side of this Rock there was a hollow Place worn a little way in like the Entrance or Door of a Cave, but there was not really any Cave or Way into the Rock at all.

On the Flat of the Green, just before this hol-

岸,但对我都没有什么用处。

这时,我的心思完全转到了别的方面:如果这岛上有野人或猛兽,我该怎样防备,怎样确保自己的安全? 对这个问题,我想出了很多方案,也仔细考虑了自己该有个怎么样的住所:是挖个洞穴呢,还是在地面上支个帐篷? 总之,我最后决定两者兼顾,至于具体的做法,我想介绍一下也不妨。

我很快注意到现在这个地方不适合居住,尤其是因为这是一块靠海的低洼地,住在这儿于健康不利,更糟糕的是附近没有淡水,因此,我决定找一个更有利于身体健康、更舒服的地点。

我对自己的处境考虑再三,发现这几个方面对我至关重要:第一是我刚提到的健康和淡水;第二是避开阳光的暴晒;第三是免遭凶猛动物的袭击,不论是野人还是野兽;第四是要能看到大海,如果上帝让什么船只从这里经过,我不致于失去获救的机会,至今我还不愿意放弃我的希望。

在寻找一个符合这些条件的地方时,我在一座小山的旁边发现了一块小平地,紧挨这块平地的山坡是如同墙壁一样陡峭的岩石,任何动物都不能从山顶上下来袭击我,在这块岩石的旁边,有一块凹进去的地面,仿佛是伸向一个山洞的入口,实际上里面根本没有山洞。

我计划就在这个凹洞前

low Place, I resolv'd to pitch my Tent: This Plain was not above an Hundred Yards broad, and about twice as long, and lay like a Green before my Door, and at the End of it descended irregularly every Way down into the Low-grounds by the Sea-side. It was on the N. N. W. Side of the Hill, so that I was shelter'd from the Heat every Day, till it came to a W. and by S. Sun, or thereabouts, which in those Countries is near the Setting.

Before I set up my Tent, I drew a half Circle before the hollow Place, which took in about Ten Yards in its Semi-diameter from the Rock, and Twenty Yards in its Diameter, from its Beginning and Ending.

In this half Circle I pitch'd two Rows of strong Stakes, driving them into the Ground till they stood very firm like Piles, the biggest End being out of the Ground about Five Foot and a Half, and sharpen'd on the Top: The two Rows did not stand above Six Inches from one another.

Then I took the Pieces of Cable which I had cut in the Ship, and I laid them in Rows one upon another, within the Circle, between these two Rows of Stakes, up to the Top, placing other Stakes in the In-side, leaning against them, about two Foot and a half high, like a Spurr to a Post, and this Fence was so strong, that neither Man or Beast could get into it or over it: This cost me a great deal of Time and Labour, especially to cut the Piles in the Woods, bring them to the Place, and drive them into the Earth.

The Entrance into this Place I made to be not by a Door, but by a short Ladder to go over the Top, which Ladder, when I was in, I lifted over

面的草地上搭我的帐篷。这块平地最多有一百码宽,其长度大约是宽度的两倍,这块平地就好像是我门前的草坪。它的尽头参参差差地低凹了下去,从各处都可通向海边的低地。这处岩壁朝着西北偏北方向,当这个地区的太阳移到西面或西南面的时候,也就是太阳快要下山的时候了,所以,我每天都可以避开太阳的直射。

搭帐篷之前,我大致丈量了一下。我以岩石壁为中心划了一个半圆,半径大约为十码,因此帐篷沿石壁的那一面全长约为二十码。

我沿着这个半圆形竖起了两排结实的木桩,木桩做成木橛子样,削得尖尖的那一头被夯入地里,木桩露出地面有五英尺半高,两排之间的距离不到六英寸。

然后,我又取出我从船上截下来的那些缆索,沿着半圆形,把它们一层一层地横放在两排木桩中间,一直堆到顶上,又用一些两英尺半高的木桩插在圈内,支着它们,仿佛柱子下的支柱;这样一个篱笆,真是牢固异常,不管是人是兽,都没法冲进来或爬进来。这个工程,耗去了我很多的时间和劳动,特别是在我从树林里把木橛砍下来,把它运到草地上,又把它们一根根地打到泥土里的时候。

至于住所的进出口,我没有在篱笆上做门,而是用一个短梯从篱笆顶上翻进来,进入

after me, and so I was compleatly fenc'd in, and fortify'd, as I thought, from all the World, and consequently slept secure in the Night, which otherwise I could not have done, tho', as it appear'd afterward, there was no need of all this Caution from the Enemies that I apprehended Danger from.

Into this Fence or Fortress, with infinite Labour, I carry'd all my Riches, all my Provisions, Ammunition and Stores, of which you have the Account above, and I made me a large Tent, which, to preserve me from the Rains that in one Part of the Year are very violent there, I made double, viz. One smaller Tent within, and one larger Tent above it, and cover'd the uppermost with a large Tarpaulin which I had sav'd among the Sails.

And now I lay no more for a while in the Bed which I had brought on Shore, but in a Hammock, which was indeed a very good one, and belong'd to the Mate of the Ship.

Into this Tent I brought all my Provisions, and every thing that would spoil by the Wet, and having thus enclos'd all my Goods, I made up the Entrance, which till now I had left open, and so pass'd and re-pass'd, as I said, by a short Ladder.

When I had done this, I began to work my Way into the Rock, and bringing all the Earth and Stones that I dug down out thro' my Tent, I laid 'em up within my Fence in the Nature of a Terras, that so it rais'd the Ground within about a Foot and a Half; and thus I made me a Cave just behind my Tent, which serv'd me like a Cellar to my House.

It cost me much Labour, and many Days, before all these Things were brought to Perfection, and therefore I must go back to some other Things

里面后再收好梯子。这样,我四面都受保护,完全与外界隔绝,夜里就可以高枕无忧了。不过,我后来发现,对我所担心的敌人,根本不必如此戒备森严。

我又花了极大的力气,把前面讲到的我的全部财产、全部粮食、弹药武器和补给品,一一搬到篱笆里面,或者可以说搬到这个堡垒里来。我又给自己搭了一个大帐篷用来防雨,因为这儿一年中有一个时期常下倾盆大雨。我搭的这个帐篷是双层的,就是说,里面是个小帐篷,外面是个大帐篷,大帐篷顶上再蒙上一大块柏油帆布,这块柏油帆布是我早先从船帆中留下的。

如今我再也不睡搬上岸来的那张床了,而是换了一个吊床睡;这吊床实在是件好东西,它本是船上大副的。

我把全部粮食和一切不能受潮的东西搬进帐篷,就这样把一切东西都弄到围栅之后,我才把一直留着的出入口堵上,用我说过的短梯进出。

随后我又开始挖凿岩壁,我把挖出来的泥土、石砾通过帐篷运出去,在篱笆下堆成一个约一英尺半高的土台,帐篷后面挖出的山洞,正好当地窖使用。

我花了大力气,费了不知多少时间才干完这些活,接着,该做那些一直叫我念念不

— 70 —

which took up some of my Thoughts. At the same time it happen'd after I had laid my Scheme for the setting up my Tent and making the Cave, that a Storm of Rain falling from a thick dark Cloud, a sudden Flash of Lightning happen'd, and after that a great Clap of Thunder, as is naturally the Effect of it; I was not so much surpris'd with the Lightning as I was with a Thought which darted into my Mind as swift as the Lightning it self: O my Powder! My very Heart sunk within me, when I thought, that at one Blast all my Powder might be destroy'd, on which, not my Defence only, but the providing me Food, as I thought, entirely depended; I was nothing near so anxious about my own Danger, tho' had the Powder took fire, I had never known who had hurt me. Such Impression did this make upon me, that after the Storm was over, I laid aside all my Works, my Building, and Fortifying, and apply'd my self to make Bags and Boxes to separate the Powder, and keep it a little and a little in a Parcel, in hope, that whatever might come, it might not all take Fire at once, and to keep it so apart that it should not be possible to make one part fire another: I finish'd this Work in about a Fortnight, and I think my Powder, which in all was about 240 l. weight was divided in not less than a Hundred Parcels; as to the Barrel that had been wet, I did not apprehend any Danger from that, so I plac'd it in my new Cave, which in my Fancy I call'd my Kitchin, and the rest I hid up and down in Holes among the Rocks, so that no wet might come to it, marking very carefully where I laid it.

In the Interval of time while this was doing I went out once at least every Day with my Gun, as well to divert my self, as to see if I could kill any thing fit for Food, and as near as I could to acquaint my self with what the Island produc'd. The first time I went out I presently discover'd that

忘的事情啦。就在我计划支帐篷、挖山洞之际,乌云忽地布满天空,大雨倾盆而下,一道道闪电划破长空,雷声轰鸣不绝于耳。一个念头闪电般地掠过脑际,叫我惊骇之至:噢,我的火药!我的火药有可能一下子全被毁掉,我的心猛地一沉,因为我不仅靠它自卫,还要靠它猎取食物。这时如果火药着火爆炸,我自己还不知道怎样死的呢!可我一点也没有考虑自己的危险。受了这场惊吓,等暴雨一停,我便把所有的事情,如建住所、修防御之事,全都抛在一边,专心致志地做些袋子和盒子,一包一包地把火药分开来装,希望不论发生什么事情,火药不致于立刻全部被毁,又把火药分开保存,省得着火后这包引着那包。我花了两个礼拜的工夫才做完了这项工作。我所有的火药加起来有二百四十磅,最后至少分装成了一百小袋。至于那桶进了海水的湿火药,我倒不担心会有什么危险,所以,我把它移到了新掘的山洞里(我管这个洞叫我的厨房呢);其余那些我则将它们藏在岩壁上的小洞里,这样就不会受潮了。同时,我在各个收藏处都仔仔细细地做了记号。

在这些日子里,我每天至少要带上枪出门一次,这不仅是为了出门散散心,而且是为了看看能打点什么吃食回来,再就是为了了解一下岛上有些什么特产与资源。第一次

there were Goats in the Island, which was a great Satisfaction to me; but then it was attended with this Misfortune to me, viz. That they were so shy, so subtile, and so swift of Foot, that it was the difficultest thing in the World to come at them: But I was not discourag'd at this, not doubting but I might now and then shoot one, as it soon happen'd, for after I had found their Haunts a little, I laid wait in this Manner for them: I observ'd if they saw me in the Valleys, tho' they were upon the Rocks, they would run away as in a terrible Fright; but if they were feeding in the Valleys, and I was upon the Rocks, they took no Notice of me, from whence I concluded, that by the Position of their Opticks, their Sight was so directed downward, that they did not readily see Objects that were above them; so afterward I took this Method, I always clim'd the Rocks first to get above them, and then had frequently a fair Mark. The first shot I made among these Creatures, I kill'd a She-Goat which had a little Kid by her which she gave Suck to, which griev'd me heartily; but when the Old one fell, the Kid stood stock still by her till I came and took her up, and not only so, but when I carry'd the Old one with me upon my Shoulders, the Kid follow'd me quite to my Enclosure, upon which I laid down the Dam, and took the Kid in my Arms, and carry'd it over my Pale, in hopes to have bred it up tame, but it would not eat, so I was forc'd to kill it and eat it my self; these two supply'd me with Flesh a great while, for I eat sparingly; and sav'd my Provisions (my Bread especially) as much as possibly I could. Having now fix'd my Habitation, I found it absolutely necessary to provide a Place to make a Fire in, and Fewel to burn; and what I did for that, as also how I enlarg'd my Cave, and what Conveniences I made, I shall give a full Account of in its Place: But I must first give some little Account of my

出去，就发现岛上有许多山羊，这使我欣喜万分，可是很快又由喜变忧，因为我发现这些山羊既胆小又狡猾，而且跑起来速度飞快，想要靠近它们非常困难。但我并不灰心丧气，相信迟早总有一天能想出办法打到它们。事实果真如此。很快我就发现了山羊的一个特点：如果我在山谷里出现，哪怕它们在山岩上，也会被惊吓得仓皇逃窜；但如果它们在山谷里吃草，我却站在山岩上，它们就不会注意到我而逃跑了。我断定它们因为视觉器管的部位的关系，仅仅可以望见下面的东西，而不能看见上面的东西。后来我就利用它们这个缺陷，先爬到山上去，从山顶朝着羊群射击；结果常常打到。我第一次放枪，就射中了一头正在哺育小羊的母羊，我感到十分悲伤。老羊倒地后，那小羊还站在那儿一动不动，我把老羊背在肩上带回家，小羊也一直跟着我。我把母羊放在地下，把小羊抱进木栅里，希望能养驯它，以便它能够给我作伴。但是小羊坚决不吃任何食物，我只好把它杀掉吃了。这两只羊我吃了许多天，我吃得很省。因为我要尽量节省粮食，特别是面包。现在既然已经把住处固定下来，我觉得有一件万不可省的事，就是要弄一个生火的地方，并且弄些柴来烧。至于我怎样做这件事，怎样扩大我的石洞，并怎样准备一些其他生活条件，我下面再详细叙

self, and of my Thoughts about Living, which it may well be suppos'd were not a few.

I had a dismal Prospect of my Condition, for as I was not cast away upon that Island without being driven, as is said, by a violent Storm quite out of the Course of our intended Voyage, and a great Way, viz. some Hundreds of Leagues out of the ordinary Course of the Trade of Mankind, I had great Reason to consider it as a Determination of Heaven, that in this desolate Place, and in this desolate Manner I should end my Life; the Tears would run plentifully down my Face when I made these Reflections, and sometimes I would expostulate with my self, Why Providence should thus compleatly ruine its Creatures, and render them so absolutely miserable, so without Help abandon'd, so entirely depress'd, that it could hardly be rational to be thankful for such a Life.

But something always return'd swift upon me to check these Thoughts, and to reprove me; and particularly one Day walking with my Gun in my Hand by the Sea-side, I was very pensive upon the Subject of my present Condition, then Reason as It were expostulated with me t'other Way, thus: Well, you are in a desolate Condition 'tis true, but pray remember, Where are the rest of you? Did not you come Eleven of you into the Boat, where are the Ten? Why were not they sav'd and you lost? Why were you singled out? Is it better to be here or there? and then I pointed to the Sea. All Evils are to be consider'd with the Good that is in them, and with what worse attends them.

述。现在我必须先把我的处境以及我对于目前生活的看法略谈一谈,因为,不难设想,这方面有不少问题可以谈谈。

我感到自己前景暗淡。因为,我被凶猛的风暴刮到这荒岛上,远离原定的航线,远离人类正常的贸易航线有数百里格(一里格约等于三英里)之遥。我想,这完全是出于天意,让我孤苦伶仃,在凄凉中了却余生。想到这些,我的眼泪不禁夺眶而出。有时我不禁犯疑,苍天为什么要这样作践自己所创造的生灵,害得他如此不幸,如此孤立无援,又如此沮丧寂寞呢!在这样的环境中,有什么理由要我们认为生活于我们是一种恩赐呢?

可是,每当我这样想的时候,立刻又有另一种思想出现在我的脑海里,并责怪我不应有上述这些念头。特别是有一天,我手里提着枪,走在海滩边上,闷闷不乐地想着自己目前的处境,这时,理智却同样来反问我了:"对,你的处境确实孤寂凄凉,可是请你不要忘记,你们中间其他的人如今在哪儿呢?你们不是有十一个人进了舢板吗?其他十个人呢?为什么不是他们活了下来而你死掉呢?为什么独独让你活了下来?是待在这个地方好呢,还是待在他们那地方好?"说着,我的手向海上指了指。所以,考虑到所有坏事的时候,应当想到坏事中还有好事,还应当想到,坏事中

Then it occurr'd to me again, how well I was furnish'd for my Subsistence, and what would have been my Case if it had not happen'd, Which was an Hundred Thousand to one, that the Ship floated from the Place where she first struck and was driven so near to the Shore that I had time to get all these Things out of her: What would have been my Case, if I had been to have liv'd in the Condition in which I at first came on Shore, without Necessaries of Life, or Necessaries to supply and procure them? Particularly said I aloud, (tho' to my self) what should I ha' done without a Gun, without Ammunition, without any Tools to make any thing, or to work with, without Clothes, Bedding, a Tent, or any manner of Covering, and that now I had all these to a Sufficient Quantity, and was in a fair way to provide my self in such a manner, as to live without my Gun when my Ammunition was spent; so that I had a tollerable View of subsisting without any Want as long as I liv'd; for I consider'd from the beginning how I would provide for the Accidents that might happen, and for the time that was to come, even not only after my Ammunition should be spent, but even after my Health or Strength should decay.

I confess I had not entertain'd any Notion of my Ammunition being destroy'd at one Blast, I mean my Powder being blown up by Lightning, and this made the Thoughts of it so surprising to me when it lighten'd and thunder'd, as I observ'd just now.

And now being to enter into a melancholy Relation of a Scene of silent Life, such perhaps as was never heard of in the World before, I shall take it from its Beginning, and continue it in its Order. It was, by my Account, the 30th. of Sept. when, in the Manner as above said, I first set Foot upon this horrid Island, when the Sun being, to us, in its Autumnal Equinox, was almost just over my

还可能有更坏的情况呢。

于是我又想到自己的生存条件是多么完备。这只有十万分之一的机遇让我们的船脱离搁浅地方,飘到海岸附近,让我把船上的东西搬上岸。如果不是这样,我的境况又会怎样呢?如果我处在刚上岸时的境地,没有生活必需品,没有获取它们的手段,又会怎样呢?"尤其是,"我大声对自己说,"如果我没有枪弹,没有工具,没有衣物、被褥、帐篷或者其他任何形式的遮盖物,又会怎样呢?"可是现在,我却有大量的物品,即使我的弹药用完了,没有枪,我同样可以很好地养活自己,只要我活着,我是不会为生存而发愁的,因为从一上岸我就考虑到怎样应付意外的事故,考虑到了将来的日子,不只考虑到我的弹药用完后的日子,甚至考虑到我的健康和精力衰退以后的日子。

必须承认,我起先并没有考虑到我的火药会被雷电引爆而全部毁于一瞬,所以,那次雷电交加,我忽然想到这一层的时候,便吓得魂不附体,正如我上文所说的那样。

现在,我已过上了一忧郁、孤独的生活,这样的生活也许是人类历史上闻所未闻的。我将从头开始,按顺序将它记录下去。根据我的估算,我是于九月三十日,经历了那场强大的飓风之后,踏上这座可怕的孤岛的,当时正好是秋

— 74 —

Head, for I reckon'd my self, by Observation, to be in the Latitude of 9 Degrees 22 Minutes North of the Line.

After I had been there about Ten or Twelve Days, it came into my Thoughts, that I should lose my Reckoning of Time for want of Books and Pen and Ink, and should even forget the Sabbath Days from the working Days; but to prevent this I cut it with my Knife upon a large Post, in Capital Letters, and making it into a great Cross I set it up on the Shore where I first landed, viz. I came on Shore here on the 30th of Sept. 1659. Upon the Sides of this square Post I cut every Day a Notch with my Knife, and every seventh Notch was as long again as the rest, and every first Day of the Month as long again as that long one, and thus I kept my Kalander, or weekly, monthly, and yearly reckoning of Time.

In the next place we are to observe, that among the many things which I brought out of the Ship in the several Voyages, which, as above mention'd, I made to it, I got several things of less Value, but not all less useful to me, which I omitted setting down before; as in particular, Pens, Ink, and Paper, several Parcels in the Captain's, Mate's, Gunner's, and Carpenter's keeping, three or four Compasses, some Mathematical Instruments, Dials, Perspectives, Charts, and Books of Navigation, all which I huddel'd together, whether I might want them or no; also I found three very good Bibles which came to me in my Cargo from England, and which I had pack'd up among my things; some Portugueze Books also, and among them two or three Popish Prayer-Books, and several other Books, all which I carefully secur'd. And I must not forget, that we had in the Ship a Dog and two Cats, of whose eminent History I may have occasion to say something in its place;

分,太阳差不多正在我的头顶之上,依我观测,我位于北纬九度二十二分。

上岛十一二天以后,我忽然想到,我没有那么多纸张笔墨作记录,以后肯定会把日期给忘记,甚至弄不清楚安息日和工作日了。为避免这种情况的发生,我用刀在一根木头柱子上以大写字母的形式刻下这样一句话:"一六五九年九月三十日在此上岸。"我把柱子做成一个大十字架,竖立在初次上岸的地方。然后,我就在十字架上刻凹痕记录日子,每一天刻一条凹痕,每七天刻一条长一倍的凹痕,每一个月刻一条再长一倍的凹痕。就这样,我有了自己的日历、周历、月历和年历。

还需要强调的是,我从船上带回来几件十分重要的东西,诸如钢笔、墨水、纸、船长、大副、炮手的行李箱,木匠的工具箱,三、四个罗盘,一部分数学仪器、日规、望远镜、地图、有关航海方面的书籍。不论有无大的用处,我都放在一处。我还发现了三本装帧精美的《圣经》,这是和我的英国货物一起来的;启程的时候,我就把《圣经》装在我的行李包中。我还细心地保存着几本葡文的祈祷书和其他书籍。同时还有一件不应该忘记的事情,就是我们船上还有一条狗和两只猫,关于它们的历史,我下面还要谈到。我把两只猫都带到岸上;至于那条狗,它是在我第一次搬东西上

for I carry'd both the Cats with me, and as for the Dog, he jump'd out of the Ship of himself and swam on Shore to me the Day after I went on Shore with my first Cargo, and was a trusty Servant to me many Years; I wanted nothing that he could fetch me, nor any Company that he could make up to me, I only wanted to have him talk to me, but that would not do: As I observ'd before, I found Pen, Ink and Paper, and I husbanded them to the utmost, and I shall shew, that while my Ink lasted, I kept things very exact, but after that was gone I could not, for I could not make any Ink by any Means that I could devise.

And this put me in mind that I wanted many things, notwithstanding all that I had amass'd together, and of these, this of Ink was one, as also Spade, Pick-Axe, and Shovel to dig or remove the Earth, Needles, Pins, and Thread; as for Linnen, I soon learn'd to want that without much Difficulty. This want of Tools made every Work I did go on heavily, and it was near a whole Year before I had entirely finish'd my little Pale or surrounded Habitation: The Piles or Stakes, which were as heavy as I could well lift, were a long time in cutting and preparing in the Woods, and more by far in bringing home, so that I spent some times two Days in cutting and bringing home one of those Posts, and a third Day in driving it into the Ground; for which Purpose I got a heavy Piece of Wood at first, but at last bethought my self of one of the Iron Crows, which however tho' I found it, yet it made driving those Posts or Piles very laborious and tedious Work.

But what need I ha' been concern'd at the Tediousness of any thing I had to do, seeing I had time enough to do it in, nor had I any other Em-

岸的第二天自动跳下船来，泅到岸上，来找我的，后来做了我多年的忠实奴仆。我并不想要它替我衔什么东西，也不想要它替我做个什么伴，我只想要它同我说说话，但是它却办不到。自从我找到笔、墨水和纸以后，我用得非常节省。事实证明，如果有墨水，我就可以把事情记得非常清楚；如果墨水完了，我就记不成了，因为我想不出任何办法来制造墨水。

这使我想到，尽管我已收集了这么多东西，我还缺少很多很多东西，墨水就是其中之一。其他的东西像挖土或搬土用的铲子、鹤嘴斧、铁锹，以及针线什么的我都没有。至于内衣内裤之类，虽然缺乏，不久我也便习惯了。由于缺乏适当的工具，一切工作进行得特别吃力。我花了差不多整整一年的时间，才把我的小木栅或围墙建筑好。就拿砍木桩而言，木桩很重，我只能竭尽全力选用我能搬得动的。我花很长时间在树林里把树砍下来削好，至于搬回住处就更费时间了。所以，我有时花两天工夫砍好一根桩子并把它弄回来，第三天就花在把它打进地里去；为了这一目的，我先是用一根沉重的木棍，可后来我想起还有铁撬棍，便找来了一根，不过我发现，用它来打桩既费劲又麻烦。

但既然干这个活很有必要，而我又有足够的时间去干，那么我又何必计较什么麻

ployment if that had been over, at least, that I could foresee, except the ranging the Island to seek for Food, which I did more or less every Day.

I now began to consider seriously my Condition, and the Circumstance I was reduc'd to, and I drew up the State of my Affairs in Writing, not so much to leave them to any that were to come after me, for I was like to have but few Heirs, as to deliver my Thoughts from daily poring upon them, and afflicting my Mind; and as my Reason began now to master my Despondency, I began to comfort my self as well as I could, and to set the good against the Evil, that I might have something to distinguish my Case from worse, and I stated it very impartially, like Debtor and Creditor, the Comforts I enjoy'd, against the Miseries I suffer'd, Thus, Evil

I am cast upon a horrible desolate Island, void of all hope of Recovery.

I am singl'd out and separated, as it were, from all the World to be miserable.

I am divided from Mankind, a Solitaire, one banish'd from humane Society.

I have not Clothes to cover me.

I am without any Defence or Means to resist any Violence of Man or Beast.

I have no Soul to speak to, or relieve me.

Good.

But I am alive, and not drown'd as all my Ship's Company was.

But I am singl'd out too from all the Ship's Crew to be spar'd from Death; and he that miraculously sav'd me from Death, can deliver me from this Condition.

烦呢？何况根据我的预计，我完成了这一工作之后，并没有其他事要做，除非是去岛上各处走走，寻找猎物，而这件事我每天都在做着，只是时间有多有少而已。

我开始慎重考虑自己的现况，并且我一一记下每天的经历，不是为了给后来者看，因为我不认为会有人上这个岛来，我这样做是为了把折磨我的纷乱思绪一吐为快。在理智的作用下，我的心情开始好转，不再那么沉重、沮丧，我掂量着自己处境的优势和劣势，觉得自己还不算太糟糕，索性就按照生意簿上负债人和借债人的格式公平地列出优劣势，用以自勉：

劣势

我被抛弃在一个可怕的孤岛上，没有逃出去的希望。

我现在与世隔绝，悲苦万分。

我被隔离在人类之外，被放任于人类社会之外，像个隐士。

我没有衣服穿。

我没有防御能力，也没有办法去抵御野人或野兽的袭击。

我没人可以交谈，也没有人来解救我。

优劣。

但我活着，没有像我的同伴那样被淹死。

但我也被从全体船员中脱离出来，免于一死。上帝用神力留我一命，定然会救我摆脱困境。

But I am in a hot Climate, where if I had Clothes I could hardly wear them.

But I am cast on an Island, where I see no wild Beasts to hurt me, as I saw on the Coast of Africa: And what if I had been Shipwreck'd there?

But God wonderfully sent the Ship in near enough to the Shore, that I have gotten out so many necessary things as will either supply my Wants, or enable me to supply my self even as long as I live.

Upon the whole, here was an undoubted Testimony, that there was scarce any Condition in the World so miserable, but there was something Negative or something Positive to be thankful for in it; and let this stand as a Direction from the Experience of the most miserable of all Conditions in this World, that we may always find in it something to comfort our selves from, and to set in the Description of Good and Evil, on the Credit Side of the Accompt.

Having now brought my Mind a little to relish my Condition, and given over looking out to Sea to see if I could spy a Ship, I say, giving over these things, I began to apply my self to accommodate my way of Living, and to make things as easy to me as I could.

I have already describ'd my Habitation, which was a Tent under the Side of a Rock, surrounded with a strong Pale of Posts and Cables, but I might now rather call it a Wall, for I rais'd a kind of Wall up against it of Turfs, about two Foot thick on the Out-side, and after some time, I think it was a Year and Half, I rais'd Rafters from it leaning to the Rock, and thatch'd or cover'd it with Bows of Trees, and such things as I could get to keep out the Rain, which I found at some times of the Year very violent.

尚有存粮,不至饿死。四季气候炎热,无需穿戴。

所处荒岛未曾见到猛兽。倘若我覆舟非洲沿岸,又该如何?

上帝奇妙地把大船送到岸边,我取下的物品终身受用不尽。

总起来说,事实证明,我当前的不幸处境,是世界上很少有的,可是,即使在这样的处境中,也有一些消极的东西或积极的东西值得感谢。我希望世上的人都要从我这最不幸的处境中取得一个经验教训,这教训就是:在最不幸的处境之中,我们也可以找到聊以自慰的事情,把好处和坏处对照起来,可以归入帐目的"贷方金额"方面。

这时既然已使自己慢慢习惯与喜欢上眼下的环境,我就把整天盼望船来之类的事抛在脑后,开始筹画如何度过每一天,如何生活得更好。

前面我已描述过自己的住所,那是一个搭在山岩下的帐篷,四周用木桩和缆索做成坚固的木栅环绕着。现在,我可以把木栅叫做围墙了,因为我在木栅外面用草皮堆成了一道两英尺来厚的墙,并在大约一年半的时间里,在围墙和岩壁之间搭了一些屋椽,上面盖些树枝或其他可以弄到的东西用来挡雨。因为,我发现,

I have already observ'd how I brought all my Goods into this Pale, and into the Cave which I had made behind me: But I must observe too, that at first this was a confus'd Heap of Goods, which as they lay in no Order, so they took up all my Place, I had no room to turn my self; so I set my self to enlarge my Cave and Works farther into the Earth, for it was a loose sandy Rock, which yielded easily to the Labour I bestow'd on it; and so when I found I was pretty safe as to Beasts of Prey, I work'd side-ways to the Right Hand into the Rock, and then turning to the Right again, work'd quite out and made me a Door to come out, on the Out-side of my ale or Fortification.

This gave me not only Egress and Regress, as it were a back Way to my Tent and to my Store-house, but gave me room to stow my Goods.

And now I began to apply my self to make such necessary things as I found I most wanted, as particularly a Chair and a Table, for without these I was not able to enjoy the few Comforts I had in the World, I could not write, or eat, or do several things with so much Pleasure without a Table.

So I went to work; and here I must needs observe, that as Reason is the Substance and Original of the Mathematicks, so by stating and squaring every thing by Reason, and by making the most rational Judgment of things, every Man may be in time Master of every mechanick Art. I had never handled a Tool in my Life, and yet in time by Labour, Application, and Contrivance, I found at last that I wanted nothing but I could have made it, especially if I had had Tools; however I made abundance of things, even without Tools, and

一年之中总有一段时间大雨如注。

我已经讲过，我是如何把所有的东西搬进自己这寨子，搬进我在帐篷后挖出的那个山洞的。我还得说明的是，这些东西起先只是胡乱堆在一起，既然是杂乱无章地摊在那里，也就占掉了所有的地方，弄得我连转个身也困难；于是我动手把那山洞再挖大挖深，好在那砂岩并不坚实，只要我肯花力气，挖起来倒也容易；所以当我感到已无需担心有猛兽来袭时，我便在山洞的右壁上挖进了一段距离，然后再朝右拐了个方向继续挖，终于在寨子外的岩壁上钻了出来，接着就在这洞口安上一个门。

这条道儿正好通向我的贮藏室和帐篷后面，不仅进出方便，而且还可以搁置物品。

现在我又忙于制作一些最需要的东西，特别是椅子和桌子。没有这些东西，我无法享受到我在这个世界上所拥有的一点有限的舒适。没有桌子，我写字、吃饭、做其他一些事情都觉得索然无味。

我开始动手；这里我必须指出，理性既是数学的本质和基础，我们对一切事物都加以理性地分析、比较、判断，每个人迟早都会掌握一门手艺。我生平从未用过任何工具，但久而久之，通过劳动、努力和发明，我终于发现，如果有工具，我想要的东西我都能做，但即使没有工具，我也做出了许多东西，有些东西尽管所用

some with no more Tools than an Adze and a Hatchet, which perhaps were never made that way before, and that with infinite Labour: For Example, If I wanted a Board, I had no other Way but to cut down a Tree, set it on an Edge before me, and hew it flat on either Side with my Axe, till I had brought it to be thin as a Plank, and then dubb it smooth with my Adze. It is true, by this Method I could make but one Board out of a whole Tree, but this I had no Remedy for but Patience, any more than I had for the prodigious deal of Time and Labour which it took me up to make a Plank or Board: But my Time or Labour was little worth, and so it was as well employ'd one way as another.

However, I made me a Table and a Chair, as I observ'd above, in the first Place, and this I did out of the short Pieces of Boards that I brought on my Raft from the Ship: But when I had wrought out some Boards, as above, I made large Shelves of the Breadth of a Foot and Half one over another, all along one Side of my Cave, to lay all my Tools, Nails, and Iron-work, and in a Word, to separate every thing at large in their Places, that I might come easily at them; I knock'd Pieces into the Wall of the Rock to hang my Guns and all things that would hang up.

So that had my Cave been to be seen, it look'd like a general Magazine of all Necessary things, and I had every thing so ready at my Hand, that it was a great Pleasure to me to see all my Goods in such Order, and especially to find my Stock of all Necessaries so great.

And now it was when I began to keep a Journal of every Day's Employment, for indeed at first I was in too much Hurry, and not only Hurry as to Labour, but in too much Discomposure of Mind,

的工具只是一把手斧和小斧，而且付出了巨大的劳动，恐怕从来没有人这样做过。比如，假如需要一块木板，我只好砍下一整棵树，把它横躺在我面前，然后就要用长柄斧把它的两侧削平，等把它削得有木板那么厚了，再用手斧将它刨得光滑。用这种方法，我只能从一棵树上取出一块木板。但没有别的办法，只有耐着性子去干，正如我不得不花费大量的时间与繁重的劳动一样。再说，我的时间或我的劳动反正不值钱，无论是花在这个方面还是花在别的方面都是一个样。

尽管艰难，但正如我刚才所说的，我首先为自己做了一张桌子和一把椅子。所用的木板是我用木筏从大船上运来的。此外，运用上述方法削出了一些木板之后，我又靠着山洞的一边做了几层架子，每层的宽度都是一英尺半，把工具、铁钉和铁器等东西按类归放在上面，以便取用。我还在墙上钉进许多小木楔，用来挂枪和其他东西。

如果有人见过我的山洞，一定会以为这是个生活物资仓库，里面品种繁多，摆放有序，取用方便。每每看着自己这库存丰富、井井有条的山洞，我心中就充满了欣慰和满足。

现在，我开始记日记了，想通过这种方式把每天的工作和生活都记录下来。在这以前，我的日子过得很匆忙，

and my Journal would ha' been full of many dull things: For Example, I must have said thus. Sept. the 30th. After I got to Shore and had escap'd drowning, instead of being thankful to God for my Deliverance, having first vomited with the great Quantity of salt Water which was gotten into my Stomach, and recovering my self a little, I ran about the Shore, wringing my Hands and beating my Head and Face, exclaiming at my Misery, and crying out, I was undone, undone, till tyr'd and faint I was forc'd to lye down on the Ground to repose, but durst not sleep for fear of being devour'd.

Some Days after this, and after I had been on board the Ship, and got all that I could out of her, yet I could not forbear getting up to the Top of a little Mountain and looking out to Sea in hopes of seeing a Ship, then fancy at a vast Distance I spy'd a Sail, please my self with the Hopes of it, and then after looking steadily till I was almost blind, lose it quite, and sit down and weep like a Child, and thus encrease my Misery by my Folly.

But having gotten over these things in some Measure, and having settled my houshold Stuff and Habitation, made me a Table and a Chair, and all as handsome about me as I could, I began to keep my Journal, of which I shall here give you the Copy (tho' in it will be told all these Particulars over again) as long as it lasted, for having no more Ink I was forc'd to leave it off.

不但忙于工作，而且心情也不好，假使记日记，一定要记许多乏味的事情。例如我一定会这样记："九月三十日。我逃出性命，上得岸来，把胃里的海水吐了出来，苏醒了一会儿。这时我不但不首先感谢上帝救我活命，反而在岸上跑来跑去，尽自扭自己的手，打自己的头和脸，大叫大嚷我的不幸，嚷着'我完了，我完了!'一直嚷到精疲力竭，才不得不倒在地上休息。但又不敢睡着，生怕被什么东西吃掉。"

几天之后，甚至在我把船上可以搬动的东西都运上岸之后，我还是每天爬到小山顶上，呆呆地望着海面，希望能看到船只经过。妄想过甚，有时仿佛看到极远处有一片帆影，于是欣喜若狂，以为有了希望；这时，我望眼欲穿，帆影却消失得无影无踪，我便一屁股坐在地上，像小孩似地大哭起来。这种愚蠢的行为，反而增加了我的烦恼。

但是这种情况总算在一定程度上过去了。我安顿好了住处和生活用品，做好了一桌一椅，尽可能把我的环境整理得舒舒服服之后，便开始写日记；下面，我为你们抄录了日记的原文（虽然上面所有提及的具体情况将有重复），当然全文并不很长，因为墨水一用完，我就只得搁笔了。

Part 2

The JOURNAL

a dreadful Storm, in the offing, came on Shore on this dismal unfortunate Island, which I call'd the Island of Despair, all the rest of the Ship's Company being drown'd, and my self almost dead.

All the rest of that Day I spent in afflicting my self at the dismal Circumstances I was brought to, viz. I had neither Food, House, Clothes, Weapon, or Place to fly to, and in Despair of any Relief, saw nothing but Death before me, either that I should be devour'd by wild Beasts, murther'd by Savages, or starv'd to Death for Want of Food. At the Approach of Night, I slept in a Tree for fear of wild Creatures, but slept soundly tho' it rain'd all Night.

October 1. In the Morning I saw to my great Surprise the Ship had floated with the high Tide, and was driven on Shore again much nearer the Island, which as it was some Comfort on one hand, for seeing her sit upright, and not broken to Pieces, I hop'd, if the Wind abated, I might get on board, and get some Food and Necessaries out of her for my Relief; so on the other hand, it renew'd my Grief at the Loss of my Comrades, who I imagin'd if we had all staid on board might have sav'd the Ship, or at least that they would not have been all drown'd as they were; and that had the Men been sav'd, we might perhaps have built us a Boat out of the Ruins of the Ship, to have carried us to some other Part of the World. I spent great Part of this Day in perplexing my self on these things; but at length seeing the Ship almost dry, I went upon the Sand as near as I could, and then swam on board; this Day also it continu'd raining, tho' with n'o Wind at all.

第二部

日 记

在一场可怕的风暴中,我所乘的船在离岸不远的海上失事,船上的伙伴全遭没顶之灾,只有我九死一生地来到这寂无人烟的凄凉小岛,这个岛,我称作绝望岛。

我整天为自己来到这么一个凄凉的环境而悲痛不已。我没有食物、房子、衣服和武器;没有可去的地方;没有得救的希望,只有死路一条:不是被野兽吃掉、被野人杀死,就是死于饥饿。夜晚来临,我因害怕野兽而睡在树上,尽管下了一夜的雨,我睡得很香。

十月一日。早晨,我极其吃惊地看到,船随着涨潮浮了起来,被冲得离海岸更近了。一方面,这对我是一个安慰,我看到船仍直立在那里,没有被打成碎片。我希望,如果风力减弱了,我可以上船找些食物和必需品来维持生计;另一方面,它又让我陷入失去同伴的悲痛之中。我想,如果我们当时都在船上,我们或许可以挽救我们的船,至少,他们不至于会被淹死。若是他们也能获救,我们就可以用船的残骸造一艘舢板,把我们带到其他地方。在这一天的大部分时间里,我都对这件事而痛苦懊丧。但是,后来我看到大船上并没有进多少水,我便走向沙滩的尽头,然后游水上了大

From the 1st of October, to the 24th. All these Days entirely spent in many several Voyages to get all I could out of the Ship, which I brought on Shore, every Tide of Flood, upon Rafts. Much Rain also in these Days, tho' with some Intervals of fair Weather: But, it seems, this was the rainy Season.

Oct. 20. I overset my Raft, and all the Goods I had got upon it, but being in shoal Water, and the things being chiefly heavy, I recover'd many of them when the Tide was out.

Oct. 25. It rain'd all Night and all Day, with some Gusts of Wind, during which time the Ship broke in Pieces, the Wind blowing a little harder than before, and was no more to be seen, except the Wreck of her, and that only at low Water. I spent this Day in covering and securing the Goods which I had sav'd, that the Rain might not spoil them.

Oct. 26. I walk'd about the Shore almost all Day to find out a place to fix my Habitation, greatly concern'd to secure my self from an Attack in the Night, either from wild Beasts or Men. Towards Night I fix'd upon a proper Place under a Rock, and mark'd out a Semi-Circle for my Encampment, which I resolv'd to strengthen with a Work, Wall, or Fortification made of double Piles, lin'd within with Cables, and without with Turf.

From the 26th. to the 30th. I work'd very hard in carrying all my Goods to my new Habitation, tho' some Part of the time it rain'd exceeding hard.

The 31st. in the Morning I went out into the

船。这一天虽然没有一丝风息,但雨一直下个不停。

十月一日至十月二十四日。这些天来,我每天都到大船上去,去了许多次,每次趁着潮水用我的木筏把船上的东西全都运到了岸上。这些天仍然是阴雨连绵,其间或也有些晴好天气。不过,现在看来好像是雨季。

十月二十日。今天,木筏搁浅倾斜,所有运载之物都落入水中。好在翻排的地方水不深,落入水中的东西也很重,故没被水冲走。退潮以后,我去捞回了许多。

十月二十五日。雨伴着阵阵大风持续了一天一夜,后来,风越刮越猛。大船终于未能挺过狂风而支离破碎了,只有在退潮后才能看到它坍塌在水中的残骸。今日全天忙于覆盖从船上搬下来的物品,以免被雨水淋坏。

十月二十六日。我在海边上跑了差不多一整天,希望找一个地方来作我的住处,我最关心的是不让野兽或野人夜间来袭击我。傍晚,我终于在一个小山的下面找到了我的地方,在那里画了一个半圆圈作为宿营的地方,决定沿着那半圆圈安上两层木桩,盘上缆索,外面加上草皮,作成一个坚固的工事、围墙或堡垒。

二十六日至三十日。我埋头苦干,把全部货物搬到新的住地,虽然有时大雨倾盆。

三十一日。早晨我带枪

Island with my Gun to see for some Food, and discover the Country, when I kill'd a She-Goat, and her Kid follow'd me home, which I afterwards kill'd also because it would not feed.

November. 1. I set up my Tent under a Rock, and lay there for the first Night, making it as large as I could with Stakes driven in to swing my Hammock upon.

Nov. 2. I set up all my Chests and Boards, and the Pieces of Timber which made my Rafts, and with them form'd a Fence round me, a little within the Place I had mark'd out for my Fortification.

Nov. 3. I went out with my Gun and kill'd two Fowls like Ducks, which were very good Food. In the Afternoon went to work to make me a Table.

Nov. 4. This Morning I began to order my times of Work, of going out with my Gun, time of Sleep, and time of Diversion, viz. Every Morning I walk'd out with my Gun for two or three Hours if it did not rain, then employ'd my self to work till about Eleven a-Clock, then eat what I had to live on, and from Twelve to Two I lay down to sleep, the Weather being excessive hot, and then in the Evening to work again: The working Part of this Day and of the next were wholly employ'd in making my Table, for I was yet but a very sorry Workman, tho' Time and Necessity made me a compleat natural Mechanick soon after, as I believe it would do any one else.

Nov. 5. This Day went abroad with my Gun and my Dog, and kill'd a wild Cat, her Skin pretty soft, but her Flesh good for nothing: Every

深入孤岛腹地,一则为了找点吃的,一则为了查看一下小岛环境。我打死了一只母山羊,它的一只小羊跟着我回家,后来我把它也杀了,因为它不肯吃食。

十一月一日。我在山脚下架了一个很大的帐篷,里面又钉了几个木桩用来挂吊床,在这儿我安安稳稳地睡了第一夜。

十一月二日。我把所有的箱子、木板,以及做木筏用的木料,沿着半圆形内侧堆成一个临时性的围墙,作为我的防御工事。

十一月三日。外出打猎,打到两只野鸭,肉很鲜美。下午开始用砍成的木板做桌子。

十一月四日。今早上我设计了什么时候工作,什么时候狩猎,什么时间睡眠,什么时候娱乐。我的计划是这样的:每天早晨,如果不下雨,就带枪出去跑上二三小时,回来后再工作到十一点左右;然后就有什么吃什么;十二点至二点为午睡时间,因为这儿天炎热异常;傍晚再开始工作。今天和明天的全部工作时间,我都用来做桌子。目前我还是个拙劣的工匠,做一样东西要花很多时间。但不久我就成了一个熟练工了。什么事做多了就熟能生巧,另一方面也是迫于需要。我相信,这在其他任何人都是办得到的。

十一月五日。今天我带着枪和狗出去,打死了一只野猫,它的毛皮挺柔软,但它的

Creature I kill'd I took off the skins and preserv'd them: Coming back by the Sea Shore, I saw many Sorts of Sea Fowls which I did not understand, but was surpris'd and almost frighted with two or three Seals, which, while I was gazing at, not well knowing what they were, got into the Sea and escap'd me for that time.

Nov. 6. After my Morning Walk I went to work with my Table again, and finish'd it, tho' not to my liking; nor was it long before I learn'd to mend' it.

Nov. 7. Now it began to be settled fair Weather. The 7th, 8th, 9th, 10th, and Part of the 12th. (for the 11th was Sunday) I took wholly up to make me a Chair, and with much ado brought it to a tolerable Shape, but never to please me, and even in the making I pull'd it in Pieces several times. Note, I soon neglected my keeping Sundays, for omitting my Mark for them on my Post, I forgot which was which.

Nov. 13. This Day it rain'd, which refresh'd me exceedingly, and cool'd the Earth, but it was accompany'd with ferrible Thunder and Lightning, which frighted me dreadfully for fear of my Powder; as soon as it was over, I resolv'd to separate my Stock of Powder into as many little Parcels as possible, that it might not be in Danger.

Nov. 14, 15, 16. These three Days I spent in making little square Chests or Boxes, which might hold about a Pound or two Pound, at most, of Powder, and so putting the Powder in, I stow'd it in Places as secure and remote from one another as possible. On one of these three Days I kill'd a

肉实在没法吃。反正我打到野兽之后,总是把皮剥下,好好保存起来。回到岸边时,我看到许多种类的海鸟,但是都叫不出名称;同时,我也看到了两三只海豹,一时没想到它们就是海豹,不免大为惊奇地愣愣看着,而这时它们就趁机窜进海水,从我眼前逃脱了。

十一月六日。早晚散步回来,我又开始制作桌子,正好今天完工。桌子做得不太合我的胃口,不久,我把它又改进了一下。

十一月七日天气开始好转。七日、八日、九日、十日和十二日的半天(11日根据我的推算是礼拜日)都用来制作椅子。很费力地做成一把椅子,样子还过得去,虽然在制作过程中我拆了好多次,但还是不能让我十分满意。附记:我不久就把星期日忽略了,因为我忘了往柱子上刻印痕,也分不清到底是哪天了。

十一月十三日。今天下了一场雨,让我感到格外凉爽,地面的热气也降了下来。但下雨的时候又夹杂着可怕的雷电,把我吓得要命,因为我担心起我的火药来。所以,雷雨刚过,我便决定,把我储存的火药量分成许多小包,以免遭到危险。

十一月十四日、十五日、十六日。这三天我都用来做一些小箱子或小盒子,每只最多能装一两磅火药,然后把火药一一装入小盒子,再把小盒子分开放置,妥善保存。另外,

large Bird that was good to eat, but I know not what to call it.

Nov. 17. This Day I began to dig behind my Tent into the Rock to make room for my farther Conveniency: Note, Two Things I wanted exceedingly for this Work, viz. A Pick-axe, a Shovel, and a Wheel-barrow or Basket, so I desisted from my Work, and began to consider how to supply that Want and make me some Tools; as for a Pickaxe, I made use of the Iron Crows, which were proper enough, tho' heavy; but the next thing was a Shovel or Spade, this was so absolutely necessary, that indeed I could do nothing effectually without it, but what kind of one to make I knew not.

Nov. 18. The next Day in searching the Woods I found a Tree of that Wood, or like it, which, in the Brasils they call the Iron Tree, for Its exceeding Hardness, of this, with great Labour and almost spoiling my Axe, I cut a Piece, and brought it home too with Difficulty enough, for it was exceeding heavy.

The excessive Hardness of the Wood, and having no other Way, made me a long while upon this Machine, for I work'd it effectually by little and little into the Form of a Shovel or Spade, the Handle exactly shap'd like ours in England, only that the broad Part having no Iron shod upon it at Bottom, it would not last me so long, however it serv'd well enough for the uses which I had occasion to put it to; but never was a Shovel, I believe, made after that Fashion, or so long a making.

I was still deficient, for I wanted a Basket or a

打下一只叫不出名的大鸟,肉很好吃。

十一月十七日。今天开始在帐篷背后的山墙下挖掘山洞,以扩大住所空间,好有足够的地方去整齐地摆放物品,便于拿用。附记:进行挖洞工作,我还缺少三样工具,一把鹤嘴锄、一把铲子、一辆推土车或一只箩筐。所以挖洞之前,必须先考虑置办这些必要的工具。鹤嘴锄可以用起货钩替代,虽然稍微重了点,倒还是能凑合用。但此外我还需要一把铲子,这件东西很要紧,没有它,什么工作都作不好,但我又不知道怎样去做它一把。

十一月十八日。今天我在树林里找了半天,终于发现一种树,在巴西,人们叫它"铁树",因为它非常坚硬。我费了很大的气力,几乎把我的斧子都砍坏了,才把它砍下一块来,又费了很大的困难,才把它弄回来,因为它实在太重了。

这木料实在硬,可是我又没有别的法子,只好在这东西上面花很多的时间。我慢慢把木块削成铲子的形状,铲柄完全像英国铲子一样,只是铲头没有包上铁,所以没有正式的铁铲那么耐用。不过,必要时用一下也还能勉强对付。我想,世界上没有一把铲子是做成这个样子的,也决不会花这么长的时间才做成一把铲子。

虽然有了鹤嘴锄和铲子,

Wheelbarrow, a Basket I could not make by any Means, having no such things as Twigs that would bend to make Wicker Ware, at least none yet found out; and as to a Wheel-barrow, I fancy'd I could make all but the Wheel, but that I had no Notion of, neither did I know how to go about it; besides I had no possible Way to make the Iron Gudgeons for the Spindle or Axis of the Wheel to run in, so I gave it over, and so for carrying away the Earth which I dug out of the Cave, I made me a Thing like a Hodd, which the Labourers carry Morter in, when they serve the Bricklayers.

This was not so difficult to me as the making the Shovel; and yet this, and the Shovel, and the Attempt which I made in vain, to make a Wheel-Barrow, took me up no less than four Days, I mean always, excepting my Morning Walk with my Gun, which I seldom fail'd, and very seldom fail'd also bringing Home something fit to eat.

Nov. 23. My other Work having now stood still, because of my making these Tools; when they were finish'd, I went on, and working every Day, as my Strength and Time allow'd, I spent eighteen Days entirely in widening and deepening my Cave, that it might hold my Goods commodiously.

Note, During all this Time, I work'd to make this Room or Cave spacious enough to accommodate me as a Warehouse or Magazin, a Kitchen, a Dining-room, and a Cellar; as for my Lodging, I kept to the Tent, except that some Times in the wet Season of the Year, it rain'd so hard, that I could not keep my self dry, which caused me afterwards to cover all my Place within my Pale with long Poles in the Form of Rafters leaning against

但工具还是不够,我还缺少一只箩筐或一辆推土车。箩筐我没有办法做,因为我没有像编藤皮用的细软的枝条,至少现在我还没有找到。要说做辆推土车,依我想,其它部分都做得成,唯独那轮子不行,因为怎么去做那轮子,我简直一筹莫展;再说,还要为轮轴做两个铁的轴承,这更是不可能办到的事,所以对做推土车的事,我也就死了心;结果我想起了小工替砖瓦工送砂浆用的砂浆桶,就做了个这样的桶,用来装运挖洞时掘出的泥沙和石块。

制作桶、铲子,加上做了一半才放弃的推土车花了我四天多的工夫,当然,要除开每天清晨的狩猎活动,这我从来没拉下过,而且总能带回家可吃的东西。

十一月二十三日。由于忙于做工具,其他工作被迫停止,直到工具做完才开始。只要力气和时间允许,我便继续天天工作。我花了十八天的时间来扩宽和加深我的山洞,以便它能宽绰地放下我的东西。

附记:在这段时间里,我的工作是扩大我的房屋或山洞,能供我做仓库或军火库、厨房、餐厅和地窖使用。至于我个人,仍然居住在帐篷里。只是在湿季里雨水特别大,经常弄得我全身湿淋淋的。因为这个缘故,我后来在篱墙和岩壁之间搭上了一些长杆子

the Rock, and load them with Flaggs and large Leaves of Trees like a Thatch.

December 10th, I began now to think my Cave or Vault finished, when on a Sudden, (it seems I had made it too large) a great Quantity of Earth fell down from the Top and one Side, so much, that in short it frighted me, and not without Reason too; for if I had been under it I had never wanted a Grave-Digger: Upon this Disaster I had a great deal of Work to do over again; for I had the loose Earth to carry out; and which was of more Importance, I had the Seiling to prop up, so that I might be sure no more would come down.

Dec. 11. This Day I went to Work with it accordingly, and got two Shores or Posts pitch'd upright to the Top, with two Pieces of Boards a cross over each Post, this I finish'd the next Day; and setting more Posts up with Boards, in about a Week more I had the Roof secur'd; and the Posts standing in Rows, serv'd me for Partitions to part of my House.

Dec. 17. From this Day to the Twentieth I plac'd Shelves, and knock'd up Nails on the Posts to hang every Thing up that could be hung up, and now I began to be in some Order within Doors.

Dec. 20. Now I carry'd every Thing into the Cave, and began to furnish my House, and set up some Pieces of Boards, like a Dresser, to order my Victuals upon, but Boards began to be very scarce with me; also I made me another Table.

（像橡子似的），又在上面盖上菖薄叶子或大的树叶，把它盖得像个茅屋。

十二月十日。现在，我觉得我的山洞或地窖总算完工了，可是，好像是我把它挖得太大了，突然有大量的泥沙从洞的顶上和洞的一边坍塌下来，掉下的泥土很多。总之，我非常害怕。我的害怕不是没有道理，因为，一旦被埋在下面，我连个掘墓人都用不着呢。这场灾难又给我带来了大量的工作，不但要把落下的泥土搬运出去，还必须设法给洞顶安装天花板，以防泥土再次坍塌下来。

十二月十一日。今天按照昨日的计划动手加固山洞的洞顶。我用两根柱子作为天花板的支撑物，在柱子顶部搭上两块交叉摆放的木板撑住洞顶。这项工作第二天完工。随后的一个星期里继续这一加固工作，又撑起许多细柱和木板，终于把洞顶搞得相当的坚实牢固，万无一失。洞内一根根直立的柱子，正好把洞室隔成了好几间。

十二月十七日。本日到二十日，我在洞内装了大量的分层的木架，并且在柱上钉了许多钉子，以便用来悬挂应挂的东西。现在房里已经初具规模，就像一家杂货铺。

十二月二十日。我把一切东西都搬到洞里，并且开始布置我的房子。我把一些木板搭起来，仿佛一个碗架，好摆吃的东西，但木板已经愈来

Dec. 24. Much Rain all Night and all Day, no stirring out.

Dec. 25. Rain all Day.

Dec. 26. No Rain, and the Earth much cooler than before, and pleasanter.

Dec. 27. Kill'd a young Goat, and lam'd another so as that I catch'd it, and led it Home in a String; when I had it Home, I bound and splinter'd up its Leg which was broke, N. B. I took such Care of it, that it liv'd, and the Leg grew well, and as strong as ever; but by my nursing it so long it grew tame, and fed upon the little Green at my Door, and would not go away: This was the first Time that I entertain'd a Thought of breeding up some tame Creatures, that I might have Food when my Powder and Shot was all spent.

Dec. 28, 29, 30. Great Heats and no Breeze; so that there was no Stirring abroad, except in the Evening for Food; this Time I spent in putting all my Things in Order within Doors.

January 1. Very hot still, but I went abroad early and late with my Gun, and lay still in the Middle of the Day; this Evening going farther into the Valleys which lay towards the Center of the Island, I found there was plenty of Goats, tho' exceeding shy and hard to come at, however I resolv'd to try if I could not bring my Dog to hunt them down.

Jan. 2. Accordingly, the next Day, I went out with my Dog, and set him upon the Goats; but I was mistaken, for they all fac'd about upon the Dog, and he knew his Danger too well, for he would not come near them.

愈少了。我又做了一张桌子。

十二月二十四日。整日整夜大雨，没有出门。

十二月二十五日。整日下雨。

十二月二十六日。无雨，地面上比前两天凉爽得多了。

十二月二十七日。打死了一只小山羊，同时又把另外一只小山羊的腿打瘸了，于是把它捉住，用绳子牵了回来。到家之后，我把它的断腿绑起来，上了夹板。附记：在我的精心照料下，受伤的小山羊活下来了，腿也长好了，而且长得很结实。由于我长期抚养，小山羊渐渐驯服起来，整日在我住所门前的草地上吃草，不肯离开。这诱发了我一个念头：我可以饲养一些易于驯服的动物，将来一旦弹药用完也不愁没有东西吃。

十二月二十八日、二十九、三十日。酷热无风，整天在家，到傍晚才外出寻食。整日在家里整理东西。

一月一日。照旧很热，我早晚带着枪出去一次，中午时静静地睡觉；今天傍晚我走得比较远，来到了朝岛的中心地带伸展的一处山谷里，发现那儿有很多野山羊，不过它们极其容易受惊，很难猎取；但我有了主意，准备以后带狗来试试，看能不能追上它们。

一月二日。我就在这一天带狗出去，命它冲向山羊，我犯了一个错误，它们非但不怕，反而正面朝它扑来。狗深知其危险，不敢靠近它们。

Jan. 3. I began my Fence or Wall; which being still jealous of my being attack'd by some Body, I resolv'd to make very thick and strong.

N. B. This Wall being describ'd before, I purposely omit what was said in the Journal; it is sufficient to observe, that I was no less Time than from the 3rd of January to the 14th of April, working, finishing, and perfecting this Wall, tho' it was no more than about 24 Yards in Length, being a half Circle from one Place in the Rock to another Place about eight Yards from it, the Door of the Cave being in the Center behind it.

All this Time I work'd very hard, the Rains hindering me many Days, nay sometimes Weeks together; but I thought I should never be perfectly secure 'till this Wall was finish'd; and it is scarce credible what inexpressible Labour every Thing was done with, especially the bringing Piles out of the Woods, and driving them into the Ground, for I made them much bigger than I need to have done.

When this Wall was finished, and the Out-side double fenc'd with a Turff-Wall rais'd up close to it, I persuaded my self, that if any People were to come on Shore there, they would not perceive any Thing like a Habitation; and it was very well I did so, as may be oberv'd hereafter upon a very remarkable Occasion.

During this Time, I made my Rounds in the Woods for Game every Day when the Rain admitted me, and made frequent Discoveries in these Walks of something or other to my Advantage; particularly I found a Kind of wild Pidgeons, who built not as Wood Pidgeons in a Tree, but rather as House Pidgeons, in the Holes of the Rocks; and

一月三日。我开始修筑篱笆或围墙,我仍旧害怕遭人袭击,决定修得厚重、结实一些。

附记:我已在前面描述过这道围墙,有关这部分的日记就不再旧话重提。从一月三日到四月十四日我一直抓紧时间工作,尽力把围墙修筑得完美些,尽管它长不过二十四码,以洞口为中心,形成一个半圆形。从半圆处的岩壁上端到另一头距离大约八码左右。

这段时间我尽力工作,下雨使我耽搁了许多天,有时是一连几个星期。我想,如果不把围墙修好,我永远不会有真正的安全。我付出每一项劳动都无法形容,令人难以置信,尤其是得把木桩从树林里运出来,并把它打入地里,实在非常吃力,因为我把木桩做得太大了,实际上并不需要这么大。

这堵墙完工之后,我又紧靠着它,在外面用草皮垒起了一道土墙,这才放了心。即使有人在这座岛上登岸,他们肯定看不出这里面有人居住。我幸亏这样做了,因为后来发生的事充分说明我这样做是有道理的。

在这期间,只要天不下雨,我就经常到树林里转转,打打猎。但在散步的同时,我经常发现一些多少对我有用的东西。值得一提的是,我发现了一种鸽子,它们不像斑尾林鸽那样在树上筑巢,而是像

taking some young ones, I endeavoured to bread them up tame, and did so; but when they grew older they flew all away, which perhaps was at first for Want of feeding them, for I had nothing to give them; however I frequently found their Nests, and got their young ones, which were very good Meat.

And now, in the managing my houshold Affairs, I found my self wanting in many Things, which I thought at first it was impossible for me to make, as indeed as to some of them it was; for Instance, I could never make a Cask to be hooped, had a small Runlet or two, as I observed before, but I cou'd never arrive to the Capacity of making one by them, tho? I spent many Weeks about it; I could neither put in the Heads, or joint the Staves so true to one another, as to make them hold Water, so I gave that also over.

In the next Place, I was at a great Loss for Candle; so that as soon as ever it was dark, which was generally by Seven-a-Clock, was oblig'd to go to Bed: I remembered the Lump of Bees-wax with which I made Candles in my African Adventure, but I had none of that now; the only Remedy had was, that when I had kill'd a Goat, sav'd the Tallow, and with a little Dish made of Clay, which I bak'd in the Sun, to which I added a Wick of some Oakum, I made me a Lamp; and this gave me Light, tho' not a clear steady Light like a Candle; in the Middle of all my Labours it happen'd, that rumaging my Things, I found a little Bag, which, as I hinted before, had been fill'd with Corn for the feeding of Poultry, not for this Voyage, but before, as I suppose, when the Ship came from Lisbon; what little Remainder of Corn

家鸽那样,把巢筑在岩壁上的洞里。我捉了几只这样的小鸽子带回家去,设法把它们驯养起来。可是它们一长大就都飞走了。这大概是因为我没经常给它们喂食的缘故,但我实在是没什么东西可喂它们。不过我常常能找到这种鸽子的窝,可以捉一些子鸽回家打打牙祭。这种鸽子的肉非常好吃。

在料理家务的过程中,我发现还缺乏许多东西。而且有些东西我确实根本无法制造出来,比方箍水桶这件事,我就无能为力。我前面说过,我有一两只小桶,我想照样打一只新的。但是,尽管我花了几个星期的工夫,还是没本事照样做出个桶来;我无法给桶安上底板,也难以把一块块桶板拼接得密不透水,所以不得不放弃了这一打算。

其次,我少的是蜡烛。所以一般到了七点钟左右,只要天一黑,我就不得不上床睡觉。我还记得,当初在非洲那次冒险出逃时,我是有一大块黄蜡可用来做蜡烛的,但现在可没这东西了;唯一的解决办法是:每当杀死一只山羊的时候,我就把羊油留下来,拿一个用阳光晒成的小泥盘,放上一点补船用的麻絮做灯心,做成一盏灯,这总算给了我一点光亮,虽然没有蜡烛那样亮。当我从事这些劳动的时候,我偶然翻翻我的东西,找到了一个小布袋。我上面已经提过,这个布袋原来是用来

had been in the Bag, was all devour'd with the Rats, and I saw nothing in the Bag but Husks and Dust; and being willing to have the Bag for some other Use, I think it was to put Powder in, when I divided it for Fear of the Lightning, or some such Use, I shook the Husks of Corn out of it on one Side of my Fortification under the Rock.

It was a little before the great Rains, just now mention'd, that I threw this Stuff away, taking no Notice of any Thing, and not so much as remembering that I had thrown any Thing there; when about a Month after, or thereabout, I saw some few Stalks of something green, shooting out of the Ground, which I fancy'd might be some Plant I had not seen, but I was surpriz'd and perfectly astonish'd, when, after a little longer Time, I saw about ten or twelve Ears come out, which were perfect green Barley of the same Kind as our European, nay, as our English Barley.

It is impossible to express the Astonishment and Confusion of my Thoughts on this Occasion; I had hitherto acted upon no religious Foundation at all, indeed I had very few Notions of Religion in my Head, or had' entertain'd any Sense of any Thing that had befallen me, otherwise than as a Chance, or, as we lightly say, what pleases God; without so much as enquiring into the End of Providence in these Things, or his Order in governing Events in the World: But after I saw Barley grow there, in a Climate which I know was not proper for Corn, and especially that I knew not how it came there, It startl'd me strangely, and I began to suggest, that God had miraculously caus'd this Grain to grow without any Help of Seed sown, and that it was so directed purely for my Sustenance, on that wild miserable Place.

装那些喂家禽的谷类的,并且还不是因为这次旅行用的,可能是为上次从里斯本出发时用的。袋里的一点谷类早已被老鼠吃光了,只看到有一点尘土和谷皮。后来因为想把布袋派别的用场(我记得,当我害怕雷电,把火药分开的时候,我曾用它装火药),我就把那点谷皮抖在岩石下面的围墙里面。

我扔掉这些东西,正是上面提到的那场大雨之前不久的事。扔掉后也就完了,再也没有想起这件事情。大约一个月之后,我发现地上长出了绿色的茎干。起初我以为那只是自己以前没有注意到的某种植物罢了。但不久以后,我看到长出了十一二个穗头,与欧洲的大麦,甚至与英国的大麦一模一样,这使我十分惊讶。

我又惊愕,又困惑,心里的混乱难以用笔墨形容。在那以前,我为人处世根本就不以宗教信条为准,事实上,我脑子里可以说毫无宗教观念,对于落到自己头上的事,无非是认为机运所致,要不,就像我们平时说的那样,轻轻巧巧地将这归因于天意;至于上苍为什么要做这些事,为什么对世上的事作这样或那样的安排,我是向来不去刨根究底的。但见到那儿长出了大麦,想到了那地方本是不该长大麦的,却偏偏莫名其妙地长了出来,我不由得大吃一惊,开始相信创造奇迹的上帝,认为

This touch'd my Heart a little, and brought Tears out of my Eyes, and I began to bless my self, that such a Prodigy of Nature should happen upon my Account; and this was the more strange to me, because I saw near it still all along by the Side of the Rock, some other straggling Stalks, which prov'd to be Stalks of Ryce, and which I knew, because I had seen it grow in Africa when I was ashore there.

I not only thought these the pure Productions of Providence for my Support, but not doubting, but that there was more in the Place, I went all over that Part of the Island, where I had been before, peering in every Corner, and under every Rock, to see for more of it, but I could not find any; at last it occur'd to my Thoughts, that I had shook a Bag of Chickens Meat out in that Place, and then the Wonder began to cease; and I must confess, my religious Thankfulness to God's Providence began to abate too upon the Discovering that all this was nothing but what was common; tho' I ought to have been as thankful for so strange and unforseen Providence, as if it had been miraculous; for it was really the Work of Providence as to me, that should order or appoint, that 10 or 12 Grains of Corn should remain unspoil'd, (when the Rats had destroy'd all the rest,) as if it had been dropt from Heaven; as also, that I should throw it out in that particular Place, where it being in the Shade of a high Rock, it sprang up immediately; whereas, if I had thrown it anywhere else, at that Time, it had been burnt up and destroy'd.

I carefully sav'd the Ears of this Corn you may be sure in their Season, which was about the End of June; and laying up every Corn, resolv'd to sow them all again, hoping in Time to have some Quantity sufficient to supply me with Bread; But

是他不凭播种,就叫地上长出了庄稼,其目的无非是要让我在这凄凉的荒岛上生存下去。

我的心一阵颤栗,泪水汩汩而下。大自然的奇迹会降临到我头上,我感到十分荣幸;更叫我啧啧称奇的是,沿着岩壁零星地生长着另一种小苗,一看便知是稻苗,因为我在非洲海岸上见过。

我相信这是上帝的恩赐,这地方肯定还有不少。我仔细搜索了我所到过的每个地方,找遍了每一个角落,每一块岩石,希望找到更多的青苗,但再也没有找到一根。最后,我才突然想起我曾在这个地方抖落过那个盛谷类的袋子,便不再感到惊异了。可以说,当我发现这只不过是一件很平常的事时,我对上苍的那种感激之心也便开始低落了,实际上我还是应该感谢上苍给我带来这件意外而离奇的事的。这样的安排是上天的杰作,当时那十几粒老鼠吃剩的谷种没有被毁掉,仿佛从天而降的一样,而我又恰好把它扔在一个特殊的地方,正是高高的岩石下的阴影里,它立刻便长了出来,而如果我那时把它扔在别处,恐怕早被太阳晒死了。

大约在六月底,收获大麦的季节到了,我自然小心地将这些谷穗收了起来。我将每一粒谷子都收藏得很好,计划再把它们全种下去;指望到时

it was not till the 4th Year that I could allow my self the least Grain of this Corn to eat, and even then but sparingly, as I shall say afterwards in its Order; for I lost all that I sow'd the first Season, by not Observing the proper Time; for I sow'd it just before the dry Season, so that it never came up at all, at least, not as it would ha' done: Of which in its Place.

Besides this Barley, there was, as above, 20 or 30 Stalks of Ryce, which I preserv'd with the same Care, and whose Use was of the same Kind or to the same Purpose, (viz.) to make me Bread, or rather Food; for I found Ways to cook it up without baking, tho' I did that also after some Time. But to return to my Journal, I work'd excessive hard these three or four Months to get my Wall done; and the 14th of April I closed it up, contriving to go into it, not by a Door, but over the Wall by a Ladder, that there might be no Sign in the Out-side of my Habitation.

April 16. I finish'd the Ladder, so I went up with the Ladder to the Top, and then pull'd it up after me, and let it down in the In-side: This was a compleat Enclosure to men for within I had Room enough, and nothing could come at me from without, unless it could first mount my Wall.

The very next Day after this Wall was finish'd, I had almost had all my Labour overthrown at once, and my self kill'd; the Case was thus, As I was busy in the Inside of it, behind my Tent, just in the Entrance into my Cave, I was terribly frighted with a most dreadful surprising Thing indeed; for all on a sudden I found the Earth come crumbling down from the Roof of my Cave, and

能有足够的粮食做面包吃。不过,到了第四个年头,我才吃到了一点点这些种子长的粮食,而且吃得非常仔细。这是后话,暂且不说。由于没有在适当的时间播种,我在第一季节里播下的种子全都失掉了,因为,我是在旱季到来之前下的种,所以,它们根本出不了芽,至少说,出苗率太低。具体情形,暂且不表。

除了大麦,还有二三十个稻穗也被我小心翼翼地保存起来,也是希望将来种多了做面包或者煮着吃。我通常把这些粮食烘烤着吃,后来发现煮着也很好吃呢。好了,还是让我们回到日记上来吧。这三四个月来,为修缮围墙,我工作得十分卖力。到四月十四日,我把围墙完全封闭了起来,我没给围墙留门,只是用一架梯子越墙而过,为的是不让外人看出这里有人居住。

四月十六日。我把梯子做完了。我用梯子爬上墙头,然后把它收了起来,放在里面。现在我的围墙可以说十分严密了;因为从墙里面说,我有充分的空间供我使用,从墙外面说,谁也不能走到里面来,除非先爬上我的墙头。

这座墙造成的第二天,我几乎全功尽弃,并且险些丧掉我的性命。事情是这样的:正当我在帐篷后面的山洞口忙着干活时,突然发生了一件可怕的事情,把我吓得魂不附体。山洞顶上突然倒塌下大量的泥土和石块,从岩壁上也

from the Edge of the Hill over my Head, and two of the Posts I had set up in the Cave crack'd in a frightful Manner; I was heartily scar'd, but thought nothing' of what was really the Cause, only thinking that the Top of my Cave was falling in, as some of it had done before; and for Fear I shou'd be bury'd in it, I run foreward to my Ladder, and not thinking my self safe there neither, I got over my Wall for Fear of the Pieces of the Hill which I expected might roll down upon me: I was no sooner stepp'd down upon the firm Ground, but I plainly saw it was a terrible Earthquake, for the Ground I stood on shook three Times at about eight Minutes Distance, with three such Shocks, as would have overturn'd the strongest Building that could be suppos'd to have stood on the Earth, and a great Piece of the Top of a Rock, which stood about half a Mile from me next the Sea, fell down with such a terrible Noise, as I never heard in all my Life, I perceiv'd also, the very Sea was put into violent Motion by it; and I believe the Shocks were stronger under the Water than on the Island.

I was so amaz'd with the Thing it self, having never felt the like, or discours'd with any one that had, that I was like one dead or stupify'd; and the Motion of the Earth made my Stomach sick like one that was toss'd at Sea; but the Noise of the falling of the Rock awak'd me as it were, and rousing me from the stupify'd Condition I was in, fill'd me with Horror, and I thought of nothing then but the Hill falling upon my Tent and all my houshold Goods, and burying all at once; and this sunk my very Soul within me a second Time.

After the third Shock was over, and I felt no

有泥土和石头滚下来,把我竖在洞里的两根柱子一下子都压断了,发出了可怕的爆裂声,我惊慌失措,完全不知道究竟发生了什么事,以为只不过像上回那样发生了塌方,洞顶有一部分塌了下来。我怕被土石埋在底下,立即跑向梯子。后来觉得在墙内还不安全,怕山上滚下来的石块打着我,我爬到了围墙外面。等到我下了梯子站到平地上,我才明白发生了可怕的地震。因为在八分钟的时间里,我脚下的地面震动了三次,这三次震动极其猛烈,不仅足以摧毁地面上任何想象中最坚固的建筑物,就连海边一座小山的山顶也崩裂了一大块,发出我从未听见过的吓人的轰隆声滚了下来,落进离我半英里外的海里。只见海水也激得浪花飞溅,波涛汹涌。我敢肯定,海水下的震动比岛上的震动更为剧烈。

我从未经历过地震,也从未听到有这种经历的人谈起过地震,这时就惊得不知所措,呆若木鸡;再说,脚下的地面动个不停,就像在海上颠簸,让人胃里难受;但是山岩落水的轰然巨响,使我猛地一惊,从那目瞪口呆的状态中回过神来,又感到心惊肉跳起来,头脑里唯一的存念就是倘若宅前的小山塌到帐篷上,我所有的物资就会埋进去,一想到这里,我的心再次格登一下沉了下去。

第三次震动结束后,有一

more for some Time, I began to take Courage, and yet I had not Heart enough to go over my Wall again, for Fear of being buried alive, but sat Still upon the Ground, greatly cast down and disconsolate, not knowing what to do: All this while I had not the least Serious religious Thought, nothing but the common, Lord ha' Mercy upon me; and when it was over, that went away too.

While I sat thus, I found the Air over-cast, and grow cloudy, as if it would Rain; soon after that the Wind rose by little and little, so that, in less than half an Hour, it blew a most dreadful Hurricane: The Sea was all on a Sudden cover'd over with Foam and Froth, the Shore was cover'd with the Breach of the Water, the Trees were torn up by the Roots, and a terrible Storm it was; and this held about three Hours, and then began to abate, and in two Hours more it was stark calm, and began to rain very hard.

All this while I sat upon the Ground very much terrify'd and dejected, when on a sudden it came into my thoughts, that these Winds and Rain being the Consequences of the Earthquake, the Earthquake it self was spent and over, and I might venture into my Cave again: With this Thought my Spirits began to revive, and the Rain also helping to persuade me, I went in and sat down in my Tent, but the Rain was so violent, that my Tent was ready to be beaten down with it, and I was forc'd to go into my Cave, tho' very much afraid and uneasy for fear it should fall on my Head.

This violent Rain forc'd me to a new Work, viz. To cut a Hole thro' my new Fortification like a Sink to let the Water go out, which would else have drown'd my Cave. After I had been in my

会儿我没再感到震动,恢复了一点勇气,但仍怕被活埋,不敢越墙入内。我坐在地上,神情沮丧、心烦意乱、无所适从。即使在这时候,除了一般性地叫叫"上帝,可怜可怜我吧!"之外,我仍旧没有什么严肃的宗教意识;地震过去后,这种想法也抛到了脑后。

我就那样呆呆地坐着。这时,我发现天空阴暗下来,乌云密布,天要下雨了。不久,渐渐地刮起了风,不到半小时的时间,竟变成了可怕的飓风。顷刻间,海面上波涛汹涌,海岸上浪花飞溅,树也被连根拔起,实在是一场令人惧怕的风暴。狂风持续了大约三个小时,然后便渐渐减弱;又过了两个多小时,便是死一般的静,接着就下起了瓢泼大雨。

在这期间,我一直坐在地上,既恐惧,又沮丧。我忽然想到,这狂风还有暴雨一定是地震造成的,既然地震本身的威力已经过去了,我或许可以冒险回到我的山洞里去。想到这一点,我的精神又开始恢复,再说,大雨也逼着我回去。于是,我便爬进了我的围墙,坐到了我的帐篷里。可是瓢泼大雨的势头是那么凶猛,恨不得要把帐篷冲垮似的,我万般无奈,只好躲进了我的山洞。当然我仍旧心存恐惧,生怕被小山压死。

这场大雨又给我找了一件非做不可的事情,得在围墙脚下开一个小洞,挖一条排水沟,排放墙内的积水,免得山

Cave some time, and found still no more Shocks of the Earthquake follow, I began to be more compos'd; and now to support my Spirits, which indeed wanted it very much, I went to my little Store and took a small Sup of Rum, which however I did then and always very sparingly, knowing I could have no more when that was gone.

It continu'd raining all that Night, and great Part of the next Day, so that I could not stir abroad, but my Mind being more compos'd, I began to think of what I had best do, concluding that if the Island was subject to these Earthquakes, there would be no living for me in a Cave, but I must consider of building me some little Hut in an open Place which I might surround with a Wall as I had done here, and so make my self secure from wild Beasts or Men; but concluded, if I staid where I was, I should certainly, one time or other, be bury'd alive.

With these Thoughts I resolv'd to remove my Tent from the Place where it stood, which was just under the hanging Precipice of the Hill, and which, if it should be shaken again, would certainly fall upon my Tent: And I spent the two next Days, being the 19th and 20th of April, in contriving where and how to remove my Habitation.

The fear of being swallow'd up alive, made me that I never slept in quiet, and yet the Apprehensions of lying broad without any Fence was almost equal to it; but still when I look'd about and saw how every thing was put in order, how pleasantly conceal'd I was, and how safe from Danger, it made me very loath to remove.

In the mean time it occur'd to me that it would require a vast deal of time for me to do this, and that I must be contented to run the Venture where I was, till I had form'd a Camp for my self, and

洞被淹没。我在山洞里坐了一会儿后，没有再感到有任何震动，便慢慢镇定下来。我想到该喝点酒给自己压压惊，壮壮胆，便走到贮藏室里，倒了一杯甘蔗酒喝。我对于我的甘蔗酒一向喝得很节省，因为我知道，喝完以后就没有了。

这场大雨当晚下了一整夜，第二天又下了大半天，因此我整天不能出门。但我心里已经安定得多了，于是我开始考虑今后的措施。我的结论是，既然岛上地震这样多，住在山洞实在不是办法，必须考虑在一块平地上造一个小茅屋，四面照这里的样子围上一道墙，以防野兽野人的袭击；如果在这里住下去，我是迟早要被活埋的。

想到这里，我决定要把帐篷从原来的地方搬开。现在的帐篷正好搭在小山的悬崖下面，如果再发生地震，那悬崖塌下来必定砸倒帐篷。于是我花了两天的时间，即四月十九日和二十日，来计划新的住址以及搬家的方法。

我唯恐被活埋，整夜不得安睡。但想到睡在外面，四周毫无遮挡，心里又同样害怕。我环顾四周，只见样样东西都安置得井井有条，更感到自己这么舒舒服服地待在这隐蔽的地方，不用为遭受袭击而担心，我又舍不得搬走了。

与此同时，我还想到，要搬家可得花很多时间，因为我先得为自己安营扎寨，把新的住所弄妥了，然后才能搬过

had secur'd it so as to remove to it: So with this Resolution I compos'd my self for a time, and resolv'd that I would go to work with all Speed to build me a Wall with Piles and Cables, &c. in a Circle as before, and set my Tent up in it when it was finish'd, but that I would venture to stay where I was till it was finish'd and fit to remove to. This was the 21st.

April 22. The next Morning I began to consider of Means to put this Resolve in Execution, but I was at a great loss about my Tools; I had three large Axes and abundance of Hatchets, (for we carried the Hatchets for Traffick with the Indians) but with much chopping and cutting knotty hard Wood, they were all full of Notches and dull, and tho' I had a Grindstone, I could not turn it and grind my Tools too, this cost me as much Thought as a Statesman would have bestow'd upon a grand Point of Politicks, or a Judge upon the Life and Death of a Man. At length I contriv'd a Wheel with a String, to turn it with my Foot, that I might have both my Hands at Liberty: Note, I had never seen any such thing in England, or at least not to take Notice how it was done, tho' Since I have observ'd it is very common there; besides that, my Grindstone was very large and heavy. This Machine cost me a full Week's Work to bring it to Perfection.

April 28, 29. These two whole Days I took up in grinding my Tools, my Machine for turning my Grindstone performing very well.

April 30. Having perceiv'd my Bread had been low a great while, now I took a Survey of it, and reduc'd my self to one Bisket-cake a Day, which made my Heart very heavy.

May 1. In the Morning looking towards the

去，在这期间，我只能冒些风险，住在这老地方。主意既定，我一时间也就安下心来，决意像先前那样，全力以赴地用木桩和锚缆等东西筑起一道围墙，待围墙筑成后，就在那里面支起个帐篷，但是在它们完工以前，在它们符合要求以前，我只能冒险住在原处。这是二十一日的事。

四月二十二日。第二天清晨，我开始实施这项计划，但工具奇缺。我有三把大斧头和一大堆原打算跟印第安人做生意的小斧头。由于不断地砍削多节的硬木，这些工具都又钝又布满缺口。虽然我有磨轮，但无法使它转动起来磨刀，叫我伤透脑筋。我想即使是一个面临重大抉择的政治家，一个要行使生杀大权的法官也不见得比我更劳神。最后，我终于发明了一个带绳子的轮子，可以用脚带动，这样就能腾出双手磨刀。附记：在英国我从未见过这类东西，我至少不曾注意到它是怎样做成的，尽管它是极普通的东西。此外，我的磨轮又大又重，我用了足足一个星期的时间，机器才运转正常。

四月二十八日、二十九日。这两天我都忙于磨砺我的工具，磨轮机转动很正常。

四月三十日。许久以来我就发现面粉已经不多了，现在我又检查了一遍，把甜点心减为每天一块，这种景况令我更加担忧。

五月一日。今天早晨，我

Sea-side, the Tide being low, I saw something lye on the Shore bigger than ordinary, and it look'd like a Cask; when I came to it, I found a small Barrel, and two or three Pieces of the Wreck of the Ship, which were driven on Shore by the late Hurricane, and looking towards the Wreck itself, I thought it seem'd to lye higher out of the Water than it us'd to do; I examin'd the Barrel which was driven on Shore, and soon found it was a Barrel of Gunpowder, but it had taken Water, and the Powder was cak'd as hard as a Stone; however I roll'd it farther on Shore for the present, and went on upon the Sands as near as I could to the Wreck of the Ship to look for more.

When I came down to the Ship I found it strangely remov'd, The Fore-castle which lay before bury'd in Sand, was heav'd up at least Six Foot, and the Stern which was broke to Pieces and parted from the rest by the Force of the Sea soon after I had left rummaging her, was toss'd, as it were, up, and cast on one Side, and the Sand was thrown so high on that Side next her Stern, that whereas there was a beat Place of Water before, so that I could not come within a Quarter of a Mile of the Wreck without swimming, I could now walk quite up to her when the Tide was out; I was surpriz'd with this at first, but soon concluded it must be done by the Earthquake, and as by this Violence the Ship was more broken open than formerly, so many Things came daily on Shore, which the Sea had loosen'd, and which the Winds and Water rolled by Degrees to the Land.

This wholly diverted my Thoughts from the Design of removing my Habitation; and I busied my self mightily that Day especially, in searching whether I could make any Way into the Ship, but I found nothing was to be expected of that Kind,

朝海上望去,只见潮水已经降了下来,又看到沙滩上有个比较大的东西,看上去很像一只木桶。我走近一看,果然是一只木桶,另外还有几块从那只大船上散下来的残片,它们都是被最近那场飓风刮上来的。再看那条破船,它仿佛比以前高出水面不少。我检查了一下那只被卷上岸来的木桶,很快便发现,那原来是一只火药桶。但是,它已经进了水,火药被浸得像石头一样硬。虽然如此,我还是先将它朝岸上滚了滚,然后又朝水边走去,走到离那条破船最近的地方,想再搞些东西上来。

靠近船边时,我发现它的位置的确有了很大变动,本来埋在沙里的船头现在至少抬高了六英尺左右。至于船尾,自从我最后一次上船后不久就被巨浪打碎,脱离了船身,现在又被海水冲到了一边。本来船尾旁边有一大片水洼,要想到达破船边,须先游过这四百多米宽的水洼。可是现在,水洼里高高地堆着泥沙,只要退潮,就可以从岸边一直走到船跟前。我起初感到十分诧异,后来想到这大概是地震造成的后果。破船经过这次猛烈的地震更破得不像样了,每天总有东西被海浪打下来,再被冲到岸上。

这个发现使我暂时中断了搬家计划。当天,我便想方设法要到船上去。但我发现,船上已没有什么东西可拿了,因为船的内部已经塞满了泥

for that all the In-side of the Ship was choack'd up with Sand: However, as I had learn'd not to despair of any Thing, I resolv'd to pull every Thing to Pieces that I could of the Ship, concluding, that every Thing I could get from her would be of some Use or other to me.

May 3. I began with my Saw, and cut a Piece of a Beam thro', which I thought held some of the upper Part or Quarter-Deck together, and when I had cut it thro', I clear'd away the Sand as well as I could from the Side which lay highest; but the Tide coming' in, I was oblig'd to give over for that Time.

May 4. I went a fishing, but caught not one Fish that I durst eat of, till I was weary of my Sport, when just going to leave off, I caught a young Dolphin. I had made me a long Line of some Rope Yarn, but I had no Hooks, yet I frequently caught Fish enough, as much as I card to eat; all which I dry'd in the Sun, and eat them dry.

May 5. Work'd on the Wreck, cut another Beam asunder, and brought three great Fir Planks off from the Decks, which I ty'd together, and made swim on Shore when the Tide of Flood came on.

May 6. Work'd on the Wreck, got several Iron Bolts out of her, and other Pieces of Iron Work, work'd very hard, and came Home very much tyr'd, and had Thoughts of giving it over.

May 7. Went to the Wreck again, but with an Intent not to work, but found the Weight of the Wreck had broke itself down, the Beams being cut, that several Pieces of the Ship seem'd to lie loose, and the In-side of the Hold lay so open, that I could see into it, but almost full of Water and Sand.

May 8. Went to the Wreck, and carry'd an

沙。不过我已经形成了对所有的事情都抱有希望的脾气，就决定尽最大努力把船全部拆下来，因为我确信这些东西将来肯定会派上用场。

五月三日。我动手用锯子把一根船骨锯断，这根船骨仿佛是支撑着那上甲板或后甲板的。锯断之后，我便尽量清除那堆积得很高的泥沙。但是不久潮水就来了，我只好暂时放弃我的工作。

五月四日。出去钓鱼，但没有钓到一条我敢吃的鱼，当我感到十分厌倦，正要离开的时候，却钓到一只小海豚。我用绞绳的麻丝做了一根长长的钓鱼线，但我没有鱼钩。不过我还是常能钓到鱼吃；我把钓到的鱼都晒干了再吃。

五月五日。在破船上干活。又锯断了一根船梁。从甲板上取下三块松木板，把板捆在一起，趁涨潮时把它们飘到岸上。

五月六日。继续上破船干活。从船上取下几根铁条和一些铁器。工作得很辛苦，回来时累坏了，很想放弃这种工作。

五月七日。又到破船上去，但不想再干活了。却发现被我锯断两根横梁之后，破船连其自身的重量也承受不了，终于垮了下来，一些船板似乎也已散落，使船舱内部暴露了出来，我朝那里一看，只见满是水和泥沙。

五月八日。带了一根起

Iron Crow to wrench up the Deck, which lay now quite clear of the Water or Sand; I wrench'd open two Planks, and brought them on Shore also with the Tide: I left the Iron Crow in the Wreck for next Day.

May 9. Went to the Wreck, and with the Crow made Way into the Body of the Wreck, and felt several Casks, and loosen'd them with the Crow, but could not break them up; I felt also the Roll of English Lead, and could stir it, but it was too heavy to remove.

May 10, 11, 12, 13, 14. Went every Day to the Wreck, and got a great deal of Pieces of Timber, and Boards, or Plank, and 2 or 300 Weight of Iron.

May 15. I carry'd two Hatchets to try if I could not cut a Piece off of the Roll of Lead, by placing the Edge of one Hatchet, and driving it with the other; but as it lay about a Foot and a half in the Water, I could not make any Blow to drive the Hatchet.

May 16. It had blow'd hard in the Night, and the Wreck appear'd more broken by the Force of the Water; but I stay'd so long in the Woods to get Pidgeons for Food, that the Tide prevented me going to the Wreck that Day.

May 17. I saw some Pieces of the Wreck blown on Shore, at a great Distance, near two Miles off me, but resolv'd to see what they were, and found it was a Piece of the Head, but too heavy for me to bring away.

May 24. Every Day to this Day I work'd on the Wreck, and with hard Labour I loosen'd some Things so much with the Crow, that the first

货钩去破船,现在甲板上没有水和泥沙,我就可以用起货钩把甲板撬起来。我撬起了两块长木板,也靠潮水把它们弄到岸上。那根起货钩棒就留在破船上了,因为明天还要用。

五月九日。上破船后,用起货钩挖开一条进入船内的路,摸到几只桶子,用货钩扒开泥沙,让它们漂起来,但我没法打开它们。我还摸到一卷英国铅皮,能挪动它,但太重,无法搬走。

五月十日、十一日、十二日、十三日、十四日。每天去破船,弄到许多圆木、木板和二三百斤重的铁器。

五月十五日。我带了两把小斧,把一只小斧的刃放在铅皮上,用另一只去破,想试试能否砍下一块铅皮,但由于它是在一英尺半深的水里,我竟无法砍掉。

五月十六日。刮了一夜的大风,受到水的冲击,破船更显得破旧不堪,我很长时间都在树林里逮鸽子吃,后来潮水上涨,我就没有到破船上去。

五月十七日。我看到离我这儿差不多两英里的沙滩上,有些被风浪推上岸来的破船的残片,我决定去看个究竟。走近一看,原来是船头的一块木头。可是,它太重了,我搬不回来。

五月二十四日。这些天来(包括今天),我都在破船上干活。我费了不少苦力,用起

blowing Tide several Casks floated out, and two of the Seamens Chests; but the Wind blowing from the Shore, nothing came to Land that Day, but Pieces of Timber, and a Hogshead which had some Brazil Pork in it, but the Salt-water and the Sand had spoil'd it.

I continu'd this Work every Day to the 15th of June, except the Time necessary to get Food, which I always appointed, during this Part of my Employment, to be when the Tide was up, that I might be ready when it was ebb'd out, and by this Time I had gotten Timber, and Plank, and Iron-Work enough, to have builded a good Boat, if I had known how; and also, I got at several Times, and in several Pieces, near 100 Weight of the Sheet-Lead.

June 16. Going down to the Sea-side, I found a large Tortoise or Turtle; this was the first I had seen, which it seems was only my Misfortune, not any Defect of the Place, or Scarcity; for had I happen'd to be on the other Side of the Island, I might have had Hundreds of them every Day, as I found afterwards; but perhaps had paid dear enough for them.

June 17. I spent in cooking the Turtle; I found in her threescore Eggs; and her Flesh was to me at that Time the most savoury and pleasant that ever I tasted in my Life, having had no Flesh, but of Goats and Fowls, since I landed in this horrid Place.

June 18. Rain'd all Day, and I stay'd within. I thought at this Time the Rain felt Cold, and I was

货钩把破船的几个地方撬得很开了,撬开之后,一次潮水便将几只木桶和两只水手的箱子浮了起来。可是由于风是从岸上往海上吹过去,风向不对,所以漂到岸上来的只有几块木料和一桶巴西猪肉。猪肉早被海水泡坏,而且浸满泥沙,无法食用了。

我就这样除了觅食就是上船干活,一直干到六月十五日。在这期间,我规定自己涨潮时外出猎食,退潮时上船干活。经过多日的辛苦劳动,卸下了许多木料和铁器。假如我懂得怎样造船,这些船料笃定能造出一只很好的小艇。此外,我还想尽办法先后弄到了几块铅皮,差不多有一百多磅重呢。

六月十六日。在海边意外发现了一只很大的海龟或者陆龟。这是我首次在岛上发现这种动物,我觉得在这个孤岛上这种动物不常见到,是由于我运气不好,并非由于岛上没有;如果我在岛的另一边登陆入住,那么我一定每天能够弄到几百个,不过也不会有很多益处。

六月十七日。我把那海龟拿来煮,在它的肚子里,发现了六十个龟蛋。这时候,我觉得它的肉是我生平所尝到的最香最美的肉类,因为自从我来到这可怕的地方以后,除了山羊和飞禽之外,我没有吃过别的肉。

六月十八日。整天下雨,没有出门。我觉得这回的雨

something chilly, which I knew was not usual in that Latitude.

June 19. Very ill, and shivering, as if the Weather had been cold.

June 20. No Rest all Night, violent Pains in my Head, and feaverish.

June 21. Very ill, frighted almost to Death with the Apprehensions of my sad Condition, to be sick, and no Help: Pray'd to GOD for the first Time since the Storm off of Hull, but scarce knew what I said, or why; my Thoughts being all confused.

June 22. A little better, but under dreadful Apprehensions of Sickness.

June 23. Very bad again, cold and shivering, and then a violent Head-ach.

June 24. Much better.

June 25. An Ague very violent; the Fit held me seven Hours, cold Fit and hot, with faint Sweats after it.

June 26. Better; and having no Victuals to eat, took my Gun, but found my self very weak; however I kill'd a She-Goat, and with much Difficulty got it Home, and broil'd some of it, and eat; I wou'd fain have stew'd it, and made some Broath, but had no Pot.

June 27. The Ague again so violent, that I lay a-Bed all Day, and neither eat or drank. I was ready to perish for Thirst, but so weak, I had not Strength to stand up, or to get my self any Water to drink: Pray'd to God again, but was light-headed, and when I was not, I was so ignorant,

有点冷,身上有些寒意;在这个纬度上,这是不常有的事。

六月十九日。我病得很重,身子直发抖,好像天气太冷了。

六月二十日。整夜不能入睡,头很痛,并发热。

六月二十一日。全身不舒服。想到自己生病而无人照顾的惨状,不禁怕得要死。自从在赫尔市出发遭遇风暴以来,我第一次祈祷上帝。至于为什么祈祷,祈祷些什么,连自己也说不清楚,因为思绪混乱极了。

六月二十二日。身子稍稍舒服一点,但因为生病,还是害怕极了。

六月二十三日。又大为不妙,冷得直打哆嗦,接着便是剧烈的头痛。

六月二十四日。大有好转。

六月二十五日。疟疾来势凶猛;这次发作了七个小时,一阵发冷之后就是发热,发作之后出了一点虚汗。

六月二十六日。有所好转;由于没有食物,我带了枪外出,但觉得身体很虚弱;尽管如此,我还是射杀了一只母山羊,千辛万苦地把它弄了回来,割下来一些肉烤了吃;我很想煮一些肉并烧点汤,但是没有锅。

六月二十七日。猛烈的发作又开始了。我整天在床上不吃不喝,差点渴死。但我根本没有力气站起来,为自己取一些水。我想向上帝祈祷,却感到头晕目眩。等我稍好一些

that I knew not what to say; only I lay and cry'd, Lord look upon me, Lord pity me, Lord have Mercy upon me: I suppose I did nothing else for two or three Hours, till the Fit wearing off, I fell asleep, and did not wake till far in the Night; when I wak'd, I found my self much refresh'd, but weak, and exceeding thirsty: However, as I had no Water bin my whole Habitation, I was forc'd to lie till Morning, and went to sleep again: In this second Sleep, I had this terrible Dream.

I thought, that I was sitting on the Ground on the Outside of my Wall, where I sat when the Storm blew after the Earthquake, and that I saw a Man descend from a great black Cloud, in a bright Flame of Fire, and light upon the Ground: He was all over as bright as a Flame, so that I could but just bear to look towards him; his Countenance was most inexpressibly dreadful, impossible for Words to describe; when he stepp'd upon the Ground with his Feet, I thought the Earth trembl'd, just as it had done before in the Earthquake, and all the Air look'd, to my Apprehension, as if it had been fill'd with Flashes of Fire.

He was no sooner landed upon the Earth, but he moved forward towards me, with a long Spear or Weapon in his Hand, to kill me; and when he came to a rising Ground, at some Distance, he spoke to me, or I heard a Voice so terrible, that it is impossible to express the Terror of it; all that I can say, I understood, was this, Seeing all these Things have not brought thee to Repentance, nom thou shalt die: At which Words, I thought he lifted up the Spear that was in his Hand, to kill me.

No one, that shall ever read this Account, will expect that I should be able to describe the Horrors of my Soul at this terrible Vision, I mean, that even while it was a Dream, I even dreamed of those Horrors; nor is it any more possible to de-

后，又不知跟上帝说什么好，只会躺在床上叫道："上帝惠顾我！上帝可怜我！上帝发发慈悲吧！"有两三个小时，我什么也不能做，直到发作停止。我倒头睡去，到半夜才醒来。醒来后，我感到自己神清气爽多了，但仍很虚弱，而且渴得要命。房里已没有水，我只得躺到天明，才呼呼睡去。这次睡着后，我做了一个噩梦：

我想我是在墙头外的地上坐着，当时正是地震后狂风大作的时候。我看见一个人从一片乌云中降下，带着火光降落到地面，他周身像火焰一样闪亮，我只有硬撑着才能看他一下。他的面容狰狞可怕，无法描述。当他的脚落到地上时，大地都震颤了，就像先前地震时一样，我觉得空中都充满了可怕的烈焰。

他落地之后，立刻向我走来，手中拿着一根长矛，一副要戳杀我的样子。当他走到离我不远的一个高坡上时，开始冲我说起话来。他说话的声音极其可怕吓人，实在无法形容。他对我说的话，我只听懂了一句："既然发生的这一切都没能使你悔悟，现在就要你去死！"他边说着边举起手中的长矛，向我杀将过来。

任何人将来有机会读到我这段记载，必然会想到，我面对这样的梦景，心里的恐怖该多么难以描绘，虽然这仅仅是一个梦，一个可怕的梦。即

scribe the Impression that remain'd upon my Mind when I awak'd and found it was but a Dream.

I had alas! no divine Knowledge; what I had received by the good Instruction of my Father was then worn out by an uninterrupted Series, for 8 Years, of Seafaring Wickedness, and a constant Conversation with nothing but such as were like my self, wicked and prophane to the last Degree: I do not remember that I had in all that Time one Thought that so much as tended either to looking upwards toward God, or inwards towards a Reflection upon my own Ways: But a certain Stupidity of Soul, without Desire of Good, or Conscience of Evil, had entirely overwhelm'd me, and I was all that the most hardened, unthinking, wicked Creature among our common Sailors, can be supposed to be, not having the least Sense, either of the Fear of God in Danger, or of Thankfulness to God in Deliverances.

In the relating what is already past of my Story, this will be the more easily believ'd, when I shall add, that thro' all the Variety of Miseries that had to this Day befallen me, I never had so much as one Thought of it being the Hand of God, or that it was a just Punishment for my Sin; my rebellious Behaviour against my Father, or my present Sins which were great; or so much as a Punishment for the general Course of my wicked Life. When I was on the desperate Expedition on the desert Shores of Africa, I never had so as one Thought of what would become of me; or one to od to direct me whether I should go, or to keep me from the Danger which apparently surrounded me, as well from voracious Creatures as cruel Savages: But I was meerly thoughtless of a God, or a Providence; acted like a meer Brute from the Principles of Nature, and by the Dictates of common Sense only, and indeed hardly that.

使在我醒来之后,明知是一场梦,遗留在我脑海里的印象还是无法描绘。

咳!我是一个没有善恶观念的人;八年以来,我毫无间断地过着水手的罪恶生活,并且一直跟一些和我一样罪大恶极、不信上帝的人混在一起,我小时候从我父亲那里受到的一点良好教海,早已消失。这么多年来,我不记得自己曾经敬仰过上帝,也没有反省过自己的行为。我生性愚蠢,善恶不分。即使在一般水手中,我也算得上是个邪恶之徒:冷酷无情,轻率鲁莽,危难中不知敬畏上帝,遇救时也不知道对上帝感恩。

从我前面的自述中,读者可以知道,至今我已遭遇了种种灾难,但我从未想到这一切都是上帝的意旨,也从未想到这一切都是对我罪孽的惩罚,是对我背逆父亲的行为、对我当前深重的罪行,以及对我邪恶生涯的惩罚。当初我不顾一切,在非洲不毛的海岸边航行时,我从没有想到自己会有什么遭遇,从没有希望上帝指引我航向,从没祈求上帝保佑我远离危险,让我不受凶猛的野兽和残忍的野人侵袭,而这些显然就在我四周。我偏偏没想到有上帝,有天意;只是像一头凭天性行动的畜生,一味地凭一点常识我行我素,而事实上,就连凭常识行动也谈不上。

Part 3

When I was deliver'd and taken up at Sea by the Portugal Captain, well us'd, and dealt justly and honourably with, as well as charitably, I had not the least Thankfulness on my Thoughts: When again I was shipwreck'd, ruin'd, and in Danger of drowning on this Island, I was as far from Remorse, or looking on it as a Judgment; I only said to my self often, that I was an unfortunate Dog, and born to be always miserable. It is true, when I got on Shore first here, and found all my Ship's Crew drown'd, and my self spar'd, I was surpriz'd with a Kind of Extasie, and some Transports of Soul, which, had the Grace of God assisted, might have come up to true Thankfulness; but it ended where it begun, in a meer common Flight of Joy, or as I may say, being glad I was alive, without the least Reflection upon the distinguishing Goodness of the Hand which had preserv'd me, and had singled me out to be preserv'd, when all the rest were destroy'd; or an Enquiry why Providence had been thus merciful to me; even just the same common Sort of Joy which Seamen generally have after they are got safe ashore from a Shipwreck, which they drown all in the next Bowl of Punch, and forget almost as soon as it is over, and all the rest of my Life was like it.

Even when I was afterwards, on due Consideration, made sensible of my Condition, how I was cast on this dreadful Place, out of the Reach of humane Kind, out of all Hope of Relief, or Prospect of Redemption, as soon as I saw but a Prospect of living, and that I should not starve and perish for Hunger, all the Sense of my Affliction wore off, and I begun to be very easy, apply'd my self to the Works proper for my Preservation and Supply, and was far enough from being afflicted at my Condition, as a Judgment from Heaven, or as the

第 三 部

当初,那位葡萄牙船长把我从海里救了起来,对我慷慨仁慈,公平无欺,我却一点也没有想到要感谢上帝。当我又一次遇到船只失事,几乎淹死在海里时,我既没有悔恨之意,也未把这看作上天的判决。我只对自己说,我是个倒霉蛋,天生就这么不幸。不错,当我第一次踏上陆地,发现所有人都淹死而我独存的时候,一种发自心灵深处的狂喜油然而生,这种喜悦之情如果借助上帝的仁慈,可以化作一片感激之情。可是,这种狂喜很快变为一种平凡的快感,高兴看到自己活着,仅此而已。我绝对没有扪心自问,我能活命是不是上帝的特殊恩典;为什么上帝单单挑了我死里逃生,其他人竟无一生还;为什么我独受上天青睐。我的高兴只是像普通水手那样,当船只失事后逃命上岸来,喝几杯潘趣酒高兴高兴,过去后也便忘记了,我生来就是这样的。

甚至到了后来,经过认真的思考,我对自己所处的环境有了切实的认识:我被抛在怎样一个可怕的地方,这里远离人类,没有任何获救的希望。即使这样,但一想到我还能勉强生活,不会因饥饿而死,我的所有痛苦感觉都消失了。我的心情开始怡然轻松起来,投入到各种维持自己生存的各项工作中,一点也不为自己

Hand of God against me; these were Thoughts which very seldom enter'd into my Head.

The growing up of the Corn, as is hinted in my Journal, had at first some little Influence upon me, and began to affect me with Seriousness, as long as I thought it had something miraculous in it; but as soon as ever that Part of the Thought was remov'd, all the Impression which was rais'd from it, wore off also, as I have noted already.

Even the Earthquake, tho' nothing could be more terrible in its Nature, or more immediately directing to the invisible Power which alone directs such Things, yet no sooner was the first Fright over, but the Impression it had made went off also. I had no more Sense of God or his Judgments, much less of the present Affliction of my Circumstances being from his Hand, than if I had been in the most prosperous Condition of Life.

But now when I began to be sick, and a leisurely View of the Miseries of Death came to place itself before me; when my Spirits began to sink under the Burthen of a strong Distemper, and Nature was exhausted with the Violence of the Feaver; Conscience that had slept so long, begun to awake, and I began to reproach my self with my past Life, in which I had so evidently, by uncommon Wickedness, provok'd the Justice of God to lay me under uncommon Strokes, and to deal with me in so vindictive a Manner.

These Reflections oppress'd me for the second or third Day of my Distemper, and in the Violence, as well of the Feaver, as of the dreadful Reproaches of my Conscience, extorted some Words from me, like praying to God, tho' I cannot say they

的处境感到烦恼了,不把我的遭遇看作是上帝对我的裁决,也不把它看作是上帝对我的惩罚。是的,我的脑子里很少有这样的想法。

我在前面的日记里曾经提到过土里长出谷子的事。那件事,开始对我颇有影响,让我深受感动,觉得那是神意的作用。可是,当我一明白那是怎么一回事的时候,对那件事的所有感触便很快淡忘了。这一点,我前面已经提到。

再说地震,这应该是大自然中最为可怕、与冥冥神力最相关联的现象了,可我也只是在最初惊恐战栗的瞬间想到过上帝及其神力,地震一过,那些印象又随即消失了。我还是那样,既不觉得有所谓的上帝,也不觉得我所处的可悲处境是出于上帝的安排,好像我一直生活得十分平安富足似的。

但如今这场大病,死亡的悲惨境遇渐渐在我面前清晰起来。由于病痛,我精神极度颓丧;由于发热,我浑身没有一点力气。这时,我那已泯灭很长时间的良心开始苏醒,并开始责备自去的生活。在此之前,我已经用不可饶恕的罪恶惹得上帝给我严厉的惩罚,对我如此严酷,用这种报应的手段来对待我。

这些观念,在我生病的第二天和第三天,给了我很大的压力;在发热和良心谴责的交逼下,我才勉强发出几句类似祷告的话,虽然这些话并不算

were either a Prayer attended with Desires or with Hopes; it was rather the Voice of meer Fright and Distress; my Thoughts were confus'd, the Convictions great upon my Mind, and the Horror of dying in such a miserable Condition rais'd Vapours into my Head with the meer Apprehensions; and in these Hurries of my Soul, I know not what my Tongue might express: but it was rather Exclamation, such as, Lord! what a miserable Creature am I? If I should be sick, I shall certainly die for Want of Help, and what will become of me! Then the Tears burst out of my Eyes, and I could say no more for a good while.

In this Interval, the good Advice of my Father came to my Mind, and presently his Prediction which I mention'd at the Beginning of this Story, viz. That if I did take this foolish Step, God would not bless me, and I would have Leisure hereafter to reflect upon having neglected his Counsel, when there might be none to assist in my Recovery. Now, said I aloud, My dear Father's Words are come to pass: God's Justice has overtaken me, and I have none to help or hear me: I rejected the Voice of Providence, which had mercifully put me in a Posture or Station of Life, wherein I might have been happy and easy; but I would neither see it my self, or learn to know the Blessing of it from my Parents; I left them to mourn over my Folly, and now I am left to mourn under the Consequences of it: I refus'd their Help and Assistance who wou'd have lifted me into the World, and wou'd have made every Thing easy to me, and now I have Difficulties to struggle with, too great for even Nature itself to support, and no Assistance, no Help, no Comfort, no Advice; then I cry'd out, Lord be my Help, for I am in great Distress.

是一种出于至诚的祈祷,只能说是一种恐怖和受难的呼声。这时我的思想非常混乱,我心里深深地感到自己有罪;一想到自己要在这种不幸的情形下死去,我的脑子里便充满了恐怖的影子。在这种心灵的混乱中,我简直不知道自己嘴里要说什么话,只是一味地喊着:"主啊,我多么不幸啊! 若是我病了,我一定要因为无人照料而送掉性命,我怎么得了啊?"于是我的眼泪夺眶而出,半天说不出话来。

这时,我想起了父亲的忠告,也想到了他老人家的预言。这些我在故事一开始就提到了。父亲说,如果我执意采取这种愚蠢的行动,那么,上帝一定不会保佑我。当我将来呼救无门时,我会后悔自己没有听从他的忠告。这时,我大声地说,现在,父亲的话果然应验了:上帝已经惩罚了我,谁也不能来救我,谁也不能来听我的呼救了。我拒绝了上天的好意,上天原本对我十分慈悲,把我安排在一个优裕的生活环境中,让我幸福舒适地过日子。可是,我自己却身在福中不知福,又不听父母的话来认识这种福份。我不辞而别,让他们为我的愚蠢行径痛心疾首,而如今事情弄到了这个结果,轮到我自己痛心疾首了。我的父母一向愿意帮我在世上安身立命,把样样事情都为我安排妥帖,但我却不要他们的帮助,如今我困难重重,却要自己去一一对付,

This was the first Prayer, if I may call it so, that I had made for many Years: But I return to my Journal.

June 28. Having been somewhat refresh'd with the Sleep I had had, and the Fit being entirely off, I got up; and tho' the Fright and Terror of my Dream was very great, yet I consider'd, that the Fit of the Ague wou'd return again the next Day, and now was my Time to get something to refresh and support my self when I should be ill; and the first Thing I did, I fill'd a large square Case Bottle with Water, and set it upon my Table, in Reach of my Bed; and to take off the chill or aguish Disposition of the Water, I put about a Quarter of a Pint of Rum into it, and mix'd them together; then I got me a Piece of the Goat's Flesh, and broil'd it on the Coals, but could eat very little; I walk'd about, but was very weak, and withal very sad and heavy-hearted in the Sense of my miserable Condition; dreading the Return of my Distemper the next Day; at Night I made my Supper of three of the Turtle's Eggs, which I roasted in the Ashes, and eat, as we call it, in the Shell; and this was the first Bit of Meat I had ever ask'd God's Blessing to, even as I cou'd remember, in my whole Life.

After I had eaten, I try'd to walk, but found my self so weak, that I cou'd hardly carry the Gun, (for I never went out without that) so I went but a little Way, and sat down upon the Ground, looking out upon the Sea, which was just before me, and very calm and smooth: As I sat here, some such Thoughts as these occurred to me.

而这些困难之大，就连自然界本身也都承受不了，何况我孤身一人，没有帮手，没有慰藉，没有指点。"说到这里，我喊了起来，"上帝呀，帮帮我吧！我可是在大难之中啊！"

这是我多年来第一次祈祷，如果我能称之为祈祷的话；不过我还是回到日记吧。

六月二十八日。一觉醒来，我感到好受一些，没再打摆子，我爬起来，虽说噩梦的恐惧久久没有消失，但我意识到第二天疟疾又会发作，现在正是吃点东西、恢复点力气对付将来发病的时候。我首先把一个大四方瓶子装满水，把它放在床边的桌子旁，为了驱掉水里的寒性和消毒，我又往水里放了四分之一品脱的甘蔗酒，和水混在一起。然后拿出一块羊肉，把它放在火上烤了烤，但吃的很少。我四处走了走，觉得身体无力，想到自己目前的悲惨处境，更害怕明天疟疾又发作，我既悲哀又苦闷。晚上我拿了三个龟蛋在灰里烤熟，剥了皮吃掉，算作晚饭。在我一生的记忆里，这是我第一次吃肉时祈求上帝的祝福。

吃完之后，我想出去走走，可发现自己太虚弱了，连持枪的力气都没有（我出门总是要带枪的），没走多远就坐到了地上。现在，大海就在我的眼前，我朝海上看去，只见海面风平浪静，平滑如镜。就在我坐在这里的当儿，我的脑

What is this Earth and Sea of which I have seen so much, whence is it produc'd, and what am I, and all the other Creatures, wild and tame, humane and brutal, whence are we?

Sure we are all made by some secret Power, who form'd the Earth and Sea, the Air and Sky; and who is that?

Then it follow'd most naturally, It is God that has made it all: Well, but then it came on strangely, if God has made all these Things, He guides and governs them all, and all Things that concern them; for the Power that could make all Things, must certainly have Power to guide and direct them.

If so, nothing can happen in the great Circuit of his Works, either without his Knowledge or Appointment.

And if nothing happens without his Knowledge, he knows that I am here, and am in this dreadful Condition; and if nothing happens without his Appointment, he has appointed all this to befal me.

Nothing occurr'd to my Thought to contradict any of these Conclusions; and therefore it rested upon me with the greater Force, that it must needs be, that God had appointed all this to befal me; that I was brought to this miserable Circumstance by his Direction, he having the sole Power, not of me only, but of every Thing that happen'd in the World. Immediately it follow'd, Why has

子中却涌起了这些奇思怪想：

虽然我陆路水路走了无数,但是,大地与海洋究竟是什么? 它们是从哪里来的? 我和其他一切生灵,所有野生的和驯养的,文明的和野蛮的,究竟是些什么? 又从何而来?

无疑,所有这一切都是由一种隐秘的力量创造出来的,这种力量创造了所有的生灵,创造了陆地、大海和天空。可是,这种力量又是什么呢?

显然,最合理的答案应该是:这种力量就是上帝,上帝创造了这一切。由此,可以得出以下结论:既然上帝创造了一切,那么,他当然也在指导支配着这一切,以及一切与之相关的东西。因为上帝既能造出万物来,当然也有能力来指导它们,支配它们。

假如是这样,那么,在他所创造的天地范围内,也就没有一件事的发生不是他所知道的,不是他所安排的了。

既然没有一件事的发生不是他所知道的,那么他自然也知道我现在是在这个岛上,是在这种可怕的情形之下了。假如没有一件事的发生不是他所安排的,那么我这些灾难自然也是他所安排的了。

我想不出有任何理由能推翻这些结论。这使我更加坚信,我遭遇的这些灾难,都是上帝安排的;正是上帝的指使,使我陷入了当前的悲惨境遇。上帝不仅对我,而且对世间万物,都有绝对的支配权力。于是,我马上又想到:"上

God done this to me? What have I done to be thus us'd?

My Conscience presently check'd me in that Enquiry, as if I had blasphem'd, and methought it spoke to me like a Voice; WRETCH! dost thou ask what thou hast done! look back upon a dreadful mis-spent Life, and ask thy self what thou hast not done? ask, Why is it that thou wert not long ago destroy'd? Why wert thou not drown'd in Yarmouth Roads? Kill'd in the Fight when the Ship was taken by the Sallee Man of War? Devour'd by the wild Beasts on the Coast of Africa? Or, Drown'd HERE, when all the Crew perish'd but thy self? Dost thou ask, What have I done?

I was struck dumb with these Reflections, as one astonish'd, and had not a Word to say, no not to answer to my self, but rise up pensive and sad, walk'd back to my Retreat, and went up over my Wall, as if I had been going to Bed, but my Thoughts were sadly disturb'd, and I had no Inclination to Sleep; so I sat down in my Chair, and lighted my Lamp, for it began to be dark: Now as the Apprehension of the Return of my Distemper terrify'd me very much, it occurr'd to my Thought, that the Brasilians take no Physick but their Tobacco, for almost all Distempers; and I had a Piece of a Roll of Tobacco in one of the Chests, which was quite cur'd, and some also that was green and not quite cur'd.

I went, directed by Heaven no doubt; for in this Chest I found a Cure, both for Soul and Body, I open'd the Chest, and found what I look'd for, viz. the Tobacco; and as the few

帝为什么要这么对待我？我到底做了什么坏事，上帝才这么惩罚我呢？"

这时，我的良心立刻制止我提出这样的问题，好像我亵渎了神明；我好像听到良心对我说："你这罪孽深重的人啊，你竟还要问你作下了什么坏事？回头看看你半生的罪孽吧！问问你自己，你什么坏事没有作过？你还该问一下，你本来早就死了，为什么现在还能活着？为什么你没有在雅木斯港外的锚地中淹死？为什么在遭到萨利海盗船的攻击时，你没有被打死？为什么没有在非洲海岸被野兽吃掉？还有，你同船的人都在这儿丢了性命，为什么你偏偏没有淹死？难道你还要问：我干过什么坏事吗？"

这么一想，我惊得瞠目结舌，无话可说，不，是无言可对，只得心事重重地站起身来，往回走去，翻过了围墙，就好像我是要回来睡一觉似的，而事实上，我心里十分烦闷，根本就不想睡觉；于是我往椅子上一坐，又把灯点亮了，因为天色已暗了下来。一想到又会发疟疾我就惶惶不安。我蓦地想起巴西人没别的药，几乎用烟草治百病。我的箱子里正好有一张加过工的烟叶和一些未加工的青烟叶。

毫无疑问，上天在为我指点迷津；因为我在箱子里找到了治愈灵与肉的良药。我打开箱子，发现我要找的东西

Books, I had sav'd, lay there too, I took out one of the Bibles which I mention'd before, and which to this Time I had not found Leisure, or so much as Inclination to look into; I say, I took it out, and brought both that and the Tobacco with me to the Table.

What Use to make of the Tobacco, I knew not, as to my Distemper, or whether it was good for it or no; but I try'd several Experiments with it, as if I was resolv'd it should hit one Way or other: I first took a Piece of a Leaf, and chew'd it in my Mouth, which indeed at first almost stupify'd my Brain, the Tobacco being green and strong, and that I had not been much us'd to it; then I took some and steeped it an Hour or two in some Rum, and resolv'd to take a Dose of it when I lay down; and lastly, I burnt some upon a Pan of Coals, and held my Nose close over the Smoke of it as long as I could bear it, as well for the Heat as almost for Suffocation.

In the Interval of this Operation, I took up the Bible and began to read, but my Head was too much disturb'd with the Tobacco to bear reading, at least that Time; only having open'd the Book casually, the first Words that occurr'd to me were these, Call on me in the Day of Trouble, and I will deliver, and thou shalt glorify me.

The Words were very apt to my Case, and made some Impression upon my Thoughts at the Time of reading them, tho' not so much as they did afterwards; for as for being deliver'd, the Word had no Sound, as I may say, to me; the Thing was so remote, so impossible in my Apprehension of Things, that I began to say as the Children of Israel did, when they were promis'd Flesh to eat, Can God spread a Table in the Wilderness? so I began to say, Can God himself deliver me from this Place? and as it was not for many Years that any Hope appear'd, this prevail'd very often upon

——烟草。我保留的几本书也在里面,我拿出一本前面提过的《圣经》,这本书本来是我既抽不出时间,也无意去阅读的。我把它取出来后,便把《圣经》和烟叶都放到桌子上。

我不知道如何用烟草治我的病,也不知道对治病是否有好处,但我用它做了几次试验,我好像下了决心,总会找到一种办法似的。我先拿了一片烟叶,在嘴里咀嚼,开始确实使我脑袋发麻,因为烟叶劲很大,这样做使我也不习惯。然后,我又拿了些烟叶,放到甘蔗酒里浸泡了一两个小时,决定睡觉时喝上一剂。最后,我又在炭盆里烧了一些,并把鼻子凑上去,尽量忍受着烟熏以及那简直令人窒息的热气。

在这一过程当中,我翻开《圣经》,读了起来。可是,我的脑子给烟草熏得发昏,读不下去,至少当时是这样。当我心不在焉地把它翻开时,首先进入眼帘的却是这样一段话:"要在患难之日求告我,我必搭救你,你也要荣耀我。"

这段话很适合我的情形,所以,当我读到它的时候,特别感动,当然,还不及后来感动。至于"搭救"之类的话,倒没怎么让我动心,因为我的前景很渺茫,不可能有获救的希望。开始,以色列人在上帝许诺给他们肉吃的时候,他们曾这样疑问:"上帝在旷野岂能摆设筵席?"我起初也问:"上帝能把我从这种地方拯救出去吗?"因为许多年以后才出现

my Thoughts: But however, the Words made a great Impression upon me, and I mused upon them very often. It grew now late, and the Tobacco had, as I said, doz'd my Head so much, that I inclin'd to sleep; so I left my Lamp burning in the Cave, least I should want any Thing in the Night, and went to Bed; but before I lay down, I did what I never had done in all my Life, I kneel'd down and pray'd to God to fulfil the Promise to me, that if I call'd upon him in the Day of Trouble, he would deliver me; after my broken and imperfect Prayer was over, I drunk the Rum in which I had steep'd the Tobacco, which was so strong and rank of the Tobacco, that indeed I could scarce get it down; immediately upon this I went to Bed, I found presently it flew up in my Head violently, but I fell into a sound Sleep, and wak'd no more 'till by the Sun it must necessarily be near Three a-Clock in the Afternoon the next Day; nay, to this Hour, I'm partly of the Opinion, that I slept all the next Day and Night, and 'till almost Three that Day after; for otherwise I knew not how I should lose a Day out of my Reckoning in the Days of the Week, as it appear'd some Years after I had done: for if I had lost it by crossing and re-crossing the Line, I should have lost more than one Day: But certainly I lost a Day in my Accompt, and never knew which Way.

Be that however one Way or th' other, when I awak'd I found my self exceedingly refresh'd, and my Spirits lively and chearful; when I got up, I was stronger than I was the Day before, and my Stomach better, for I was hungry; and in short, I

了获救的希望,所以这个疑问一直在我的脑海中盘旋。但是,不管怎么说,《圣经》上的这句话确实给我留下了深刻的印象,使我时常回味其中的含意。夜已经深了,我也被烟草熏得迷迷糊糊,困意渐浓。于是我准备睡觉。我让灯继续在山洞里点燃着,以防晚上有什么不方便。接着,我做了一件有生以来从未做过的事:我跪在地上,虔诚地向上帝祈祷,求他应允,如果有一天我在患难中向他呼告,请他务必搭救我。我断断续续颠三倒四地说完了祈祷词,便开始进行最后一种烟草疗法。我把那浸了烟叶的甘蔗酒喝了下去;酒性非常凶烈,而且烟味刺人,我几乎喝不下去。喝完之后,我立刻上了床。不一会儿,我便觉得酒力直冲顶门,非常有力。我昏昏睡去,一直到第二天下午三点钟才醒过来。不,我甚至疑心我第二天又睡了一天一夜;一直到第三天三点钟才醒;若不是这样,我就无法解释我为什么把日子少算了一天(这是我几年以后才发现的)。要说我画的线,有时多画了一根,有时少画了一根,为什么单单只漏掉一天呢。事实是,我的确把日子漏记了一天,至于怎么漏的,我也不知道。

不管怎么说,醒来时我觉得精神焕发,身体也完全恢复了活力。起床后,我感到力气也比前一天大多了,并且胃口也开了,因为我肚子感到饿

had no Fit the next Day, but continu'd much alter'd for the better; this was the 29th.

The 30th was my well Day of Course, and I went abroad with my Gun, but did not care to travel too far, I kill'd a Sea Fowl or two, something like a brand Goose, and brought them Home, but was not very forward to eat them; so I ate some more of the Turtle's Eggs, which were very good: This Evening I renew'd the Medicine which I had suppos'd did me good the Day before, viz. the Tobacco steep'd in Rum, only I did not take so much as before, nor did I chew any of the Leaf, or hold my Head over the Smoke; however, I was not so well the next Day, which was the first of July, as I hop'd I shou'd have been; for I had a little Spice of the cold Fit, but it was not much.

July 2. I renew'd the Medicine all the three Ways, and doz'd my self with it as at first; and doubled the Quantity which I drank.

3. I miss'd the Fit for good and all, tho' I did not recover my full Strength for some Weeks after; while I was thus gathering Strength, my Thoughts run exceedingly upon this Scripture, I will deliver thee, and the Impossibility of my Deliverance lay much upon my Mind in Barr of my ever expecting it: But as I was discouraging my self with such Thoughts, it occurr'd to my Mind, that I pored so much upon my Deliverance from the main Affliction, that I disregarded the Deliverance I had receiv'd; and I was, as it were, made to ask my self such Questions as these, viz. Have I not been deliver'd, and wonderfully too, from Sickness? from the most distress'd Condition that could be, and that as so frightful to me, and what Notice I had taken of it? Had I done my Part?

了。一句话,第二天疟疾没有发作,身体逐渐复原;这一天是二十九日。

三十日当然身体更好了,我重又带枪外出,但不敢走得太远。打死了一两只像黑雁那样的海鸟带回家,可又不想吃鸟肉,就又煮了几个龟蛋吃,味道挺不错。傍晚,我又给自己治起病来,因为我昨天就觉得这治疗对我颇有用处;我又把烟叶浸在甘蔗酒中,只是喝得没上回多,也不把烟叶放在嘴里咀嚼或点着了烟叶再凑过头去嗅;然而第二天七月一日,我却没怎么好,没我所希望的那样好,因为我身子感到有点发冷,但总算并不厉害。

七月二日。我把三种治疗办法全又做了一遍,而且把喝下去的分量增加了一倍,结果我的头又像上回那样昏昏沉沉的。

七月三日。好几个星期我的体力都未恢复,虽说如此,我不再打摆子。在调养期间,我念念不忘这句箴言:"我必搭救你。"但我很难相信我会真正被搭救,似乎连期待这点都不应该。就在我患得患失、心烦意乱之际,我猛然想到,我一心一意想从现在这种状况中挣脱出来,却忽视了我已得到的解救。我扪心自问:"难道我没有奇迹般地被从病魔中解救出来吗?难道这不是把我从最痛苦、最令我害怕的状况中解救出来?我可曾注意到这方面?我可曾尽了

God had deliver'd me, but I had not glorify'd him; that is to say, I had not own'd and been thankful for that as a Deliverance, and how cou'd I expect greater Deliverance?

This touch'd my Heart very much, and immediately I kneel'd down and gave God Thanks aloud, for my Recovery from my Sickness.

July 4. In the Morning I took the Bible, and beginning at the New Testament, I began seriously to read it, and impos'd upon my self to read a while every Morning and every Night, not tying my self to the Number of Chapters, but as long as my Thoughts shou'd engage me: It was not long after I set seriously to this Work, but I found my Heart more deeply and sincerely affected with the Wickedness of my past Life: The Impression of my Dream reviv'd, and the Words, All these Things have not brought thee to Repentance, ran seriously in my Thought: I was earnestly begging of God to give me Repentance, when it happen'd providentially the very Day that reading the Scripture, I came to these Words, He is exalted a Prince and a Saviour, to give Repentance, and to give Remission: I threw down the Book, and with my Heart as well as my Hands lifted up to Heaven, in a Kind of Extasy of Joy, I cry'd out aloud, Jesus, thou Son of David, Jesus, thou exalted Prince and Saviour, give me Repentance!

This was the first Time that I could say, in the true Sense of the Words, that I pray'd in all my Life; for now I pray'd with a Sense of my Condition, and with a true Scripture View of Hope founded on the Encouragement of the Word of God; and from this Time, I may say, I began to have Hope that God would hear me.

Now I began to construe the Words mentioned

自己该尽的责任？上帝搭救了我，但我没有荣耀他，就是说，我没对自己得救表示感谢，这样我又怎能指望得到更大的搭救呢？"

我心里触动很大，立即跪下来，并大声地感谢上帝让我从疾病中得以康复。

七月四日。早晨，我拿起《圣经》，翻开《新约》，开始认真地读看，并逼着自己每天早晚都要读，只要精神集中就读下去，并没有限定章数。我这样认真地读下去，没多久我的心便被以前自己的罪恶生活而深深地打动了，梦中的印象又重现了，我反复思考着这句话："这些事情没能让你悔改。"一日，正当我恳求上帝赐给我悔改之心的时候，仿佛受到了神的指引，恰好读到了《新约》中的这段话："上帝且用右手将他高举，叫他作君主，作救主，将悔改的心和赦罪的恩，赐给以色列人。"我放下经书，将手举在空中，心向天国，满怀着一腔狂喜，大声叫道："耶稣啊，耶稣，大卫之子，既然上帝举你为君王和救主，那就请赐给我悔改之心吧！"

可以说，这是我有生以来，第一次用合乎规范的方式祈祷。因为在这次祈祷中，我真正联想到了自己的处境，真正受到了上帝言辞的鼓励，真正抱着一种符合《圣经》精神的虔诚态度。也可以说，正是从这时候起，我才真正希望上帝能够听到我的祷告。

现在，对于"你若求告我，

above, Call on me, and I will deliver you, in a different Sense from what I had ever done before; for then I had no Notion of any thing being call'd Deliverance, but my being deliver'd from the Captivity I was in; for tho' I was indeed at large in the Place, yet the Island was certainly a Prison to me, and that in the worst Sense in the World; but now I learn'd to take it in another Sense: Now I look'd back upon my past Life with such Horrour, and my Sins appear'd so dreadful, that my Soul sought nothing of God, but Deliverance from the Load of Guilt that bore down all my Comfort: As for my Solitary Life it was nothing; I did not SO much as pray to be deliver'd from it, or think of it; It was all of no Consideration in Comparison to this: And I add this Part here, to hint to whoever shall read it, that whenever they come to a true Sense of things, they will find Deliverance from Sin a much greater Blessing, than Deliverance from Affliction.

But leaving this Part, I return to my Journal.

My Condition began now to be, tho' not less miserable as my Way of living, yet much easier to my Mind; and my Thoughts being directed, by a constant reading the Scripture, and praying to God, to things of a higher Nature: I ad a great deal of Comfort within, which till now I knew nothing of; also, as my Health and Strength returned, I bestirr'd my self to furnish my self with every thing that I anted, and make my Way of living as regular as I could.

From the 4th of July to the 24th, I was chiefly

我必搭救你"这句话,我产生了一种全新的、与以前截然不同的观点,理解的角度与以前也大不一样了。过去我认为,"搭救"就是要把我从当前的困境中解救出来。因为我在这个地方虽然无拘无束,可是我认为这个海岛实在是我的一个监牢,而且是世界上最坏的监牢。可是现在,我已懂得用另一种眼光去对待它。现在,我只感到自己过去的生活太可憎了,自己的罪孽太可怕了,因此我对上帝别无他求,只求他把我从这些使我昼夜不安的罪恶重担下解救出来。至于我的孤苦伶仃的生活,那简直算不了什么。我无意祈求上帝把我从这里救出来,也没有这种念头。相形之下,这件事完全不关紧要。我在这里说这一段话,就是要提醒那些读到我的日记的人,要他们明白,一个人在明白事理以后,就会觉得,被上帝从罪恶中救出来,比被上帝从患难中救出来,幸福更大。

现在,闲话少说,重回到日记上来吧。

我当前的境况是:虽然生活依然很艰苦,但精神却轻松多了。由于读《圣经》和祈祷,思想变得高尚了,内心也有了更多的安慰,这种宽慰的心情我以前从未有过。同时,健康和体力也已恢复,我重又振作精神,安排工作,并恢复正常的生活。

从七月四日至十四日,我

employ'd walking about with my Gun in my Hand, a little and a little, at a Time, as a Man that was gathering up his Strength after a Fit of Sickness: For it is hardly to be imagin'd, how low I was, and to what Weakness I was reduc'd. The Application which I made Use of was perfectly new, and perhaps what had never cur'd an Ague before, neither can recommend it to any one to practise, by this Experiment; and tho' it did carry off the Fit, yet it rather contributed to weakening me; for I had frequent Convulsions in my Nerves and Limbs for some Time.

I learn'd from it also this in particular, that being abroad the rainy Season was the most pernicious thing to my Health that could be, especially in those Rains which came ended with Storms and Hurricanes of Wind; for as the in which came in the dry Season was always most accompany'd with such Storms, so I found that Rain was much more dangerous than the Rain which fell in September and October.

I had been now in this unhappy Island above 10 Months, all Possibility of Deliverance from this Condition, seem'd to be entirely taken from me; and I firmly believed, that no humane Shape had ever set Foot upon that Place: Having now secur'd my Habitation, as I thought, fully to my Mind, I had a great Desire to make a more perfect Discovery of the Island, and to see what other Productions I might find, which I yet knew nothing of.

It was the 15th of July that I began to take a more particular Survey of the Island it self: I went up the Creek first, where, as I hinted, I brought my Rafts on Shore; I found after I came about two Miles up, that the Tide did not flow any higher, and that it was no more than a little Brook of running Water, and very fresh and good; but this be-

主要的活动是带枪外出，四处走走。但就像病后康复的人那样，我总是走点路就歇会儿，歇过了再走点路。因为，我病后身体之衰弱，已到了难以想象的地步。我用来给自己治病的办法完全是别出心裁的，也许从来就没用这种办法治好过疟疾，所以我不敢把自己的这种尝试向大家推荐；这种办法虽然使我的病不再发作，却也使我身体受到损害，因为在相当一段时间里，我的四肢常常会抽筋。

从这次生病我得到了一个教训：雨季出门对我的健康真是再有害不过，而伴随着狂风或飓风下的雨，对健康的害处则更大。但在旱季里，下雨的时候老要刮这样的大风。所以，我发现，旱季下的雨，比九月、十月下的雨对人更有害。

我到这孤岛已经有十个多月了。看来任何脱离目前处境的可能性都不存在了。我完全相信，人类的足迹在我之前从未踏上过这个孤岛。现在，我的住所和生活都已安定，所以我就十分渴望按照自己的心愿对海岛作一次更为全面的勘察，看看还有哪些我尚未发现的物产。

七月十五日我开始对这座孤岛进行特别考查。我先沿着我以前撑进木筏的那条河逆流而上，约走了两英里，发现潮水不再涨过来，河流缩小成一条小溪，溪水甜美而无咸味。但这会儿是旱季，有的

ing the dry Season, there was hardly any Water in some Parts of it, at least, not enough to run in any Stream, so as it could be perceiv'd.

On the Bank of this Brook I found many pleasant Savana's, or Meadows; plain, smooth, and cover'd with Grass; and on the rising Parts of them next to the higher Grounds, where the Water, as it might be supposed, never overflow'd I found a great deal of Tobacco, green, and growing to great and very strong Stalk; there were divers other Plants which I had no Notion of, or Understanding about, and might perhaps have Vertues of their own, which I could find out.

I searched for the Cassava Root, which the Indians in all that climate make their Bread of, but I could find I saw large Plants of Alloes, but did not then understand them. I saw several Sugar Canes, but wild, and for Cultivation, imperfect. I contented my self with these Discoveries for this Time, and came back musing with my self what Course I might take to know the Vertue and Goodness of any of the Fruits or Plants which I should discover; but could bring it to no Conclusion; for in short, I had made so little Observation while I wad in the Brasils, that I knew little of the Plants in the Field, at least very little that might serve me to any Purpose now in my Distress.

The next Day, the 16th, I went up the same Way again, and after going something farther than I had gone the Day before, I found the Brook, and the Savana's began to cease, and the Country became more woody than before; in this Part I found different Fruits, and particularly I found Mellons upon the Ground in great Abundance, and Grapes upon the Trees; the Vines had spread indeed over the Trees, and the Clusters of Grapes were just

地方都干涸了,至少已不能形成水流。

在这小溪的边上,我看到一片一片的草地,它们开阔而平坦,令人心旷神怡;这些草地一直延伸到看来永无水淹之虞的高地,而在草地和高地之间的斜坡上,我看见还长有许多烟草,它们的叶子碧绿,茎儿非常粗壮;还有其他多种植物,都是我不曾见过的,也想不出它们究竟是什么,它们也许各有用处,但是我一时还无法了解。

我到处寻找木薯的块根,那是热带印第安人用来做面包的东西,可是找不到。我看到许多很大的芦荟,但当时还不知道它们的用处。我又看见一些甘蔗,然而都是野生的,因为没有人工培植,都不大好。我认为这回发现了不少东西,在回家的路上,心里寻思着用什么方法可以知道我所发现的水果和植物的性质和用处,然而毫无结果。主要因为我在巴西的时候观察得太少,所以对于野生的植物都不大知道,不能在这困难之中对我有什么用处。

第二天,十六日,我再次去那个地方。我又向前多走了一些,发现小溪和草地都开始少起来,而树木却逐渐茂盛。在这一带,我发现了大量的各种各样的果子,尤其是发现了许多瓜类和葡萄,葡萄长得很繁茂,葡萄藤爬满树枝,葡萄一串串的,又红又大。发

now in their Prime, very ripe and rich: This was a surprising Discovery, and I was exceeding glad of them; but I was warn'd by my Experience to eat sparingly of them, remembring, that when I was ashore in Barbary, the eating of Grapes kill'd several of our English Men who were Slaves there, by throwing them into Fluxes and Feavers: But I found an excellent Use for these Grapes, and that was to cure or dry them in the Sun, and keep them as dry'd Grapes or Raisins are kept, which I thought would be, as indeed they were, as wholesom as agreeable to eat, when no Grapes might be to be had.

I spent all that Evening there, and went not back to my Habitation, which by the Way was the first Night, as I might say, I had lain from Home. In the Night I took my first Contrivance, and got up into a Tree, where I slept well, and the next Morning proceeded upon my Discovery, travelling near four Miles, as I might judge by the Length of the Valley, keeping still due North, with a Ridge of Hills on the South and North-side of me.

At the End of this March I came to an Opening, where the Country seem'd to descend to the West, and a little Spring of fresh Water which issued out of the Side of the Hill by me, run the other Way, that is due East; and the Country appear'd so fresh, so green, so flourishing, every thing being in a constant Verdure, or Flourish of Spring, that it looked like a planted Garden.

I descended a little on the Side of that delicious Vale, surveying it with a secret Kind of Pleasure, (tho' mixt with my other afflicting Thoughts) to think that this was all my own, that I was King and Lord of all this Country indefeasibly, and had a Right of Possession; and if I could convey it, I might have it in Inheritance, as compleatly as any

现这些我简直高兴极了。但此刻我很清醒,不能吃多了,记得在非洲的巴巴里海岸登陆时,有几个被海盗俘虏的英国人,由于葡萄吃得太多,都患痢疾和热病死了。但是,我还是想出了一个很好的方法利用这些葡萄,就是把它们放在太阳下晒干,制成葡萄干收藏起来。我相信葡萄是很好吃的,在不是葡萄成熟的季节,就可以吃葡萄干,既富有营养又好吃。后来事实证明确实如此。

那晚我就留在那里,没有回家。顺便说一句,这是我第一次在外面过夜。到了夜里,我还是拿出老办法,爬上一棵大树,舒舒服服地睡了一夜。第二天早上,我又继续我的考察。根据那个山谷的长度来判断,我走了将近四英里,而且一直是在朝正北方向走,我的南面和北面,都有一脉连绵起伏的山峦。

走到这次远足的尽头处,我面前是片开阔地,地势似乎有点朝西倾斜,而我身侧的小山上,涌出一股清泉,朝正东方向流去;这地方看上去草木繁茂,欣欣向荣,真是永葆青翠的春日景象,简直就像是人工种植的大花园。

我走进这个幽静怡人的山谷,环顾四周,暗自欣喜:这一切都是我的,我是这里无法废除的国王,当然,恼火的是,我只身一人,一个臣民也没有。不过,如果我可以转让的话,我就能完全像英国的领主

Lord of a Mannor in England. I saw here Abundance of Cocoa Trees, Orange, and Lemmon, and Citron Trees; but all wild, and very few bearing any Fruit, at least not then: However, the green Limes that I gathered, were not only pleasant to eat, but very wholesome; and I mix'd their Juice afterwards with Water, which made it very wholesome, and very cool, and refreshing.

I found now I had Business enough to gather and carry Home; and I resolv'd to lay up a Store, as well of Grapes, as Limes and Lemons, to furnish my self for the wet Season, which I knew was approaching.

In Order to this, I gather'd a great Heap of Grapes in one Place, and a lesser Heap in another Place, and a great Parcel of Limes and Lemons in another Place; and taking a few of each with me, I travell'd homeward, and resolv'd to come again, and bring a Bag or Sack, or what I could make to carry the rest Home.

Accordingly, having spent three Days in this Journey, I came Home; so I must now call my Tent and my Cave: But, before I got thither, the Grapes were spoil'd; the Richness of the Fruits, and the Weight of the Juice having broken them, and bruis'd them, they were good for little or nothing; as to the Limes, they were good, but I could bring but a few.

The next Day, being the 19th, I went back, having made me two small Bags to bring Home my Harvest: But I was surpriz'd, when coming to my Heap of Grapes, which were so rich and fine when I gather'd them, I found them all spread about, trod to Pieces, and dragg'd about, some here, some there, and Abundance eaten and devour'd:

那样，把土地传给子孙。我在这儿找到大量的可可树、桔子树、柠檬树和香橼树。但这些都是野生植物，不生果子，至少当时我没看到。但我采摘的酸橙非常好吃，也有利于健康。我后来在橙汁里兑上水，制成清凉可口、滋养补身的饮料。

我知道我应该把这些果子收集起来并送回家去，我决心把它们像贮存葡萄那样，把酸橙和柠檬都收集起来，供我在雨季里吃，我知道，雨季马上就要来了。

为此，我采集了一大堆葡萄放在一个地方，又采集了一小堆放在另外一个地方，还把采集到的一大堆橙子和柠檬堆到一个地方。然后，我每样都取了一点，开始往回走。我打算下次再来时带个口袋什么的，把其余的也运回去。

就这样，这次出行花掉了我三天的时间，三天之后，就回到了我的家中（该称它为我的帐篷和山洞）。可是，就在半路上，这些葡萄就已破损掉了；由于它们的汁液太丰富，太饱满，结果都给压烂了，我几乎没法吃它们了。至于那些酸橙子，倒是没坏，可惜没带几个回来。

第二天，七月十九日，我带上事先做好的两个小口袋去装运我的丰收果实。可是当我来到葡萄堆前的时候，不禁大吃一惊。昨天还是个个饱满、粒粒完好、堆得好好的水果堆。现在却被拖得东一

By this I concluded, there were some wild Creatures thereabouts, which had done this; but what they were, I knew not.

However, as I found there there was no laying them up on Heaps, and no carrying them away in a Sack, but that one Way they would be destroy'd, and the other Way they would be crush'd with their own Weight. I took another Course; for I gather'd a large Quantity of the Grapes, and hung them up upon the out Branches of the Trees, that they might cure and dry in the Sun; and as for the Limes and Lemons, I carry'd as many back as I could well stand under.

When I came Home from this Journey, I contemplated with great Pleasure the Fruitfulness of that Valley, and the Pleasantness of the Scituation, the Security from Storms on that Side the Water, and the Wood, and concluded, that I had pitch'd upon a Place to fix my Abode, which was by far the worst Part of the Country. Upon the Whole I began to consider of removing my Habitation; and to look out for a ace equally safe, as where I now was scituate, if possible, in that pleasant fruitful Part of the Island.

This Thought run long in my Head, and I was exceeding fond of it for some Time, the Pleasantness of the Place tempting me; but when I came to a nearer View of it, and to consider that I was now by the Sea-Side, where it was at least possible that something might happen to my Advantage, and by the same ill Fate that brought me hither, might bring some other unhappy Wretches to the same Place; and tho' it was scarce probable that any such Thing should ever happen, yet to enclose my self among the Hills and Woods, in the Center of the Island, was to anticipate my Bondage, and to render such an Affair not only Improbable, but Impossible; and that therefore I ought not by any

串,西一粒,皮破汁淌,一片狼藉,好像还有许多被吃掉了。看情形,是附近一带的野兽搞的,至于是什么野兽,我就不得而知了。

我因此发现,把葡萄采下堆在一处或用口袋装回家都不是好办法,不是被野兽糟蹋,就是被挤坏压坏。于是我想出了一个新的办法。我采集了许多葡萄,把它们挂在一些树的外枝上,让太阳把它们晒干。至于那些酸橙和柠檬,我却尽量把它们背了一些回来。

我自从这次出门回来,经常带着愉快的心情想着那山谷的物产丰富,地势宜人,而且靠近河水和树林,不怕暴风雨的袭击。我看出我所选定的住处,实在是全岛最坏的地方。总之,我开始考虑搬家的问题,打算在风景宜人、物产丰富的岛的那一边,找一个和我现在所住的地方同样安全的场所。

搬家的念头在我头脑里盘旋了很久,那地方风光明媚,特别诱人,有时,这种念头特别强烈;但仔细一想,住在海边也有住在海边的好处,说不定还有一些别的倒霉蛋,像我一样,交上恶运,来到这座荒岛上。当然,这种事情发生的希望确实微乎其微,但把自己关闭在岛中央的山林里,无异于把自己禁闭起来。那时,这种事情不仅没有希望发生,就连可能性也没有了。思前想后,觉得家还是不搬为好。

Means to remove.

However, I was so Enamour'd of this Place, that I spent much of my Time there, for the whole remaining Part of the Month of July; and tho' upon second Thoughts I resolv'd as above, not to remove, yet I built me a little kind of a Bower, and surrounded it at a Distance with a strong Fence, being a double Hedge, as high as I could reach, well stak'd, and fill'd between with Brushwood; and here I lay very secure, sometimes two or three Nights together, always going over it with a Ladder, as before; so that I fancy'd now I had my Country-House, and my Sea-Coast-House: And this Work took me up to the Beginning of August.

I had but newly finish'd my Fence, and began to enjoy my Labour, but the Rains came on, and made me stick close to my first Habitation; for tho' I had made me a Tent like the other, with a Piece of a Sail, and spread it very well; yet I had not the Shelter of a Hill to keep me from Storms, nor a Cave behind me to retreat into, when the Rains were extraordinary.

About the Beginning of August, as I said, I had finish'd my Bower, and began to enjoy my self. The third of August, I found the Grapes I had hung up were perfectly dry'd, and indeed, were excellent good Raisins of the Sun; so I began to take them down from the Trees, and it was very happy that I did so; for the Rains which follow'd would have spoil'd them, and I had lost the best Part of my Winter Food; for I had above two hundred large Bunches of them. No sooner had I taken them all down, and carry'd most of them Home to my Cave, but it began to rain, and from hence,

话虽这么说，我对这地方还是极其着迷的，所以在七月份剩下的那些日子里，我有好多的时间是在那儿消磨的；另一方面，虽然我经过上述那种考虑，已决定不搬家了，但还是给自己搭起个小茅屋，并在这茅屋四周筑起了一道坚固的围栅；这道围栅同茅屋间留有一些距离，实际上是两排扎得很深很稳的桩子，都有我一人一手高，两排桩子之间以从树的主干上砍下的枝枝桠桠充填，进进出出照旧是用梯子；我睡在这儿非常安全，有时一连睡上两三夜，所以我觉得现在我是既有海滨住宅，也有乡间别墅了。为了建这住所，我一直干到了八月初。

我刚刚完成围栅工程，正为自己的劳作自鸣得意的时候，雨下来了，迫使我躲进老住宅闭门不出。新住宅也有帐篷，像第一个那样用帆布做的，铺得非常平整，但没有山挡住暴风雨，雨下得太大时，也没有山洞躲避。

正如我所说的，八月初的时候，我已完成了我的新茅屋。当我准备好好享受一下时，八月三日，我发现我挂在树上的葡萄已经干透了，而且是极好的葡萄干。于是我便动手把它们从树上取下来，我对自己这样的做法很高兴，否则，继之而来的大雨就会把它们全部毁掉，我也就失去了冬季里最好的食物。我足足挂了二百串，我把这些葡萄刚刚

which was the fourteenth of August, it rain'd more or less, every Day, till the Middle of October; and sometimes so violently, that I could not stir out of my Cave for several Days.

In this Season I was much surpriz'd with the Increase of my Family; I had been concern'd for the Loss of one of my Cats, who run away from me, or as I thought had been dead, and I heard no more Tale or Tidings of her, till to my Astonishment she came Home about the End of August, with three Kittens; this was the more strange to me, because tho' I had kill'd a wild Cat, as I call'd it, with my Gun; yet I thought it was a quite differing Kind from our European Cats; yet the young Cats were the same Kind of House breed like the old one; and both my Cats being Females, I thought it very strange: But from these three Cats, I afterwards came to be so pester'd with Cats, that I was forc'd to kill them like Vermine, or wild Beasts, and to drive them from my House as much as possible.

From the fourteenth of August to the twenty sixth, incessant Rain, so that I could not stir, and was now very careful not to be much wet. In this Confinement I began to be straitned for Food, but venturing out twice, I one Day kill'd a Goat, and the last Day, which was the twenty sixth, found a very large Tortoise, which was a Treat to me, and my Food was regulated thus; I eat a Bunch of Raisins for my Breakfast, a Piece of the Goat's Flesh, or of the Turtle for my Dinner broil'd; for to my great Misfortune, I had no Vessel to boil or stew any Thing; and two or three of the Turtle's

取下来把大部分带回家时,天便开始下雨。从这时,即八月十四日起,直到十月中旬,几乎每天都下雨。有时雨水很大,我一连几天都无法走出山洞。

在这个季节中,我惊奇地发现,我的家里又添了新成员;我本来有两只猫,但后来少掉了一只。我心里很是着急,心想,它要么是跑掉了,要么就是死了。总之,我不知道它的下落,没有了它的消息。但是,让我感到震惊的是,大约在八月底,它忽然回来了,而且带着三只小猫。更叫我惊奇的是,我以前虽然用枪打死过一只野猫,因为我觉得它跟我的欧洲猫不是同一个品种,可是,现在看来,这些小猫都跟老猫一样,都是家种,而我的两只老猫是母的,所以,我好生奇怪,不知道这些小猫是怎么生的。可是,这三只小猫后来越生越多。闹得我不得安宁,我不得不像捕杀害虫和野兽一样追杀它们,尽量把它们从我的家中赶走。

从八月十四日到二十六日,大雨一直下个不停。我现在不大敢冒雨外出,生怕再被雨淋出病来。可就这么被雨困在家中,眼见着家中的存粮日益减少。无奈,我冒险外出了两次,第一次打死了一只山羊。第二次,就是二十六日那天,捉住了一只奇大无比的陆龟,美美地吃了一顿。我每天的进食一般这样安排:早上吃一串葡萄干;中午吃一块烤羊

Eggs for my Supper.

During this Confinement in my Cover, by the Rain, I work'd daily two or three Hours at enlarging my Cave, and by Degrees work'd it on towards one Side, till I came to the Out-Side of the Hill, and made a Door or Way out, which came beyond my Fence or Wall, and so I came in and out this Way; but I was not perfectly easy at lying so open; for as I had manag'd my self before, I was in a perfect Enclosure, whereas now I thought I lay expos'd, and open for any Thing to come in upon me; and yet I could not perceive that there was any living Thing to fear, the biggest Creature that I had yet seen upon the Island being a Goat.

September the thirtieth, I was now come to the unhappy Anniversary of my Landing. I cast up the Notches on my Post, and found I had been on Shore three hundred and sixty five Days. I kept this Day as a Solemn Fast, Setting it apart to Religious Exercise, prostrating my self on the Ground with the most serious Humiliation, confessing my Sins to God, acknowledging his Righteous Judgments upon me, and praying to him to have Mercy on me, through Jesus Christ; and having not tasted the least Refreshment for twelve Hours, even till the going down of the Sun, I then eat a Bisket Cake, and a Bunch of Grapes, and went to Bed, finishing the Day as I began it.

I had all this Time observ'd no Sabbath-Day; for as at first I had no Sense of Religion upon my Mind, I had after some Time omitted to distinguish the Weeks, by making a longer Notch than ordinary for the Sabbath-Day, and so did not really know what any Of the Days were; but now having cast up the Days, as above, I found I had been there a Year; so I divided it into Weeks, and

肉或烤龟肉,没有蒸煮食物的器皿,只好烤着吃;晚上吃两三个海龟蛋。

我被雨困在家里的期间,每天工作两三小时,扩大我的山洞,逐渐把它向一边开辟,一直开到山外面,打出一个旁门或者出路,通到围墙外面。于是,我就从这条路出进。但这样空荡荡地睡觉,我始终有点不放心,因为我以前总是把自己安置在一个四周不通风的地方,而现在我却睡在一个四门大开的地方,任何东西都可以来袭击我。其实,我倒看不出有什么生物值得我害怕,我在岛上所见过的最大的动物,就是一只山羊。

九月十三日。到今天我正好来到荒岛一周年。这是一个不幸的日子。我计算了一下柱子上的刻痕,发现我已上岸三百六十五天了。我把这天定为斋戒日,并举行了宗教仪式,以极端虔诚谦卑的心情跪伏在地上,向上帝忏悔我的罪行,接受他对我公正的惩罚,求他通过耶稣基督可怜我,饶恕我。从早到晚,十二个小时中我不吃不喝,直到太阳下山,我才吃了几块饼干和一串葡萄干,然后就上床睡觉。

在这以前的那段日子里,我是一向不管安息日不安息日的;起先,这是因为我心里没有一点宗教观念,隔了一阵子以后,我在那根木柱子上按日刻痕时,不再为标出一个个星期而把安息日的一道刻得长些,把平日的一道刻得短

— 124 —

set apart every seventh Day for a Sabbath; though I found at the End of my Account I had lost a Day or two in my Reckoning.

A line after this my Ink began to fail me, and so I contented my self to use it more sparingly, and to write down only the most remarkable Events of my Life, without continuing a daily Memorandum of other Things.

The rainy Season, and the dry Season, began now to appear regular to me, and I learn'd to divide them so, as to provide for them accordingly. But I bought all my Experience before I had it; and this I am going to relate, was one of the most discouraging Experiments that I made at all: I have mention'd that I had sav'd the few Ears of Barley and Rice, which I had so surprizingly found spring up, as I thought, of themselves, and believe there was about thirty Stalks of Rice, and about twenty of Barley; and now I thought it a proper Time to sow it after the Rains, the Sun being in its Southern Position going from me.

Accordingly I dug up a Piece of Ground as well as I could with my wooden Spade, and dividing it into two Parts, I sow'd my Grain; but as I was sowing, it casually occur'd to my Thoughts, That I would not sow it all at first, because I did not know when was the proper Time for it; so I sow'd about two Thirds of the Seed, leaving about a Handful of each.

It was a great Comfort to me afterwards, that I did so, for not one Grain of that I sow'd this Time came to any Thing; for the dry Months following, the Earth having had no Rain after the Seed was sown, it had no Moisture to assist its Growth, and

些,所以事实上也弄不清每一天到底是星期几;可现在我已如上述那样把日子都统计了一下,也就知道自己已来了一年,于是就把这一年分成一个个星期,把每个星期里的第七天列为安息日;不过算到结果,我发现我的计算中少了一两天。

时隔不久,我的墨水告急,不得不非常节省地用,只记下生活中一些不寻常的事件,日常细末琐事只好略过不提。

我逐渐捕捉到雨季和旱季的规律,学会划分它们,以便有备无患。掌握这个规律我是付出代价的,下面我要谈一项令人沮丧的实验。记得我在前面曾经提到过,当初我惊奇地发现,岩壁脚下竟然冒出了一些谷苗,其中大约有三十棵水稻,二十棵大麦,它们成熟之后,我把谷穗都收了起来。好了,现在雨季刚过,太阳的位置已经偏南,我想,这一定是播种的好时节。

于是我就用木锹掘了一块地,把它分成两部分,把种子种下去。在种的时候,我闪念想到:我开始时不要全部种下去吧,因为我不知道何时下种最合适,我就把种子种了三分之二,其他的留了下来以备不测。

事后我发现,我这样做真是万幸,因为我这次播下去的种子一粒也没有出。在那之后,一连几个月都是干旱;下种后由于没有雨水滋润,土中

never came up at all, till the wet Season had come again, and then it grew as if it had been but newly sown.

Finding my first Seed did not grow, which I easily imagin'd was by the Drought, I fought for a moister Piece of Ground to make another Trial in, and I dug up a Piece of Ground near my new Bower, and sow'd the rest of my Seed in February, a little before the Vernal Equinox; and this having the rainy Months of March and April to water it, sprung up very pleasantly, and yielded a very good Crop; but having Part of the Seed left only, and not daring to sow all that I had I had but a small Quantity at last, my whole Crop not amounting to above half a Peck of each kind.

But by this Experiment I was made Master of my Business, and knew exactly when the proper Season was to sow; and that I might expect two Seed Times, and two Harvests every Year.

While this Corn was growing, I made a little Discovery which was of use to me afterwards: As soon as the Rains were over, and the Weather began to settle, which was about the Month of November, I made a Visit up the Country to my Bower, where though I had not been some Months, yet I found all Things just as I left them. The Circle or double Hedge that I had made, was not only firm and entire; but the Stakes which I had cut out of some Trees that grew thereabouts, were all shot out and grown with long Branches, as much as a Willow-Tree usually shoots the first Year after lopping its Head. I could not tell what Tree to call it, that these Stakes were cut from. I was surpriz'd, and yet very well pleas'd, to see the young Trees grow; and I prun'd them, and led them up to grow as much alike as I could; and it is scarce credible how beautiful a Figure they grew into in three Years; so that though the Hedge

没有潮气,种子便没有发出芽。等到雨季重来时,种子才发了芽,就像刚种下去似的。

看到播下去的种子没能长出来,我料定是由于土地干旱的缘故,便决定另找一块湿润的土地再进行尝试。二月春分的前几天,我在新居茅舍附近刨出了一块地,把留下的种子又播撒了一部分。紧接其后就是三四月份的雨季。由于水足土润,种子不久便冒出芽来,而且长势旺盛,最终获得了好收成。但是因为种子本来剩得就不多,而且又没敢全部撒下,所以每样差不多只收了五升而已。

不过这次的经验,使我在这方面成了内行,我知道什么时候该播种,并且知道我每年能够种植两季。

在这些庄稼从播种到成熟这段时间,我有了一个十分有用的小发现。连绵的大雨渐渐过去,十一月前后,天气开始稳定,我到内地的茅屋去了一次,我已经好几个月没有去那里了,一切如旧。那道围墙不但坚固完整,连那些木桩,也都发了芽,生出很长的枝子,好像前一年修剪过的柳树似的。我也忘了从哪些树上砍下的木桩。看见这些小树都活了,我心里高兴极了。于是我开始修剪枝叶,刻意让这些树按我的要求生长。三年以后,它们居然长得体态非常美观,几乎使人难以相信。虽然我的围栅直径达二十五码,然而这些树却很快地把它

made a Circle of about twenty five Yards in Diameter, yet the Trees, for such I might now call them, soon cover'd it; and it was a compleat Shade, sufficient to lodge under all the dry Season.

This made me resolve to cut some more Stakes, and make me a Hedge like this in a Semicircle round my Wall; I mean that of my first Dwelling, which I did; and placing the Trees or Stakes in a double Row, at about eight Yards distance from my first Fence, they grew presently, and were at first a fine Cover to my Habitation, and afterward serv'd for a Defence also, as I shall observe in its Order.

I found now, That the Seasons of the Year might generally be divided, not into Summer and Winter, as in Europe; but into the Rainy Seasons, and the Dry Seasons, which were generally thus, Half February, March, Half April, Rainy, the Sun being then on, or near the Equinox.

Half April, May, June, July, Half August, Dry, the Sun being then to the North of the Line.

Half August, September, Half October, Rainy, the Sun being then come back.

Half October, November, December, January, Half February, Dry, the Sun being then to the South of the Line.

The Rainy Season sometimes held longer or shorter, as the Winds happen'd to blow; but this was the general Observation I made: After I had found by Experience, the ill Consequence of being abroad in the Rain. I took Care to furnish my self with Provisions before hand, that I might not be oblig'd to go out; and I sat within Doors as much as possible during the wet Months.

完全遮起来,使它成为一个绿叶成荫的地方,在旱季里住在底下,非常合适。

我看到这种情况,决定再砍些桩子,照样打一个半圆形的围栅,把我的第一个住所围起来。我不久就这样做了。我把那些树或者木桩排成两行,离开我的旧墙大约八码左右。它们不久也都长大起来,起初对于我的住宅只是一个良好的荫蔽,后来却成了我的防御工事。关于这些,我将在后面再叙述。

现在我知道,在这儿不像欧洲那样,一年分为夏季和冬季,而是分为雨季和旱季。一年之中的时间大致划分如下:二月后半月三月四月前半月多雨,太阳在赤道上,或靠近赤道。

四月后半月、五月、六月、七月、八月前半月干旱,太阳在赤道北面。

八月后半月、九月、十月前半月多雨,太阳回到赤道上。

十月半、十一月、十二月、一月、二月半少雨,太阳在赤道以南。

这是我观察到的大致情形,但雨季有时略有长短,这就看是不是刮风了。既然凭自己的体验,已经知道外出时淋雨的害处,我就注意事先把食物备足,以免今后发生不得不出去觅食的情形;备足了食物,到了雨季,就可以尽量不

This Time I found much Employment, (and very suitable also to the Time) for I found great Occasion of many Things which I had no way to furnish my self with, but by hard Labour and constant Application; particularly, I try'd many Ways to make my self a Basket, but all the Twigs I could get for the Purpose prov'd so brittle, that they would do nothing. It prov'd of excellent Advantage to me now, That when I was a Boy, I used to take great Delight in standing at a Basketmaker's, in the Town where my Father liv'd, to see them make their Wicker-ware; and being as Boys usually are, very officious to help, and a great Observer of the Manner how they work'd those Things, and sometimes lending a Hand, I had by this Means full Knowledge of the Methods of it, that I wanted nothing but the Materials; when it came into my Mind, That the Twigs of that Tree from whence I cut my Stakes that grew, might possibly be as tough as the Sallow's, and Willows, and Osiers in England, and I resolv'd to try.

Accordingly the next Day, I went to my Country-House, as I call'd it, and cutting some of the smaller Twigs, I found them to my Purpose as much as I could desire; whereupon I came the next Time prepar'd with a Hatchet to cut down a Quantity, which I soon found, for there was great Plenty of them; these I set up to dry within my Circle or Hedge, and when they were fit for Use, I carry'd them to my Cave, and here during the next Season, I employ'd my self in making, as well as I could, a great many Baskets, both to carry Earth, or to carry or lay up any Thing as I had occasion; and tho' I did not finish them very handsomly, yet I made them sufficiently serviceable for my Purpose; and thus afterwards I took Care never to be without them; and as my Wicker-ware decay'd, I made more, especially, I made

出去了。

我发现许多需要添置的东西都要经过艰苦劳作和不断实验才能制成。特别是我试过许多方法制作筐子,但我能找到的枝条都很脆,派不上用场。有一件事叫我占了不少便宜,小时候,我父亲住的城市里有藤器店,我特别喜欢去。我站在一旁看他们编织,像一般小男孩那样,巴巴地等他们叫我帮忙。就这样我看会了他们怎样编藤器,有时候也上前搭一下手。此刻一整套技术在手,缺的就是原料。我猛然想起我做木桩的那种树的枝条可能跟英国的柳条一样坚韧,我决定试一试。

第二天,我到我的乡间别墅(我总是这样称呼它)那边去了,砍下了一些细枝条。回来一看,发现它们非常合用,令我非常满意。所以,我第二次再去的时候,便带了一把长柄斧,打算砍下一大批下来,因为我很快便发现,这样的枝条那里很多。我将砍下的枝条都放在别墅的篱墙里晒,等它们晒到适用的程度,我再把它们运进我的山洞。所以,在下一个季节中,我主要是在洞中做筐子,而且尽量多做些,一方面是为了用来运土,同时也是为了在必要的时候,贮藏或运送别的东西。尽管这些

strong deep Baskets to place my Corn in, instead of Sacks, when I should come to have any Quantity of it.

Having master'd this Difficulty, and employ'd a World of Time about it, I bestirr'd my self to see if possible how to supply two Wants: I had no Vessels to hold any Thing that was Liquid, except two Runlets which were almost full of Rum, and some Glass-Bottles, some of the common Size, and others which were Case-Bottles square, for the holding of Waters, Spirits, etc. I had not so much as a Pot to boil any Thing, except a great Kettle, which I sav'd out of the Ship, and which was too big for such Use as I desir'd it, viz. To make Broth, and stew a Bit of Meat by it self. The Second Thing I would fain have had, was a Tobacco-Pipe; but it was impossible to me to make one, however, I found a Contrivance for that too at last.

I employ'd my self in Planting my Second Rows of Stakes or Piles and in this Wicker working all the Summer, or dry Season, when another Business took me up more Time than it could be imagin'd I could spare.

I mention'd before, That I had a great Mind to see the whole Island, and that I had travell'd up the Brook, and so on to where I built my Bower, and where I had an Opening quite to the Sea on the other Side of the Island; I now resolv'd to travel quite Cross to the Sea-Shore on that Side; so taking my Gun, a Hatchet, and my Dog, and a larger Quantity of Powder and Shot than usual, with two Bisket Cakes, and a great Bunch of Raisins in my Pouch for my Store, I began my

筐子我做得不那么美观，但很适用，足以满足我的需要。所以，后来我的身边就从来没有缺过筐子，因为这些藤器坏朽之后，我就再做一些。尤其到了后来，当我的谷子多起来时，我就做了一些又深又结实的筐子来装，而不必用布袋了。

我花了很多时间，解决了这个编筐的困难后，便激励自己，看看是否有可能满足另外两种需求。首先，我没有盛液体的器皿，仅有两只水桶，但差不多都装满了甘蔗酒，也有一些玻璃瓶子，有些形状一样，也有些是方形的，但都是用来盛水和烈酒等等。我连煮东西用的锅都没有，只有一只从船上取出来的大壶，但比我要用的大出许多，不能用它来做汤和煮肉用。其次，我想要一只烟斗，但一下子无法作出来。不过后来，我还是想出了一个办法。

整个夏季或者说旱季中，我一直忙着给旧居打树篱、编藤器。与此同时，我还干了另一件事。占去的时间比预想的要多得多。

前面说过，我一心想巡游全岛，以了解海岛概况，现在我接着上回的路程往下走。我从上次走过的小溪尽头继续向前，走到我盖茅屋的那片开阔地，从那里向下，可以走到海岛的另一头，我决定去岛那头的海边看看。于是，我带上枪、斧子和我的爱犬，还带了比平常多的火药和子弹，再

Journey; when I had pass'd the Vale where my Bower stood as above, I came within View of the Sea, to the West, and it being a very clear Day, I fairly descry'd Land, whether an Island or a Continent, I could not tell; but it lay very high, extending from the West, to the W. S. W. at a very great Distance; by my Guess it could not be less than Fifteen or Twenty Leagues off.

I could not tell what Part of the World this might be, otherwise than that I know it must be Part of America, and as I concluded by all my Observations, must be near the Spanish Dominions, and perhaps was all Inhabited by Savages, where if I should have landed, I had been in a worse Condition than I was now; and therefore I acquiesced in the Dispositions of Providence, which I began now to own, and to believe, order'd every Thing for the best; I say, I quieted my Mind with this, and left afflicting my self with Fruitless Wishes of being there.

Besides, after some Pause upon this Affair, I consider'd, that if this Land was the Spanish Coast, I should certainly, one Time or other, see some Vessel pass or re-pass one Way or other; but if not, then it was the Savage Coast between the Spanish Country and Brasils, which are indeed the worst of Savages; for they are Cannibals, or Men-eaters, and fail not to murther and devour all the humane Bodies that fall into their Hands.

With these Considerations I walk'd very leisurely forward, I found that Side of the Island where I now was, much pleasanter than mine, the open or Savanna Fields sweet, adorn'd with Flowers and Grass, and full of very fine Woods. I saw Abundance of Parrots, and fain I would have caught

带上两大块饼干和一大串葡萄干，就此启程上路了。我走过茅屋所在的山谷，从那儿朝西望，便看到了大海。一天，天气很晴朗，我可以很清楚地望见对面的陆地，也不知道是一个海岛还是一片大陆，只知道它的地势很高，从西方直向西南偏西伸展过去，伸展得很远，依我猜测，至少有十五海里到二十海里那么长。

我说不清这是什么地方，不过根据我的一点观测知识判断，大概是美洲的一部分，靠近西班牙的领地，说不定上面全住着野人；如果我在那面上岸，我的情况一定比现在要坏。现在，我更愿意听天由命，并感到这种安排是尽善尽美的。这样一想，我就感到心平气和了，我不再自寻烦恼，妄想到海对面的陆地上去了。

另外，我经过了一番思考，得出了如下的结论：如果这片陆地确实是属于西班牙领地的海岸，那么迟早会有船只经过；如果没有船只在那边的海岸来往，那儿肯定是位于西班牙领地和巴西之间的蛮荒海岸，上面住着最野蛮的土人。这些土人都是吃人的野人，任何人落入他们的手里，都会给他们吃掉。

这么思量了一番之后，我就不慌不忙地朝前踱去。我觉得，同我位于岛上另一端那住所的环境比较，面前的这片地方叫人赏心悦目多了：开阔的绿草地上野花缤纷，处处是

one, if possible to have kept it to be tame, and taught it to speak to me. I did, after some Pains taking, catch a young Parrot, for I knock'd it down with a Stick, and having' recover'd it, I brought it home; but it was some Years before I could make him speak: However, at last I taught him to call me by my Name very familiarly: But the Accident that follow'd, tho' it be a Trifle, will be very diverting in its Place.

I was exceedingly diverted with this Journey: I found in the low Grounds Hares, as I thought them to be, and Foxes, but they differ'd greatly from all the other Kinds I had met with; nor could I satisfy my self to eat them, tho' I kill'd several: But I had no Need to be ventrous; for I had no Want of Food, and of that which was very good too; especially these three Sorts, viz. Goats, Pidgeons, and Turtle or Tortoise; which, added to my Grapes, Leaden-hall Market could not have furnish'd a Table better than I, in Proportion to the Company; and tho' my Cafe was deplorable enough, yet I had great Cause for Thankfulness, that I was not driven to any Extremities for Food; but rather Plenty, even to Dainties.

I never travell'd in this Journey above two Miles outright in a Day, or thereabouts; but I took so many Turns and Returns, to see what Discoveries I could make, that I came weary enough to the Place where I resolv'd to sit down for all Night; and then I either repos'd my self in a Tree, or surrounded my self with a Row of Stakes set upright in the Ground, either from one Tree to another, or so as no wild Creature could come at me, without Waking me.

青翠欲滴的树丛。我还看见了许多鹦鹉,要是有可能,真想捉一只来,把它养得乖乖的,再教它同我说说话。花了一番工夫,我总算捉到了一只小鹦鹉,这是我用一根树枝把它敲下来的;我等它睁开眼来以后,把它带回了家里,但是教会它说话却是几年以后的事情了。尽管如此,我到底还是教会了它,让它亲亲热热地叫我的名字。这件事后来还引起点意外,虽说是小事一桩,其本身倒还颇为有趣呢。

这趟旅行玩得很愉快。我在低地找到兔子和狐狸(我认为是这两种动物)。它们跟我以前见过的有很大的不同。我打了几只,却不想吃,我无须冒险,因为食品不缺,而且都颇上档次,特别是这三种:山羊、鸽子、海龟或陆龟,再佐以葡萄,雷登赫尔市场也摆不出如此丰盛的筵席。虽然我境况凄凉,我仍旧有理由感谢上苍,没有让我为填饱肚子而疲于奔命。我有的是吃的,而且不乏美味珍馐。

在这次旅行中,我每天的行程从来不超过两英里,因为我总是迂回前进,东绕西转,看能否有什么新的发现,所以,在走到一个地方,打算坐下来过夜时,我总是一身疲惫。我要么睡到树上去,要么在我的四周插一圈木桩,要么用木桩将两棵树连在一起,要么采取别的办法。总之,要是有野兽袭来,我肯定会被惊

As soon as I came to the Sea Shore, I was surpriz'd to see that I had taken up my Lot on the worst Side of the Island; for here indeed the Shore was cover'd with innumerable Turtles, whereas on the other Side I had found but three in a Year and half. Here was also an infinite Number of Fowls, of many Kinds, some which I had seen, and some which I had not seen of before, and many of them very good Meat; but such as I knew not the Names of, except those call'd Penguins.

I could have shot as many as I pleas'd, but was very sparing of my Powder and Shot; and therefore had more Mind to kill a she Goat, if I could, which I could better feed on; and though there were many Goats here more than on my Side the Island, yet it was with much more Difficulty that I could come near them, the Country being flat and even, and they saw me much sooner than when I was on the Hill.

I confess this Side of the Country was much pleasanter than mine, but yet I had not the least Inclination to remove; for as I was fix'd in my Habitation, it became natural to me, and I seem'd all the while I was here, to be as it were upon a Journey, and from Home: However, I travell'd along the Shore of the Sea, towards the East, I suppose about twelve Miles; and the setting up a great Pole upon the Shore for a Mark, I concluded I would go Home again; and that the next Journey I took should be on the other Side of the Island, East from my Dwelling, and so round till I came to my Post again: Of which in its Place.

I took another Way to come back than that I went, thinking I could easily keep all the Island so

当我走到海边时，更加意外地发现，我居住的岛那边可以算是全岛最差的地方了。在这边的海滩上，海龟多得不计其数，可在我那边，一年半的时间里，我只碰到过三只。此外，这里还有无数的飞禽，种类繁多，有些我以前见过，有些我从未见过。我知道这其中有不少飞禽的肉都很好吃。不过这些海鸟中，除了企鹅，其他的鸟类我都叫不上名字。

只要我愿意我可以打到更多的飞禽，但我对自己的弹药很节约。这时我很想打到一只大山羊，这样我就可以美美地吃上一顿。这里的山羊虽比我原来所在的那边多得多，但我要想走近它们，却更加困难，因为这里地势平坦宽阔，它们比在山上更容易看到我。

我承认这一带地方比我那边可爱得多，但我还是无意搬家，因为我在那边已经住定了，已经习惯了；我在这边的期间，总觉得是在旅行，不是在家里。我沿着海边向东走，据我估计大约走了十二英里。于是我在海岸上立了一根柱子，作为记号，决定暂时回家，并决定下次出发时采取相反的方向，从我的住所沿着海岸向东走，兜上一个圈子，仍旧走到我所立的柱子为止。这是后话。

回家时我走了另一条路，我以为，只要我注意全岛的地

much in my View, that I could not miss finding my first Dwelling by viewing the Country; but I found my self mistaken; for being come about two or three Miles, I found my self descended into a very large Valley; but so surrounded with Hills, and those Hills cover'd with Wood, that I could not see which was my Way by any Direction but that of the Sun, nor even then, unless I knew very well the Position of the Sun at that Time of the Day.

It happen'd to my farther Misfortune, That the Weather prov'd hazey for three or four Days, while was in this Valley; and not being able to see the Sun, I wander'd about very uncomfortably, and at last was oblig'd to find out the Sea Side, look for my Post, and come back the same Way I went; and then by easy Journies I turn'd Homeward, the Weather being exceeding hot, and my Gun, Ammunition, Hatchet, and other Things very heavy.

In this Journey my Dog surpriz'd a young Kid, and seiz'd upon it, and I running in to take hold of it, caught it, and sav'd it alive from the Dog: I had a great Mind to bring it Home if I could; for I had often been musing, Whether it might not be possible to get a Kid or two, and so raise a Breed of tame Goats, which might supply me when my Powder and Shot should be all spent.

I made a Collar to this little Creature, and with a String which I made of some Rope-Yarn, which I always carry'd about me, I led him along, tho' with some Difficulty, till I came to my Bower, and there I enclos'd him, and left him; for I was very impatient to be at Home, from whence I had been absent above a Month.

I cannot express what a Satisfaction it was to me, to come into my old Hutch, and lye down in my Hamock-Bed: This little wandring Journey, without settled Place of Abode, had been so un-

势就不会迷路以致于找不到我在海边的居所。但我想错了。走了两三英里后,我发现自己进入了一个大山谷,四周群山环绕,山上丛林密布,除非看太阳才能辩出东西南北,可是此刻太阳也无助于辩别方向,因为我不知道这时是上午、中午还是下午。

更为倒霉的是,我进入那山谷后的三四天里,偏偏碰上云雾迷漫的天气,连太阳也看不见;我心里很不安地胡乱走着,最后只得再摸到海边,找到那根柱子,然后循原路回去;这时天气酷热,我的枪支、弹药、斧子等等东西都很重,所以我就不慌不忙地慢慢往回走。

这次外出期间,我的狗发现了一只小山羊,便冲过去咬它;我连忙奔上前去,捉住了山羊,把它从狗嘴里救了下来,保住了它的性命。我决心带它回家,因为我时常考虑捉一两只小山羊驯养,繁殖成群,这样我的弹药用尽后,我仍能吃上羊肉。

我给小山羊做了一个项圈,用随身时刻带着的股线搓成一根绳牵它走,费了不少力气把它带到别墅,关在里面就不管了,我迫不及待地想回家,我已在外面游荡了一个多月。

我不知道怎样描述回到老宅,躺在吊床上的那份惬意。这趟小小的游历风餐露宿、居无定所,别扭极了,相比

— 133 —

pleasant to me, that my own House, as I call'd it to my self, was a perfect Settlement to me, compar'd to that; and it rendred every Thing about me so comfortable, that I resolv'd I would never go a great Way from it again, while it should be my Lot to stay on the Island.

I repos'd my self here a Week, to rest and regale my self after my long Journey; during which, most of the Time was taken up in the weighty Affair of making a Cage for my Poll, who began now to be a meer Domestick, and to be mighty well acquainted with me. Then I began to think of the poor Kid, which I had penn'd in within my little Circle, and resolv'd to go and fetch it Home, or give it some Food; accordingly I went, and found it where I left it; for indeed it could not get out, but almost starv'd for want of Food: I went and cut Bows of Trees, and Branches of such Shrubs as I could find, and threw it over, and having fed it, I ty'd it as I did before, to lead it away; but it was so tame with being hungry, that I had no need to have ty'd it; for it follow'd me like a Dog; and as I continually fed it, the Creature became so loving, so gentle, and so fond, that it became from that Time one of my Domesticks also, and would never leave me afterwards.

The rainy Season of the Autumnal Equinox was now come, and I kept the 30th of Sept. in the same solemn Manner as before, being the Anniversary of my Landing on the Island, having now been there two Years, and no more Prospect of being deliver'd, than the first Day I came

之下,我的房子简直是一个尽善尽美的住处,舒适而温馨。我家里的一切都使我生活得十分舒服满意。我下定决心,如果我命中注定要呆在这个岛上,我以后再也不离家出门了。

我在家里休息了一个星期,为的是长期旅行之后使自己放松一下。这期间大部分时间,我都在做一件重要的事情,即为我的鹦鹉波儿做一只笼子。它现在已经变得非常驯服,而且同我非常熟悉。这时,我才想起了我那可怜的小山羊,它还被关在栏里。我决定把它牵回来,或给它吃些东西。于是,我便到那边去了,发现它还在那里。其实,它是难以从那逃出来的,不过,因为没有草吃,它都快要饿死了。我去砍来一些树枝和灌木之类的枝条,扔给了它。让它吃完之后,我又像上次那样,将它拴起,往回牵。由于饥饿的缘故,它非常温顺。我真的没有必要拴它,因为它像一只狗似的,老老实实地跟在我的身后。由于我的不断喂养,这个小东西后来竟变得那么可爱,那么温顺,那么讨人喜欢。从那时起,它便成了我的家畜之一,而且,从此以后竟不肯离开我。

秋分时节,雨季又开始了。在九月三十日登岛纪念日这天,我还是像去年一样,严肃而虔诚地守了斋戒日。我来这孤岛已整整两年了,而获救的希望却和两年前上岛

there. I spent the whole Day in humble and thankful Acknowledgments of the many wonderful Mercies which my Solitary Condition was attended with, and without which it might have been infinitely more miserable. I gave humble and hearty Thanks that God had been pleas'd to discover to me, even that it was possible I might be more happy in this Solitary Condition, than I should have been in a Liberty of Society, and in all the Pleasures of the World. That he could fully make up to me, the Deficiencies of my Solitary State, and the want of Humane Society by his Presence, and the Communications of his Grace to my Soul, supporting, comforting, and encouraging me to depend upon his Providence here, and hope for his Eternal Presence hereafter.

It was now that I began sensibly to feel how much more happy this Life I now led was, with all its miserable Circumstances, than the wicked, cursed, abominable Life I led all the past Part of my Days; and now I chang'd both my Sorrows and my Joys; my very Desires alter'd, my Affections chang'd their Gusts, land my Delights were perfectly new, from what they were at my first Coming, or indeed for the two Years past.

Before, as I walk'd about, either on, my Hunting, or for viewing the Country, the Anguish of my Soul at my Condition, would break out upon me on a sudden, and my very Heart would die within me, to think of the Woods, the Mountains, the Desarts I was in; and how I was a Prisoner lock'd up with the Eternal Bars and Bolts of the Ocean, in an uninhabited Wilderness, without Redemption: In the midst of the greatest Composures of my Mind, this would break out upon me like a Storm, and make me wring my Hands, and weep like a Child: Sometimes it would take me in the middle of my Work, and I would immediately

时一样渺茫。整整一天,我怀着恭顺感恩的心情追念上帝布施于我的种种恩惠,如果没有这些,我孤独的生活就会更加凄惨悲苦。我谦卑地、衷心地感谢上帝,正是上帝使我明白,我目前这种孤独寂寞的生活要比人世间自由快乐的生活更为幸福,因为,现在上帝来到了我的身边,与我同在,与我的心灵交流沟通,支持我、安慰我、鼓励我去依赖天命,追随天意,这完全弥补了我孤寂生活的种种缺陷,消除了远离人群与世隔绝的痛苦。

我现在开始充分地感觉到,我现在所过的生活,尽管非常不幸,比起我过去那种罪恶的、可诅咒的、可憎的生活来,还是幸福得多。我现在完全改变了对于忧愁和欢乐的看法;我的愿望已经与旧时大不相同,我的性情已经完全发生变化,跟我初来的时候相比,甚至跟过去两年相比,我的爱好已经转移到新的方向。

过去,当我到各处打猎,或勘查岛上环境时,一想到自己的处境,我的灵魂就会痛苦不堪;想到自己被困在这些树林、山谷和沙滩中间,被困在渺无人烟的荒野里,我觉得自己就像是个囚犯,那茫茫的大海就是我牢狱的铁栅栏,并且永无出狱之日。一想到这些,我总是忧心如焚。即使在我心境最宁静的时候,这种念头也会像暴风雨一样突然向我袭来,使我扭扯双手,像小孩

sit down and sigh, and look upon the Ground for an Hour or -two together; and this was still worse to me; for if I could burst out into Tears, or vent my self by Words, it would go off, and the Grief having exhausted it self would abate.

But now I began to exercise my self with new Thoughts; I daily read the Word of God, and apply'd all the Comforts of it to my present State: One Morning being very sad, I open'd the Bible upon these Words, I will never, never leave thee, nor forsake thee; immediately it occurr'd, That these Words were to me, Why else should they be directed in such a Manner, just at the Moment when I was mourning over my Condition, as one forsaken of God and Man? Well then, said I, if God does not forsake me, of what ill Consequence can it be, or what matters it, though the World should all forsake me, seeing on the other Hand, if I had all the World, and should lose the Favour and Blessing of God, there wou'd be no Comparison in the Loss.

From this Moment I began to conclude in my Mind, That it was possible for me to be more happy in this forsaken Solitary Condition, than it was probable I should ever have been in any other Particular State in the World; and with this Thought I was going to give Thanks to God for bringing me to this Place.

I know not what it was, but something shock'd my Mind at that Thought, and I durst not speak the Words: How canst thou be such a Hypocrite, (said I, even audibly) to pretend to be thankful for a Condition, which however thou may'st en-

子一样号啕痛哭。有时在劳动中,这种念头也会突然袭来,我就会立刻坐下来,长吁短叹,两眼死盯着地面,一两个小时一动也不动,这就更令人痛苦了。因为,假如我能哭出来,或者用语言发泄出来,苦恼就会过去,悲哀发泄出来后,心情也会好一些。

但现在,我开始以新的思想来锻炼自己,每天读上帝的书,把书中的话结合我目前的处境,从而获得慰藉。有一天早上,我颇为抑郁不安,翻开《圣经》时,一眼就见到了这样一句话:"我必不撇下你,也不丢弃你。"我马上想到,这完全是对我而发的,要不然,为什么恰恰在我为自己的处境悲伤时,在我感到自己被上帝、被世人抛弃时,让我读到这句话呢?"好吧,"我说道,"既然上帝不抛弃我,那么即使世人抛弃我,又有什么坏处,又有什么关系? 反过来说,就算我重归世人中间,却丧失了上帝的眷顾和祝福,这个损失之大才是无可比拟的。"

从这一刻起,我开始思忖,我现在这种孤寂、被抛弃的现状比我经历过的世上其他特殊状况幸福得多。想到这儿,我决定向上帝谢恩,感谢他把我带到这个地方。

不知怎地,突然间我为自己有这种想法大感吃惊,半天不敢出声。"你怎么变得如此虚伪,"我差点大声叫起来,"假装对这种处境表示感谢,在勉

deavour to be contented with, thou would'st rather pray heartily to be deliver'd from; so I stopp'd there: But though I could not say, I thank'd God for being there; yet I sincerely gave Thanks to God for opening my Eyes, by whatever afflicting Providences, to see the former Condition of my Life, and to mourn for my Wickedness, and repent. I never open'd the Bible, or shut it, but my very Soul within me, bless'd God for directing my Friend in England, without any Order of mine, to pack it up among my Goods; and for assisting me afterwards to save it out of the Wreck of the Ship.

Thus, and in this Disposition of Mind, I began my third Year: and tho' I have not given the Reader the Trouble of so particular Account of my Works this Year as the first; yet in General it may be observ'd, That I was very seldom idle; but having regularly divided my Time, according to the several daily Employments that were before me, such as, First, My Duty to God, and the Reading the Scriptures, which I constantly set apart some Time for thrice every Day. Secondly, The going Abroad with my Gun for Food, which generally took me up three Hours in every Morning, when it did not Rain. Thirdly, The ordering, curing, preserving, and cooking what I had kill'd or catch'd for my Supply; these took up great Part of the Day; also it is to be considered that the middle of the Day when the Sun was in the Zenith, the Violence of the Heat was too great to stir out; so that about four Hours in the Evening was all the Time I could be suppos'd to work in; with this Exception, That sometimes I chang'd my Hours of Hunting and Working, and went to work in the Morning, and Abroad with my Gun in the Afternoon.

为其难地让自己过得满意的同时，又巴不得上帝开恩让自己脱困？"于是，我便停止了说话。尽管我不能说我感谢上帝把我带到了这里，但我还是要诚心地感谢上帝，他为了使我睁开眼睛看清我的生活方式，给了我种种命运的磨难，让我为我的罪恶而悲痛和忏悔。我感激上帝让我的英国朋友，没有经过我的嘱咐，便把《圣经》放在我的货物中；感激上帝后来又帮助我把《圣经》从破船上救出来。

我怀着这样的心情，跨入了第三个年头。虽然没有像头一年那样，把这一年当中所做的事情一件一件地都写出来，劳神诸位去读，但总的来说，我几乎从未有过偷懒的时候。我总是把每天的时间划分得很有规律，来做我每天应做的事情。比如：首先，我每天都花出一定的时间，读一次《圣经》，以尽我对上帝的天职；其次，如果不下雨，我就持枪出门找吃的，这通常要花掉我上午三个小时；再次，将我所打到或捉到的东西加以整理、晒制、收藏、或者烤制，作为我的储存。这些事情往往要消耗掉我一天的大部分时间。此外，还得考虑除去中午的时间，因为正午时分，太阳正当头顶，这时的天气异常炎热，根本无法出门。因此，每天真正能够用于工作的时间，只有傍晚的四个小时。我有时还把巡猎和工作的时间互换一下，下午外出猎食。

To this short Time allow'd for Labour, I desire may be added the exceeding Laboriousness of my Work; the many Hours which for want of Tools, want of Help, and want of Skill, every Thing I did, took up out of my Time: For Example, I was full two and forty Days making me a Board for a long Shelf, which I wanted in my Cave; whereas two Sawyers with their Tools, and a Saw-Pit, would have cut six of them out of the same Tree in half a Day.

My Case was this, It was to be a large Tree, which was to be cut down, because my Board was to be a broad one. This Tree I was three Days a cutting down, and two more cutting off the Bows, and reducing it to a Log, or Piece of Timber. With inexpressible hacking and hewing I reduc'd both the Sides of it into Chips, till it begun to be light enough to move; then I turn'd it, and made one Side of it smooth, and flat, as a Board from End to End; then turning that Side downward, cut the other Side, till I brought the plank to be about three Inches thick, and smooth on both Sides. Any One may judge the Labour of my Hands in such a Piece of Work; but Labour and Patience carry'd me through that and many other Things: I only observe this in Particular, to shew, The Reason why so much of my Time went away with so little Work, viz. That what might be a little to be done with Help and Tools, was a vast Labour, and requir'd a prodigious Time to do alone, and by hand.

But notwithstanding this, with Patience and Labour I went through many Things; and indeed every Thing that my Circumstances made necessary to me to do, as will appear by what follows.

每天可用于工作的时间是那么的短暂,可是必须完成的工作却异常艰苦。下面就给读者说说工作的艰苦性吧。这里每一样工作,都会因为缺乏工具、助手和经验而花费掉大量的时间。譬如,我整整花了四十二天才做了一块用作洞内架子的长板,其实如果有两个人用两把锯子,半天就可以从一棵树上弄下六块来。

而我必须先伐一棵很大的树,由于我所要的板子很宽,这用去三天的工作时间,然后费两天的时间把枝子砍下来,砍成一块木料,然后经过不计其数的砍斫,把两面砍成碎片,以便我一个人能够拿得动,然后把它平放在地面,把它的一面从头至尾削得又光又平,像一块板子一样。然后把这一面翻下去,削那一面,一直把它削成三英寸多厚,两面光滑为止。任何人都可以判断得出,做这样一种工作,我的两手要付出多少劳力;但劳力和耐心终于使我完成了这件工作以及其他的工作。我把这件事特别提出来,就是要说明我为什么在这样少的工作中花费了这么多的时间;也就是要说明,一件工作,如果有助手和工具,本来是一件轻而易举的事情,若是单靠一个人空手去做,便要花很大的劳力和很多的时间。

尽管如此,靠了耐心和劳动,我完成了大量的工作。下面,我将叙述我如何为生活环境所迫,完成了许多必不可少

I was now, in the Months of November and December, expecting my Crop of Barley and Rice. The Ground I had manur'd or dug up for them was not great; for as I observ'd, my Seed of each was not above the Quantity of half a Peck; for I had lost one whole Crop by sowing in the dry Season; but now my Crop promis'd very well, when on a sudden I found I was in Danger of losing it all again by Enemies of several Sorts, which it was scarce possible to keep from it; as First, The Goats, and wild Creatures which I call'd Hares who tasting the Sweetness of the Blade, lay in it Night and Day, as soon as it came up, and eat it so close, that it could get no Time to shoot up into Stalk.

This I saw no Remedy for, but by making an Enclosure about it with a Hedge, which I did with a great deal of Toil; and the more, because it requir'd Speed. However, as my Arable Land was but small, suited to my Crop, I got it totally well fenc'd, in about three Weeks Time; and shooting some of the Creatures in the Day Time, I set my Dog to guard it in the Night, tying him up to a Stake at the Gate, where he would stand and bark all Night long; so in a little Time the Enemies forsook the Place, and the Corn grew very strong, and well, and began to ripen apace.

But as the Beasts ruined me before, while my Corn was in the Blade; so the Birds were as likely to ruin me now, when it was in the Ear; for going along by the Place to see how it throve, I saw my little Crop surrounded with Fowls of I know not how many Sorts, who stood as it were watching till I should be gone: I immediately let fly among

的工作。

现在正是十一、十二月之间,即将收获大麦和稻子。我耕种和施肥的面积不大,因为,上面说过,我所有的种子每样只不过半斗,而又因第一次在旱季播种,把播下去的种子完全毁了。但这一次却丰收在望。然而,我突然发现,庄稼受到好几种敌人的威胁,而且这些敌人简直难以对付,全部收获又将丧失殆尽。首先,就是山羊和像野兔似的野物,它们尝到了禾苗的甜味后,等禾苗一长出来,就昼夜伏在田里,把长出地面的禾苗吃光,禾苗根本就无法长出茎秆来。

一看这情形,我知道只有一个解决办法,那就是把我这块田围起来。于是我又辛辛苦苦地干了起来,因为我不仅要把田围起来,而且得早日完工。幸好我种的庄稼不多,要圈起来的面积也很小,花了大概三个星期的时间就把这片地全都圈好了;我白天里一看见这些动物就开枪,晚上就把狗拴在那门口的一根木桩上,让它一整夜守在那里叫啊叫的;结果没过多久,我那些对头就不来了,于是我的庄稼长得苗壮起来,很快便开始成熟了。

但是,就像以前那些野兽在庄稼刚出叶的时候骚扰我一样,庄稼抽穗时那些鸟类又来侵袭我了。一次我去地里看我的庄稼长得怎么样了,就看见一大群飞禽围着我那点可怜的庄稼,我不知道它们有

them (for I always had my Gun with me) I had no sooner shot, but there rose up a little Cloud of Fowls, which I had not seen at all, from among the Corn it self.

This touch'd me sensibly, for I foresaw, that in a few Days they would devour all my Hopes, that I should be starv'd, and never be able to raise a Crop at all, and what to do I could not tell: However I resolv'd not to loose my Corn, if possible, tho' I should watch it Night and Day. In the first Place, I went among it to see what Damage was already done, and found they had spoil'd a good deal of it, but that as it was yet too Green for them, the Loss was not so great, but that the Remainder was like to be a good Crop if it could be sav'd.

I staid by it to load my Gun, and then coming away I could easily see the Thieves sitting upon all the Trees about me, as if they only waited till I was gone away, and the Event proved it to be so; for as I walk'd off as if I was gone, I was no sooner out of their sight, but they dropt down one by one into the Corn again. I was so provok'd that I could not have Patience to stay till more came on, knowing that every Grain that they eat now, was, as it might be said, a Peck-loaf to me in the Consequence; but coming up to the Hedge, I fir'd again, and kill'd three of them. This was what I wish'd for; so I took them up, and serv'd them as we serve notorious Thieves in England, (viz.) Hang'd them in Chains for a Terror to others; it is impossible to imagine almost, that this should have such an Effect, as it had; for the Fowls wou'd not only not come at the Corn, but in short they forsook all that Part of the Island, and I could never see a Bird near the Place as long as my Scare-Crows hung there.

多少种,它们都站在那里,看着我,等我离开。我马上朝它们放了一枪(我总是随身带枪),枪一响,又从庄稼地里惊起一大群,而我刚才却根本没发现它们。

我大吃一惊,因为我预见到几天之内,这些鸟就会吃光我的全部希望,我会挨饿,而且不可能再有庄稼种。我不知道如何是好,于是便决定日夜守护,如果可能,一定要保全庄稼。首先我到地里查看一下损坏情况,发现它们已经糟踏了不少,但因为庄稼还发青,不太好吃,所以损失不算大,如果好好保护其余的部分,还会有好收成。

我站在田边,把我的枪装好,然后,当我走开时,我一眼便看见,蹲在我周围树上的这些"盗贼"仿佛都在等我走开;事实证明,确实是这样。因为,当我开始往回走,假装离开时,它们一看见我走得不见了,一个个又下到了庄稼地里。这使我大为恼火,忍无可忍,我等不得它们都下来后再扑过去,因为我明白,它们现在所吃的每一粒,可以说都是我将来的"度命粮"。我立即折回篱笆旁边,又放了一枪,打死了其中的三只。这总算合了我的心愿;我把它们拾了起来,采用了英国惩治恶贼的办法,也就是说,用一根链子将它们挂起来,以吓唬它们的同类。没承想这办法居然非常灵验,从此以后,那些鸟不但不再到庄稼地里来,就连岛的

This I was very glad of, you may be sure, and about the latter end of December, which was our second Harvest of the Year, I reap'd my Crop.

I was sadly put to it for a Scythe or a Sicle to cut it down, and all I could do was to make one as well as I could out of one of the Broad Swords or Cutlasses, which I sav'd among the Arms out of the Ship. However, as my first Crop was but small I had no great Difficulty to cut it down; in short, I reap'd it my Way, for I cut nothing off but the Ears, and carry'd it away in a great Basket which I had made, and so rubb'd it out with my Hands; and at the End of all my Harvesting, I found that out of my half Peck of Seed, I had near two Bushels of Rice, and above two Bushels and half of Barley, that is to say, by my Guess, for I had no Measure at that time.

However, this was a great Encouragement to me, and I foresaw that in time, it wou'd please God to supply me with Bread: And yet here I was perplex'd again, for I neither knew how to grind or make Meal of my Corn, or indeed how to clean it and part it; nor if made into Meal, how to make Bread of it, and if how to make it, yet I knew not how to bake it; these things being added to my Desire of having a good Quantity for Store, and to secure a constant Supply, I resolv'd not to taste any of this Crop but to preserve it all for Seed against the next Season, and in the mean time to employ all my Study and Hours of Working to accomplish this great Work of Providing my self with Corn and Bread.

It might be truly said, that now I work'd for

这一边都不大来了。在示众的死鸟吊挂的期间,附近竟然连一只鸟也看不到。

这甭提让我有多高兴了。就这样转眼之间到了十二月底,这是第二茬庄稼收获的季节,我终于收割了我的庄稼。

说到收割庄稼,就又出现了令我为难的问题,没有收割用的镰刀。这该怎么办呢?无奈之中,只好将我从船上武器堆中找来的一把腰刀改作镰刀。第一次的收成分量很少,所以割起来没有多大困难。并且我的割法也与众不同,因为我只是把穗子割下来,用我自己做的筐子搬走,再用双手把它们搓下来。收获完毕之后,我发现那半斗种子差不多打了两斛稻谷,两斛半麦;这当然是根据我个人的猜测,因为当时我手边没有量器。

这对于我是一个很大的鼓励,我已经预见到,早晚有一天我会有面包吃。可是,现在我又感到为难了。因为我既不知道怎样把谷粒磨成粉,甚至根本不知道怎样脱谷,怎样筛去秕糠;即使能把谷粒磨成粉,我也不知道怎样把粉做成面包;即使做成了面包,也不知怎样烤面包。另外,我想多积一点粮食,以保证不断供应。为此,我决定不吃这次收获的谷物,而是全部留起来做种子,待下一季再播种。同时,我决定用全部时间全力研究磨制面粉和烤制面包这一艰巨的工作。

人们常说"为面包而工

my Bread; 'tis a little wonderful, and what I believe few People have thought much upon, (viz.) the strange multitude of little Things necessary in the Providing, Producing, Curing, Dressing, Making and Finishing this one Article of Bread.

I that was reduced to a meer State of Nature, found this to my daily Discouragement, and was made more and more sensible of it every Hour, even after I had got the first Handful of Seed-Corn, which, as I have said, came up unexpectedly, and indeed to a surprize.

First, I had no Plow to turn up the Earth, no Spade or Shovel to dig it. Well, this I conquer'd, by making a wooden Spade, as I observ'd before; but this did my Work in but a wooden manner, and tho' it cost me a great many Days to make it, yet for want of Iron it not only wore out the sooner, but made my Work the harder, and made it be perform'd much worse.

However this I bore with, and was content to work it out with Patience, and bear with the badness of the Performance. When the Corn was sow'd, I had no Harrow, but was forced to go over it my self and drag a great heavy Bough of a Tree over it, to Scratch it, as it may be call'd, rather than Rake or Harrow it.

When it was growing and grown, I have observ'd already, how many things I wanted, to Fence it, Secure it, Mow or Reap it, Cure and

作"，其意思是"为生存而工作"，而现在，我可以说是真的为"面包"而工作了。想来也真有点叫人惊异，要做成区区一个面包，竟还有准备种子、种出庄稼、翻晒谷物、加工粮食和最后制作这一连串必不可少的繁琐程序，说来也真是奇怪；但我相信，很少有人会在这件事上多费心思。

我已落到面对洪荒的境地，这情况每天纠缠着我，事实上，甚至在我弄到那第一把作为种子的谷粒之后——前面我已说过，这完全是意外收获，当时着实叫我惊诧了一阵——我每天想着这事就泄气，而且随着每个小时的过去，我越来越感受到这一点。

第一，我没有犁来翻地，没有锄头或铲子来掘地。前面已经说过，我做了一把木头铲子，初步克服了这个困难，可是这把铲子使用起来很不得力；虽然我花了不少日子才把它做出来，但因为没有铁器，不仅坏得快，而且使我的工作更加困难，使工作效率更加恶劣。

但我总算还凑合着使用这把铲子，耐着性子慢慢干，姑且容忍着翻得乱七八糟的地。下完种后，我没有耙子，只得拖着一根很重的树枝在地里走来走去，与其说这是耙地，还不如说是给土地挠挠痒。

庄稼生长、成熟的时候，我提过我需要多少东西来做围栏，使其免遭破坏；需要收

Carry it Home, Thrash, Part it from the Chaff, and Save it. Then I wanted a Mill to Grind it, Sieves to Dress it, Yeast and Salt to make it into Bread, and an Oven to bake it, and yet all these things I did without, as shall be observ'd; and yet the Corn was an inestimable Comfort and Advantage to me too. All this, as I said, made every thing laborious and tedious to me, but that there was no help for; neither was my time so much Loss to me, because as I had divided it, a certain Part of it was every Day appointed to these Works; and as I resolv'd to use none of the Corn for Bread till I had a greater Quantity by me, I had the next six Months to apply my self wholly by Labour and Invention to furnish my self with Utensils proper for the performing all the Operations necessary for the making the Corn (when I had it) fit for my use.

But first, I was to prepare more Land, for I had now Seed enough to sow above an Acre of Ground. Before I did this, I had a Week's-work at least to make me a Spade, which when it was done was but a sorry one indeed, and very heavy, and requir'd double Labour to work with it; however I went thro' that, and sow'd my Seed in two large flat Pieces of Ground, as near my House as I could find them to my Mind, and fenc'd them in with a good Hedge, the Stakes of which were all cut of that Wood which I had set before, and knew it would grow, so that in one Year's time I knew I should have a Quick or Living-Hedge, that would want but little Repair. This Work was not so little as to take me up less than three Months, because great Part of that time was of the wet Season, when I could not go abroad.

Within Doors, that is, when it rained, and I could not go out, I found Employment on the fol-

割、加工、运输、打谷、筛选、分离秕糠、储藏粮食的工具和器皿。我还需要磨坊磨粉，筛子筛选，酵母和盐把面粉做成面包，烤炉烘烤面包。正如我所说的，这些东西我都没有。尽管如此，粮食对我来说可谓无价之宝，我能从中得到巨大的安慰。尽管我提到的这一切使我每样事情都艰辛和烦闷，但却没有办法，而我的时间也没有浪费太多。因为我已经把我的时间分成几个部分，每天用一定的时间去从事这些工作，我既然已下定决心等到下季我的粮食足够多时再做面包，我就可以把后来这六个月的时间投入到制造加工粮食所需的各种器皿中。

当然，我首先得准备更多的耕地，因为我现在的种子足够种一英亩以上。在开始这项工作之前，我先花了至少一个星期的工夫做一把铲子，但做得很难看，又很笨重，用它去干活得花双倍的力气。尽管如此，我总算攻克了这一关，并且把种子播进了两块平整的大田里。这两块我很满意，因为它们离我的住处再近不过了。我在这两块地的四周筑起了牢固的篱墙，我知道，只消一年时间，这些篱墙就会长成葱绿的屏障，而且几乎不需要整修。这项工作花掉了我三个月的时间，因为这期间，大部分时间是雨季，我没法出门。

下雨不能出门的时候，我也找些事情做。我一边做事，

lowing Occasions; always observing, that all the while I was at work I diverted my self with talking to my Parrot, and teaching him to Speak, and I quickly learn'd him to know his own Name, and at last to speak it out pretty loud P O L, which was the first Word I ever heard spoken in the Island by any Mouth but my own. This therefore was not my Work, but an assistant to my Work, for now, as I said, I had a great Employment upon my Hands, as follows, (viz.) I had long study'd by some Means or other, to make my self some Earthen Vessels, which indeed I wanted sorely, but knew not where to come at them: However, considering the Heat of the Climate, I did not doubt but if I could find out any such Clay, I might botch up some such Pot, as might, being dry'd in the Sun, be hard enough, and strong enough to bear handling, and to hold any Thing that was dry, and requir'd to be kept so; and as this was necessary in the preparing Corn, Meal, etc. which was the Thing I was upon, I resolv'd to make some as large as I could, and fit only to stand like Jarrs to hold what should be put into them.

It would make the Reader pity me, or rather laugh at me, to tell how many awkward ways I took to raise this Paste, what odd mishapen ugly things I made, how many of them fell in, and how many fell out, the Clay not being stiff enough to bear its own Weight; how many crack'd by the over violent Heat of the Sun, being set out too hastily; and how many fell in pieces with only removing, as well before as after they were dry'd; and in a word, how after having labour'd hard to find the Clay, to dig it, to temper it, to bring it home and work it; I could not make above two large earthern ugly things, I cannot call them Jarrs, in about two Months Labour.

一边同我的鹦鹉说话,一遍一遍地教它学舌,权当消遣。我很快就教会它说出自己的名字,到后来它能清楚响亮地叫自己为"波儿"。这可是自我上岛以后从别的嘴里听到的第一句话呢。教鹦鹉学舌当然不是我的工作,不过是在忙碌的工作中调剂精神罢了。目前我正在着手做一件很重要的工作。早就想设法制作一些陶器,就像前面所说,我急需这类东西,可不知道该怎么做。不过我敢肯定,这里炎热的气候,只要能找到合适的陶土,就一定能做出陶钵陶罐,似火的阳光能把陶器晒得坚挺结实,经久耐用,满足我想隔潮保存干东西的需要。这对于我当前正在进行的制造粮食和面粉的工作是必要的,因此我决定把它们尽力做大一些,摆在地上,像瓮一样,可以在里面放东西。

说起来真是又可怜又可笑,我也不知道用了多少笨拙的办法去调合陶泥,做出了多少奇形怪状的丑陋的家伙;有多少因为陶土太软,吃不住本身的重量而陷了进去,凸了出来;有多少因为晒得太早了,太阳的热力太猛而爆裂了;有多少在晒干前后一挪动就碎了。一句话,我费了很大的力气去找陶土,找到后把土挖出来,调合好,运回家,再做成泥瓮。结果,我工作了差不多两个月的时间,才做成两只大瓦罐,样子非常难看,简直无法把它们叫作缸。

However, as the Sun bak'd these Two, very dry and hard, I lifted them very gently up, and set them down again in two great Wicker-Baskets which I had made on purpose for them, that they might not break, and as between the Pot and the Basket there was a little room to spare, I stuff'd it full of the Rice and Barley Straw, and these two Pots being to stand always dry, I thought would hold my dry Corn, and perhaps the Meal, when the Corn was bruised.

Tho' I miscarried so much in my Design for large Pots, yet I made several smaller things with better Success, such as little round Pots, flat Dishes, Pitchers and Pipkins, and any things my Hand turn'd to, and the Heat of the Sun bak'd them strangely hard.

But all this would not answer my End, which was to get an earthen Pot to hold what was Liquid, and bear the Fire, which none of these could do. It happen'd after some time, making a pretty large Fire for cooking my Meat, when I went to put it out after I had done with it, I found a broken Piece of one of my Earthen-ware Vessels in the Fire, burnt as hard as a Stone, and red as a Tile. I was agreeably suppris'd to see it, and said to my self, that certainly they might be made to burn whole if they would burn broken.

This set me to studying how to order my Fire, so as to make it burn me some Pots. I had no Notion of a Kiln, such as the Potters burn in, or of glazing them with Lead, tho' I had Some Lead to do it with; but I plac'd three large Pipkins, and two or three Pots in a Pile one upon another, and plac'd my Fire-wood all round it with a great Heap of Embers under them, I ply'd the Fire with fresh Fuel round the out-side, and upon the top, till I

最后,太阳终于把这两只大瓦罐晒得非常干燥非常坚硬了。我就把它们轻轻搬起来,放进两只预先特制的大柳条筐里,防备它们破裂。在缸和筐之间的空隙处,又塞上了稻草和麦秆。现在,这两个大缸不会受潮了,以后我想就可以用来装粮食和粮食磨出来的面粉。

虽说我想做些大缸的计划大多归于破产,我做的一些小东西倒是比较成功的,其中包括好些小圆罐、扁碟子、带柄的罐子、小锅以及我顺手做出来的一些东西。它们经烈日一晒,硬得出奇。

但是所有这些东西都不符合我的目的,因为我要的是陶罐,要能够盛水,能经得起火烧,而这些东西都做不到这两点。过了好些日子后,有一回我为了烤肉而生起了一堆大火,待到肉烤熟了,我去把火灭掉时,偏巧在火堆里发现一块东西,是我用陶土做的某个器皿的碎片,但经过大火一烧,已经红得像瓦片,硬得像石头了。我又惊又喜,对自己说,碎片能烧的话,整的自然也能烧啦。

我由此开始研究怎样掌握火势来焙制几只锅来。我对陶工使用的窑一无所知,也不知道如何用铅上釉,虽说我手头有铅。我把三只大泥锅,两三只泥罐叠成一堆,四周架上木柴,木柴下面放上炭火,然后点燃泥器顶部和四周的木柴,把里面的泥器烧红但不

saw the Pots in the inside red hot quite thro', and observ'd that they did not crack at all; when I saw them clear red, I let them stand in that Heat about 5 or 6 Hours, till I found one of them, tho' it did not crack, did melt or run, for the Sand which was mixed with the Clay melted by the violence of the Heat, and would have run into Glass if I had gone on, so I slack'd my Fire gradually till the Pots began to abate of the red Colour, and watching them all Night, that I might not let the Fire abate too fast, in the Morning I had three very good, I will not say handsome Pipkins; and two other Earthen Pots, as hard burnt as cou'd be desir'd; and one of them perfectly glaz'd with the Running of the Sand.

After this Experiment, I need not say that I wanted no sort of Earthen Ware for my Use; but I must needs say, as to the Shapes of them, they were very indifferent, as any one may suppose, when I had no way of making them; but as the Children make Dirt-Pies, Or as a Woman would make Pies, that never learn'd to raise Past.

No Joy at a Thing of so mean a Nature was ever equal to mine, when I found I had made an Earthen Pot that would bear the Fire; and I had hardly Patience to stay till they were cold, before I set one upon the Fire again, with some Water in it, to boil me some Meat, which it did admirably well; and with a Piece of a Kid, I made Some very good Broth, though I wanted Oatmeal, and several other Ingredients, requisite to make it so good as I would have had it been.

My next Concern was, to get me a Stone Mortar, to stamp or beat some Corn in; for as to the Mill, there was no thought at arriving to that Perfection of Art, with one Pair of Hands. To supply this Want I was at a great Loss; for of all Trades

开裂,待它们变得通红通红以后,我把这种火势维持五六个小时不灭,其中一个器皿开始熔化,但它没有开裂,原来是陶土里的沙子被高温熔化,如果再继续下去,恐怕要烧成玻璃了。于是,我慢慢地撤了火,直到罐子的红色开始消退。我整夜地守着它,不让火退得太快。到了早晨,我便有了三只瓦锅和两个陶锅,质地很好,虽谈不上太漂亮,但烧得非常坚硬,而且其中一只由于沙土已被烧化了,似上了一层很好的釉。

这次试验后,不必说我已不缺什么需用的器皿了。不过,说到它们的造形,我得承认,它们一个个都很丑陋。这是谁都想象得到的,可我没有办法,只能像孩子们做泥饼那样瞎捣腾,只能像从未和过面的妇女做馅饼那样凑和。

我终于造出了一个能够耐火的陶锅。尽管这只是件微不足道的小东西,但它带给我的快乐,却再大不过了。我没等得及让它们冷透,就将其中的一只又放到了火上,在里面放了一点水,想煮点肉吃,结果煮得很成功。而且用羊肉煮出的那碗肉汤也极其鲜美可口,只可惜我没有燕麦片和其他配料,否则就更加棒了。

下一个要解决的棘手问题是要制做一个舂米的石臼。我深知,光靠一双手是无法做出可用的石臼的,因为对制作这东西简直不通一丁点的门

in the World I was as perfectly unqualify'd for a Stone-cutter, as for any whatever; neither had I any Tools to go about it with. I spent many a Day to find out a great Stone big enough to cut hollow, and make fit for a Mortar, and could find none at all; except what was in the solid Rock, and which I had no way to dig or cut out; nor indeed were the Rocks in the Island of Hardness sufficient, but were all of a sandy crumbling Stone, which neither would bear the Weight of a heavy Pestle, or would break the Corn without filling it with Sand; so after a great deal of Time lost in searching for a Stone, I gave it over, and resolv'd to look out for a great Block of hard Wood, which I found indeed much easier; and getting one as big as I had Strength to stir, I rounded it, and form'd it in the Out-side with my Axe and Hatchet, and then with the Help of Fire, and infinite Labour, made a hollow Place in it, as the Indians in Brasil make their Canoes. After this, I made a great heavy Pestle or Beater, of the Wood call'd the Iron-wood, and this I prepar'd and laid by against I had my next Crop of Corn, when I propos'd to my self, to grind, or rather pound my into Meal to make my Bread.

My next Difficulty was to make a Sieve, or Search,' to dress my Meal, and to part it from the Bran, and the Husk, without which I did not see it possible I could have any Bread. This was a most difficult Thing, so much as but to think on; for to be sure I had nothing like the necessary Thing to make it; I mean fine thin Canvas, or Stuff, to search the Meal through. And here I was at a full Stop for many Months; nor did I really know what to do; Linnen I had none left, but what was meer Rags; I had Goats Hair, but neither knew I how to weave it, or spin it; and had I known how, here was no Tools to work it with;

道。在三百六十行的工种中，我对石匠这门手艺是一窍不通，是地地道道的门外汉。况且，也没有适合的工具。起初我想找一块大石头，把中间挖空做成石臼，可是岛上的石头不仅全是大块岩石，无法挖开搬走，而且这些岩石都是些疏松的沙石，质地不够坚硬，一凿就碎，既经不起重杵，也捣不碎粮食，还会使粮食里掺进许多沙子。所以经过几天费时费力的寻找后，我放弃了做石臼的念头，决定找一段坚硬的木头做木臼。这办法果然切实可行多了。我弄了一大块木头(大得我勉强搬得动)，先用大小斧头把它砍得圆圆的，砍得粗具外形，然后靠了火力和无限的劳力，在它上面做了一个槽，好像巴西的印第安人做独木舟那样。做好之后，我又用铁树做了一只又大又重的杵。我把这些东西做好之后，把它们放在一边，准备等下次收到粮食时，把粮食碾捣成面粉，来做面包。

我的第二步困难，就是要做一个筛子来筛面粉，把它和糠皮分开；没有这样东西，我就不可能做面包。做筛子想想就把我难倒了。我没有任何材料可以用来做筛子，也就是那种有很细很细网眼的薄薄的布可以把面粉筛出来。这使我停工好几个月，不知怎么办才好。除了一些破布碎片外，我连一块亚麻布也没有。虽然我有山羊毛，但我根本不知道怎样纺织，即使知

all the Remedy that I found for this, was, That at last I did remember I had among the Seamens Cloaths which were sav'd out of the Ship, some Neckcloths of Callicoe, or Muslin; and with some Pieces of these, I made three small Sieves, but proper enough for the Work; and thus I made shift for some Years; how I did afterwards, I shall shew in its Place.

The baking Part was the next Thing to be consider'd, and how I should make Bread when I came to have Corn; for first I had no Yeast; as to that Part, as there was no supplying the Want, so I did not concern my self much about it: But for an Oven, I was indeed in great Pain; at length I found out an Experiment for that also, which was this; I made some Earthen Vessels very broad, but not deep; that is to say, about two Foot Diameter, and not above nine Inches deep; these I burnt in the Fire, as I had done the other, and laid them by; and when I wanted to bake, I made a great Fire upon my Hearth, which I had pav'd with some square Tiles of my own making, and burning also; but I should not call them square.

When the Fire-wood was burnt pretty much into Embers, or live Coals, I drew them forward upon this Hearth, so as to cover it all over, and there I let them lye, till the Hearth was very hot, then sweeping away all the Embers, I set down my Loaf, or Loaves, and whelming down the Earthen Pot upon them, drew the Embers all round the Out-side of the Pot, to keep in, and add to the Heat; and thus, as well as in the best Oven in the World, I bak'd my Barley Loaves, and became in little Time a meer Pastry-Cook into the Bargain;

道,这里也没有纺织工具。后来,我忽然想起一个补救办法,也是当时唯一的办法,那就是在从船上搬下来的那些水手衣服里,有几块棉布和薄纱围巾。我拿了几块出来做成三个小筛子,总算能凑合着用,这样应付了好几年。至于后来怎么办,我下面再叙述。

接下去要考虑的是,一旦我有了足够的粮食,我用什么东西去烘烤面包,怎么个烘烤法?因为我首先就没有酵母,对于这一点,我是无论如何都没法解决的,所以也就不去为这事多费神了。至于烤面包的炉子,这倒叫我真是大伤脑筋,但结果还是想出个办法可以试一下,也就是说,我先用陶土做了几个盘子,它们宽度大而深度小——直径约两英尺,深度不超过九英寸——随后像烧制其他陶器一样,我把它们烧好了,就放起来备用;我还做了些算不得怎么方正的砖坯,把它们烧制后,砌成一块专门用来烧火的砖地;待到要烘制面包时,我便在这砖地上烧起一堆大火。

当木柴烧成热炭或炽炭时,我就把它们取出放进炉膛里,把炉子盖满,一直让它把炉子烧得非常热,再把所有的火种通通扫去,然后把面包放进去,用陶盆把炉子扣住,再往陶盆外面围一层炭火,这样既可以保持炉子的热度,又可以增加热度。我这样烘烤出来的面包,可以和世界上最好的炉子烘烤出来的面包相媲

for I made my self several Cakes of the Rice, and Puddings; indeed I made no Pies, neither had I any Thing to put into them, supposing I had, except the Flesh either of Fowls or Goats.

It need not be wondred at, if all these Things took me up most Part of the third Year of my Abode here; for it is to be observ'd, That in the Intervals of these Things, I had my new Harvest and Husbandry to manage; for I reap'd my Corn in its Season, and carry'd it Home as well as I could, and laid it up in the Ear, in my large Baskets, till I had Time to rub it out; for I had no Floor to thrash it on, or Instrument to thrash it with.

And now indeed my Stock of Corn increasing, I really wanted to build my Barns bigger. I wanted a Place to lay it up in; for the Increase of the Corn now yielded me so much, that I had of the Barley about twenty Bushels, and of the Rice as much, or more; insomuch, that now I resolv'd to begin to use it freely; for my Bread had been quite gone a great while; Also I resolved to see what Quantity would be sufficient for me a whole Year, and to sow but once a Year.

Upon the whole, I found that the forty Bushels of Barley and Rice, was much more than I could consume in a Year; so I resolv'd to sow just the same Quantity every Year, that I sow'd the last, in Hopes that such a Quantity would fully provide me with Bread, etc.

All the while these Things were doing, you may be sure my Thoughts run many times upon the Prospect of Land which I had seen from the other Side of the Island, and I was not without secret Wishes that I were on Shore there, fancying the seeing the main Land, and in an inhabited Coun-

美。而且，渐渐地把我自己训练成了一个技术高明的面包师，还用稻米做了些糕点和布丁。但我却没有办法做馅饼，因为我除了飞禽肉和羊肉外，没有别的佐料。

毫无疑问，我在这儿的第三年大部分时间都花在这些事情上。我马上要提到的是，干这些活的同时，我还要收割庄稼和进行田间管理。我等庄稼成熟后收割，带回家，一穗一穗地储放在筐里，等有空的时候用手搓出谷粒，因为我既没有谷场也没有工具打谷。

现在，我的粮食储存真的大大增加了，确实有必要把我的粮仓扩展得宽大一点。我很需要一个放粮的地方，因为我的谷子已增加得如此之多，大麦约有二十蒲式耳，稻米也有这么多，或许还不止。所以，我现在可以放开来吃粮了。因为原来我从船上取下来的粮食早就吃完了。此外，我想估算一下，看我一年最多要吃多少粮，打算一年只长一茬。

试了几天后，我发现四十蒲式耳的米和麦足够我一年的口粮，还有富余，遂决定今后每年播种与今年同样数量的粮食。只要没有意外，收获的粮食能够供应我做面包和其他之用了。

在做这些事情的时候，我心里一直牵挂着另一件事情，脑中不断地想着巡游时看到的岛对岸的那片陆地。我确实存在着一种希望，希望能在那里登陆，幻想着在找到大陆

try, I might find some Way or other to convey my self farther, and perhaps at last find some Means of Escape.

But all this while I made no Allowance for the Dangers of such a Condition, and how I might fall into the Hands of Savages, and perhaps such as I might have Reason to think far worse than the Lions and Tigers of Africa. That if I once came into their Power, I should run a Hazard more than a thousand to one of being kill'd, and perhaps of being eaten; for I had heard that the People of the Carribean Coast were Canibals, or Man-eaters; and I knew by the Latitude that I could not be far off from that Shore. That suppose they were not Canibals, yet that they might kill me, as many Europeans who had fallen into their Hands had been serv'd, even when they had been ten or twenty together; much more I' that was but one, and could make little or no Defence: All these Things, I say, which I ought to have consider'd well of, and did cast up in my Thoughts afterwards, yet took up none of my Apprehensions at first; but my Head run mightily upon the Thought of getting over to the Shore.

Now I wish'd for my Boy Xury, and the long Boat, with the Shoulder of Mutton Sail, with which I sail'd above a thousand Miles on the Coast of Africk; but this was In vain. Then I thought I would go and look at our Ship's Boat, which, as I have said, was blown up upon the Shore, a great Way in the Storm, when we were first cast away. She lay almost where she did at first, but not quite; and was turn'd by the Force of the Waves and the Winds almost Bottom upward, against a high Ridge of Beachy rough Sand; but no Water about her as before.

和有人烟的地方以后,能够继续设法去其他地方,直至最后获得新生。

在这些时候,我根本没有想到这办法可能遇到的危险;没有想到我被野人逮着的可能,其实这比遇到非洲狮虎更令人恐惧;也没有想到,如果我落到他们手里,我就要冒着一种九死一生的危险,不是被他们杀死,就是被他们吃掉,因为我听说加勒比海岸的人都是吃人的,而且从纬度来看,我知道这里离加勒比海岸不会太远。再说,就算他们不是吃人的种族,他们也会把我杀死,正如他们对付其他落到他们手里的欧洲人一样,即使我们是一二十个人成群打伙走,也无济于事。而我,只不过孤身一人,一点自卫的力量都没有。这些事本来是我应该考虑的,并且后来也考虑到了,可是当时却丝毫引不起我的恐惧。我的脑子一心一意只要到对面的陆地上去。

这时,我怀念我那小仆人朱利和那只长舢船了;我和朱利架着那挂着三角帆的舢船沿非洲海岸航行了一千多英里啊!然而,光思念也于事无补。所以,我想到去看看我们大船上的那只小艇。前面已谈到过,这小艇是在我们最初遇难时被风暴刮到岸上来的。小艇差不多还躺在原来的地方,但位置略有变更,并且经风浪翻了个身,船底朝天,搁浅在一个高高的沙石滩上,四面无水。

If I had had Hands to have refitted her, and to have launch'd her into the Water, the Boat would have done well enough, and I might have gone back into the Brasils with her easily enough; but I might have foreseen, That I could no more turn her, and set her upright upon her Bottom, than I could remove the Island: However, I went to the Woods, and cut Levers and Rollers, and brought them to the Boat, resolv'd to try what I could do, suggesting to my self, That if I could but turn her down, I might easily repair the Damage she had receiv'd, and she would be a very good Boat, and I might go to Sea in her very easily.

I spar'd no Pains indeed, in this Piece of fruitless Toil, and spent, I think, three or four Weeks about it; at last finding it impossible to heave it up with my little Strength, I fell to digging away the Sand, to undermine it, and so to make it fall down, setting Pieces of Wood to thrust and guide it right in the Fall.

But when I had done this, I was unable to stir it up again, or to get under it, much less to move it forward, towards the Water; so I was forc'd to give it over; and yet, though I gave over the Hopes of the Boat, my desire to venture over for the Main increased, rather than decreased, as the Means for it seem'd impossible.

This at length put me upon thinking, Whether it was not possible to make my self a Canoe, or Periagua, such as the Natives of those Climates make, even without Tools, or, as I might say, without Hands, viz. of the Trunk of a great Tree. This I not only thought possible, but easy, and pleas'd my self extreamly with the Thoughts of making it, and with my having much more Conve-

要是我有几个帮手把它修理一下，再把它弄下水，这条小艇还是挺管用的，驾上它，我也就可以轻而易举地驶回巴西；照理说，我应该看出来，凭我一个人是没法使它翻个身的，我要它再船底朝下，就像要搬动这座海岛一样不可能。但是我却去了林子里，砍了一些可用作撬棒和滚木的树，把它们搬到船边，一心想要试试；我提醒自己：只要能把船翻转过来，那么一些损坏的部分就很容易修理，它仍能成为一条易于操纵的好船，让我有可能驾着出海。

在这个毫无结果的苦役中，我费尽周折，花了约三四个星期的时间。最后，发现靠我这点微薄的力量不可能把它举起来，我又一次扎进挖掘中，想把它下面挖空，让它落下来，再安置一些木头，在它落下来时把它翻转过来。

可是无论我怎么卖力地干它还是岿然不动，我无法挖到船底下，更不用说把它移到水边，只得罢手。但是，尽管我已经放弃了对小艇的希望，但我要到大陆去冒险的愿望，不仅没有因为无法实现而减退，反而更加强烈了。

最后，我想到，既没有工具，又没有人手，是否可以像热带气候中的土著人那样，用一个大树干给自己做一个独木舟。我想这不仅是可能的，而且很容易。我一想到这一点心里就非常高兴。而且比起黑人或印第安人来，我有许

nience for it than any of the Negroes or Indians; but not at all considering the particular Inconveniences which I lay under, more than the Indians did, viz. Want of Hands to move it, when it was made, into the Water, a Difficulty much harder for me to surmount, than all the Consequences of Want of Tools could be to them; for what was it to me, That when I had chosen a vast Tree in the Woods, I might with much Trouble cut it down, if after I might be able with my Tools to hew and dub the Out-side into the proper Shape of a Boat, and burn or cut out the In-side to make it hollow, so to make a Boat of it: If after all this, I must leave it just there where I found it, and was not able to launch it into the Water.

One would have thought, I could not have had the least Reflection upon my Mind of my Circumstance, while I was making this Boat; but I should have immediately thought how I should get it into the Sea; but my Thoughts were so intent upon my Voyage over the Sea in it, that I never once consider'd how I should get it off of the Land; and it was really in its own Nature more easy for me to guide it over forty five Miles of Sea, than about forty five Fathom of Land, where it lay, to set it afloat in the Water.

I went to work upon this Boat, the most like a Fool, that ever Man did, who had any of his Senses awake. I pleas'd my self with the Design, without determining whether I was ever able to undertake it; not but that the Difficulty of launching my Boat came often into my Head; but I put a stop to my own Enquiries into it, by this foolish Answer which I gave my self, Let's first make it, I'll warrant I'll find some Way or other to get it along, when 'tis done.

This was a most preposterous Method; but the Eagerness of my Fancy prevail'd, and to work I

多便利条件。但是,我全然没有考虑到,比起印第安人来,我也有极为不利的条件。当我把船做好后,由于缺乏人帮忙,也难以把它推到水里。对我来说,这个困难,远比土著人没有工具的困难更难以克服。试想,我从树林里选中一棵大树,费千辛万苦把它砍下,然后用工具把它削成船的形状,再把里面烧空凿空,终于将一棵树做成一只船,可是,做成之后,我只能把它留在原来的地方,没法将它推到水中,这种劳动对我又有什么意义呢?

别人肯定会认为,我在造这样一只舢板的时候,至少会设身处地地想一想,看到不能把它推到水中。可是,我当时所有的心思都放在驾舟航海上了,竟未多想木舟如何入水的问题。而实际上一个人在陆地上把船推动四十五英寻后下到水里,比驾驶它在海里航行四十五英里还要困难得多!

我就像是一个大傻瓜,没头没脑地着手造船的工作,并为自己的造船计划深感得意,根本顾不上深究它到底是否可行。其实我也不是一点都没想到过,但每当一想到困难而疑惑时,我都是用"船到桥头自然直"这句俗语糊弄自己,总是对自己说:"先把船造好再说,到时总会有法子解决的。"

这想法太幼稚了;但由于太急于求成,我就不顾一切地

went. I fell'd a Cedar Tree: I question much whether Solomon ever had such a One for the Building of the Temple at Jerusalem. It was five Foot ten Inches Diameter at the lower Part next the Stump, and four Foot eleven Inches Diameter at the End of twenty two Foot, after which it lessen'd for a while, and then parted into Branches: It was not without infinite Labour that I fell'd this Tree: I was twenty Days hacking and hewing at it at the Bottom. I was fourteen more getting the Branches and Limbs, and the vast' spreading Head of it cut off, which I hack'd and hew'd through with Axe and Hatchet, and inexpressible Labour: After this, it cost me a Month to shape it, and dub it to a Proportion, and to something like the Bottom of a Boat, that it might swim upright as it ought to do. It cost me near three Months more to clear the In-side, and work it out so, as to make an exact Boat of it: This I did indeed without Fire, by meer Malett and Chissel, and by the dint of hard Labour, till I had brought it to be a very handsome Periagua, and big enough to have carry'd six and twenty Men, and consequently big enough to have carry'd me and all my Cargo.

When I had gone through this Work, I was extremely delighted with it. The Boat was really much bigger than I ever saw a Canoe, or Periagua, that was made of one Tree, in my Life. Many a weary Stroke it had cost, you may be sure; and there remain'd nothing but to get it into the Water; and had I gotten it into the Water, I make no question but I should have began the maddest Voyage, and the most unlikely to be perform'd, that ever was undertaken.

But all my Devices to get it into the Water fail'd me; tho' they cost me infinite Labour too. It lay about one hundred Yards from the Water, and not more: But the first Inconvenience was, it was up Hill towards the Creek; well, to take away this

做了下去。我伐倒一株很大的杉树,我敢肯定连所罗门王在建耶路撒冷圣殿时,也未必使用过如此大的木料。树脚的直径达到五英尺十英寸,在二十二英尺处的树干直径也达到四英尺十一英寸,再往上便渐渐细下去,分为大量枝桠。这棵树太大了,我用二十天的工夫才砍倒,然后又花了两星期的时间才把巨大的枝桠和浓密的枝叶砍下来。然后,我又花了一个月的工夫把它刮得略具规模,成为船底的形状,使它可以船底朝下浮在水里。又花了将近三个月的工夫把它的内部挖空,把它做得完全像一只舢板。我做这一步的时候,并不用火去烧,只用槌子和凿子把它一点一点地凿空,一直把它造成一个很体面的独木舟,其大可以容纳二十六个人,因此可以把我和所有的东西装进去。

我完成这个工程之后,对它非常满意。这艘舢板比我们以前看到的任何独木舟都大。当然,做成这只大型独木舟我是费尽心血的。现在,剩下的就是下水问题了。要是我的独木舟真的下水了,我肯定会进行一次有史以来最疯狂、最不可思议的航行了。

尽管我想尽办法,费尽力气,可就是无法使船移动一步。舢板所在的位置离水仅一百码,决不会再多。第一个难处是,从舢板所在的位置到

Discouragement, I resolv'd to dig into the Surface of the Earth, and so make a Declivity: This I begun, and it cost me a prodigious deal of Pains; but who grutches Pains, that have their Deliverance in View: But then this was work'd through, and this Difficulty manag'd, it was still much at one; for I could no more stir the Canoe, than I could the other Boat.

Then I measur'd the Distance of Ground, and resolv'd to cut a Dock, or Canal, to bring the Water up to the Canoe, seeing I could not bring the Canoe down to the Water: Well, I began this Work, and when I began to enter into it, and calculate how deep it was to be dug, how broad, how the Stuff to be thrown out, I found, That by the Number of Hands I had, being none but my own, it must have been ten or twelve Years before I should have gone through with it; for the Shore lay high, so that at the upper End, it must have been at least twenty Foot Deep; so at length, tho' with great Reluctancy, I gave this Attempt over also.

This griev'd me heartily, and now I saw, tho' too late, the Folly of beginning a Work before we count the Cost; and before we judge rightly of our own Strength to go through with it.

In the middle of this Work, I finish'd my fourth Year in this Place, and kept my Anniversary with the same Devotion, and with as much Comfort as ever before; for by a constant Study, and serious Application of the Word of God, and by the Assistance of his Grace, I gain'd a different Knowledge from what I had before. I entertain'd different Notions of Things. I look'd now upon the World as a Thing remote, which I had nothing to do with, no Expectation from, and indeed no Desires

河边,正好是一个向上的斜坡。为此,我决定把地面掘起,掘出一个向下的斜坡。于是,我立即动手进行这项工程,并且也历尽艰辛。但只要看到了希望,谁又会为受苦受累而抱怨呢?然而,当我把这件活干完,把这个困难克服以后,情况依然如故,因为我以前既弄不动那只小艇,现在也弄不动这只独木船。

眼看没法把独木舟弄到水边,我只得把地面的距离量了一量,决心挖一条沟渠,把水引到独木舟的跟前;好吧,我又得干这个活了,可当我刚着手干时,我核算了一下,这条沟渠挖多深和多宽,怎么把挖起的土甩出去;我发现靠我一双手,我需要十到十二年才能完工,因为河岸很高,至少要挖二十英尺深才够标准。就这样,我极不情愿地放弃了这个打算。

我极度伤心,但也一下子明白了,不盘算盘算代价,不量力而行就开始一项工作是多么愚蠢,可惜认识到这一点已经太晚。

在进行这项工程的过程中,我度过了自己在这儿的第四个年头,我仍旧虔诚地举行周年纪念日,仍旧活得舒心自在。对上帝之语我不断研究,认真执行,仰仗他的仁慈,我产生了全新的世界观,对事物有了不同的看法。我把世间看作一个很遥远的事物,我同它没有任何关系,没有任何期

about: In a Word, I had nothing indeed to do with it, nor was ever like to have; so I thought it look'd as we may perhaps look upon it hereafter, viz. as a Place I had liv'd in, but was come out of it; and well might I say, as Father Abraham to Dives, Between me and thee is a great Gulph fix'd.

In the first Place, I was remov'd from all the Wickedness of the World here. I had neither the Lust of the Flesh, the Lust of the Eye, or the Pride of Life. I had nothing to covet; for I had all that I was now capable of enjoying: I was Lord of the whole Mannor; or if I pleas'd, I might call my self King, or Emperor over the whole Country which I had Possession of. There were no Rivals. I had no Competitor, none to dispute Sovereignty or Command with me. I might have rais'd Ship Loadings of Corn; but I had no use for it; so I let as little grow as I thought enough for my Occasion.

望,也没有任何要求。总之,我确实同它没有任何关连,而且永远也不会同它有关系了。所以,我对它的看法,就像我们来世对它的看法一样,我们曾在那里住过,但已经离开了那里。我也可以用亚伯拉罕对财主们说的那句话:"在你我之间是一道鸿谷深渊。"

首先,我在这里已摆脱了人世间的一切罪恶,我没有肉欲,没有视觉的贪欲,没有生活中的虚荣,我一无所求。凡是我能享受的,我都拥有,我就是整片这个土地上的君主。在属于我的这片土地上,只要我高兴,我可以称自己是国王,或者皇帝。我在这里没有对手,没有人跟我竞争,没有人争夺我的主权地位,或者统治权。我本可以种出成船成船的谷子,但我用不着那么多,我能吃多少就种多少。

Part 4

I had Tortoise or Turtles enough; but now and then one, was as much as I could put to any use. I had Timber enough to have built a Fleet of Ships. I had Grapes enough to have made Wine, or to have cur'd into Raisins, to have loaded that Fleet, when they had been built. But all I could make use of, was, All that was valuable. I had enough to eat, and to supply my Wants, and, what was all the rest to me? If I kill'd more Flesh than I could eat, the Dog must eat it, or the Vermin. If I sow'd more Corn than I could eat, it must be spoil'd. The Trees that I cut down, were lying to rot on the Ground. I could make no more use of them than for Fewel; and that I had no Occasion for, but to dress my Food.

In a Word, The Nature and Experience of Things dictated to me upon just Reflection, That all the good Things of this World, are no farther good to us, than they are for our Use; and that whatever we may heap up indeed to give others, we enjoy just as much as we can use, and no more. The most covetous griping Miser in the World would have been cur'd of the Vice of Covetousness, if he had been in my Case; for I possess'd infinitely more than I knew what to do with. I had no room for Desire, except it was of Things which I had not, and they were but Trifles, though indeed of great Use to me. I had, as I hinted before, a Parcel of Money, as well Gold as Silver, about thirty six Pounds Sterling: Alas! There the nasty sorry useless Stuff lay; I had no manner of Business for it; and I often thought

第四部

我有充足的海龟或陆龟供我享用,但在我偶尔想吃的时候,才去弄个把来。我所拥有的木材,足够建造一支船队。我还有充足的葡萄,用它们酿出的葡萄酒或晒成的葡萄干,可以装满一支船队的每一条船——假如我真的建造出一支船队的话。可是多又有什么用? 我只能使用自己需要的那部分。所以,当自己够吃够用的时候,多余的便毫无价值了。如果捕获的猎物多得自己吃不了,不去喂狗就得招虫咬;生产的粮食多得吃不了,不毁于霉变就毁于虫蛀。还有,树木砍倒不用,堆在地上就会腐烂,除了偶尔烹煮食物当作柴薪外,就别无他用了。

总之,事理和经验使我认识到,评价世间万物的好坏,关键要看其是否有用,唯其最为宝贵。我们只能尽最大可能的去享受,多余的实在是一无用处;我们所积存的,最好都赠给别人去享受。即使是世上最贪婪的、最吝啬的守财奴到了我这份上,也要变成好人;因为我如今有数不清的财产,却不知道如何消耗它们。我唯一希望的就是再有些生活缺乏的那些必需的东西;这些东西虽然对我有用,然而都是小东西。前文我曾经提到,我有一包钱币,金子银子都有,大约值三十六英镑。但它

with my self, That I would have given a Handful of it for a Gross of Tobacco-Pipes, or for a Hand-Mill to grind my Corn; nay, I would have given it all for Sixpenny-worth of Turnip and Carrot Seed out of England, or for a Handful of Pease and Beans, and a Bottle of Ink: As it was, I had not the least advantage by it, or Benefit from it; but there it lay in a Drawer, and grew mouldy with the Damp of the Cave, in the wet Season; and if I had had the Drawer full of Diamonds, it had been the same Case; and they had been of no manner of Value to me, because of no Use.

I had now brought my State of Life to be much easier in it self than it was at first, and much easier to my Mind, as well as to my Body. I frequently sat down to my Meat with Thankfulness, and admir'd the Hand of God's Providence, which had thus spread my Table in the Wilderness. I learn'd to look more upon the bright Side of my Condition, and less upon the dark Side; and to consider what I enjoy'd, rather than what I wanted; and this gave me sometimes such secret Comforts, that I cannot express them; and which I take Notice of here, to put those discontented People in Mind of it, who cannot enjoy comfortably what God has given them; because they see, and covet something that he has not given them: All our Discontents about what we want, appear'd to me, to spring from the Want of Thankfulness for what we have.

Another Reflection was of great Use to me, and doubtless would be so to any one that should fall

们对我已无任何意义，就扔在那里。我常常想，我情愿用一大把金钱去换一只烟斗，或者换一个磨谷子的手磨。不但如此，我甚至情愿把它全部都付出去，去换价值六个便士的英国莱菔和红萝卜种子，或是去换一把豆子和一瓶墨水。可是现在，我却从它们得不到一点利益，一点好处。它们只是空放在一个抽屉里，由于雨季洞里潮湿，已经生了霉。就算现在我的抽屉里堆满了钻石，情况也是一样，还是对我一点价值都没有，因为没有用。

与当初上岛时相比，我已大大地改善了自己的生活状况。我不仅生活舒适，而且心情也安逸。每当我坐下来吃饭，总会有一种感激之情，惊异上帝万能，竟然能在旷野为我摆设筵席。我已学会多看看自己生活中的光明面，少看看生活中的黑暗面；多想想自己所得到的享受，少想想所缺乏的东西。这种态度使我内心感到的由衷安慰，实难言表。在这儿，我写下这些话，就是希望那些不知满足的人能有所觉醒：他们之所以不能舒舒服服地享受上帝的恩赐，正是因为他们老是在期望和贪求他们还没有得到的东西。我感到，我们老是感到缺少什么东西而不满足，是因为我们对已经得到的东西缺少感激之情。

另外还有一种想法对我也大有帮助，而且对任何像我

into such Distress as mine was; and this was, To compare my present Condition with what I at first expected it should be; nay, with what it would certainly have been, if the good Providence of God had not wonderfully order'd the Ship to be cast up nearer to the Shore, where I not only Could come at her, but could bring what I got out of her to the Shore, for my Relief and Comfort; without which, I had wanted for Tools to work, Weapons for Defence, or Gun-Powder and Shot for getting my Food.

I spent whole Hours, I may say whole Days, in representing to my self in the most lively Colours, how I must have acted, if I had got nothing out of the Ship. How I could not have so much as got any Food, except Fish and Turtles; and that as it was long before I found any of them, I must have perish'd first. That I should have liv'd, if I had not perish'd, like a meer Savage. That if I had kill'd a Goat, or a Fowl, by any Contrivance, I had no way to flea' or open them, or part the Flesh from the Skin, and the Bowels, or to cut it up; but must gnaw it with my Teeth, and pull it with my Claws like a Beast.

These Reflections made me very sensible of the Goodness of Providence to me, and very thankful for my present Condition, with all its Hardships and Misfortunes: And this Part also I cannot but recommend to the Reflection of those, who are apt in their Misery to say, Is any Affliction like mine! Let them consider, How much worse the Cases of some People are, and their Case might have been, if Providence had thought fit.

I had another Reflection which assisted me also to comfort my Mind with Hopes; and this was,

一样遭到不幸的人也肯定如此;这就是:看看自己目前的情况,再比比当初我所预期的情况,或者不如说比比我本来必然会面对的情况,幸而凭着上帝的善意,奇迹般地让船搁到了离岸较近的地方,使我不仅得以上船,还使我可以把我从船上找到的东西运到岸上,让我赖以生存和度日,而要是没有这些,我就没有干活的工具,自卫的武器以及射杀猎物的弹药。

我有时一连几小时,甚至好几天在脑海里尽可能生动地再现这样一个情景:如果我没有弄到船上的物资,我怎么过日子;如果我除了海龟肉和鱼之外什么食品都没有,该怎么办。其实等等我搞到这些东西时已经许多天过去了,那时我早已奄奄待毙了。如果我没死,那也只能像一个纯粹的野人一样活着。如果我设法打了一只小羊或鸟,我没办法剥皮开膛,或把肉跟皮及肚肠分开,或把它切碎,我只能像野兽一样用牙咬,用手撕。

这些想法使我非常感激造物主对我的仁慈,对自己当前充满苦难和不幸的环境非常感激,我写这段话也是想提醒一下,那些自受苦难,常说"谁像我这样苦啊!"这句话的人们,让他们想想,还有许多人的状况,比起他们还要坏得多,如果造物主愿意的话,他们的状况也许会更糟。

此外,我还想到一点。这一点也让我看到希望,让我的

comparing my present Condition with what I had deserv'd, and had therefore Reason to expect from the Hand of Providence. I had liv'd a dreadful Life, perfectly destitute of the Knowledge and Fear of God. I had been well instructed by Father and Mother; neither had they been wanting to me, in their early Endeavours, to infuse a religious Awe of God into my Mind, a Sense of my Duty, and of what the Nature and End of my Being, requir'd of me. But alas! falling early into the Sea-faring Life, which of all the Lives is the most des-titute of the Fear of God, though his Terrors are always before them; I say, falling early into the Seafaring Life, and into Seafaring Company, all that little Sense of Religion which I had entertain'd, was laugh'd out of me by my Mess-Mates, by a harden'd despising of Dangers; and the Views of Death, which grew habitual to me; by my long Absence from all Manner of Opportu-nities to converse with any thing but what was like my self, or to hear any thing that was good, or tended towards it.

So void was I of every Thing that was good, or of the least Sense of what I was, or was to be, that in the greatest Deliverances I enjoy'd, such as my Escape from Sallee; my being taken up by the Portuguese Master of the Ship; my being planted so well in the Brasils; my receiving the Cargo from England, and the like; I never had once the Word Thank God, so much as on my Mind, or in my Mouth; nor in the greatest Distress, had I so much as a Thought to pray to him, or so much as to say, Lord have Mercy upon me; no nor to men-tion the Name of God, unless it was to swear by, and blaspheme it.

I had terrible Reflections upon my Mind for many Months, as I have already observ'd, on the Account of my wicked and hardned Life past; and

心灵得到安慰。就是说,我将我现在的处境,跟我从造物主那里应得的惩罚作了一番比较。我以前过着一种可怕的生活,对上帝完全没有认识,也不知道对他敬畏。我从我父母那里曾受到过良好的教育,但他们当初并没有努力向我灌输敬畏上帝的宗教观念,并没有教我明白,什么是我的天职,什么是我的生活目的。可是,唉!我过早地开始了我的航海生涯,而那些水手都是些最不懂得敬畏上帝的人,尽管死亡的恐怖时时摆在他们面前。由于在长期的海上生活中与水手们耳鬓厮磨,我的那一点宗教观念早就在伙伴的嘲笑之中,在自己对各种危险从逐渐习惯到视死如归的过程之中,在长久听不到有益教导的岁月之中,一点一点从脑海中消失殆尽了。

那时的我全无善念,浑浑噩噩,即使在得到上帝多次的大恩大惠,诸如出逃萨利,受救于葡萄牙船长,在巴西安居乐业,得到英国货物等等,我也从未在口中或心里念叨一句"感谢上帝!"之类的话。同样,即使自己身陷极端的危难之中,也从未想到向上帝祈祷,或是说上一声"上帝啊,可怜可怜我吧!"诸如此类的话。甚至除了用他来发誓、亵渎他之外,我就根本不说上帝的名字。

我在前文已经提到,有几个月我心怀恐惧地回想过去那罪恶而无情的生活。当我

when I look'd about me and considered what particular Providences had attended me since my coming into this Place, and how God had dealt bountifully with me; had not only punished me less than my Iniquity had deserv'd, but had so plentifully provided for me; this gave me great hopes that my Repentance was accepted, and that God had yet Mercy in store for me.

With these Reflections I work'd my Mind up, not only to Resignation to the Will of God in the present Disposition of my Circumstances; but even to a sincere Thankfulness for my Condition, and that I who was yet a living Man, ought not to complain, seeing I had not the due Punishment of my Sins; that I enjoy'd so many Mercies which I had no reason to have expected in that Place; that I ought never more to repine at my Condition but to rejoyce, and to give daily Thanks for that daily Bread, which nothing but a Croud of Wonders could have brought. That I ought to consider I had been fed even by Miracle, even as great as that of feeding Elijah by Ravens; nay, by a long Series of Miracles, and that I could hardly have nam'd a Place in the unhabitable Part of the World where I could have been cast more to my Advantage: A Place, where as I had no Society, which was my Affliction on one Hand, so I found no ravenous Beast, no furious Wolves or Tygers to threaten my Life, no venomous Creatures or poisonous, which I might feed On to my Hurt, no Savages to murther and devour me.

In a word, as my Life was a Life of Sorrow, one way, so it was a Life of Mercy, another; and I wanted nothing to make it a Life of Comfort, but to be able to make my Sence of God's Good-

睁开眼睛,想到上帝自我落难孤岛之后给我的众多益处,对我如何地宽大,不但没有按我所犯的罪恶所应得的惩治我,还处处给我方便时,我内心马上又充满了希望,感觉到上帝已经接受了我的忏悔,并且对我表示了怜悯。

通过这样的反省,我心里便开始坚定下来,不但心平气和地接受了上帝对我当前处境的安排,甚至对我的现状怀着一种衷心的感谢。我觉得我现在既然保住了性命,就不应该抱怨,因为我没有受到应得的惩罚。我觉得,我已经得到了许多我所不应该期望的慈悲。我觉得,我绝不应该对于我的境遇表示不满,应该满心欢喜,为每天有面包吃表示感谢,因为我能够吃到它,完全是奇事中的奇事。我觉得,我应该认为我是在被奇迹养活着,这种奇迹之伟大,不亚于以利亚之受到乌鸦的养活。老实说,我简直是被一系列的奇迹养活着。在世界上所有荒无人烟的地区,我感到没有一个地方会比我现在流落的荒岛更好了。虽说这儿远离人世,形单影只,使我非常苦恼,但这儿没有吃人的野兽,没有凶猛的虎狼害我性命,没有毒人的动物和植物,吃下去会把我毒死,更没有野人会把我杀了吃掉。

总而言之,我的生活,在一方面看来,确实是一种可悲的生活;在另一方面看来,却也是一种蒙恩的生活。我并

ness to me, and Care over me in this Condition, be my daily Consolation; and after I did make a just Improvement of these things, I went away and was no more sad.

I had now been here so long, that many Things which I brought on Shore for my Help, were either quite gone, or very much wasted' and near spent.

My Ink, as I observed, had been gone some time, all but a very little, which I eek'd out with Water a little and a little, till it was so pale it scarce left any Appearance of black upon the Paper: As long as it lasted, I made use of it to minute down the Days of the Month on which any remarkable Thing happen'd to me, and first by casting up Times past: I remember that there was a strange Concurrence of Days, in the various Providences which befel me; and which, if I had been superstitiously inclin'd to observe Days as Fatal or Fortunate, I might have had Reason to have look'd upon with a great deal of Curiosity.

First I had observed, that the same Day that I broke away from my Father and my Friends, and run away to Hull, in order to go to Sea; the same Day afterwards I was taken by the Sallee Man of War, and made a Slave.

The same Day of the Year that I escaped out of the Wreck of that Ship in Yarmouth Rodes, that same Day-Year afterwards I made my escape from Sallee in the Boat.

The same Day of the Year I was born on (viz.) the 30th of September, that same Day, I had my Life so miraculously saved 26 Year after, when I was cast on Shore in this Island, so that my wicked Life, and my solitary Life begun both on a

不需要什么东西来使自己的日子过得舒心些,只求能体会上帝对我的善意和眷念,让我虽然在这种环境里,每天都能有这种体会作为生活中的慰藉;在对自己的遭遇提高了认识以后,我就不再愁肠百结,而是一心向前了。

我在岛上已待了很长的时间,我弄上岸来过日子用的许多东西,有的已完全用完,有的不是已几乎用完,便是已用得差不多了。

我提过我的墨水只剩下很少的一点,我一点一点地往里面兑水,直到它在纸上再也留不下任何痕迹。只要还能写得出来,我就记下每周的大事。回顾一下我过去的经历,我记得那些不同的灾难在日期上却形成奇怪的巧合。如果我迷信日期会给人带来福祸,我会饶有兴趣地推崇这种信仰。

我首先注意到,我从父亲和亲友中逃出来,到赫尔去航海的那一天,同我后来在萨利的战斗中沦为奴隶那天是同一天。

我从雅木斯的沉船中逃出来的那天同我从萨利逃出的那天是同一天。

我出生的那天,九月三十日,同二十六年后,我奇迹般地获救,被冲上岸来到这个岛上,正是同一天。因此,可以说,我罪恶的生活和孤寂的生

Day.

The next Thing to my Ink's being wasted, was that of my Bread, I mean the Bisket which I brought out of the Ship; this I had husbanded to the last degree, allowing my self but one Cake of Bread a Day for above a Year, and yet I was quite without Bread for near a Year before I got any Corn of my own, and great Reason I had to be thankful that I had any at all, the getting it being, as has been already observed, next to miraculous.

My Cloaths began to decay too mightily: As to Linnen, I had had none a good while, except some chequer'd Shirts which I found in the Chests of the other Seamen, and which I carefully preserved, because many times I could bear no other Cloaths on but a Shirt; and it was a very great help to me that I had among all the Men's Cloaths Of the Ship almost three dozen Of Shirts. There were also several thick Watch Coats of the Seamens, which were left indeed, but they were too hot to wear; and tho' it is true, that the Weather was so violent hot, that there was no need of Cloaths, yet I could not go quite naked; no, tho' I had been inclin'd to it, which I was not, nor could not abide the thoughts of it, tho' I was all alone.

The Reason why I could not go quite naked, was, I could not bear the heat of the Sun so well when quite naked, as with some Cloaths on; nay, the very Heat frequently blistered my Skin; whereas with a Shirt on, the Air itself made some Motion, and whistling under that Shirt was twofold cooler than without it; no more could I ever bring my self to go out in the heat of Sun, without a Cap or a Hat; the heat of the Sun beating with such Violence as it does in that Place, would give me the Head-ach presently, by darting so directly on my Head, without a Cap or Hat on, so that I could not bear it, whereas, if I put on

活同是从这一天开始的。

除了我的墨水已经用完之外,我从木船上取下来的饼干也吃光了。那些饼干,我吃得仔细得不能再仔细了,在一年多的时间中,我每天只让自己吃一块。尽管如此,在打到谷子之前,我已有一年多的时间没有粮食吃了。所以,地里能长出谷物,我没有理由不感激上帝,况且,正如我前面所说的,这一切简直是奇迹。

我的衣服也渐渐破烂不堪。至于亚麻衬衫,这些我都保存得很好。因为在许多时候,我热得穿不住别的衣服,只穿一件衬衫。好在我从船上的水手服装中找到了三打衬衫。我另外还有几件水手穿的值更大衣,但都比较厚,穿起来太热了。按说,这里天气酷热,倒也用不着穿什么衣服,可是我总不能赤身裸体一丝不挂吧。不,我可不愿意那样。尽管这里只有我一个人,也不打算这么做,甚至不愿意让自己有这种念头。

再说,我不想赤身裸体还另有原因。这里的阳光炽热灼人,如果不穿点衣服,根本无法忍受阳光的暴晒,皮肤很快就会被晒出泡来。如果穿上点衣服,空气就可以在它下面流通,使我比不穿衣服时双倍地凉快。同时,在大太阳下面不戴帽子出门,我也办不到,因为太阳的热力是那样强,射在我的没有帽子的头上,不大工夫就把我晒得头痛难忍;可是,如果戴上帽子,那

my Hat, it would presently go away.

Upon those Views I began to consider about putting the few Rags I had, which I call'd Cloaths, into some Order; I had worn out all the Wast-coats I had, and my Business was now to try if I could not make Jackets out of the great Watch-Coats which I had by me, and with such other Materials as I had, so I set to Work a Taylering, or rather indeed a Botching, for I made most piteous Work of it. However, I made shift to make two or three new Wastcoats, which I hoped wou'd serve me a great while; as for Breeches or Drawers, I made but a very sorry shift indeed, till afterward.

I have mentioned that I saved the Skins of all the Creatures that I kill'd, I mean four-footed ones, and I had hung them up stretch'd out with Sticks in the Sun, by which means some of them were so dry and hard that they were fit for little but others it seems were very useful. The first thing I made of these was a great Cap for my Head, with the Hair on the out Side to shoor off the Rain; and this I perform'd so well, that after this I made me a Suit of Cloaths wholly of these Skins, that is to say, a Wastcoat, and Breeches open at Knees, and both loose, for they were rather wanting to keep me cool than to keep me warm. I must not omit to acknowledge that they were wretchedly made; for if I was a bad Carpenter, I was a worse Tayler. However, they were such as I made very good shift with; and when I was abroad, if it happen'd to rain, the Hair of my Wastcoat and Cap being outermost, I was kept very dry.

就不要紧了。

根据这种情况，我便开始考虑把我的那些破烂衣服整理一下。我已经把我所有的背心都穿破了，我现在要办的事就是设法用我手边的值更大衣，加上一些别的材料，做两件背心。于是我做起裁缝来。其实，我根本不懂缝纫工作，只是胡乱缝合起来罢了。我的手艺可以说是再糟也没有了。尽管如此，我还是勉强做成了两三件新背心，希望能穿一段时间。至于短裤，我直到后来才马马虎虎做出几条很不像样的东西。

我前面提到过，凡是我打死的野兽，我都把毛皮保存起来，所谓野兽，我指的是四足动物。我把毛皮用棍子支在太阳下晒干，有的被晒得又干又硬，简直没有什么用处了；但有的倒还合用。我首先用这些毛皮做了顶帽子，把毛翻在外面，可以挡雨。帽子做得还可以，我就又用一些毛皮做了一套衣服，包括一件背心和一条长仅及膝的短裤。这一身衣裤都做得很宽松，因为我穿它们的目的不是保暖，而是为了遮阳、图凉快。同时，我也千万不能忘了承认，这身衣服做得实在不妙，因为如果说我是个糟糕的木匠，那么我这个裁缝就更加糟糕了。但尽管如此，它们到底还是挺管用的，只是得将就些；所以我在屋外时，要是下起雨来，我的上衣和帽子既然都是毛皮在外的，我身上就不会淋湿。

After this I spent a great deal of Time and Pains to make me an Umbrella; I was indeed in great want of one, and had a great Mind to make one; I had seen them made in the Brasils, where they are very useful in the great Heats which are there. And I felt the Heats every jot as great here, and greater too, being nearer the Equinox; besides, as I was oblig'd to be much abroad, it was a most useful thing to me, as well for the Rains as the Heats. I took a world of Pains at it, and was a great while before I could make any thing likely to hold; nay, after I thought I had hit the Way, I spoil'd 2 or 3 before I made one to my Mind; but at last I made one that answer'd indifferently well: The main Difficulty I found was to make it to let down. I could make it to spread, but if it did not let down too, and draw in, it was not portable for me any Way but just over my Head, which wou'd not do. However, at last, as I said, I made one to answer, and covered it with Skins, the Hair upwards, So that it cast off the Rains like a Penthouse, and kept off the Sun so effectually, that I could walk out in the hottest of the Weather with greater Advantage than I could before in the coolest, and when I had no need of it, cou'd close it and carry it under my Arm.

Thus I liv'd mighty comfortably, my Mind being entirely composed by resigning to the Will of God, and throwing my self wholly upon the Disposal of his Providence. This made my Life better than sociable, for when I began to regret the want of Conversation, I would ask my self whether thus conversing mutually with my own Thoughts, and, as I hope I may say, with even God himself by Ejaculations, was not better than the utmost Enjoyment of humane Society in the World.

这以后，我花了大量时间和精力做一把伞，我太需要一把伞了，早就想做一把。我曾在巴西见过如何制伞，那儿的炎热气候是造成出门一定要带伞的原因。我感到这儿靠近赤道，跟那儿一样炎热，甚至更热。再说，我不得不经常出门，伞能遮阳，又能挡雨，对我来说再有用不过。我费了很大的劲，花了很长时间，才做出一把。做伞实在不易，在我自信找到了窍门之后，仍然做坏了二三把，直到最后才做出了一把像样的勉强能用的伞。我发现，主要的困难是能把它放下来，我可以把它撑开，但如果不能把它放下收起来，没有任何携带办法，而只能顶在头上，对我来说是不实用的。到最后，正如我前面所说，我终于勉强做出了一把，用兽皮盖住，毛皮朝上，这样它就像一座小茅屋似的可以挡雨，也能够有效地遮阳，使我能够在最炎热的天气里出门比在最寒冷的天气里出门更便利，而当我不需要它时，还可以把它收起来，夹在胳膊底下携带。

就这样，我活得非常舒服，内心也非常平静，因为我完全顺从上帝的意志，将自己完全交托给他，听从神意的一切安排。这使我的生活比那种有交往的生活更美好，因为，当我因没有人与我交往而觉得遗憾时，就反问自己：跟自己的思想交谈，或者，通过自己的祷告跟上帝交谈，不是

I cannot say that after this, for five Years, any extraordinary thing happened to me, but I liv'd on in the same Course, in the same Posture and Place, just as before; the chief things I was employ'd in, besides my yearly Labour of planting my Barley and Rice, and curing my Raisins, of both which I always kept up just enough to have sufficient Stock of one Year's Provisions beforehand. I say, besides this yearly Labour, and my daily Labour of going out with my Gun, I had one Labour to make me a Canoe, which at last I finished. So that by digging a Canal to it of six Foot wide, and four Foot deep, I brought it into the Creek, almost half a Mile. As for the first, which was so vastly big, as I made it without considering before-hand, as I ought to do, how I should be able to launch it; so never being able to bring it to the Water, or bring the Water to it, I was oblig'd to let it lye where it was, as a Memorandum to teach me to be wiser next Time: Indeed, the next Time, tho' I could not get a Tree proper for it, and in a Place where I could not get the Water to it, at any less Distance, than as I have said, near half a Mile; yet as I saw it was practicable at last, I never gave it over: and though I was near two Years about it, yet I never grutch'd my Labour, in Hopes of having a Boat to go off to Sea at last.

However, though my little Periagua was finish'd; yet the Size of it was not at all answerable to the Design which I had in View, when I made the first; I mean, Of venturing over to the Terra Firma, where it was above forty Miles broad; accordingly, the Smallness of my Boat assisted to put an End to that Design, and now I thought no more of it: But as I had a Boat, my

比人世间最美好的享乐还要美好吗?

转眼间,我上岛已有五个年头了,五年中的后几年里,没有发生什么特别的事情,我的生活方式和环境也没多大的变化。我每年的主要工作还是照例种麦种稻,晒制葡萄干,并把这两样活命之物贮藏起来,以供自己当年食用。我主要的日常工作也不外乎每天持枪外出巡猎等。值得一提的事情是,在这期间我又造了一只独木舟,并且最终让它下了水。为此,我挖了一条宽六英尺、深四英尺,长为半英里的水渠,把独木舟引到了小河里。以前造的那只独木舟,由于太大而始终无法推入水里,也无法把水引过来。本应在动手之前考虑周全,却因为我头脑发热而未能想到,现在只好让这只庞大的独木舟留在原地作为纪念,好教训自己下一次应该学得聪明些。所以这一次,尽管没有离得比较近的树木,可是因为觉得肯定不会再次失败,还是不肯放弃;虽然费了两年的工夫才做成,我却感到十分欣慰,因为我觉得终于有船能够漂在海上了。

不过,虽然舢板已做成,大小却与我开始时的计划相差甚远,无法渡过四十英里以外的海面到大陆上去。由于船做得太小了,我也就放弃了这个计划,不再幻想到那边的大陆去。可是,现在既然有了一只舢板,我的第二步计划就

next Design was to make a Tour round the Island; for as I had been on the other Side, in one Place, crossing as I have already describ'd it, over the Land; so the Discoveries I made in that little Journey, made me very eager to see other Parts of the Coast; and now I had a Boat, I thought of nothing but sailing round the Island.

For this Purpose, that I might do every Thing with Discretion and Consideration, I fitted up a little Mast to my Boat, and made a Sail to it, out of some of the Pieces of the Ship's Sail, which lay in store; and of which I had a great Stock by me.

Having fitted my Mast and Sail, and try'd the Boat, I found she would sail very well: Then I made little Lockers, or Boxes, at either End of my Boat, to put Provisions, Necessaries and Ammunition, etc. into, to be kept dry, either from Rain, or the Sprye of the Sea; and a little long hollow Place I cut in the In-side of the Boat, where I could lay Gun, making a Flap to hang down over it to keep it dry.

I fix'd my Umbrella also in a Step at the Stern, like a Mast, to stand over my Head, and keep the Heat of the Sun off of me like an Auning; and thus I every now and then took a little Voyage upon the Sea, but never went far out, nor far from the little Creek; but at last being eager to view the Circumference of my little Kingdom, I resolv'd upon my our, and accordingly I victuall'd my Ship for the Voyage, putting in two Dozen of my Loaves (Cakes I should rather All them) of Barley Bread, an Earthen Pot full of parch'd Rice, a Food I eat a great deal of, a little Bottle of Rum, half a Goat, and Powder and Shot for killing more, and two large Watch-coats, of those which, as I mention'd before, I had sav'd out of the Seamen's Chests; these I took, one to lye upon,

是坐船绕岛环行一周；因为，前面讲过，我曾经从陆地上越过本岛，抵达岛的那一头，在那次小小的旅行当中，我发现了一些事物，使我很想看看沿岸的其他部分。现在既然已有了一只舢板，我就一心一意要沿岛航行一周。

为了达到这个目的，为了把样样事情做得既周到又慎重，我在我的舢板上安装了一根小小的桅杆，用我贮藏已久的帆布给它做了一面帆。

安装好了桅杆和帆之后，我决定坐船试航一番，结果发现舢板走得相当不错。于是，我在船的两头都做了小抽屉或者可以说是小盒子，里面放粮食、日用品和弹药之类的东西，免得被雨水或浪花打湿。另外，我又在船舷内挖了一条长长的槽，用来放枪，还做了块垂板可盖住长槽，以防枪支受潮。

我还在船尾做了个支架，把伞像桅杆似地撑在那儿，算是个遮篷，挡去我头上的阳光；我时不时就这样去海上转转，但从来都不远离那条小河，不远去海上；但最后由于实在想看看我这小小独立王国的边界，我决心去航行一圈，便把准备在旅途中吃的食物搬上船去，总共有二十几只大麦面包(我觉得，叫它们大麦饼更为贴切)，满满的一罐炒米，这是我吃得很多的食品，一小瓶甘蔗酒，半只山羊肉，还带了些弹药，准备多打些山羊来；前面提到过，我在

and the other to cover me in the Night.

It was the sixth of November, in the sixth Year of my Reign, or my Captivity, which you please, That I set out on this Voyage, and I found it much longer than I expected; for though the Island it self was not very large, yet when I me to the East Side of it, I found a great Ledge of Rocks lye out above two Leagues into the Sea, some above Water, some under it; and beyond that, a Shoal of Sand, lying dry half a League more; so that I was oblig'd to go a great Way out to Sea to double the Point.

When first I discover'd them, I was going to give over my Enterprise, and come back again, not knowing how far it might oblige me to go out to Sea; and above all, doubting how I should get back again; so I came to an Anchor; for I had made me a kind of an Anchor with a Piece of a broken Graplin, which I got out of the Ship.

Having secur'd my Boat, I took my Gun, and went on Shore, climbing up upon a Hill, which seem'd to over-look that Point, where I saw the full Extent of it, and resolv'd to venture.

In my viewing the Sea from that Hill where I stood, I perceiv'd a strong, and indeed, a most furious Current, which run to the East, and even came close to the Point; and I took the more Notice of it, because I saw there might be some Danger; that when I came into it, I might be carry'd out to Sea by the Strength of it, and not be able to make the Island again; and indeed, had I not gotten first up upon this Hill, I believe it would have

水手们的箱子里找到好些衣服,拿回来收着,这回我从中取了两件值更穿的大衣,准备夜里睡觉时,一件垫在身下,一件盖在身上。

今天是十一月六日,是统治此地也好,还是被囚禁此地也好,反正我已在这里度过了第六个年头,也就在这一天我踏上旅途。我发现旅程比我估算的要大,因为,虽然岛不大,但当我驶到东海岸时,发现一排礁石延伸到两海里远的海里,有明礁,也有暗礁,越过这条礁石带,是一片约半海里长的沙滩,这样的话,我只得驶向更远的海面绕过这个海角。

起初当发现这种情况后,我立即决定放弃我的航行,顺原路返回来,因为我不知要在海上走出去多远,重要的是我拿不准自己能否回来。于是,我抛下一只锚,这只锚是用我从轮船上取下来的一只铁钩子打做的。

我停泊好我的船,拿起枪上了岸,爬上可以俯瞰那个海角的小山,从山上我看清了海角的全貌,并打算继续冒险航行。

从我脚下这座小山朝海面望去,我看到有一股异常强大汹涌的急流向东面流去,一直流到岬角附近。我对这股急流特别注意,因为,一旦我的船开进急流中,肯定会遇到危险,甚至会被它强劲的力量冲到海中间去,再也回不了岛上。要是不爬到这座山上来

been so; for there was the same Current on the other Side the Island, only, that it set off at a farther Distance; and I saw there was a strong Eddy under the Shore; so I had nothing to do but to get in out of the first Current, and I should presently be in an Eddy.

I lay here, however, two Days; because the Wind blowing pretty fresh at E.S.E. and that being just contrary to the said Current, made a great Breach of the Sea upon the Point; so that it was not safe for me to keep too close to the Shore for the Breach, nor to go too far off because of the Stream.

The third Day in the Morning, the Wind having abated over Night, the Sea was calm, and I ventur'd; but I am a warning Piece again, to all rash and ignorant Pilots; for no sooner was I come to the Point, when even I was not my Boat's Length from the Shore, but I found my self in a great Depth of Water, and a Current like the Sluice of a Mill: It carry'd my Boat a long with it with such Violence, That all I could do, could not keep her so much as on the Edge of it; but I found it hurry'd me farther and farther out from the Eddy, which was on my left Hand. There was no Wind stirring to help me, and all I could do with my Paddlers signify'd nothing, and now I began to give my self over for lost; for as the Current was on both Sides the Island, I knew in a few Leagues Distance they must joyn again, and then I was irrecoverably gone; nor did I see any Possibility of avoiding it; so that I had no Prospect before me but of Perishing; not by the Sea, for that was calm enough, but of starving for Hunger. I had indeed found a Tortoise on the Shore, as big almost as I could lift, and had toss'd it into the

看一看,我还真的会遇上这样的危险呢,因为岛的另一边也有这样的急流,只不过那股急流离岸边远一些。我还发现,这里的海岸下面有一股强劲的涡流。所以,即使我能摆脱刚才所说的那股急流,也一定会立即被旋进这股涡流。

我的舢板一连在这里停泊了两天。因为一直刮着大风,风向东南偏东,正好和那股急流的方向相逆,所以海角一带波涛汹涌。这样一来我就无法航行了,因为如果靠岸航行,会碰上大浪,可离岸航行,又会卷入急流,我只好按兵不动。

到了第三天早晨,由于风力在夜间已减弱,所以海面风平浪静,于是我起锚开航,冒险前进。这次继续航行的结果,几乎让我陷入绝境,再次为鲁莽无知的驾船人作了前车之鉴。我驾舟刚刚靠近海角,在离海岸不是很远的地方,就稀里糊涂地进入了一片深水区域,并且遇上了一股急流,就像磨坊底下的水流一样急。这股急流来势汹汹地把我的船向前冲去,我费尽九牛二虎之力,想叫船沿着这股急流的边上走,可是办不到,结果我被它冲得愈来愈离开了我左边的那股涡流。刚好这时候没有一点风可以帮我的忙,我拼命地打着我的双桨,还是无济于事。这时候,我开始觉得自己要完蛋了。因为我知道岛的两边都有急流,必然在几海里以外汇合在一处,

Boat; and I had a great Jar of fresh Water, that is to say, one of my Earthen Pots; but what was all this to being driven into the vast Ocean, where to be sure, there was no Shore, no main Land, or Island, for a thousand Leagues at least.

And now I saw how easy it was for the Providence of God make the most miserable Condition Mankind could be in worse. Now I look'd back upon my desolate solitary Island, the most pleasant Place in the World, and all the Happiness my Heart could wish for, was to be but there again. I stretch'd out my Hands to it with eager Wishes. O happy Desart said I, I shall never see thee more. O miserable Creature, said I, whether am I going: Then I reproach'd my Self with my unthankful Temper, and how I had repin'd at my solitary Condition; and now what would I give to be on Shore there again. Thus we never see the true State of our Condition, till it is illustrated to us by its Contraries; nor know how to value what we enjoy, but by the want of it. It is scarce possible to imagine the Consternation I was now in, being driven from my beloved Island (for so it appear'd to me now to be) into the wide Ocean, almost two Leagues, and in the utmost Despair of ever recovering it again. However, I work'd hard, till indeed my Strength was almost exhausted, and kept my Boat as much to the Northward, that is, towards the Side of the Current which the Eddy lay on, as possibly I could; when about Noon, as the Sun pass'd the Meridian, I thought I felt a little Breeze of Wind in my Face, springing up from the

到了那时,我的灭亡就更加无可挽救了。更糟糕的是,我完全看不出有什么办法可以逃避,因此,除了死亡之外,我没有任何希望;倒不是死在海里,因为大海这时倒很平静;而是因为没东西吃,活活饿死。说起吃的粮食,我在岸上已经捉到一只十分沉重的陆龟,扔到船上;除了这些我还有一大罐清水;可如果在没有岛屿的汪洋大海当中,这些东西根本无任何作用。

如今我才懂得了,上帝是太容易给人类的环境雪上加霜了。现在我觉得没有比孤岛更快乐的地方了,而我心里最大的渴望就是返回孤岛。我怀着热切的心愿向它伸出双手:"幸福荒芜的小岛啊,"我说,"我将永远看不到你了!"然后,我又对自己说:"你这倒霉的家伙,你将去何方!"我开始责备自己身在福中不知福的脾气,责备自己不应该抱怨孤独的生活。现在,我愿意付出任何代价,只要能让我重新回到岸上!可是,我们一般凡人,不亲自经历更恶劣的环境,就永远看不到自己原来所处环境的优越性;不落到山穷水尽的地步,就不懂得珍惜自己原来享受的一切。我眼看自己被冲进茫茫的大海,离开我那可爱的小岛有六海里多远,现在我从心底里感到我的小岛确实可爱无比。看到已没有回岛的希望,我内心的惶恐简直难以形容。但我还在拼死地干着,直干到几乎筋疲力尽

S. S. E. This chear'd my Heart a little, and especially when in about half an Hour more, it blew a pretty small gentle Gale. By this Time I was gotten at a frightful Distance from the Island, and had the least Cloud or haizy Weather interven'd, I had been undone another Way too; for I had no Compass on Board, and should never have known how to have steer'd towards the Island, if I had but once lost Sight of it; but the Weather continuing clear, I apply'd my self to get up my Mast again, spread my Sail, standing away to the North, as much as possible, to get out of the Current.

Just as I had set my Mast and Sail, and the Boat began to stretch away, I saw even by the Clearness of the Water, some Alteration of the Current was near; for where the Current was so strong, the Water was foul; but perceiving the Water clear, I found the Current abate, and presently I found to the East, at about half a Mile, a Breach of the Sea upon some Rocks; these Rocks I found caus'd the Current to part again, and as the main Stress of it ran away more Southerly, leaving the Rocks to the North-East; so the other return'd by the Repulse of the Rocks, and made a strong Eddy, which run back again to the North-West, with a very sharp Stream.

They who know what it is to have a Reprieve brought to them upon the Ladder, or to be rescued from Thieves just a going to murther them, or, who have been in such like Extremities, may guess what my present Surprise of Joy was, and how gladly I put my Boat into the Stream of this Eddy, and the Wind also freshening, how gladly I spread my Sail to it, running chearfully before the Wind,

的地步，为的是尽量让船往北靠，就是说，要让船靠近那道急流与涡流相接的边沿处；中午前后，当太阳刚过头顶时，我觉得脸上有微风吹拂，风向是东南。我心情为之一振，特别是过了半个小时左右，风力已颇有点强劲了。可这时我同那孤岛之间的距离已非常吓人，只要空中再有一点阴云或雾霭，我就会以另一种方式完蛋；因为我的船上没带罗盘，只要我一看不见那个岛，也就不知往哪儿行驶才好。幸亏天气依然晴好，于是我动手把桅杆又竖了起来，把帆张了起来，尽量朝北驶去，为的是驶出那股急流。

我刚刚竖起桅杆，扯满帆，让舢板自个儿行走的时候，发现海水变清，我由此判断附近急流有变化，因为，强劲的急流往往造成海水混浊，水清了，说明水流也不会那么湍急了，接着我发现在东方，大约半英里处，海水在礁石上激起白花花的大浪，我注意到，这群礁石把急流一分为二，主流朝南涌动，另一股被岩石撞回，形成凶猛的漩涡，又顺着西北方向奔腾而去。

那些要上绞刑架时又得到赦免，或是要被强盗杀害时又得到解救，或是经历过类似绝处逢生事情的人们，不难猜出此刻我内心的那无以伦比的喜悦，也不难猜出我怀着怎样愉快的心情把舢板撑进了这股涡流，以及我怎样满怀喜

and with a strong Tide or Eddy under Foot.

This Eddy carried me about a League in my Way back again directly towards the Island, but about two Leagues more to the Northward than the Current which carried me away at first; so that when I came near the Island, I found my self open to the Northern Shore of it, that is to say, the other End of the Island opposite to that which I went out from.

When I had made something more than a League of Way by the help of this Current or Eddy, I found it was spent and serv'd me no farther. However, I found that being between the two great Currents, (viz.) that on the South Side which had hurried me away, and that on the North which lay about a League on the other Side. I say between these two, in the wake of the Island, I found the Water at least still and running no Way, and having still a Breeze of Wind fair for me, I kept on steering directly for the Island, tho' not making such fresh Way as I did before.

About four a-Clock in the Evening, being then within about a League of the Island, I found the Point of the Rocks which occasioned this Disaster, stretching out as is describ'd before to the Southward, and casting off the Current more Southwardly, had of Course made another Eddy to the North, and this I found very strong, but not directly setting the Way my Course lay which was due West, but almost full North. However having a fresh Gale, I stretch'd a-cross this Eddy slanting North-west, and in about an Hour came within about a Mile of the Shore, where it being smooth Water, I soon got to Land.

When I was on Shore I fell on my Knees and

悦地把帆扯起,乘风破浪向前行驶。

这股涡流,一直将我向小岛的方向推送,往回推送了约三英里。只是我的航线向北偏移了许多,离起先将我冲下海的那股急流约有六英里多。因此,当船行到小岛附近时,我发现,我已来到了它的北侧,就是说,我到了小岛的另一端,跟我的出发地相反的一端。

就这样,在这股涡流的推送下,我向前行了三英里多路。这时,我发现它的势力已经耗尽,不再对我有帮助了。不过,我又看到,我的船已处于南北两大急流的中间,南边的那股就是把我冲向外海的急流,它与北边那股急流之间相距一里格远。我现在已靠近海岛,又在急流中间的平缓地带,所以海面平静,海水也不大流动,风向也很顺,于是,我就慢慢地向岛上划去。

下午四点钟左右的时候,我划到了离岛不到三英里的地方,远远地又看到了惹起此次险情的那片海角。它向南延伸,把岛南边的那股急流进一步向南方逼过去,同时又分出一股涡流一直向北方流去。这股涡流湍急凶猛,与我西行的航线并不一致。由于风很大,我就从斜里穿过这股涡流,向西北插过来;不到半小时,离岸只有一英里了;这一带海面很平,我不久便上了岸。

我上岸之后,立刻跪在地

gave God Thanks for my Deliverance, resolving to lay aside all Thoughts of my Deliverance by my Boat, and refreshing my self with such Things as I had, I brought my Boat close to the Shore in a little Cove that I had spy'd under some Trees, and lay'd me down to sleep, being quite spent with the Labour and Fatigue of the Voyage.

I was now at a great Loss which Way to get Home with my Boat, I had run so much Hazard, and knew too much the Case to think of attempting it by the Way I went out, and what might be at the other Side (I mean the West Side) I knew not, nor had I any Mind to run any more Ventures; so I only resolved in the Morning to make my Way Westward along the Shore and to see if there was no Creek where I might lay up my Frigate in Safety, so as to have her again if I wanted her; in about three Mile or thereabout coasting the Shore, I came to a very good Inlet or Bay about a Mile over, which narrowed till it came to a very little Rivulet or Brook, where I found a very convenient Harbour for my Boat and where she lay as if she had been in a little Dock made on Purpose for her. Here I put in, and having stow'd my Boat very safe, I went on Shore to look about me and see where I was.

I soon found I had but a little past by the Place where I had been before, when I travell'd on Foot to that Shore; so taking nothing out of my Boat, but my Gun and my Umbrella, for it was exceeding hot, I began my March: The Way was comfortable enough after such a Voyage as I had been upon, and I reach'd my old Bower in the Evening, where I found every thing standing as I left it; for I always kept it in good Order, being, as I said before, my Country House.

下，感谢上帝搭救我脱离大难，并且决心放弃一切坐舢板离开荒岛的思想。我把所带的东西随便吃了几口，把舢板拉到岸边，拉进我在几棵树底下找到的一个小湾里，就倒在地上睡了，因为我已经被航行中的辛劳和疲倦弄得筋疲力竭了。

我完全不知道从哪条路坐船回家。我遇到了这么多危险，知道照原路回去是十分危险的，而海岛的另一边，也就是西边的情况，我又一无所知，更无心再去冒险。所以，我决定第二天早晨沿海岸西行，看看能不能找到一条小河停泊我的小战舰，以便需要的时候再来取它。我驾船沿岸行驶约三英里，找到了一个小湾，约一英里宽，愈往里愈窄，最后成了一条小溪。这对于我的舢板倒是一个进出方便的港口，就仿佛是专门为它建立的舢板坞似的。我把舢板停放妥当后，便上了岸。我环顾四周，看看到底到了什么地方。

我很快便发现自己到过这儿东面一点的地方，而当初我是走陆路到达那处海岸的；我把大多数的东西都留在船上，只拿了枪和伞，因为阳光太猛，便开始登程出发。走过了那样的一段水路，现在这陆路就相当好走了；傍晚时分，我抵达了我的那间小茅屋，那儿一切照旧，仍然是我离开时的样子，因为我既把这儿说成是我的乡间别墅，这里的一切

I got over the Fence, and laid me down in the Shade to rest my Limbs; for I was very weary, and fell asleep: But judge you, if you can, that read my Story, what a Surprize I must be in, when I was wak'd out of my Sleep by a Voice calling me by my Name several times, Robin, Robin, Robin Crusoe, poor Robin Crusoe, where are you Robin Crusoe? Where are you? Where have you been?

I was so dead asleep at first, being fatigu'd with Rowing, or Paddling, as it is call'd, the first Part of the Day, and with walking the latter Part, that I did not wake thoroughly, but dozing between sleeping and waking, thought I dream'd that some Body spoke to me: But as the Voice continu'd to repeat Robin Crusoe, Robin Crusoe, at last I began to wake more perfectly, and was at first dreadfully frighted, and started up in the utmost Consternation: But no sooner were my Eyes open, but I saw my Poll sitting on the Top of the Hedge; and immediately knew that it was he that spoke to me; for just in such bemoaning Language I had used to talk to him, and teach him; and he had learn'd it so perfectly, that he would sit upon my Finger, and lay his Bill close to my Face, and cry, Poor Robin Crusoe, Where are you? Where have you been? How come you here? And such things as I had taught him.

However, even though I knew it was the Parrot, and that indeed it could be no Body else, it was a good while before I could·compose my self: First, I was amazed how the Creature got thither, and then, how he should just keep about the Place, and no where else: But as I was well satisfied it could be no Body but honest Poll, I got it over; and holding out my Hand, and calling him

都是安排得井井有条的。

我越过围篱,摊手摊脚地躺倒在树荫下。我累极了,倒头就睡。如果你读了我的故事,你可以想象当我被一种声音唤醒时,我有多震惊。那种声音反复叫着我的名字:"鲁滨,鲁滨,鲁滨·克鲁索! 可怜的鲁滨·克鲁索! 你在哪儿?你在哪儿? 你跑到哪里去了?"

这一天里,起初,我一方面摇桨摇得很累,另一方面走路走得很累,所以睡得像死去一般,完全没有清醒过来。这时,迷迷糊糊正处于半醒半睡状态,仿佛梦见有人同我说话,但那声音不断重复着"鲁滨·克鲁索,鲁滨·克鲁索",最后我终于完全醒过来了。起初我真害怕,恐惧极了,但当我眼睛刚一睁开,我就看见我的波儿正站在篱笆墙上,立刻我便知道原来是它在同我说话。因为我过去常向它说这些悲哀的话,并教它说这些话,它学得惟妙惟肖。有时就站在我的手指上,把它的嘴贴近我的脸,喊着:"可怜的鲁滨·克鲁索! 你从哪里来? 你在哪儿呀? 你怎么到这儿来的呀?"以及一些诸如此类我教它的话。

然而,尽管我知道是我的鹦鹉在跟我说话——其实,除了它,不可能有别人——但还是过了好一会儿,情绪才平静下来。首先,我感到诧异的是,这个小家伙是怎么跑到这个地方来的;其次,它怎么恰好就守在这里,而不是别处。不

by his Name Poll, the sociable Creature came to me, and sat upon my Thumb, as he used to do, and continu'd talking to me, Poor Robin Crusoe, and how did I come here? and where had I been? just as if he had been overjoy'd to see me again; and so I carry'd him Home along with me.

I had now had enough of rambling to Sea for some time, and had enough to do for many Days to sit still, and reflect upon the Danger I had been in: I would have been very glad to have had my Boat again on my Side of the Island; but I knew not how it was practicable to get it about as to the East Side of the Island, which I had gone round; I knew well enough there was no venturing that Way; my very heart would shrink, and my very Blood run chill but to think of it: And as to the other Side of the Island, I did not know how it might be there; but supposing the Current ran with the same Force against the Shore at the East as it pass'd by it on the other, I might run the same Risk of being driven down the Stream, and carry'd by the Island, as I had been before, of being carry'd away from it; so with these Thoughts I contented my self to be without any Boat, though it had been the Product of so many Months Labour to make it, and of so many more to get it unto the Sea.

In this Government of my Temper, I remain'd near a Year, liv'd a very sedate retir'd Life, as you may well suppose; and my Thoughts being very much composed as to my Condition, and fully comforted in resigning my self to the Dispositions

过,发现跟我说话的不是别人,而是我的波儿,我感到十分欣慰,也就不再惊恐了;我伸出手来,唤了一声它的名字"波儿",这只讨人喜欢的鸟儿,便向我飞来,和往常一样,站到了我的大拇指上,并且不停地跟我交谈:"可怜的鲁滨·克鲁索!"它问我怎么到这里来的,问我去了什么地方,就好像它再次见到我,多么兴高采烈似的。于是,我便带着它一同回了家。

我在海上漂泊了那么多天,受了那么多的罪,现在很想静静地休息几天,好好地回想一下这几天的危险经历。我还是很想把我的小独木舟弄到岛这边来,靠家近一点,可又实在想不出什么可行的办法来。岛的东部,我已走过一遭,并有所领教,再也不想去那里冒险了。一想起这次的冒险经历,我就会心惊胆寒,战栗不安。而我对岛西海岸的情况更是一无所知,如果那边的激流也像东边的一样湍急,我就会碰到同样的危险,被卷入急流而冲离海岸。想来想去,最后终于打算放弃舢板。虽说我费了那么长的时间把舢板制成,又花了更多的时间挖渠引水,把它放入海里,可我现在没法弄回来,也就不再想它了。

差不多有一年的工夫,我压制着自己的性子,过着一种恬静优闲的生活。我对于自己的环境,抱着一种非常心平气和的态度,同时把自己的命

of Providence, I thought I liv'd really very happily in all things, except that of Society.

I improv'd my self in this time in all the mechanick Exercises which my Necessities put me upon applying my self to, and I believe cou'd, upon Occasion, make a very good Carpenter, especially considering how few Tools I had.

Besides this, I arriv'd at an unexpected Perfection in my Earthen Ware, and contriv'd well enough to make them with a Wheel, which I found infinitely easyer and better; because I made things round and shapable, which before were filthy things indeed to look on. But I think I was never more vain of my own Performance, or more joyful for any thing I found out, than for my being able to make a Tobacco-Pipe. And tho' it was a very ugly clumsy thing, when it was done, and only burnt red like other Earthen Ware, yet as it was hard and firm, and would draw the Smoke, I was exceedingly comforted with it, for I had been always used to smoke, and there were Pipes in the Ship, but I forgot them at first, not knowing that there was Tobacco in the Island; and afterwards, when I search'd the Ship again, I could not come at any Pipes at all.

In my Wicker Ware also I improved much, and made abundance of necessary Baskets, as well as my Invention shew'd me, tho not very handsome, yet they were such as were very handy and convenient for my laying things up in, or fetching things home in. For Example, if I kill'd a Goat abroad, I could hang it up in a Tree, flea it, and dress it, and cut it in Pieces, and bring it home in a Basket, and the like by a Turtle, I could cut it up, take out the Eggs, and a Piece or two of the Flesh, which was enough for me, and bring them

运完全交给上天来安排，因此过得十分幸福，除了没有人同我往来之外，别无缺憾。

在这期间，我为了应付生活的需要，在各种技术上都有一些进步。我相信，总有一天，我会成为一名手艺高超的木匠，尤其是在工具缺乏的条件下，我也能有所作为。

此外，令人难以预料的是，我的陶器也做得相当完美。我想出了一个好方法，用一只轮盘来制造陶器，做起来又容易又好看。现在我做出来的器皿又圆又有样子，而过去做出来的东西看了也叫人恶心。但使我感到最自豪最高兴的是，居然还做成功了一只烟斗。尽管我做出来的这只烟斗又粗劣又难看，并且烧得和别的陶器一样红，可是却坚实耐用，烟管也抽得通。有了它，我就有了极大的安慰，因为我在过去是一直抽烟的，在那大船上就有好几个烟斗，但由于不知道这岛上有烟草，当初也就把它们忘了；后来再去船上找时，却连一个都没有找到。

在编柳条的技术方面，我也大有长进，并做出了大量的筐筐篓篓，反正需要什么样的，我就想办法编出来；虽说这些筐筐篓篓不怎么美观，但是用来放放东西，或者用来把东西搬回家来，却是非常方便的。比方说我在外面打死了一只野羊，可以把它往树上一挂，然后剥皮、放血、去头、去内脏，再切成一块一块的，放进

home in a Basket, and leave the rest behind me. Also large deep Baskets were my Receivers for my Corn, which I always rubb'd out as soon as it was dry, and cured, and kept it in great Baskets.

I began now to perceive my Powder abated considerably, and this was a Want which it was impossible for me to supply, and I began seriously to consider what I must do when I should have no more Powder; that is to say, how I should do to kill any Goat. I had, as is observ'd in the third Year of my being here, kept a young Kid, and bred her up tame, and I was in hope of getting a He-Goat, but I could not by any Means bring it to pass, 'till my Kid grew an old Goat; and I could never find in my Heart to kill her, till she dy'd at last of meer Age.

But being now in the eleventh Year of my Residence, and, as I have said, my Ammunition growing low, I set my self to study some Art to trap and snare the Goats, to see whether I could not catch some of them alive, and particularly I wanted a She-Goat great with young.

To this Purpose I made Snares to hamper them, and I do believe they were more than once taken in them, but my Tackle was not good, for I had no Wire; and I always found them broken, and my Bait devoured.

At length I resolv'd to try a Pit-fall, so I dug several large Pits in the Earth, in Places where I had observ'd the Goats used to feed, and over these Pits I plac'd Hurdles of my own baking too, with a great Weight upon them; and several times I put Ears of Barley, and dry Rice, without setting the Trap, and I could easily perceive that the

篮子里带回来;弄到个海龟也一样,我把它剖开,取出龟蛋,割下够我吃的肉放在篮里带回家,其余的就丢掉不要。一些大而深的筐子是用来盛粮食的。这些庄稼一晒干,我就搓出谷粒,加工处理,然后存放在大筐里,而不是谷仓里。

我注意到弹药已用去不少,这种必需品是无法补充的,我开始认真考虑一旦弹药没了,我该怎么办。也就是说,我用什么方法杀死山羊。前面我曾提到,上岛第三年,我捉到了一只雌的小山羊,经过驯养,它长大了。我希望弄到一只公羊与它配对,但一直没有成功。直到我的小羊变成了老羊,我不忍心杀它,最后让它寿终正寝。

现在,已是我来此居住的第十一年。我已说过,我的弹药正在减少,我决心试用夹子或陷阱的办法来捕捉山羊,看看我能否逮到几只活的,尤其是我非常想要一只怀孕的母山羊。

为此,我制作了几只夹子来捕捉它们,我确信它们曾不止一次地落到里边,但由于没有金属丝,我的装备做得不好。我总是发现被它们弄坏,诱饵被它们吃光。

后来,我决定用陷阱试一试。我在山羊经常吃草的地方挖了几处大陷阱,然后,又在陷阱上盖上我亲手做的篱笆,再在上面压一些重物。有几次,我在里面放了一些大麦穗和一些干稻子,但没有设圈

Goats had gone in and eaten up the Corn, for I could see the Mark of their Feet. At length I set three Traps in one Night, and going the next Morning I found them all standing, and yet the Bait eaten and gone: This was very discouraging. However, I alter'd my Trap, and, not to trouble you with Particulars, going one Morning to see my Trap, I found in one of them a large old He-Goat, and in one of the other, three Kids, a Male and two Females.

As to the old one, I knew not what to do with him, he was so fierce I durst not go into the Pit to him; that is to say, to go about to bring him away alive, which was what I wanted. I could have kill'd him, but that was not my Business, nor would it answer my End. So I e'en let him out, and he ran away as if he had been frighted out of his Wits: But I had forgot then what I learn'd afterwards, that Hunger will tame a Lyon. If I had let him stay there three or four Days without Food, and then have carry'd him some Water to drink, and then a little Corn, he would have been as tame as one of the Kids, for they are mighty sagacious tractable Creatures where they are well used.

However, for the present I let him go, knowing no better at that time; then I went to the three Kids, and taking them one by one, I tyed them with Strings together, and with some Difficulty brought them all home.

套。我后来一眼便看出，山羊是到过里面的，并把谷子都吃掉了，因为我看得出它们的脚印。再后来，我一个晚上设下了三个圈套。第二天早晨去看时，发现三个圈套都原封不动，而诱饵却被吃掉了，不见了。这真叫人灰心丧气。随后，我改制了陷阱，这其中的具体过程就不再细说了。总之，我终于在一个陷阱里套住了一只老公羊，在另一个陷阱里套住了三只小羊，一只公的，两只母的。

那只老公羊凶悍性野，简直不知怎么对付。我不敢走下陷阱，更不敢靠过去活捉它。当然，可以把它打死，可这不是现在该干的事，也不符合我的初衷，我的本意就是想活捉它。现在活捉不成，就只好把它给放了。这只老公羊一出陷阱，便像吓掉了魂似地逃之夭夭了。可我当时却忘了，我完全可以采用饥饿的办法制服它。连狮子都可以被饥饿驯服，如果我使它在陷阱里饿三、四天，不给它东西吃，然后再给它喝一点水吃一点谷子，它一定可如同小羊那般驯服，如果适当饲养这些山羊，它们就都会成为伶俐易驯的生灵。

可是，当时我还不知道有更好的办法，只好把它放走。然后，我就走到那些小羊那边去，把它们一只一只提出来，用细绳把它们拴在一起，又费了不少的困难，才把它们带回来。

It was a good while before they wou'd feed, but throwing them some sweet Corn, it tempted them and they began to be tame; and now I found that if I expected to supply my self with Goat-Flesh when I had no Powder or Shot left, breeding some up tame was my only way, when perhaps I might have them about my House like a Flock of Sheep.

But then it presently occurr'd to me, that I must keep the tame from the wild, or else they would always run wild when they grew up, and the only Way for this was to have some enclosed Piece of Ground, well fenc'd either with Hedge or Pale, to keep them in so effectually, that those within might not break out, or those without break in.

This was a great Undertaking for one Pair of Hands, yet as I saw there was an absolute Necessity of doing it, my first Piece of Work was to find out a proper Piece of Ground, viz. where there was likely to be Herbage for them to eat, Water for them to drink, and Cover to keep them from the Sun.

Those who understand such Enclosures will think I had very little Contrivance, when I pitch'd upon a Place very proper for all these, being a plain open Piece of Meadow-Land, or Savanna, (as our People call it in the Western Collonies,) which had two or three little Drills' of fresh Water in it, and at one end was very woody. I say they will smile at my Forecast, when I shall tell them I began my enclosing of this Piece of Ground in such a manner, that my Hedge or Pale must have been at least two Mile about. Nor was the Madness of it so great as to the Compass, for if it was ten Mile about I was like to have time enough to do it in. But I did not consider that my Goats would be as wild in so much Compass as if they had had the whole Island, and I should have so much Room to

它们好久都不肯吃东西；后来我丢给它们一些新鲜的玉米，吊它们的胃口，它们才慢慢驯服起来。我认为，如果我打算在弹药用尽之后能够吃到羊肉，唯一的办法就是养一些驯羊；将来说不定我家里会有一大群呢。

想到这里，我忽然又想到，我一定要隔开驯羊和野羊，否则它们长大后又会变野了。唯一的办法，就是找一块地方，用篱笆或木栅将四面牢牢地围起来，令里边的不会逃走，外边的不会冲进来。

我孤身一人，要圈地修筑篱笆无疑是一项巨大的工程，可这样做又是绝对必要的。所以，我首先得找到一块合适的地方，那儿既要有青草供山羊吃，又要有水供它们喝，并且还要有荫凉的地方供它们歇息。

我找到了一个十分合适的地方，以上三个条件样样具备。这是一大片平坦的草原，也就是西部殖民者所说的热带或亚热带那种树木稀疏的草原。草原上有两三条小溪，水流清澈，小溪尽头有不少树木。凡是对这类圈地之事有所了解的人，一定会认为我有些想入非非，而且如果我告诉他们，我已开始行动，根据我所要圈的这块地，篱笆或木栅将至少绵延两英里长，那么他们肯定会笑话我。倒不是这长度太大，因为即使要树篱十英里长，我也有足够的时间去

chace them in, that I should never catch them.

My Hedge was begun and carry'd on, I believe, about fifty Yards, when this Thought occurr'd to me, so I presently stopt short, and for the first beginning I resolv'd to enclose a Piece of about 150 Yards in length, and 100 Yards in breadth, which as it would maintain as many as I should have in any reasonable time, so as my Flock encreased, I could add more Ground to my Enclosure.

This was acting with some Prudence, and I went to work with Courage. I was about three Months hedging in the first Piece, and till I had done it I tether'd the three Kids in the best part of it, and us'd them to feed as near me as possible to make them familiar; and very often I would go and carry them some Ears of Barley, or a handful of Rice, and feed them out of my Hand; so that after my Enclosure was finished, and I let them loose, they would follow me up and down, bleating after me for a handful of Corn.

This answer'd my End, and in about a Year and half I had a Flock of about twelve Goats, Kids and all; and in two Years more I had three and forty, besides several that I took and kill'd for my Food. And after that I enclosed five several Pieces of Ground to feed them in, with little Pens to drive them into, to take them as I wanted, and Gates out of one Piece of Ground into another.

But this was not all, for now I not only had

做;而是这范围大得近乎疯狂,因为我没有考虑到,我的羊在这么大的一个范围里,其活动余地之大,同它们可以在整个岛上乱跑并无多大区别,而今后我要捉它们时,也就得在这个范围里追来追去,哪里还捉得住!

我开始动手做我的篱笆,但一直到做了五十码的时候,我才意识到了这一点。因此,我立刻停下来,决定开始先圈一块长一百五十码,宽一百码的地方。这在相当长一段时间内,可以容纳我的羊群,而当我的羊群增加时,我可以扩建我的篱笆。

这种办法还切实可行,所以我鼓足干劲,忙碌起来。用了大约三个月的时间我围好了第一块地。直到这篱笆完成时为止,我一直把我的三只小羊拴在最好的地方,使它们尽可能地在我身边吃东西,同我混熟。我常常带一些麦穗或一把谷子,让它们从我手上吃,篱笆修好后,我放开它们,让它们在篱笆内自由走动,它们仍老是跟在我后面咩咩地叫,求我给它们一把谷子。

我如愿以偿,一年半以后,我有大大小小十二只羊。又过了两年,除了杀掉吃掉之外我的羊增加到三十四只。这以后,我又围了五六块地放养羊群,同时我还插了一些小的篱笆,需要捉住它们的时候,就把它们赶到小篱笆里,五块地之间彼此还有门相通。

不过,好处还远不止这

Goats Flesh to feed on when I pleas'd, but Milk too, a thing which indeed in my beginning I did not so much as think of, and which, when it came into my Thoughts, was really an agreeable Surprize. For now I set up my Dairy, and had sometimes a Gallon or two of Milk in a Day. And as Nature, who gives Supplies of Food to every Creature, dictates even naturally how to make use of it; so I that had never milk'd a Cow, much less a Goat, or seen Butter or Cheese made, very readily and handily, tho' after a great many Essays and Miscarriages, made me both Butter and Cheese at last, and never wanted it afterwards.

How mercifully can our great Creator treat his Creatures, even in those Conditions in which they seem'd to be overwhelm'd in Destruction. How can he sweeten the bitterest Providences, and give us Cause to praise him for Dungeons and Prisons. What a Table was here spread for me in a Wilderness, where I saw nothing at first but to perish for Hunger.

It would have made a Stoick smile to have seen me and my little Family sit down to Dinner; there was my Majesty the Prince and Lord of the whole island; I had the Lives of all my Subjects at my absolute Command. I could hang, draw, give Liberty, and take it away, and no Rebels among all my Subjects.

Then to see how like a King I din'd too all alone, attended by my Servants, Poll, as if he had

些。因为,我现在不但有羊肉供我尽情享用,而且还有羊奶喝呢。这一层我起先没怎么想到,忽然想到这一层时,真是惊喜万分。现在,我已搭起了我的挤奶棚,有时,一天能挤到一两加仑的羊奶。看来,造物主不仅赐给每一个生命以食物,而且还指点他们,按照自然的法则去利用这些食物。我从来没有挤过牛奶,更不用说挤羊奶,也没有见过人家怎么做黄油和乳酪,但经过了许多尝试和失败之后,居然把黄油和乳酪做得很好,而且,后来一直不缺这两样东西吃。

伟大的造物主对自己亲手创造的生灵是多么慈悲啊!哪怕他们濒临灭亡、身处绝境也决不抛弃他们。他能把世间最苦难的命运变得甜蜜,即使我们身陷囹圄也会对他加以赞美。在这片最初认为只能把我饿死的荒野之中,上帝给我摆下了多么丰盛的筵席啊!

你要是看到我和我的小家庭坐在一处用饭的情形,即使你是一个斯多噶派的哲学家,你也不禁要微笑。我坐在那里,简直像全岛的君王。我对于我的全部臣民拥有绝对生杀之权;我可以把它们吊死,开膛破腹,给他们自由,或是剥夺他们的自由;而且,在我的臣民中间,根本没有叛逆者。

你看我用餐的时候,俨然像一位国王,一个人高高地坐

been my Favourite, was the only Person permitted to talk to me. My Dog who was now grown very old and crazy, and had found no Species to multiply his Kind upon, sat always at my Right Hand, and two Cats, one on one Side the Table, and one on the other, expecting now and then a Bit from my Hand, as a Mark of special Favour.

But these were not the two Cats which I brought on Shore at first, for they were both of them dead, and had been interr'd near my Habitation by my own Hand; but one of them having multiply'd by I know not what Kind of Creature, these were two which I had preserv'd tame, whereas the rest run wild in the Woods, and became indeed troublesom to me at last; for they would often come into my House, and plunder me too, till at last I was obliged to shoot them, and did kill a great many; at length they left me with this Attendance, and in this plentiful Manner I lived; neither could I be said to want any thing but Society, and of that in some time after this, I was like to have too much.

I was something impatient, as I have observ'd, to have the Use of my Boat; though very loath to run any more Hazards; and therefore sometimes I sat contriving Ways to get her about the Island, and at other Times I sat my self down contented enough without her. But I had a strange Uneasiness in my Mind to go down to the Point of the Island, where, as I have said, in my last Ramble, I went up the Hill to see how the Shore lay, and how the Current set, that I might see what I had to do: This Inclination encreas'd upon me every Day, and at length I resolv'd to travel thither by Land, following the Edge of the Shore. I did so: But had

在上面，臣仆们在旁边侍侯着。波儿仿佛是我的宠臣，只有它才被允许与我讲话。我的爱犬现在已又老又昏聩了，它总是坐在我右手；而那两只猫则各坐一边，不时地希望从我手里得到一点赏赐，并把此视为一种特殊的恩宠。

这两只猫已不是我最初从破船上带下来的那两只了，那两只早就死了，我亲自把它们葬在我的住所附近。不过其中一只不知同什么动物交配，生下了许多小猫。这两只就是我从那些小猫中留下来驯养起来的，其余的都跑到树林里成了野猫。那些野猫后来给我添了不少麻烦，因为它们经常跑到我家里来劫掠我的东西。最后我不得不开枪杀了许多，终于使它们全都跑掉，留下我同这些贴身侍从过着吃喝不愁的生活。可以说，现在我什么也不缺，要说缺，也只缺同我一样的人，但此后过了些日子，我倒差点一下子就嫌太多了。

我曾经说过，我有点迫不及待地想用用我那只舢板，但同时又不愿再冒风险，所以有时我坐在那里冥思苦索，想把它弄回岛的这边来，有时则颇为满足地一坐，觉得没有它也够好的了。但在我脑海里，总是有种奇怪的感觉，叫我安定不下来，总是想去岛上那个海走一趟——上回出门时，我曾爬上山去看海岸的情况、急流的走向以确定我该怎么办。我有一种说不出来的冲劲，很

any one in England been to meet such a Man as I was, it must either have frighted them, or rais'd a great deal of Laughter; and as I frequently stood still to look at my self, I could not but smile at the Notion of my travelling though Yorkshire with such an Equipage, and in such a Dress: Be pleas'd to take a Scetch of my Figure as follows, I had a great high shapeless Cap, made of a Goat's Skin, with a Flap hanging down behind, as well to keep the Sun from me, as to shoot the Rain off from running into my Neck; nothing being so hurtful in these Climates, as the Rain upon the Flesh under the Cloaths.

I had a short Jacket of Goat-Skin, the Skirts coming down to about the middle of my Thighs; and a Pair of open-knee'd Breeches of the same, the Breeches were made of the Skin of an old Hegoat, whose Hair hung down such a Length on either Side, that like Pantaloons it reach'd to the middle of my Legs; Stockings and Shoes I had none, but had made me a Pair of some-things, I scarce know what to call them, like Buskins to flap over my Legs, and lace on either Side like Spatter-dashes; but of a most barbarous Shape, as indeed were all the rest of my Cloaths.

I had on a broad Belt of Goats-Skin dry'd, which I drew together with two Thongs of the same, instead of Buckles, and in a kind of a Frog on either Side of this. Instead of a Sword and a Dagger, hung a little Saw and a Hatchet, one on one Side, one on the other. I had another Belt not so broad, and fasten'd in the same Manner, which hung over my Shoulder; and at the End of it, un-

想再去一趟那个山上能望见的海角。这种愿望一天比一天强烈,我最终决定沿海岸步行到那儿去。如果让英国人见到我的模样,他们不是吓一跳,就是会发出一片哄笑。我常静静地伫立着,打量自己,一想到自己以这副打扮和装备穿越约克城,不禁莞尔。我很愿意把自己的形象略微描上几笔。我头戴一顶又高又大的帽子,不像个样子,是由山羊皮制的,后边还拖着一块长长的帽边,既可以遮阳,又能挡住雨水,以免流进我的脖子。在这种气候中,雨水流到衣服和皮肉之间,是最恼人的事。

我上身穿一件由山羊皮做的短外衣,衣摆一直垂到大腿上,下穿一条开膝的裤子,也是用一只老公羊皮做的,上边有很长的毛,一直垂到我的小腿上,如同一条马裤。袜子和鞋子,我一样也没有。但我做出了一双有点像鞋袜的东西,真不知道该怎么叫它们才好。我把它们裹在两条小腿上,看上去既像鹿皮裤,又像皮绑腿。它们跟我其余所有的衣服一样,形状野蛮,难看至极。

我的腰上,系着一根用晒干的山羊皮制成的宽皮带。由于两端没有带扣,我就用两根窄羊皮系住。腰的两侧各有一个挂武器的小环,由于没有刀剑、匕首之类的东西可挂,我就挂了一把小锯子和一把斧子,一边挂一样。我另外

der my left Arm, hung two Pouches, both made of Goat's-Skin too; in one of which hung my Powder, in the other my Shot: At my Back I carry'd my Basket, on my Shoulder my Gun, and over my Head a great clumsy ugly Goat-Skin Umbrella, but which, after all, was the most necessary Thing I had about me, next to my Gun: As for my Face, the Colour of it was really not so Moletta-like as one might expect from a Man not at all careful of it, and living within nine or ten Degrees of the Equinox. My Beard I had once suffer'd to grow till it was about a Quarter of a Yard long; but as I had both Scissars and Razors sufficient, I had cut it pretty short, except what grew on my upper Lip, which I had trimm'd into a large Pair of Mahometan Whiskers, such as I had seen worn by some Turks, who I saw at Sallee; for the Moors did not wear such, tho' the Turks did; of these Muschatoes or Whiskers, I will not say they were long enough to hang my Hat upon them; but they were of a Length and Shape monstrous enough, and such as in England would have pass'd for frightful.

But all this is by the by; for as to my Figure, I had so few to observe me, that it was of no manner of Consequence; so I say no more to that Part. In this kind of Figure I went my new Journey, and was out five or six Days. I travell'd first along the Sea Shore, directly to the Place where I first brought my Boat to an Anchor, to get up upon the Rocks; and having no Boat now to take care of, I went over the Land a nearer Way to the same Height that I was upon before, when looking forward to the Point of the Rocks which lay out, and which I was oblig'd to double with my Boat, as is said above: I was surpriz'd to see the Sea all smooth and quiet, no Ripling, no Motion, no

还有一条没有这么宽的皮带，两端也是用羊皮条系的，我用它斜搭在右肩上，下端斜到左胳膊下面。我在上面挂着两个皮囊，一个装着火药，一个装着子弹。我身上背着一个筐，肩上扛着一杆枪，手上还撑着一把又丑又笨的大羊皮伞。这把伞和我的枪一样总是随身携带，是出门必不可少的物品。再看我的脸。虽说住在靠赤道只有十来度的地方，但脸色还没黑得像那些不修边幅的穆拉托人。我的胡子曾经长到九英寸那么长，不过我有好几把剪刀和剃刀，所以后来把下唇的胡子修剪得很短，只蓄上唇的胡须并修饰成穆斯林式的八字胡，就像我在萨利见到的土耳其人一样。这种式样摩尔人不大时兴，而在土耳其人当中挺流行。虽不敢说这副胡子长得可以挂我的帽子，但它的确又长又密，要是在英国给人看见，准保吓人一大跳。

不过这些都与本题无关；我不太注意外表，反正没有多少人看到我，我的外表如何是无关紧要的；因而如今暂且不提。我带着这副尊容走路，似乎走了五、六天。刚开始沿着海岸向我以前泊船登山的地方走了过去，到了那边，由于用不着看守船只，就抄了近路，爬到以前登过的那座小山岗上。然而我却没想到当我向以前绕驶的那海角一带望去时，不觉吓了一跳，因为海面风平浪静，没一点儿动静，

Current, any more there than in other Places.

I was at a strange Loss to understand this, and resolv'd to spend some Time in the observing it, to see if nothing from the Sets of the Tide had occasion'd it; but I was presently convinc'd how it was, viz. That the Tide of Ebb setting from the West, and joyning with the Current of Waters from some great River on the Shore, must be the Occasion of this Current; and that according as the Wind blew more forcibly from the West, or from the North, this Current came nearer, or went farther from the Shore; for waiting thereabouts till Evening, I went up to the Rock again, and then the Tide of Ebb being made, I plainly saw the Current again as before, only, that it run farther off, being near half a League from the Shore; whereas in my Case, it set close upon the Shore, and hurry'd me and my Canoe along with it, which at another Time it would not have done.

This Observation convinc'd me, That I had nothing to do but to observe the Ebbing and the Flowing of the Tide, and I might very easily bring my Boat about the Island again: But when I began to think of putting it in Practice, I had such a Terror upon my Spirits at the Remembrance of the Danger I had been in, that I could not think of it again with any Patience; but on the contrary, I took up another Resolution which was more safe, though more laborious; and this was, That I would build, or rather make me another Periagua or Canoe; and so have one for one Side of the Island, and one for the other.

You are to understand, that now I had, as I may call it, two Plantations in the Island; one my little Fortification or Tent, with the Wall about it under the Rock, with the Cave behind me, which by this Time I had enlarg'd into several Apartments, or Caves, one within another. One of these, which was the dryest, and largest, and had

没一点儿急流，与别的海域一模一样。

对于这个现象我简直莫名其妙，决心花些时间，看看它是否与退潮有关系。不久我就明白了它的奥妙，原来那急流是由西边退下来的潮水与沿岸某一条大河的倾泻汇合而成的；而且，要看西方的风力大还是北方的风力大，来决定急流离岸的远近。等到傍晚，我重新爬到山上，这时正值退潮，我又分明看到了那股急流，不过这回已离岸有一英里半远，不像那样近了。所不同的是，我上次来时，它恰好流得离岸很近，所以把我的船给冲走了；在别的时候，它是不会这样的。

这次观察使我确信，只要注意潮水的涨落，我可以很容易把舢板弄到我住地所在的那一边。但当我想把自己的主意付诸实施的时候，又想到了上次所经历的危险，不由心惊肉跳，连想也不敢想了。于是，我作了一个新的决定，那就是再造一条独木舟。这样，我在岛的这边有一只，岛的那边也有一只。这样做虽然比较费力，但却比较安全。

你们要知道，现在我在岛上已有了两个庄园——我也许可以这么称呼我的两处住所。一处是我的那个小小的城堡或帐篷，它倚着崖壁，前面有堵围墙，后面有个山洞，而这个洞现在已被我扩大为

a Door out beyond my Wall or Fortification; that is to say, beyond where my Wall joyn'd to the Rock, was all fill'd up with the large Earthen Pots, of which I have given an Account, and with fourteen or fifteen great Baskets, which would hold five or six Bushels each, where I laid up my Stores of Provision, especially my Corn, some in the Ear cut off short from the Straw, and the other rubb'd out with my Hand.

A for my Wall made, as before, with long Stakes or Piles, those Piles grew all like Trees, and were by this Time grown so big, and spread so very much, that there was not the least Appearance to any one's View of any Habitation behind them.

Near this Dwelling of mine, but a little farther within the Land, and upon lower Ground, lay my two Pieces of Corn-Ground, which I kept duly cultivated and sow'd, and which duly yielded me their Harvest in its Season; and whenever I had occasion for more Corn, I had more Land adjoyning as fit as that.

Besides this, I had my Country Seat, and I had now a tollerable Plantation there also; for first, I had my little Bower, as I call'd it, which I kept in Repair; that is to say, I kept the Hedge which circled it in, constantly fitted up to its usual Height, the Ladder standing always in the Inside; I kept the Trees which at first were no more than my Stakes, but were now grown very firm and tall; I kept them always so cut, that they might spread and grow thick and wild, and make the more agreeable Shade, which they did effectually to my Mind. In the Middle of this I had my Tent always standing, being a piece of a Sail spread over Poles

好几个部分,或者说,已被我扩展成好几个洞,一一相接。其中最大也最干燥的一个洞,开有一扇门,出了门也就到了我那防御工事的坚壁之外,也就是说,在那堵墙与岩壁结合处之外;这个大洞里放满了我说过的大陶罐,还有十四五只筐子,每只筐子都有五六个蒲式耳的容量,我的食粮,特别是那些谷物,就贮放在这些筐子里,它们有的是庄稼头上割下的穗子,有的是已被我搓了下来的麦粒或谷粒。

我的围墙是以前用木桩围起来的,这些木桩已长成大树,它们长得那么高,那么茂密,把我的住宅围得严严实实,谁也别想发现有人在这里居住。

这一处住宅附近,更靠近内陆的低地上有我的两块田,我按时播种耕种,两块地按时在成熟季节产粮,如果我需要更多的粮食,我就在毗邻处挖更多的同样肥沃的地。

除此以外,我还有自己的别墅,那里也有一座很不错的庄园。我有一个小茅屋(我这么称呼它),我不断地加以修整,也就是说,我总是把围着茅屋的墙修得高度相当,梯子总是放在墙里边。那些树,起初只不过是一些木桩子,现在长得又高大又结实。我总是不断地修整它们,以使它们向四周伸展,长得枝繁叶茂,绿荫重重,而这些树真是长得合乎我心意。篱墙中央,总是支

set up for that Purpose, and which never wanted any Repair or Renewing; and under this I had made me a Squab or Couch, with the Skins of the Creatures I had kill'd, and with other soft Things, and a Blanket laid on them, such as belong'd to our Sea-Bedding, which I had saved, and a great Watch-Coat to cover me; and here, whenever I had Occasion to be absent from my chief Seat, I took up my Country Habitation.

Adjoyning to this I had my Enclosures for my Cattle, that is to say, my Goats: And as I had taken an inconceivable deal of Pains to fence and enclose this Ground, so I was so uneasy to see it kept entire, lest the Goats should break thro', that I never left off till with infinite Labour I had stuck the Out-side of the Hedge so full of small Stakes, and so near to one another, that it was rather a Pale than a Hedge, and there was scarce Room to put a Hand thro' between them, which afterwards when those Stakes grew, as they all did in the next rainy Season, made the Enclosure strong like a Wall, indeed stronger than any Wall.

This will testify for me that I was not idle, and that I spared no Pains to bring to pass whatever appear'd necessary for my comfortable Support; for I consider'd the keeping up a Breed of tame Creatures thus at my Hand, would be a living Magazine of Flesh, Milk, Butter and Cheese, for me as long as I liv'd in the Place, if it were to be forty Years; and that keeping them in my Reach, depended entirely upon my perfecting my Enclosures to such a Degree, that I might be of keeping them together; which by this Method indeed I so effectually secur'd, that when these little Stakes began to grow, I had planted them so very thick, I was forced to pw some of them up again.

着我的帐篷。它是用一块帆布做成的,用柱子支着,从来不需要修理或重搭。帐篷的下面,我用我所打到的动物的皮毛和别的软东西,做了一张长沙发或软床,又用一条我们海船上睡觉用的毯子铺在上面,再用一件水手值更穿的大衣作我的被子。每当我偶尔离开我的"总部",就到我的"乡间别墅"来住。

与此相连的,便是我用来圈养山羊的篱笆。因为吃了千辛万苦来圈这块地方,所以,我总想把它弄得很严密,生怕山羊从里面钻出来。我花了无穷的力气,在篱笆的外面叉插了一圈密密的小树桩。桩和桩之间靠得那么紧,与其说这是一道篱墙,不如说它是一道栅栏,其空隙小得简直插不进一只手。到后来,经过了一个雨季,小树桩全都成活,到现在已长成了一堵坚固结实的围墙。

这一切足以说明我从来都没游手好闲过。为了丰衣足食,生活舒适,凡是需要做的事情,我都会不遗余力而为之。我认为驯养一群山羊之类的牲畜,等于替自己建立了一座肉、奶、奶油和奶酪等食品的活仓库,无论我在岛上活多久,哪怕是四十年,也会取之不尽,用之不竭。另外,要想伸手就能抓住驯养的牲畜,就得把篱笆修筑得极为严密牢固,绝不能让它们逃跑。这工作我做得非常成功,甚至后来那些树桩长大时,倒由于植得

In this Place also I had my Grapes growing, which I principally depended on for my Winter Store of Raisins; and which I never fail'd to preserve very carefully, as the best and most agreeable Dainty of my whole Diet; and indeed they were not agreeable only, but physical, whole-some, nourishing, and refreshing to the last Degree.

As this was also about half Way between my other Habitation, and the Place where I had laid up my Boat, I generally stay'd, and lay here in my Way thither; for I used frequently to visit my Boat, and I kept all Things about or belonging to her in very good Order; sometimes I went out in her to divert my self, but no more hazardous Voyages would I go, nor scarce ever above a Stone's Cast or two from the Shore, I was so apprehensive of being hurry'd out my Knowledge again by the Currents, or Winds, or any ether Accident. But now I come to a new Scene of my Life. It happen'd one Day about Noon going towards my Boat, I was exceedingly surpriz'd with the Print of a Man's naked Foot on the Shore, which was very plain to be seen in the Sand: I stood like one Thunder-struck, or as if I had seen an Apparition; I listen'd, I look'd round me, I could hear nothing, nor see any Thing, I went up to a rising Ground to look farther, I went up the Shore and down the Shore, but it was all one, I could see no other Impression but that one, I went to it again to see if there were any more, and to observe if it might not be my Fancy; but there was no Room for that, for there was exactly the very Print of a Foot, Toes, Heel, and every Part of a Foot; how it came thither, I knew not, nor could in the least imagine. But after innumerable fluttering Thoughts, like a Man perfectly confus'd and out of my self, I came Home to my Fortification, not feeling, as we say, the Ground I went on, but terrify'd to the last Degree, looking behind me at

在这里，我又培植了一些葡萄，我每年冬天贮藏的葡萄干，主要就靠它们。我照例小心翼翼把它们保藏起来，作为我食物中最好的、最可口的美味；真的，它们不仅仅好吃，而且能够去病延年，营养提神。

由于这地方正处于我的住所和我停船的地方的中途，我每次到那边去的时候，总要在这里停留一下；因为我经常要去看看我的舢板，把上面的东西整理整理。有时我也驾着它出去消遣消遣，但我再也不敢离岸太远冒险远航了，唯恐无意中被急流、大风或其他意外事故把我冲走或刮走。然而，正在这时我生活却发生了新的变化。一天中午，我正走去看我的船，忽然在海边上发现一个人的脚印；那是一个赤脚的脚印，清清楚楚地印在沙滩上。这简直把我吓坏了。我呆呆地站在那里，犹如挨了一个晴天霹雳，又像大白天见到了鬼。我侧耳倾听，又环顾四周，可什么也没有听到，什么也没有看到。我跑上高地，向远处眺望，又在海边来回跑了几遍，可还是毫无结果。除了那个脚印外，见不到别的脚印；我走回那脚印边，想看看到底是不是只有这个脚印，到底是不是我的幻觉；但毫无怀疑的余地，因为这确确实实是一只脚的脚印，脚趾、脚跟和脚的各个部分的印痕一应俱全。这脚印怎么会出现在这儿？对此我既一无所知，也完

every two or three Steps, mistaking every Bush and Tree, and fancying every Stump at a Distance to be a Man; nor is it possible to describe how many various Shapes affrighted Imagination represented Things to me in, how many wild Ideas were found every Moment in my Fancy, and what strange unaccountable Whimsies came into my Thoughts by the Way.

When I came to my Castle, for so I think I call'd it ever after this, I fled into it like one pursued; whether I went over by the Ladder as first contriv'd, or went in at the Hole in the Rock, which I call'd a Door, I cannot remember; no, nor could I remember the next Morning, for never frighted Hare fled to Cover, or Fox to Earth, with more Terror of Mind than I to this Retreat.

I slept none that Night; the farther I was from the Occasion of my Fright, the greater my Apprehensions were, which is something contrary to the Nature of such Things, and especially to the usual Practice of all Creatures in Fear: But I was so embarrass'd with my own frightful Ideas of the Thing, that I form'd nothing but dismal Imaginations to my self, even tho' I was now a great way off of it. Sometimes I fancy'd it must be the Devil; and Reason joyn'd in with me upon this Supposition: For how should any other Thing in human Shape come into the Place? Where was the Vessel that brought them? What Marks was there of any other Footsteps? And how was it possible a Man

全无法想象。我心慌意乱,神不守舍,心里七上八下地胡乱想了一阵之后,真是害怕到了极点,连忙打道回我那防御工事,也不知道自己是怎么走回来的,反正走了两三步就要回头瞧瞧,见到一些树也要疑神疑鬼,看到远处的树桩,也会误认为是个人影;一路上,许多形态各异的东西都使我想入非非,惊惶不已;而我神魂颠倒的想象中,在时时生出许多不着边际的怪念头;至于我脑海里的怪念头有多离奇,多荒诞,那就真是一言难尽了。

我一跑进我的城堡,我以后就这样称呼它好了,就立刻钻了进去,仿佛有人追赶似的。至于我是像当初设计的那样,通过梯子爬进去的,还是通过被我称为小门的山岩上的洞口爬进去的,到了第二天早晨我仍然记不起来。我逃跑时的害怕程度,就是兔子往窝里逃,狐狸往洞里逃也从不曾像我这般恐惧。

那夜我一宿未睡。通常生物离受惊地点愈远,心就愈安定,我却恰恰相反。我被种种幻想所困扰,越想越怕,即使是离它很远,却还在吓唬自己。有时候,我幻想这是魔鬼来了,为此还举出一大堆理由:其他具备人形的东西怎么上得了这个地方? 带他们上这儿来的船又在哪儿? 其他脚印呢? 人怎么能上得了这儿来? 不过,奇怪的是撒旦为什么选这么一个地方化为人形,实在无此必要,在他身后

should come there? But then to think that Satan should take human Shape upon him in such a Place where there could be no manner of Occasion for it, but to leave the Print of his Foot behind him, and that even for no Purpose too, for he could not be sure I should see it; this was an Amusement the other Way; I consider'd that the Devil might have found out abundance of other Ways to have terrify'd me than this of the single Print of a Foot. That as I liv'd quite on the other Side of the Island, he would never have been so simple to leave a Mark in a Place where 'twas Ten Thousand to one whether I should ever see it Or not, and in the Sand too, which the first Surge of the Sea upon a high Wind would have defac'd entirely: All this seem'd inconsistent with the Thing it self, and with all the Notions we usually entertain of the Subtilty of the Devil.

Abundance of such Things as these assisted to argue me out' of all Apprehensions of its being the Devil: And I presently concluded then, that it must be some more dangerous Creature, (viz.) That it must be some of the Savages of the main Land over-against me, who had wander'd out to Sea in their Canoes; and either driven by the Currents, or by contrary Winds had made the Island; and had been on Shore, but were gone away again to Sea, being as loth, perhaps, to have stay'd in this desolate Island, as I would have been to have had them.

While these Reflections were rowling upon my Mind, I was very thankful in my Thoughts, that I was so happy as not to be thereabouts at that Time, or that they did not see my Boat, by which they would have concluded that some Inhabitants had been in the Place, and perhaps have search'd farther for me: Then terrible Thoughts rack'd my Imagination about their having found my Boat, and that there were People here; and that if so, I

留下一个脚印也毫无意义,因为他不能肯定我会看见;从另一方面来看,这未免可笑。我想,如果魔鬼真的想吓唬我,他可以找到别的许多办法,断不至于用这个孤零零的脚印来吓唬我。况且,我是居住在远离脚印的岛的另一端,他不至于头脑这么简单,把脚印留在我几乎没有可能看到的地方。再说,那脚印是留在沙滩上的,只要海上一起大风,海浪就会把它冲得毫无痕迹。所以,所有这些猜想都好像站不住脚,不符合事理,因为,根据我们通常的理解,魔鬼往往是狡猾的。

所有这些推断都证明,我对魔鬼的恐惧是没有道理的。于是,我立刻就得出了另一个结论:那一定是某种更具危险性的物种在作祟。就是说,是岛对面大陆上的野人们光顾此岛了。他们大概划着独木舟在海上游荡,不是碰上了急流,就是碰上了逆风,碰巧到了我的岛上。可能他们上岸后又不愿意留在这里,所以就又返回了海上,否则我早就该发现他们了。

当这些想法在头脑中闪动的时候,我起初为自己感到十分庆幸,庆幸自己幸好当时没在现场,也没让他们发现我的舢板,要是船给他们看见了,他们一定会断定小岛上有居民,说不定要进一步搜寻我。可是紧接着,我又往可怕的方面胡思乱想起来,觉得他

should certainly have them come again in greater Numbers, and devour me; that if it should happen so that they should not find me, yet they would find my Enclosure, destroy all my Corn, carry away all my Flock of tame Goats, and I should perish at last for meer Want.

Thus my Fear banish'd all my religious Hope; all that former Confidence in God which was founded upon such wonderful Experience as I had had of his Goodness, now vanished, as if he that had fed me by Miracle hitherto, could not preserve by his Power the Provision which he had made for me by his Goodness: I reproach'd my self with my Easiness, that would not sow any more Corn one Year than would just serve me till the next Season, as if no Accident could intervene to prevent my enjoying the Crop that was upon the Ground; and this I thought so just a Reproof, that I resolv'd for the future to have two or three Years Corn beforehand, so that whatever might come, I might not perish for want of Bread.

How strange a Chequer Work of Providence is the Life of Man! and by what secret differing Springs are the Affections hurry'd about as differing Circumstance present To Day we love what to Morrow we hate; to Day we seek what to Morrow we shun; to Day we desire what to Morrow we fear; nay even tremble at the Apprehensions of; this was exemplify'd in me at this Time in the most lively Manner imaginable; for I whose only Affliction was, that I seem'd banished from human Society, that I was alone, circumscrib'd by the boundless Ocean, cut off from Mankind, and condemn'd to what I call'd silent Life; that I was as one who Heaven thought not worthy to be

们业已发现了我的舢板,并且已经发现这岛上有人了。又想,如果是那样的话,他们一定会有更多的人前来,把我吃掉;就算他们找不到我,他们也会找到我的篱笆,把我的谷物通通毁掉,把我的羊只通通劫走,最后,我只好活活地饿死。

恐惧心理驱走了我的全部宗教希望;我从前因为亲身受到上帝的好处而产生的对上帝的信仰,现在完全消失了,过去,上帝用神迹赐给我食物;而现在,我似乎认为他竟无力来保护他所赐给我的食物了。于是,我责备自己贪图安逸的生活,不肯多种一些粮食,只图能接得上下一季吃的就算了,好像不会发生什么意外似的,认为我一定能享用地里收获的谷物。这种自我谴责是有道理的,所以我决定以后一定要屯积好两三年的粮食。这样,无论发生什么事,也不致于因缺乏粮食而饿死。

天命难测,使人生显得多么光怪陆离,变化无穷啊! 在不同的环境下,人的感情又怎样变幻无常啊! 我们今天所爱的,往往是我们明天就会恨的;今天我们一心追求的,明天我们会避之唯恐不及;今天我们巴望的,明天会叫我们害怕,对,怕得甚至见它来就发抖;在这方面,当时的我就是一个绝顶生动的例子;因为我曾认为,我的最大苦恼就是被排除在人类社会之外,孤零零地被无边无际的大海所包围,

number'd among the Living, or to appear among the rest of his Creatures; that to have seen one of my own Species, would have seem'd to me a Raising me from Death to Life, and the greatest Blessing that Heaven it self, next to the supreme Blessing of Salvation, could bestow; I say, that I should now tremble at the very Apprehensions of seeing a Man, and was ready to sink into the Ground at but the Shadow or silent Appearance of a Man's having set his Foot in the Island.

Such is the uneven State of human Life: And it afforded me a great many curious Speculations afterwards, when I had a little recover'd my first Surprize; I consider'd that this was the Station of Life the infinitely wise and good Providence of God had determin'd for me, that as I could not foresee what the Ends of Divine Wisdom might be in all this, so I was not to dispute his Sovereignty, who, as I was his Creature, had an undoubted Right by Creation to govern and dispose of me absolutely as he thought fit; and who, as I was a Creature who had offended him, had likewise a judicial Right to condemn me to what Punishment he thought fit; and that it was my Part to submit to bear his Indignation, because I had sinn'd against him.

I then reflected that God, who was not only Righteous but Onmipotent, as he had thought fit thus to punish and afflict me, so he was able to deliver me; that if he did not think fit to do it, 'twas my unquestion'd Duty to resign my self absolutely and entirely to his Will; and on the other Hand, it was my Duty also to hope in him, pray

同人类隔绝,过的是一种遭到天罚的我所谓无声无息的生活;我曾认为,在上苍的眼里,我不配混迹于芸芸众生之中,不配在他创造的生灵中抛头露面;我曾认为,如果能让我见到我的一个同类,那么对我来说,简直就是起死回生,就是老天所能对我的莫大恩典,因为比这再大的恩典只能是让我的灵魂得救了;可是现在,光是想到我也许会见到一个人,我居然会不寒而栗;光是看到个人影,看到有个人悄无声息地出现在岛上,我就巴不得有个地洞可钻。

人生就是这样变幻无常。当我从第一次打击中恢复过来后,我由此而产生了许多稀奇古怪的想法,我觉得是法力无边的仁慈上帝为我规定了这种生活方式。由于我不能预见神圣智慧在这些事件中的用意,我不能对上帝的权威提出质疑,我是上帝的子民,是他创造了我,毫无疑问,他有绝对权力用他认为合适的方式安排我的命运。不仅如此,我还是个冒犯过他的罪民,他有不可辩驳的权力判定我该受什么样的惩罚。我对他的震怒应该接受和服从,因为我在他面前我是有罪的。

我转而又想到,既然上帝不仅是公正的而且是万能的,他认为应当这样来惩罚和折磨我,他当然也能拯救我。如果他认为不应当拯救我,绝对地、完全地服从他的意志也是我责无旁贷的责任。另一方

to him, and quietly to attend the Dictates and Directions of his daily Providence.

These Thoughts took me up many Hours, Days; nay, I may say, Weeks and Months; and one particular Effect of my Cogitations on this Occasion, I cannot omit, viz. One Morning early, lying in my Bed, and fill'd with Thought about my Danger from the Appearance of Savages, I found it discompos'd me very much, upon which those Words of the Scripture came into my Thoughts, Call upon me in the Day of Trouble, and I will deliver, and thou shalt glorify me.

Upon this, rising chearfully out of my Bed, my Heart was not only comforted, but I was guided and encourag'd to pray earnestly to God for Deliverance: When I had done praying, I took up my Bible, and opening it to read, the first Words that presented to me, were, Wait on the Lord, and be of good Cheer, and he shall strengthen thy Heart; wait, I say, on the Lord: It is impossible to express the Comfort this gave me. In Answer, I thankfully laid down the Book, and was no more sad, at least, not on that Occasion.

In the middle of these Cogitations, Apprehensions and Reflections, it came into my Thought one Day, that all this might be a meer Chimera of my own; and that this Foot might be the Print of my own Foot, when I came on Shore from my Boat: This chear'd me up a little too, and I began to perswade my self it was all a Delusion; that it was nothing else but my own Foot, and why might not I come that way from the Boat, as well

面,我的责任就是我对他充满希望,祈祷,静静地服从他每天的吩咐和指示。

这些想法在我的脑海中盘桓了好几个小时,好几天,不,甚至有好几个星期,好几个月。总之,这件事对我影响很大,我想了很多,特别是有一点收获我不得不在这里交待一下:一天早上,我正躺在床上,满脑子里想到的都是野人的出现会给我带来的危险。这一担心弄得我惶惶不安。可就在这时,《圣经》上的那段话又涌现在我的脑海:"要在患难之日求告我,我必搭救你,你也要荣耀我。"

想起这几句话,我仿佛受到了某种指引和鼓舞,顿时来了精神。我兴奋地下了床,开始虔诚地祷告起来,默默地祈求上帝的搭救。做完祈祷后,我又虔诚地打开《圣经》,下面这段话便一下子跃入眼帘:"等候上帝吧,你要满怀信心,坚定不移。等候上帝吧!"我简直无法用笔墨来形容这些话带给我的那种深深的安慰。我满怀感激地放下《圣经》,忧伤愁苦的心情得以暂时的安宁。

我正这样东想西想,疑神疑鬼,反省默想的时候,忽然有一天,我觉得这一切也许是我个人的幻觉,那脚印也许是我下船登岸时留下的。这样一想,我的精神稍稍为之一振,并且开始使自己相信这都是我个人的幻觉,相信那只不过是我自己的脚印。我想,我

as I was going that way to the Boat; again, I consider'd also that I could by no Means tell for certain where I had trod, and where I had not; and that if at last this was only the Print of my own Foot, I had play'd the Part of those Fools, who strive to make stories of Spectres, and Apparitions; and then are frighted at them more than any body.

Now I began to take Courage, and to peep abroad again; for I had not stirr'd out of my Castle for three Days and Nights; so that I began to starve for Provision; for I had little or nothing within Doors, but some Barley Cakes and water. Then I knew that my Goats wanted to be milk'd too, which usually was my Evening Diversion; and the poor Creatures were in great Pain and Inconvenience for want of it; and indeed, it almost spoil'd some of them, and almost dry'd up their Milk.

Heartning my self therefore with the Belief that this was nothing but the Print of one of my own Feet, and so I might be truly said to start at my own Shadow, I began to go abroad again, and went to my Country House, to milk my Flock; but to see with what Fear I went forward, how often I look'd behind me, how I was ready every now and then to lay down my Basket, and run for my Life, it would have made any one have thought I was haunted with an evil Conscience, or that I had been lately most terribly frighted, and so indeed I had.

However, as I went down thus two or three Days, and having seen nothing, I began to be a little bolder; and to think there was really nothing in it, but my own Imagination: But I cou'd not perswade my self fully of this, till I should go down to the Shore again, and see this Print of a Foot, and measure it by my own, and see if there was any Similitude or Fitness, that I might be

既然能在那地方上船,为什么不能在那地方下船呢?我又想,究竟我踩过什么地方,没踩过什么地方,我自己也无从确定。如果将来有一天发现那不过是我自己的脚印,那我就活像那些傻瓜,自己想法子编造出一套鬼怪故事,而自己倒比别人更大惊小怪。

于是,我又鼓起勇气,想到外面去看看。我已经三天三夜没有走出城堡了,家里快断粮了,只剩一些大麦饼和水。另外,我还想到,那些山羊也该挤奶了,这项工作一直是我傍晚的消遣。那些可怜的家伙好久没挤奶,一定痛苦不安。事实上,由于长久没有挤奶,有好几只几乎已挤不出奶而糟蹋掉了。

相信那不过是自己的脚印,这一切只是自己在吓自己,我就壮起胆子重新外出了,并跑到我的乡间别墅去挤羊奶。但我一边战战兢兢往前走,一边时时回头张望,准备随时随地撂下背篓逃命;谁要是见了我这副模样,准以为我是做过坏事才这样惴惴不安,要不,就是新近给吓破了胆,这倒是没错。

这样去了两三天,没发现什么意外情况,胆子也就渐渐地大了点,并开始认为确实是我捕风捉影,无中生有。不过我也没法让我完全相信这点,除非再去那岸边,重新看看那脚印,并把我的脚踏在那脚印上比比,看看脚型和大小是不

assur'd it was my own Foot: But when I came to the Place, First, It appear'd evidently to me, that when I laid up my Boat, I could not possibly be on Shore any where there about. Secondly, When I came to measure the Mark with my own Foot, I found my Foot not so large by a great deal; both these Things fill'd my Head with new Imaginations, and gave me the Vapours again, to the highest Degree; so that I shook with cold, like one in an Ague: And I went Home again, fill'd with the Belief that some Man Or Men had been on Shore there; or in short, that the Island was inhabited, and I might be surpriz'd before I was aware; and what course to take for my Security I knew not.

O what ridiculous Resolution Men take, when possess'd with Fear! It deprives them of the Use of those Means which Reason offers for their Relief. The first Thing I propos'd to my self, was, to throw down my Enclosures, and turn all my tame Cattle wild into the Woods, that the Enemy might not find them; and then frequent the Island in Prospect of the same, or the like Booty: Then to the simple' Thing of Digging up my two Corn Fields, that they might not find such a Grain there, and still be prompted to frequent the Island; then to demolish my Bower, and Tent, that they might not see any Vestiges of Habitation, and be prompted to look farther, in order to find out the Persons inhabiting.

These were the Subject of the first Night's Cogitation, after I was come Home again, while the Apprehensions which had so over-run my Mind were fresh upon me, and my Head was full of Vapours, as above: Thus Fear of Danger is ten thousand Times more terrifying than Danger it self, when apparent to the Eyes; and we find the Burthen of Anxiety greater by much, than the Evil which we are anxious about; and which was worse than all this, I had not that Relief in this

是一样，这才能断定这究竟是不是我的脚印。但我来到那里之后，第一件让我看得清楚明白的情况是：要是我把船停在那儿的话，我在岸上无论如何也不可能走到那一带去的。其次，我比划了一下，我的脚没那么大。这两件事使我心中重新充满无数新的妄念，我忧悒无比，像害了疟疾似的颤抖不已。我奔回家，满脑子想的是，已有人上岸，这岛上住上了人，也许我还未清醒过来就已遭到袭击。可该采取什么防卫措施，我茫然不知。

唉，极度惊慌的人会产生多么荒唐的计划！他们完全丧失了用理智搭救自己的能力。我首先想到的是毁掉篱笆，把全部驯羊放走，这样敌人就不会发现这儿有驯羊，也就不会经常上这个岛上来劫掠；其次，我打算索性挖掉我那块谷田，以免他们在那里找到谷物，更经常到岛上来。然后，拆掉我的茅屋和帐篷，免得让他们看出有人居住的痕迹后，再进一步搜寻，找出在此居住的人来。

这些都是我再次回到家里以后第一个晚上所想到的问题。此时，各种忧虑萦绕在我的脑海里，种种想法充满我的大脑，使我火往上冒。所以，对危险的恐惧，比所见的危险本身更能千万倍地让人胆战心惊，更糟糕的是，我平时总是听天由命，现在灾祸来了，我再也无法从中得到一些抚

— 194 —

Trouble from the Resignation I used to practice, that I hop'd to have. I look'd, I thought, like Saul, who complain'd not only that the Philistines were upon him; but that God had forsaken him; for I did not now take due Ways to compose my Mind, by crying to God in my Distress, and resting upon his Providence, as I had done before, for my Defence and Deliverance; which if I had done, I had, at least, been more cheerfully supported under this new Surprise, and perhaps carry'd through it with more Resolution.

This Confusion of my Thoughts kept me waking all Night; but in the Morning I fell asleep, and having by the Amusement of my Mind, been, as it were, tyr'd, and my Spirits exhausted; I slept very soundly, and wak'd much better compos'd than I had ever been before; and now I began to think sedately; and upon the utmost Debate with my self, I concluded, That this Island, which was so exceeding pleasant, fruitful, and no farther from the main Land than as I had seen, was not so entirely abandon'd as I might imagine: That altho' there were no stated Inhabitants who liv'd on the Spot; yet that there might sometimes come Boats off from the Shore, who either with Design, or perhaps never, but when they were driven by cross Winds, might come to this Place.

That I had liv'd here fifteen Years now, and had not met with the least Shadow or Figure of any People yet; and that if at any Time they should be driven here, it was probable they went away again as soon as ever they could, seeing they had never thought fit to fix there upon any Occasion, to this Time.

That the most I cou'd suggest any Danger from, was, from any such casual accidental Landing of straggling People from the Main, who, as it was

慰。我想,我就像扫罗那样,不仅抱怨非利士人来进攻他,而且抱怨上帝将他抛弃。因为,我没有采取适当的方法来安定我的心绪,没有在痛苦中向上帝呼救,没有像过去所做的那样,听从天命,求造物主保佑我,拯救我。倘使我那样做了,在这次新的惊恐中,至少会乐观些,或许能以更坚定的决心渡过难关。

由于胡思乱想,脑子里一片混乱,我一夜没睡着。但到了早晨,我反而睡着了。由于夜里想得太多,折腾得精疲力竭,我睡得很香。一觉醒来,心情比过去任何时候都要平静,于是我便开始进行冷静的思考。内心经过了一番激烈的思想斗争后,终于得出了这样的结论:这个岛如此景致宜人,物产丰富,又靠近那片大陆,自然不会像我以前想的那样绝无人迹。岛上虽然没人长期居留,但难免偶尔会有一些来自大陆的船只在此靠岸。他们当中,也许有人为了某种目的来到这里,但大多数肯定都只是被逆风吹过来的。

我在岛上已呆了十五年,却从未见过任何人的踪影,可想而知,有人上岛的情况非常少见。况且,即使有人有时会被逆风吹过来,他们也会设法尽快离开。恐怕到目前为止,还不曾有人会认为这里适合长期居住呢。

对我来说,最大的危险不过是大陆上那三三两两的居民偶然在此登岸,可是他们被

likely if they were driven hither, were here against their Wills; so they made no stay here, but went off again with all possible Speed, seldom staying one Night on Shore, least they should not have the Help of the Tides, and Day-light back again; and that therefore I had nothing to do but to consider of some safe Retreat, in Case I should see any Savages land upon the Spot.

Now I began sorely to repent, that I had dug my Cave so large, as to bring a Door through again, which Door, as I said, came out beyond where my Fortification joyn'd to the Rock; upon maturely considering this therefore, I resolv'd to draw me a second Fortification, in the same Manner of a Semicircle, at a Distance from my Wall, just where I had planted a double Row of Trees, about twelve Years before, of which I made mention: These Trees having been planted so thick before, they wanted but a few Piles to be driven between them, that they should be thicker, and stronger, and my Wall would be soon finish'd.

So that I had now a double Wall, and my Outer Wall was thickned with Pieces Of Timber, old Cables, and every Thing I could think of, to make it strong; having in it seven little Holes, about as big as I might put my Arm out at: In the In-side of this, I thickned my Wall to above ten Foot thick, with continual bringing Earth out of my Cave, and laying it at the Foot of the Wall, and walking upon it; and through the seven Holes, I contriv'd to plant the Musquets, of which I took Notice, that I got seven on Shore out of the Ship; these, I say, I planted like my Cannon, and fitted them into Frames that held them like a Carriage, that so I could fire all the seven Guns in two Minutes Time: This Wall I was many a weary Month a finishing, and yet never thought my self safe till it was done.

逆风吹过来，完全是出于不得已，因此他们决不肯在这里留下来，一来了就要设法赶快离开，很少在岸上过夜，否则的话，等到潮水过了，天色黑了，他们就困难了。所以我现在只须找一个安全的退路，一看到有野人登岸，就躲起来，别的事情用不着烦心。

我这时深深后悔把山洞掘得那么大，并且在围墙和岩石衔接的地方开了一个门。经过一番深思熟虑后，我决定在围墙外边，也就是我十二年前种两行树的地方，再筑起一道半圆形的防御工事。那些树原来就种得非常密，所以现在只须在树干之间再打一些木桩，就可以使树干之间的距离变得十分紧密。我很快就把这道围墙打好了。

现在，我有两道墙了。我又在外墙上用了不少木料、旧缆索及其他我能想到的东西进一步加固，并在墙上开了七个小洞，大小刚好能伸出我的手臂。在围墙里面，我又从山洞里搬了不少泥土倒在墙脚上用脚踩实。这样，把墙加宽到十多英尺宽。这七个小洞是准备放我的短枪的。我从破船上拿下了七支短枪，现在把这些枪安置在七个洞里并用架子支撑好，样子像七尊大炮。所以我可以在两分钟的时间里发射七枪。没有这堵墙，我总觉得自己不安全，于是苦干了好几个月，总算把它完成了。

When this was done, I stuck all the Ground without my Wall, for a great way every way, as full with Stakes or Sticks of the Osier like Wood, which I found so apt to grow, as they could well stand; insomuch, that I believe I might set in near twenty thousand of them, leaving a pretty large Space between them and my Wall, that I might have room to see an Enemy, and they might have no shelter from the young Trees, if they attempted to approach my outer Wall.

Thus in two Years Time I had a thick Grove and in five or six Years Time I had a Wood before my Dwelling, growing so monstrous thick and strong, that it was indeed perfectly impassable; and no Men of what kind soever, would ever imagine that there was any Thing beyond it, much less a Habitation: As for the Way which I propos'd to my self to go in and out, for I left no Avenue; it was by setting two Ladders, one to a Part of the Rock which was low and then broke in, and left room to place another Ladder upon that; so when the two Ladders were taken down, no Man living could come down to me without mischieving himself; and if they had come down, they were still on the Out-side of my outer Wall.

Thus I took all the Measures humane Prudence could suggest for my own Preservation; and it will be seen at length, that they were not altogether without just Reason; though I foresaw nothing at that Time, more than my meer Fear suggested to me.

While this was doing, I was not altogether Careless of my other Affairs; for I had a great Concern upon me, for my little Herd of Goats; they were not only a present Supply to me upon every Occasion, and began to be sufficient to me, without the Expence of Powder and Shot; but also

这件事做好以后,我就在这堵墙外空地周围遍插树枝——就是那种类似柳树的树枝,因为我已知道它们极易成活——插了很大一片地方,而且也插得尽可能地密,依我估计,很可能插了近两万枝;当然,它们同我那堵墙之间留有很大一片开阔地,所以如果有敌人想靠近我那外墙的话,他们就无法隐蔽在那些小树之后,而我也就很容易发现他们。

就这样过了两年,我就有了一片密密的树丛。五六年后,住宅前面的树林变得阴森萧煞,根本无法通行。没有人能想到在这片森林后面会有什么东西,更不会想到会有人居住在那里。我进进出出全靠两个梯子(因为我没有在树林里开道),一个安在低一些的岩石上,悬岩上有一个凹进去的地方,正好架第二个梯子。两个梯子一撤,没有人能安然无恙地从岩石上爬下来。即使能爬下来,也只会落到我的外墙外面。

就这样,为了生存,我绞尽脑汁,用尽了人类所有的智慧。后来证明,这样做不无道理,虽然当时是恐惧而不是预见驱使我采取这些防范措施。

在忙着这件事的时候,我并不是对别的事情一点也不关心,因为我一直在为我那群山羊担心。现在,它们不仅随时都可以满足我的需求,同时又不必耗费我的弹药,而且,

without the Fatigue of Hunting after the wild Ones, and I was loth to lose the Advantage of them, and to have them all to nurse up over again.

To this Purpose, after long Consideration, I could think of but two Ways to preserve them; one was to find another convenient Place to dig a Cave Under-ground, and to drive them into it every Night; and the other was to enclose two or three little Bits of Land, remote from one another and as much conceal'd as I could, where I might keep about half a Dozen young Goats in each Place: So that if any Disaster happen'd to the Flock in general, I might be able to raise them again with little Trouble and Time: And this, tho' it would require a great deal of Time and Labour, I thought was the most rational Design.

Accordingly I spent some Time to find out the most retir'd Parts of the Island; and I pitch'd upon one which was as private indeed as my Heart could wish for; it was a little damp Piece of Ground in the Middle of the hollow and thick Woods, where, as is observ'd, I almost lost my self once before, endeavouring to Come back that Way from the Eastern Part of the Island: Here I found a clear Piece of Land near three Acres, so surrounded with Woods, that it was almost an Enclosure by Nature, at least it did not want near so much Labour to make it so, as the other Pieces of Ground I had work'd so hard at.

I immediately went to Work with this Piece of Ground, and in less than a Month's Time, I had so fenc'd it round, that my Flock or Herd, call it which you please, who were not so wild now as at first they might be supposed to be, were well enough secur'd in it. So, without any farther Delay, I removed ten young She-Goats and two He-Goats to this Piece; and when they were there, I

我也不必跑得气喘吁吁去追捉那些野羊。所以，我不愿意失去它们给我带来的好处，免得又要从头驯养。

为了达到这一目的，我考虑了很长时间，最终只想到了两个保住它们的办法。一是找合适的地方挖个地洞，晚上将羊赶进去躲藏起来；另外就是再圈出两三块小圈地，每个地方只圈养六七只。这些地方应彼此相距远一点，而且越隐蔽越好。这样万一大圈地里的羊遭遇灾难，我只要花上一点时间和精力，仍然能靠小圈地里的羊再恢复发展起来。这虽然需要花较长的时间和较多的劳动，可我觉得这应该是最为可行的办法。

于是我花了一些时间，寻找岛上最幽静的地方，终于相中了一块极为合乎心愿的理想之地。这是山谷中一片小小的湿地，处于茂密的树林中间。这里也正是我曾提到过的，我先前从岛的东部回来时几乎迷路的地方。这里有一片空地，差不多有三英亩，周围被树木包围着，简直就是一道天然的屏障，至少不像我圈其他地块时那样需要费很大的力气。

我立刻开始在这里忙活起来。用了不到一个月的时间，我把它全围上了篱墙，这样我的羊群在这里就彻底安全了。我的羊群，现在已不像当初那般疯野了，相当安全。于是我一点也不敢耽搁，马上就移了十只小母羊和两只公

continued to perfect the Fence till I had made it as secure as the other, which, however, I did at more Leisure, and it took me up more Time by a great deal.

All this Labour I was at the Expence of, purely from my Apprehensions on the Account of the Print of a Man's Foot which I had seen; for as yet I never saw any human Creature come near the Island, and I had now liv'd two Years under these Uneasinesses, which indeed made my Life much less comfortable than it was before; as may well be imagin'd by any who know what it is to live in the constant Snare of the Fear of Man; and this I must observe with Grief too, that the Discomposure of my Mind had too great Impressions also upon the religious Part of my Thoughts, for the Dread and Terror of falling into the Hands of Savages and Canibals, lay so upon my Spirits, that I seldom found my self in a due Temper for Application to my Maker, at least not with the sedate Calmness and Resignation of Soul which I was wont to do; I rather pray'd to God as under great Affliction and Pressure of Mind, surrounded with Danger, and in Expectation every Night of being murther'd and devour'd before Morning; and I must testify from my Experience, that a Temper of Peace, Thankfulness, Love and Affection, is much more the proper Frame for Prayer than that of Terror and Discomposure; and that under the Dread of Mischief impending, a Man is no more fit for a comforting Performance of the Duty of praying to God, than he is for Repentance on a sick Bed: For these Discomposures affect the Mind as the others do the Body; and the Discomposure of the Mind must necessarily be as great a Disability as that of the Body, and much greater, Praying to God being properly an Act Of the Mind, not of the Body.

羊到那边去。搬过去之后,我又把我的篱墙继续加工,把它做得同原来的那个篱墙一样牢靠,所不同的是,我那原来的围墙,做起来的时候比较从容,所花费的时间也多得多。

我所以这样不辞辛苦,纯粹是由于我看到了那只脚印,产生了种种疑惧,其实,我至今还没有看见有任何人到岛上来过。就这样在这种忐忑不安的心情下我又过了两年。这种不安的心情使我的生活远远不如从前那样舒畅了。这种情况任何人都可以想象。试想一个人成天提心吊胆地生活,生怕有人会害他,这种生活会有什么乐趣呢?更令我痛心的是,这种不安的心情大大影响了我的宗教观念。因为我时刻担心落到野人或食人生番的手里,简直无心祈祷上帝;即使在祈祷的时候,也已不再有以往那种宁静和满足的心情了。我祈祷时,心情苦恼,精神负担很重,仿佛危机四伏,每夜都担心可能被野人吃掉似的。经验表明,平静、感激和崇敬的心情比恐怖和不安的心情更适于祈祷。而且,如果一个人向上帝祈祷的目的是为了求得安慰,那么正如生病后在病床上忏悔一样,怀着大祸临头的恐惧感去祈祷是同样不合适的。因为这类不安对心灵的影响,犹如疾病对肉体的影响;而不安对心灵造成的危害,必然也同疾病对肉体造成的危害一样,甚至还更严重些,因为向上帝祈

But to go on; After I had thus secur'd one Part of my little living Stock, I went about the whole Island, searching for another private Place, to make such another Deposit; when wandring more to the West Point of the Island, than I had ever done yet, and looking out to Sea, I thought I saw a Boat upon the Sea, at a great Distance; I had found a Prospective Glass, or two, in one of the Seamen's Chests, which I sav'd out of our Ship; but I had it not about me, and this was so remote, that I could not tell what to make of it; though I look'd at it till my Eyes were not able to hold to look any longer; whether it was a Boat, or not, I do not know; but as I descended from the Hill, I could see no more of it, so I gave it over; only I resolv'd to go no more out without a Prospective Glass in my Pocket.

When I was come down the Hill, to the End of the Island, where indeed I had never been before, I was presently convinc'd, that the seeing the Print of a Man's Foot, was not such a strange Thing in the Island as I imagin'd; and but that it was a special Providence that I was cast upon the Side of the Island, where the Savages never came: I should easily have known, that nothing was more frequent than for the Canoes from the Main, when they happen'd to be a little too far out at Sea, to shoot over to that Side of the Island for Harbour; likewise as they often met, and fought in their Canoes, the Victors having taken any Prisoners, would bring them over to this Shore, where according to their dreadful Customs, being all Canibals, they would kill and eat them; of which hereafter.

祷完全是一种心灵的活动,而非肉体的活动。

但还是言归正传吧。在把我那群牲畜中的一部分这样安顿好以后,我就在整个岛上东寻西找,想再觅一个隐蔽地方,以便再作一些这样的安置;我走到从前没去过的西角,朝大海观望,我觉得我看到在很遥远的海面有一条舢板,我曾在大船上的水手箱里找到过望远镜,但没带在身上,距离太远,我看不清是条什么样的船。我直勾勾地盯着那个方向看,直到视力变得一片模糊,但到底是不是船,我仍然不敢肯定。等我走下山岗,我再没见到船的影子,只得作罢,只是下决心下次出门,兜里一定要揣上望远镜。

我走下山来到我从未到过的岛的尽头,很快便确信在岛上看到一个人的脚印并不像我想象的那样奇怪;要不是上天有意安排,让我漂泊到野人从不去的那一边,我就不难知道,从对面大陆上开出的独木舟,如果在海上走得太远,就会渡过海峡,到岛上的这边来靠港,这是再寻常不过的事;而且,不同部落的独木舟在海上相遇时,往往要打仗,获胜者往往要把抓到的战俘带到海滩上来。那些人都是食人者,根据他们的惯例,他们会把战俘杀死吃掉。其具体情形,下文再表。

Part 5

When I was come down the Hill, to the Shore, as I said above, being the S. W. Point of the Island, I was perfectly confounded and amaz'd; nor is it possible for me to express the Horror of my Mind, at seeing the Shore spread with Skulls, Hands, Feet, and other Bones of humane Bodies; and particularly I observ'd a Place where there had been a Fire made, and a Circle dug in the Earth, like a Cockpit, where it is suppos'd the Savage Wretches had sat down to their inhumane Feastings upon the Bodies of their Fellow-Creatures. I was so astonish'd with the Sight of these Things, that I entertain'd no Notions of any Danger to my self from it for a long while; All my Apprehensions were bury'd in the Thoughts of such a Pitch of inhuman, hellish Brutality, and the Horror of the Degeneracy of Humane Nature; which though I had heard of often, yet I never had so near a View of before; in short, I turn'd away my Face from the horrid Spectacle; my Stomach grew sick, and I was just at the Point of Fainting, when Nature discharg'd the Disorder from my Stomach; and having vomited with an uncommon violence, I was a little reliev'd; but cou'd not bear to stay in the Place a Moment; so I gat me up the Hill again, with the Speed I cou'd, and walk'd on towards my own Habitation.

When I came a little out of that Part of the Island, I stood a while as amaz'd; and then recovering my self, I look'd with the utmost Affection of my Soul, and with a Flood Tears in my Eyes, gave God Thanks that had cast my Lot in a Part of the World, where I was distinguish'd from such dreadful Creatures as these; and that though I had esteem'd my present Condition very miserable, had yet given me so many Comforts in it, that I

第 五 部

且说从小山上下来,走到海边,走到小岛的最西端时,我不禁被惊得目瞪口呆,我心中的那份恐惧简直难以形容。只见岸边到处是头骨、手骨、脚骨和人体上其他的骨头。尤其,有个地方还曾经生过火,地上挖有一个斗鸡场大的圆坑,不难猜测,那些野蛮的畜生曾坐在这里,用他们同类的肉体举行过残忍的宴会。看到这些东西,我异常惊愕,好一段时间,我连自身的危险都忘掉了。我的全部心思都集中在这种不人道的、地狱般残忍的行为上,集注在这种毫无人性的可怕景象上。尽管我以前经常听人说到过,但却从未亲眼目睹。我再也无法继续面对这可怕的场景。我转过身去,感到一阵阵的恶心,头晕得几乎支撑不住。最后终于倾肠倒肚地呕吐了一番,把胃里的东西全部吐出来以后,才觉得稍微好受一点。我一分钟也不愿呆下去了,立即撒开腿全速跑上小山,再向自己的住所急步走去。

离开那里好一段距离以后,我仍然惊魂未定。于是我停下来就地站了一会儿,这才稍稍定下心来。这时,我满怀深情,眼含热泪地仰望着苍天,衷心感谢上帝让我诞生在世界的另一个地方,使我有幸不与这帮可恶的家伙同生共处。我感悟到,虽然我落入了

had still more to give Thanks for than to complain of; and this above all, that had even in this miserable Condition been comforted with the Knowledge of himself, and the Hope of his Blessing, which was a Felicity more than sufficiently equivalent to all the Misery which I had suffer'd, or could suffer.

In this Frame of Thankfulness, I went Home to my Castle, and began to be much easier now, as to the Safety my Circumstances, than ever I was before; for I observ'd, that these Wretches never came to this Island in search of what they could get; perhaps not seeking, not wanting, or not expecting any Thing here; and having often, no doubt, been up in the cover'd woody Part of it, without finding any Thing to their Purpose. I knew I had been here now almost eighteen Years, and never saw the least Foot-steps of Humane Creature there before; and I might be here eighteen more, as entirely conceal'd as I was now, if I did not discover my self to them, which I had no manner of Occasion to do, it being my only Business to keep my self entirely conceal'd where I was, unless I found a better sort of Creatures than Canibals to make my self known to.

Yet I entertain'd such an Abhorrence of the Savage Wretches, that I have been speaking of, and of the wretched inhuman Custom of their devouring and eating one another up, that I continu'd pensive, and sad, and kept close within my own Circle for almost two Years after this: When I say my own Circle, I mean by it, my three Plantations, viz. my Castle, my Country

目前这种不幸的境地,但上帝还是为我的生存给了许多关照,我非但不该抱怨上帝,反而应该对他感恩不尽。尤其重要的是,甚至于在这种不幸的处境中,他还给我以无上的安慰,使我得以认识他,指望他的祝福。这种幸福,足以抵偿我曾经遭受的、或可能遭受的全部不幸,而且还绰绰有余。

我怀着这种感激的心情回到我的城堡,对我的环境的安全比过去任何时期都安心得多了。我注意到,这伙坏蛋从来不是为了有所需求而到岛上来,他们并不是要到这里来寻求什么,要求什么,或指望什么。这无疑是因为他们经常在那一带树木深密的地方登岸,从来没有在那里发现过任何他们所需要的东西。据我所知,我来这里已经十八年了,从来没见过任何人类的足迹;只要我不把自己暴露给他们,把自己像目前这样完全隐蔽起来,我大可以再住上十八年。何况,我当然绝不会暴露自己,因为我唯一的目的就是很好地隐蔽自己,除非我发现比吃人生番更文明的人,才敢与他们交往。

我对这伙野蛮的畜生,对他们互相吞食这种灭绝人性的罪恶风俗真是深恶痛绝。所以,差不多有两年时间,我整天愁眉不展,郁郁寡欢,并不敢超越自己的活动范围。我所谓的活动范围,就是指我的三处庄园:我的城堡,我的

Seat, which I call'd my Bower, and my Enclosure in the Woods; nor did I look after this for any other Use than as an Enclosure for my Goats; for the Aversion which Nature gave me to these hellish Wretches, was such, that I was fearful of seeing them, as of seeing the Devil himself; nor did I so much as go to look after my Boat, in all this Time; but began rather to think of making me another; for I cou'd not think of ever making any more Attempts, to bring the other Boat round the Island to me, least I should meet with some of these Creatures at Sea, in which, if I had happen'd to have fallen into their Hands, I knew what would have been my Lot.

Time however, and the Satisfaction I had, that I was in no Danger of being discover'd by these People, began to wear off my Uneasiness about them; and I began to live just in the same compos'd Manner as before; only with this Difference, that I used more Caution, and kept my Eyes more about me than I did before, least I should happen to be seen by any of them; and particularly, I was more cautious of firing my Gun, least any of them being on the Island, should happen to hear of it; and it was therefore a very good Providence to me, that I had furnish'd my self with a tame Breed of Goats, that I needed not hunt any more about the Woods, or shoot at them; and if I did catch any of them after this, it was by Traps, and Snares, as I had done before; so that for two Years after this, I believe I never fir'd my Gun once off, though I never went out without it; and which was more, as I had sav'd three Pistols out of the Ship, I always carry'd them out with me, or at least two of them, sticking them in my Goat-skin Belt; also I furbish'd up one of the great Cut-lashes, that I had out of the Ship, and made me a Belt to put it on also; so that I was now a most formidable Fellow to look at, when I went abroad, if you add to the former Description of my self,

别墅和我那森林中的圈地。这中间,那森林中的圈地,我只是用来养羊,从不派别的用处。因为我天生憎恶那些魔鬼似的食人畜生,所以害怕看到他们,就像害怕看到魔鬼一样。这两年中,我也没有去看过那只舢板,只想另外再造一只。我根本不敢再想把那只舢板从海上弄回来,唯恐在海上碰到那些野人。那时候,若落到他们手里,我的命运就可想而知了。

但时间一长,因他们而引起的那种不安心情渐渐淡化,我自以为他们完全没有可能发现我,所以开始安安心心地同以前一样过日子,唯一不同的是我现在多加小心了,对周围的情况也比以前注意了,免得事不凑巧,被他们看见;特别是在用枪方面,我更是谨慎,生怕他们中有人正在岛上,会听见我的枪声;幸亏上天保佑我,让我驯化了一群羊供我吃喝,不必再到林子里去打猎,也不必开枪打野羊了;当然我在那以后还是捕到过野羊的,但都是用以前的办法,凭陷阱和罗网捉到的;所以据我回忆所及,在那以后的两年里,我虽说外出时总带着枪,但一次也没放过;事实上,我从大船上只取来三把手枪,每次外出,我总是全都带上,至少也带上其中的两支,把它们插在我的羊皮腰带上;我还配带了一把也是从船上弄来的大短剑,还专门为它做了一

the Particular of two Pistols, and a great broad Sword, hanging at my Side in a Belt, but without a Scabbard.

Things going on thus, as I have said, for some Time; I seem'd, excepting these Cautions, to be reduc'd to my former calm, sedate Way of Living, all these Things tended to shewing me more and more how far my Condition was from being miserable, compar'd to some others; nay, to many other Particulars of Life, which it might have pleased God to have made my Lot. It put me upon reflecting, How little repining there would be among Mankind, at any Condition of Life, if People would rather compare their Condition with those that are worse, in order to be thankful, than be always Comparing them with those which are better, to assist their Murmurings and Complainings.

As in my present Condition there were not really many Things which I wanted; so indeed I thought that the Frights I had been in about these Savage Wretches, and the Concern I had been in for my own Preservation, had taken off the Edge of my Invention for my own Conveniences; and I had dropp'd a good Design, which I had once bent my Thoughts too much upon; and that was, to try if I could not make some of my Barley into Malt, and then try to brew my self some Beer: This was really a whimsical Thought, and I reprov'd my self often for the Simplicity of it; for I presently saw there would be the want of several Things necessary to the making my Beer, that it would be impossible for me to supply; as First, Casks to preserve it in, which was a Thing, that as I have observ'd already, I cou'd never compass; no, though I spent not many Days, but Weeks, nay, Months in attempting it, but to no purpose. In

条挂剑带。你想想,在我原来的装束打扮上再加上两把短枪,一把斜挎的无鞘宽刃剑,这副出门的形象有多么狰狞可怖。

日子就这么一天一天地过着,除了采取这些防范措施,我渐渐地又回到过去那种平和、恬静的生活方式。事情愈来愈向我表明,我的处境与其他人相比较,远远算不上悲惨,与上帝愿施加给我的惩罚相比更是如此。这使我想到如果人们总是跟比自己过得差的人相比较,他们就会知恩图报;如果老跟比自己过得好的人攀比,他们就会嘀嘀咕咕抱怨个不停;而如果总是同那些处境比自己更好的人们相比,他们当然就会牢骚满腹,叫苦不迭。

就我目前的条件来说,我并不缺少什么东西。但是,我以为我由于受到那些野人的惊吓,由于时刻都在关心自己的藏身之地,我为了方便自己而创造发明的气势已经受挫。我本来做出了一个很好的计划,而且曾经费尽了心思去琢磨,即试一试能否把我的一些大麦制成麦芽,酿些啤酒。这当然是个异想开天的想法,我也时常责备自己这种愚笨的念头。因为我立刻就知道我缺少几样制造啤酒的必需物品。这几样东西我无法弄到。首先,我没有装啤酒用的大木桶。这样一个大桶,正如我前面所说,我永远也箍不成。虽然我花了好多天,甚至好多个

the next Place, I had no Hops to make it keep, no Yeast to make it work, no Copper or Kettle to make it boil; and yet all these Things, notwithstanding, I verily believe, had not these Things interven'd, I mean the Frights and Terrors I was in about the Savages, I had undertaken it, and perhaps brought it to pass too; for I seldom gave any Thing over without accomplishing it, when I once had it in my Head enough to begin it.

But my Invention now run quite another Way; for Night and Day, I could think of nothing but how I might destroy some of these Monsters in their cruel bloody Entertainment, and if possible, save the Victim they should bring hither to destroy. It would take up a larger Volume than this whole Work is intended to be, to set down all the Contrivances I hatch'd, or rather brooded upon in my Thought, for the destroying these Creatures, or at least frighting them, so as to prevent their coming hither any more; but all was abortive, nothing could be possible to take effect, unless I was to be there to do it my self; and what could one Man do among them, when perhaps there might be twenty or thirty of them together, with their Darts, or their Bows and Arrows, with which they could shoot as true to a Mark, I could with my Gun?

Sometime I contriv'd to dig a Hole under the Place where they made their Fire, and put in five or six Pound of Gun-powder, which when they kindled their Fire, would consequently take Fire,

星期，好多个月的工夫来箍它，但就是达不到目的。其次，我没有蛇麻，来使它不会变质，没有酵母来使它发酵，也没有铜壶锅之类的来烧煮它。尽管缺这少那，但我坚信，要不是有这些事情的干扰（我是指，要是没有野人让我担惊受怕），我肯定开始做了，说不定已经做成功了。因为，我这个人一旦想到要做什么，就一定要做下去，决不肯半途而废。

可是，我的发明才能却用到别的方面去了；因为我终日想的都是怎样趁这帮家伙举行残暴的人肉野餐时，把他们消灭一部分，并且将那些被他们抓来并准备吃掉的受害者解救出来。我仔细筹划着如何去消灭这些野蛮东西，至少要想法狠狠地吓唬他们一下，好使他们不敢再上岛来。各种各样的计策在脑海中像小鸡出壳一样一个接一个不断地冒出。如果把我所盘算的这些计划全部详细地记录下来，肯定能写出一部远比这本游记厚得多的谋略巨作。然而这不过是一些不成熟的纸上谈兵罢了。我如果不能付诸实践，又能产生什么作用呢？再说了，如果他们是二三十人结伙而来，拿着标枪、弓箭一类的武器，投射起来又能像我打枪那么准，我孤身一人又怎么能对付得了呢？

有时我很想在他们生火的地方挖一个小坑，再埋上五六磅火药，等他们生火的时候，必然把火药引燃，把附近

and blow up all that was near it; but as in the first Place I should be very loth to wast so much Powder upon them, my Store being now within the Quantity of one Barrel; so neither could I be sure of its going off' at any certain Time, when it might surprise them, and at best, that it would do little more than just blow the Fire about their Ears and fright them, but not sufficient to make them forsake the Place; so I laid it aside, and then propos'd, that I would place my self in Ambush, in some convenient Place, with my three Guns, all double loaded; and in the middle of their bloody Ceremony, let fly at them, when I should be sure to kill or wound perhaps two or three at every shoot; and then falling in upon them with my three Pistols, and my Sword, I made no doubt, but that if there was twenty I should kill them all: This Fancy pleas'd my Thoughts for some Weeks, and I was so full of it, that I often dream'd of it; and sometimes that I was just going to let fly at them in my Sleep.

I went so far with it in my Imagination, that I employ'd my self several Days to find out proper Places to put my self in Ambuscade, as I said, to watch for them; and I went frequently to the Place it self, which was now grown more familiar to me; and especially while my Mind was thus fill'd with Thoughts of Revenge, and of a bloody putting twenty or thirty of them to the Sword, as I may call it, the Horror I had at the Place, and at the Signals of the barbarous Wretches devouring one another, abated my Malice.

Well, at length I found a Place in the Side of the Hill, where I was satisfy'd I might securely wait, till I saw any of their Boats coming, and might then, even before they would be ready to come on Shore, convey my self unseen into Thick-

的一切都炸掉。但是,首先,我不愿意在他们身上浪费这么许多的火药,因为我的储藏量现在已经不到一桶了。再说,我又不敢保证它在特定的时间爆发,给他们以突然的打击。看起来,最多也不过把火星子炸到他们脸上,吓他们一跳,决不会使他们放弃这块地方,永不再来。因此我把这个计划放在一边,又计划找一个适当的地方埋伏起来,把我的三支枪加倍地装上弹药,等他们正热闹地举行那残忍的仪式时,向他们开火,一枪准能打死或打伤两三个;然后再带着我的三支手枪和一把腰刀向他们冲过去,如果他们只有二十个人,一定可以把他们杀个精光。这个幻想使我心里高兴了好几个星期;我因为整天想着它,连作梦都梦见它,有时甚至在睡梦里都在向他们开枪。

我对这个计划简直着了迷,竟费了好几天的工夫去寻找适当的埋伏地点。我还常到他们吃人的地点去察看,所以对那儿地势已了如指掌。尤其是我报复心切,恨不得一刀杀死他们二三十个;而在我一次次亲临现场,看到那恐怖的景象,看到那些野蛮的畜牲互相吞食的痕迹,更使我怒气冲天。

最后,我在小山坡上找到了一个地方,可以安全地把自己隐蔽起来,监视他们舢板上岛的一举一动。在他们上岸之前,我可以藏身在丛林里,

ets of Trees, in one of which there was a Hollow large enough to conceal me entirely; and where I might sit, and observe all their bloody Doings, and take my full aim at their Heads, when they were so close together, as that it would be next to impossible that I should miss my Shoot, or that I could fail wounding three or four of them at the first Shoot.

In this Place then I resolv'd to fix my Design, and accordingly I prepar'd two Muskets, and my ordinary Fowling Piece. The two Muskets I loaded with a Brace of Slugs each, and four or five smaller Bullets, about the Size of Pistol Bullets; and the Fowling Piece I loaded with near a Handful of Swan-shot, of the largest Size; I also loaded my Pistols with about four Bullets each, and in this Posture, well provided with Ammunition for a second and third Charge, I prepar'd my self for my Expedition.

After I had thus laid the Scheme of my Design, and in my Imagination put it in Practice, I continually made my Tour every Morning up to the Top of the Hill, which was from my Castle, as I call'd it, about three Miles, or more, to see if I cou'd observe any Boats upon the Sea, coming near the Island, or standing over towards it; but I began to tire of this hard Duty, after I had for two or three Months constantly kept my Watch; but came always back without any Discovery, there having not in all that Time been the least Appearance, not only on, or near the Shore; but not on the whole Ocean, so far as my Eyes or Glasses could reach every Way.

As long as I kept up my daily Tour to the Hill, to look out; so long also I kept up the Vigour of

因为那儿有一个小坑,大小正好能使我藏身。我可以稳稳当当地坐在那里,把他们食人的残忍行为看得一清二楚。而在他们彼此凑得很近时,我可以瞄准他们的脑袋,这样我准能十拿九稳地打中他们,第一枪打去,至少可以打伤他们三四个。

于是,我就选了这地方,准备在这里实施我的计划;为了这一目的,我备好了两支火枪和一支普通的鸟枪。给它们装好火药后,我在那两支火枪里分别装进了两颗形状不规则的弹丸和四五颗较小的弹丸,其大小同手枪用的差不多;在鸟枪里装进了一把最大号的打野鸭等飞禽的弹丸;还在每把手枪里装进了四颗弹丸;此外,我又备好了第二次及第三次射击的弹药,就这样我已作好了出击的准备。

我这样安排好我的方案计划外,就想象着把它付诸实施。我连续每天早晨跑到离我那所谓的城堡大约有三英里远的小山上,去观察一下海上是否有舢板驶近小岛,或是正从远处向本岛驶来。但当我连续观察了两三个月后,我就对这项艰苦的任务感到厌倦了。因为我总是毫无所获地回到家里,在这段时间里,不仅海岸上或海岸附近没有任何舢板的影子,就是在我肉眼或望远镜能够观测到的整个海面上也没有舢板的影子。

在每天到小山上巡视守望的这段时间里,我一直保持

my Design, and my Spirits seem'd to be all the while in a suitable Form, for so outragious an Execution as the killing twenty or thirty naked Savages, for an Offence which I had not at all entred into a Discussion of in my Thoughts, any farther than my Passions were at first fir'd by the Horror I conceiv'd at the natural Custom of that People of the Country, who it had been suffer'd by Providence in his wise Disposition of the World, to have no other Guide than that of their own abominable and vitiated Passions; and constantly were left, and perhaps had been so for some Ages, to act: horrid Things, and receive such dreadful Customs, as nothing but Nature entirely abandon'd of Heaven, and acted by hellish Degeneracy, could have run them into: But now, as I have said, I began to be weary of the fruitless Excursion, which I had made so long, and so far, every Morning in vain, so my Opinion of the Action it self began to alter, and I began with cooler and calmer Thoughts to consider what it was I was going to engage in. What Authority, or Call I had, to pretend to be Judge and Executioner upon these Men as Criminals, whom Heaven had thought fit for so many Ages to suffer unpunish'd, to go on, and to be as it were, the Executioners of his Judgments one upon another. How far these People were Offenders against me, and what Right I had to engage in the Quarrel of that Blood, which they shed promiscuously one upon another. I debated this very often with my self thus; How do I know what God himself judges in this particular Case? is certain these People either do not commit this as a Crime; it is not against their own Consciences reproving, or their Light reproaching them. They do not know it be Offence, and then commit it in Defiance of Divine Justice, we do in almost all the Sins we commit. They think it no ore a Crime to kill a Captive taken in War, than we do kill an Ox; nor to eat humane Flesh, than we do to eat

着实行我的计划的锐气。在整个这段时间里，我的精神都好像处于最佳状态，随时准备进行一场残酷的屠杀，一次杀死二三十个赤条条的野人。至于他们犯了什么罪，我根本没有认真考虑过，只是看不惯他们那种可怕的、非人性的习俗而怒火中烧。英明的造物主在统治世界时，好像已经抛弃了他们，任凭他们按他们自己的可怕的、堕落的本能去行事。造物主抛弃他们或许已有千百年了，随他们干着各种耸人听闻的勾当，通行着这种可怕的习俗。这些，完全是由于上天把他们抛弃所造成的，否则，他们也不会落到这种地步。可是，我天天早上徒劳无功地爬山瞭望，数日不辍，这种毫无结果的旅行已叫我生厌，我开始对这个行为本身发生了信念动摇。仔细、冷静地想想，我这是在干什么，既然上天允许这些人数世纪以来不受惩罚地照他们的方式活着，生息不止，然后一个接着一个地接受上帝的审判后死去，我又有什么权利假想这些人是罪犯而对他们判决死刑呢？这些人究竟冒犯了我什么，我有什么权利介入他们的自相残杀呢？我常扪心自问：我又如何知道上帝本人对这种特殊事例是怎样判决的呢？显然这些人不把吃人看作犯罪，他们不违拗自己的良知，不受良心的谴责，做这种事的时候，心中没有神圣审判，就像我们犯罪的时候也没有一

Mutton.

When I had consider'd this a little, it follow'd necessarily, that I was certainly in the Wrong in it, that these People were not Murtherers in the Sense that I had before condemn'd them, in my Thoughts; any more than those Christians were Murtherers, who often put to Death the Prisoners taken in Battle; or more frequently, upon many Occasions, put whole Troops of Men to the Sword, without giving Quarter, though they threw down their Arms and submitted.

In the next Place it occurr'd to me, that albeit the Usage they thus gave one another, was thus brutish and inhuman; yet it was really nothing to me: These People had done me Injury. That if they attempted me, or I saw it necessary my immediate Preservation to fall upon them, something might be said for it; but that as I was yet out of their Power, and they had really no Knowledge of me, and consequently sign upon me; and therefore it could not be just for to fall upon them. That this would justify the Conduct the Spaniards in all their Barbarities practis'd in America, and where they destroy'd Millions of these People, who however they were Idolaters and Barbarians, and had several bloody and barbarous Rites in their Customs, such as sacrificing human Bodies to their Idols, were yet, as to the Spaniards, very innocent People; and that the rooting them out of the Country, is spoken of with the utmost Abhorrence and Detestation, by even the Spaniards themselves, at this Time; and by all other Christian Nations of Europe, as a meer Butchery, a bloody and unnatural Piece of Cruelty, unjustifiable either to God or Man; and such, as for which the very Name of a Spaniard is reckon'd to be frightful and terrible to all People of Humanity, or of Christian Compas-

样,杀掉一个战争俘虏就像我们杀掉一头牛一样,吃人肉就像我们吃羊肉一样。

我接着自己的辩词往下想,自然而然地感到我起初对这件事的想法有些偏激了。我开始那么愤恨不平地把这些土人谴责为杀人犯,可他们与某些基督徒相比,并没有什么两样呀! 有些基督徒常常在战斗中残杀俘虏,更有甚者,当敌人已经放下武器,举手投降时,他们照样把成群结队的战俘毫无人道地杀光。

接着我又想到:即使这些野人一直在用着丧尽天良的手段互相掳杀,可那与我又有什么关系呢? 他们并没有伤害到我呀。如果他们伤害到我头上,那我完全有理由为了保护自己的性命,向他们发动猛烈进攻。可是我现在既没有落到他们手里,他们也不知有我这个人,也没有对我有任何阴谋,我若进攻他们,那就不公道了。我若这样做,就等于承认那些西班牙人在美洲所采取的种种野蛮行径是正当行为。他们在那里屠杀了成千上万的本地土人,——这些人民,虽然是偶像崇拜者,是野蛮人,并且在他们的风俗中有些残忍而野蛮的仪式,如象把活人祭他们的偶像等等,可是,对于西班牙人来说,他们都是无罪的。这种杀人灭种的行为,无论在西班牙人自己中间,还是在欧洲各基督教国家中间谈论起来,都引起了极端的憎恶和痛恨,认为是一

sion: As if the Kingdom of Spain were particularly Eminent for the Product of a Race of Men, who were without Principles of Tenderness, or the common Bowels of Pity to the Miserable, which is reckon'd to be a Mark of generous Temper in the Mind.

These Considerations really put me to a Pause, and to a kind of a Full-stop; and I began by little and little to be off of my Design, and to conclude, I had taken wrong Measures in my Resolutions to attack the Savages; that it was not my Business to meddle with them, unless they first attack'd me, and this it was my Business if possible to prevent; but that if I were discover'd, and attack'd, then I knew my Duty.

On the other hand, I argu'd with my self, That this really was the way not to deliver my self, but entirely to ruin and destroy my self; for unless I was sure to kill every one that not only should be on Shore at that Time, but that should ever come on Shore afterwards, if but one of them escap'd, to tell their Country People what had happen'd, they would come over again by Thousands to revenge the Death of their Fellows, and I should only bring upon my self a certain Destruction, which at present I had no manner of occasion for.

Upon the whole I concluded, That neither in Principle or in Policy, I ought one way or other to concern my self in this Affair. That my Business was by all possible Means to conceal my self from

种兽性的屠杀,一种神人共恨的残酷的不人道的暴行,以至使"西班牙人"这个名词,在一切具有人道思想或基督教同情心的人中间,成为一个可怕的字眼,就仿佛西班牙这个国家专门出产这样一种人,没有一点仁爱观念,对于不幸的人们没有一点怜悯的心肠,而这些原则,正是大国风度的标志。

基于上述考虑,我中止了执行攻击野人的计划,或至少在某些方面几乎完全停止了行动。这样,我逐渐放弃了这一计划,因为,我认为自己作出袭击那些野人的决定是错误的。我不应干预他们的内部事务,除非他们先攻击我。我应该做的是,只要可能,尽量防止他们攻击我自己。不过,现在我至少知道,如果自己一旦被发现并受到攻击,该如何对付他们了。

另外,我也认识到,这种主动攻击野人的计划不仅不能拯救自己,反而会完全彻底地毁灭自己。因为除非我有把握把每次登上这座孤岛的人杀得一个不剩,否则只要有一个人逃了回去,把发生的事告诉他部落里的人,那么就会有千百个人渡海过来,为他们的同胞报仇雪恨,这样的话,我就必死无疑,可我眼下好端端的,何必要如此呢。

总之,我的结论是:不管从原则上还是从策略上考虑,我都不该以任何方式去管这件事。我应该做的,是尽一切

them, and not to leave the least Signal to them to guess by, that there were any living Creatures upon the Island; I mean of humane Shape.

Religion joyn'd in with this Prudential, and I was convinc'd now many Ways, that I was perfectly out of my Duty, when I was laying all my bloody Schemes for the Destruction of innocent Creatures, I mean innocent as to me: As to the Crimes they were guilty of towards one another, I had nothing to do with them; they were National, and I ought to leave them to the Justice of God, who is the Governour of Nations, and knows how by National Punishments to make a just Retribution for National Offences; and to bring publick Judgments upon those who offend in a publick Manner, by such Ways as best pleases him.

This appear'd so clear to me now, that nothing was a greater Satisfaction to me, than that I had not been suffer'd to do a Thing which I now saw so much Reason to believe would have been no less a Sin, than that of wilful Murther, if I had committed it; and I gave most humble Thanks on my Knees to God, that had thus deliver'd me from Blood-Guiltiness; beseeching him to grant me the Protection of his Providence, that I might not fall into the Hands of the Barbarians; or that I might not lay my Hands upon them, unless I had a more clear Call from Heaven to do it, in Defence of my own Life.

In this Disposition I continu'd, for near a Year after this; and so far was I from desiring an Occasion for falling upon these Wretches, that in all that Time, I never once went up the Hill to see whether there were any of them in Sight, or to know whether any of them had been on Shore there, or not, that I might not be tempted to re-

可能隐蔽自己,不让他们发现;同时也要尽可能地不留下任何蛛丝马迹,让他们永远也猜不到这岛上还有着一个生灵;我是指具有人形的生灵。

这番慎重的考虑又让我有了宗教方面的顾虑。现在,我心里很明白,我制订这些残忍的计划,来消灭这些无罪的人(我是说,他们对我是无罪的),无论从哪方面看,都完全超出了我的职责范围。至于他们彼此之间的犯罪行为,那与我毫不相干,那是他们民族内部的事。我应该让上帝来作出公正的裁决,因为上帝是所有民族的统治者,自然知道怎样惩罚一个民族的集体犯罪行为,怎样将公开的裁决,加在公开的犯罪者的身上。

我现在越来越清楚,我可以确信,如果我干了这件蠢事,我所犯的罪行并不亚于故意杀人。现在我没有这么干,再没有比这更令我满意的事情了。我跪下来,向上帝表示我最谦卑的感激,感激他从那流血的罪恶中把我解救出来,我恳求他保佑我,别让我落入野人手中,也别叫我对他们动手,除非我从上天得到极为清楚的号召,为了保卫自己的生命而进行正当防卫。

就这样又过了近一年的光景;这期间,我完全不再想去碰见这帮坏蛋,因此没有再上那座小山去察看那边有无他们的踪影,去判断那边是否有人上岸了。我想,这样一来我就能够控制住自己,不会因

new any of my Contrivances against them, or be
provok'd by any Advantage which might present it
self, to fall upon them; only this I did I went and
remov'd my Boat, which I had on the other Side
the Island, and carry'd it down to the East End of
the whole Island, where I ran it into a little Cove
which I found under some high Rocks, and where
I knew, by Reason of the Currents, the Savages
durst not, at least would not come with their
Boats, upon any Account whatsoever.

With my Boat I carry'd away every Thing that I
had left there belonging to her, though not necessary for the bare going thither, viz. A Mast and
Sail which I had made for her, and a Thing like an
Anchor, but indeed which could not be call'd either Anchor or Grapling; however, it was the best
I could make of its kind: All these I remov'd, that
there might not be the least Shadow of any Discovery, or any Appearance of any Boat, or of any human Habitation upon the Island.

Besides this, I kept my self, as I said, more
retir'd than ever, and seldom went from my Cell,
other than upon my constant Employment, viz.
To milk my She-goats, and manage my little
Flock, in the Wood; which as it was quite on the
other Part of the Island, was quite out of Danger;
for certain it is, that these Savage People who
sometimes haunted this Island, never came with
any Thoughts of finding any Thing here; and consequently never wandred off from the Coast; and I
doubt not, but they might have been several
Times on Shore, after my Apprehensions of them
had made me cautious as well as before; and indeed, I look'd back with some Horror upon the
Thoughts of what my Condition would have been,
if I had chop'd upon them, and been discover'd
before that, when naked and unarm'd, except
with one Gun, and that loaden often only with

一时激动而重新拾起自己的
杀人计划，也不会因发现有机
可乘而对他们进行突然袭击
了。这期间我只做了一件事，
那就是把我停泊在岛那头的
舢板转移到岛东边来，把它藏
到我在一块巨大岩石下发现
的一个小海湾里。我知道，由
于急流的原因，野人们无论如
何也不敢或是不愿意乘舢板
到那一带去的。

我把我留在舢板上的所
有的附属品都搬了下来，这些
东西都是短程航行所不需要
的，其中包括我自己为它做的
一套桅和帆，一个锚样的东西
（这东西实在不能称为锚或四
爪锚，不过总算是我尽了最大
的努力做出来的）。我把这所
有的东西全部搬下来，免得引
人注意，叫人看出有船只和居
民的痕迹。

与此同时，我更加形踪隐
蔽，除了挤羊奶或照料林子里
的羊群，难得走出自己的蜗
居。我放羊的那片树林正好
处于岛的另一地区，没有被野
人侵扰之虞。虽然，这些野人
偶尔光顾这座海岛的时候，从
未想过能找到什么东西，所以
从未游离海岸，我相信在我因
提防他们而变得处处小心之
后，他们又来过几次。真的，我
一想到我过去出游的情况，不
禁不寒而栗。我以前外出只
带一支枪，枪里装的也是一些
小子弹。就这样我在岛上到
处东走走，西瞧瞧，看看能不
能弄到什么吃的东西。在这
种情况下，假使碰上他们，或

small Shot, I walk'd every where peeping, and peeping about the Island, to see what I could get; what a Surprise should I have been in, if when I discover'd the Print of a Man's Foot, I had instead of that, seen fifteen or twenty Savages, and found them pursuing me, and by the Swiftness of their Running, no Possibility of my escaping them.

The Thoughts of this sometimes sunk my very Soul within me, and distress'd my Mind so much, that I could not soon recover it, to think what I should have done, and how I not only should not have been able to resist them, but even should not have had Presence of Mind enough to do what I might have done; much less, what now after so much Consideration and Preparation I might be able to do: Indeed, after serious thinking of these Things, I should be very Melancholly, and sometimes it would last a great while; but I resolv'd it at last all into Thankfulness to that Providence, which had deliver'd me from so many unseen Dangers, and had kept me from those Mischiefs which I could no way have been the Agent in delivering my self from; because I had not the least Notion of any such Thing depending,' or the least Supposition of it being possible.

This renew'd a Contemplation, which often had come to my Thoughts in former Time, when first I began to see the merciful Dispositions of Heaven, in the Dangers we run through in this Life. How wonderfully we are deliver'd, when we know nothing of it. How when we are in (a Quandary, as we call it) a Doubt or Hesitation, whether to go this Way, or that Way, a secret Hint shall direct us this Way, when we intended to go that Way;

被他们发现,我该怎么办呢?因为,我没有多少自卫能力。或者,假定我当时看到的不是一个人的脚印,而是一二十个野人,一见到我就向我追来,他们善于奔跑,我是无论如何跑不过他们的,那我必定会落在他们手里!

有时想到这些,我就会吓得魂不附体,心里异常难过,半天都恢复不过来。我很难想象,在那种情况下,我会作出什么反应,依我想,不要说是进行抵抗了,恐怕一吓之下,魂飞魄散的我连自己本来能做到的也给忘得一干二净,更不用说经过了深思熟虑和仔细筹划之后,我现在具备的自卫能力了。是啊,把这些事情认真地思索一番,我常感到闷闷不乐,而且这种心情有时会持续很长一段时间;但是到头来,我总觉得要为这一切而感谢上帝,是他拯救了我,使我免遭这许多我没看见的危险,使我免遭一些灾祸,而凭我自己,我是无法从这些灾祸中逃脱的,因为我完全没有想到还有这类事会随时落在我头上,甚至没想到有发生这种事的可能性。

我以前经常有这样一种感想,那就是,当我们在人生的旅途上遇到各种凶险时,上天总是那样大慈大悲,将我们拯救出来。现在,这一感想又萦绕在我的心头。我们甚至是在不知不觉中得到了上天奇迹般的拯救。当我们身处窘境,怀疑彷徨,犹豫不决的

nay, when Sense, our own Inclination, and perhaps Business has call'd to go the other Way, yet a strange Impression upon the Mind, from we know not what Springs, and by we know not what Power, shall over-rule us to go this Way; and it shall afterwards appear, that had we gone that Way which we should have gone, and even to our Imagination ought to have gone, we should have been ruin'd and lost: Upon these, and many like Reflections, I afterwards made it a certain Rule with me, That whenever I found those secret Hints, or pressings of my Mind, to doing, or not doing any Thing that presented; or to going this Way, or that Way, I never fail'd to obey the secret Dictate; though I knew no other Reason for it, than that such a Pressure, or such a Hint hung upon my Mind: I could give many Examples of the Success of this Conduct in the Course of my Life; but more especially in the latter Part of my inhabiting this unhappy Island; besides many Occasions which it is very likely I might have taken Notice of, if I had seen with the same Eyes then, that I saw with now: But 'tis never too late to be wise; and I cannot but advise all considering Men, whose Lives are attended with such extraordinary Incidents as mine, or even though not so extraordinary, not to slight such secret Intimations of Providence, let them come from what invisible Intelligence they will, that' I shall not discuss, and perhaps cannot account for; but certainly they are a Proof of the Converse of Spirits, and the secret Communication between those embody'd, and those unembody'd; and such a Proof as can never be withstood: Of which I shall have Occasion to give some very remarkable Instances, in the Remainder of my solitary Residence in this dismal Place.

时候,当我们不知道该走这条路,还是该走那条路的时候,总有一种神秘的暗示,指示我们走这一条路(虽然我们很想走那条路);不仅如此,当我们的见识、意愿,甚至使命要我们走另一条路的时候,总有一种奇妙的力量作用于我们的精神,促使我们去走这一条路,虽然我们不知道这种力量从何而来,那究竟是一种什么力量;而这种力量事后往往证明,要是我们走了我们自以为应该走的那条路,或者我们心目中以为应该走的那条路,肯定会自取灭亡。在此基础上,我经过反复考虑,我自己找出了一条规律:不管什么时候,当我觉得心中有股神秘的暗示或力量,叫我去做什么而不去做什么,走这条路而不走那条路,我必须服从这种神秘的指示,虽然我不知道心中这种暗示或力量是什么。在我的一生中,特别是我来到这个倒霉的岛上以后,我可以找出许多这样成功的例子。此外,还有许多事情,如果我当时也用现在的眼光看问题,一定可以注意到。但只要彻悟起来,从来都不会为时太晚。我想奉劝那些有头脑的人们,在他们的生活中,也同我一样,充满了种种不寻常的变故,即使不是出乎寻常,不可轻视这种神秘的上天启示。且不管这种启示来自何种神力。关于这种启示来自何种神力这一点我不想在此讨论,也无法加以阐释。但是这种启示起码可

I believe the Reader of this will not think strange, if I confess that these Anxieties, these constant Dangers I liv'd in, and the Concern that was now upon me, put an End to all Invention, and to all the Contrivances that I had laid for my future Accommodations and Conveniencies. I had the Care of my Safety more now upon my Hands, than that of my Food. I car'd not to drive a Nail, or chop a Stick of Wood now, for fear the Noise I should make should be heard; much less would I fire a Gun, for the same Reason; and above all, I was intollerably uneasy at making any Fire, least the Smoke which is visible at a great Distance in the Day should betray me; and for this Reason I remov'd that Part of my Business which requir'd Fire; such as burning of Pots, and Pipes, etc. into my new Apartment in the Woods, where after I had been some time, I found to my unspeakable Consolation, a meer natural Cave in the Earth, which went in a vast way, and where, I dare say, no Savage, had he been at the Mouth of it, would be so hardy as to venture in, nor indeed, would any Man else; but one who like me, wanted nothing so much as a safe Retreat.

The Mouth of this Hollow, was at the Bottom of a great Rock, where by meer accident, (I would say, if I did not see abundant Reason to ascribe all such Things now to Providence) I was cutting down some thick Branches of Trees, to make Charcoal; and before I go on, I must observe the Reason of my making this Charcoal;

以证明,神灵之间可以互相交流,有形之物与无形之物之间可以神秘交往。而且,这一证明永远无法推翻。对于这一点,我能在我后半辈子孤独的生活中找出一些很有代表性的事例来加以证明。

对危险的焦虑与担忧,对人生的苦思和冥想,使我无心再像以前那样,为获得更加舒适方便的生活进行创造和设计。我这么说,想必读者一定不会觉得有什么奇怪。目前最让我烦心的不是食物问题,而是人身安全问题。我连一个钉子都不敢钉,一块木头都不敢劈,深怕声音被别人听见。至于枪,为了同样的理由,那就更不敢开了。尤其叫我担心的,是生火这件事,深怕白天老远被人看见烟火,坏我的事。因此,我把一切需要生火的事情,像烧陶罐,烧烟斗等等,都移到我那森林中的新地方去做。那地方,我去了一个时期之后,就在土层里发现了一个天然的地洞,这件事叫我感到说不出来的欣慰。地洞进去很深,我敢说,就有野人来到洞口,也没有胆子进去;老实说,除了像我这样专门想找安全退路的人,谁都不会进去。

地洞的洞口在一块大岩石底下。有一天,我正在那儿砍柴,准备用来烧炭,偶然间发现了一个洞口,这一发现我除了归诸天意外,只能说是偶然了。现在,在我继续讲我的发现之前,必须先谈谈我为什

which was thus: I was afraid of making a Smoke about my Habitation, as I said before; and yet I could not live there without baking my Bread, cooking my Meat, etc. so I contriv'd to burn some Wood here, as I had seen done in England, under Turf, till it became Chark, or dry Coal; and then putting the Fire out, I preserv'd the Coal to carry Home; and perform the other Services which Fire was wanting for at Home without Danger of Smoke.

But this is by the by: While I was cutting down some Wood here, I perceiv'd that behind a very thick Branch of low Brushwood, or Underwood, there was a kind of hollow Place; I was curious to look into it, and getting with Difficulty into the Mouth of it, I found it was pretty large; that is to say, sufficient for me to stand upright in it, and perhaps another with me; but I must confess to you, I made more hast out than I did in, when looking farther into the Place, and which was perfectly dark, I saw two broad shining Eyes of some Creature, whether Devil or Man I knew not, which twinkl'd like two Stars, the dim Light from the Cave's Mouth shining directly in and making the Reflection.

However, after some Pause, I recover'd my self, and began to call my self a thousand Fools, and tell my self, that he that was afraid to see the Devil, was not fit to live twenty Years in an Island all alone; and that I durst to believe there was nothing in this Cave that was more frightful than my self; upon this, plucking up my Courage, I took up a great Firebrand, and in I rush'd again, with the Stick flaming in my Hand; I had not gone three Steps in, but I was almost as much frighted as I was before; for I heard a very loud Sigh, like that of a Man in some Pain, and it was follow'd by a broken Noise, as if of Words half

么要烧炭。前面我已经说过，我不敢在我的住所附近生火。可是，那儿是我生活的地方，我不能不烤面包，不能不煮肉。因此，我计划按照我在英国看到的办法，拿一些木头放在草皮泥层下烧，把木头烧成木炭，熄火后再把木炭带回家。这样，如果家里需用火，就可以用木炭来烧，省得有冒烟的冒险。

这题外话只是顺便一提。话说当时我正在砍着树枝，看到密密的灌木丛后面仿佛有个洞穴般的所在；我感到好奇，想进洞去看看，好不容易地进了洞口后，我发现里面很大，不仅我可以直立，而且能容得下两个人；但是我得承认，我出洞时比进洞时要匆促得多，因为我进洞后朝里一望，只见一片漆黑中居然有两只亮晶晶的眼睛，也不知是人是鬼还是什么动物的；洞口处进来的一点微弱的光线，照在这双眼睛上反射了出来，就像两颗闪烁的寒星。

然而，稍稍歇了一会儿，我又镇定了下来，觉得自己是个地地道道的大傻瓜，心想，一个害怕魔鬼的人就不配在这座孤岛上独自生活二十年；我又想，洞里会有什么东西比我自己更可怕的呢？想到这里，我又壮起了胆子，手里拿着一个用树枝做成的火把，重新冲了进去。可是，才走了两三步，我几乎跟刚才一样，又给吓了一跳。因为，这回听见一声很响的呻吟，就像一个人

express'd, and then a deep Sigh again: I stepp'd back, and was indeed struck with such a Surprize, that it put me into a cold Sweat; and if I had had a Hat on my Head, I will not answer for it, that my Hair might not have lifted it off. But still plucking up my Spirits as well as I could, and encouraging my self a little with considering that the Power and Presence of God was every where, and was able to protect me; upon this I stepp'd forward again, and by the Light of the Firebrand, holding it up a little over my Head, I saw lying on the Ground a most monstrous frightful old He-goat, just making his Will, as we say, and gasping for Life, and dying indeed of meer old Age.

I stirr'd him a little to see if I could get him out, and he essay'd to get up, but was not able to raise himself; and I thought with my self, he might even lie there; for if he had frighted me so, he would certainly fright any of the Savages, if any of them should be so hardy as to come in there, while he had any Life in him.

I was now recover'd from my Surprize, and began to look round me, when I found the Cave was but very small, that is to say, it might be about twelve Foot over, but in no manner of Shape, either round or square, no Hands having ever been employ'd in making it, but those of meer Nature: I observ'd also, that there was a Place at the farther Side of it, that went in farther, but was so low, that it requir'd me to creep upon my Hands and Knees to go into it, and whither I went I knew not; so having no Candle, I gave it over for some Time; but resolv'd to come again the next Day, provided with Candles, and a Tinder-box,

发出的痛苦的呻吟；紧接着，就是一阵断断续续的声音，像是有人在含含糊糊地讲话，然后又是一声呻吟。于是，我又退了出来。说真的，我给吓出了一身冷汗；要是我此刻头上戴着帽子，真不敢保证，我竖起的头发会不会要把它顶落在地。但我还是强打起精神，一边给自己壮胆，一边想，上帝的神力和足迹是无所不在的，他一定能保护我。想到这儿我又鼓起勇气，向前走去。我举着火把，把它举过头顶，借着火光一看，我看到地上正躺着一只硕大无比、老得可怕的山羊，好像正在交待我们所说的遗嘱，一边无奈地喘着气，显然已经快要死了。

我推了它一下，想看看能不能把它赶出去。它也打算站起来，但却站不起来了。我想了想，觉得还是由它躺在那里吧。因为它既然已把我吓了一跳，它当然也会吓着那些野人，如果那些野人在它还活着时胆敢进来的话。

我这时已从惊吓中完全回过神来，开始定下心观察洞中的情况。我发现洞里面不算太大，方圆不过十二英尺。不过，它既不是圆形，也不是方形，说不上是什么形状。这里没有人工开凿的痕迹，完全是一个天然形成的洞穴。我又发现在洞的尽端，还有一个更深的洞，实在看不清楚通向何方。这洞的入口很低，非得爬着进去才行。因为那里伸手不见五指，随身又没带着蜡

which I had made of the Lock of one of the Muskets, with some wild-fire in the Pan.

Accordingly the next Day, I came provided with six large Candles of my own making; for I made very good Candles now of Goat's Tallow; and going into this low Place, I was oblig'd to creep upon all Fours, as I have said, almost ten Yards; which by the way, I thought was a Venture bold enough, considering that I knew not how far it might go, nor what was beyond it. When I was got through the Strait, I found the Roof rose higher up, I believe near twenty Foot; but never was such a glorious Sight seen in the Island, I dare say, as it was, to look round the Sides and Roof of this Vault, or Cave; the Walls reflected 100 thousand Lights to me from my two Candles; what it was in Rock, whether Diamonds, or any other precious Stones, or Gold, which I rather suppos'd it to be, I knew not.

The Place I was in, was a most delightful Cavity, or Grotto, of its kind, as could be expected, though perfectly dark; the Floor was dry and level, and had a sort of small lose Gravel upon it, so that there was no nauseous or venemous Creature to be seen, neither was there any damp, or wet, on the Sides or Roof: The only Difficulty in it was the Entrance, which however as it was a Place of Security, and such a Retreat as I wanted, I thought that was a Convenience; so that I was really rejoyc'd at the Discovery, and resolv'd without any Delay, to bring some of those Things which I was most anxious about, to this Place; particularly, I resolv'd to bring hither my Magazine of Powder, and all my spare Arms, viz. Two Fowling-Pieces, for I had three in all; and three Muskets,

烛,我只好决定第二天带上蜡烛和火绒盒再来。那只火绒盒是我用短枪枪栓改制而成的,里面还有一盘火药作为火种。

第二天,我带来六支自制的大蜡烛,我已能用羊油制作上好的蜡烛,蜡坯很硬,正好裹住烛蕊,烛蕊有时用破布,或股线或一种像荨麻草的晒干的草制成。要爬进这个小洞,就像我曾说过的那样,我必须手脚并用。我爬了将近十码远,真够刺激的,因为我不知道这洞有多深,也不知道洞里面是什么。待我穿过这个洞,眼前豁然开朗,洞顶升高了将近二十英尺;在这岛上,我敢说还从未见过如此瑰丽的景象。烛光中,四周和洞顶霞光万丈,绚丽辉煌。这里的岩石含有什么,是钻石还是其他宝石,或者是金子,我说不清楚,我想多半是金子吧。

我现在所来到的地方,实在是一个最美观的洞穴,虽然里面黑洞洞地没有一点光线。地上又干燥又平坦,上面铺着一层细碎的沙石,所以在里面再也看不见什么令人厌恶的或有毒的虫蛇之类,同时,顶上和四壁上也一点都不潮湿。它唯一的缺点就是它的入口;可是,这正是我所需要的安全地点,我所需要的那种退路,因此,我倒觉得这个缺点于我有利。因此我对于这个发现真是非常高兴,决定一刻也不耽搁,把我最放心不下的一部分东西搬到这地方来,特别是

for of them I had eight in all; so I kept at my Castle only five, which stood ready mounted like Pieces of Cannon, on my out-most Fence; and were ready also to take out upon any Expedition.

Upon this Occasion of removing my Ammunition, I took occasion to open the Barrel of Powder which I took up out of the Sea, and which had been wet; and I found that the Water had penetrated about three or four Inches into the Powder, on every Side, which caking and growing hard, had preserv'd the inside like a Kernel in a Shell; so that I had near sixty Pound of very good Powder in the Center of the Cask, and this was an agreeable Discovery to me at that Time; so I carry'd all away thither, never keeping above two or three Pound of Powder with me in my Castle, for fear of a Surprize of any kind: I also carry'd thither all the Lead I had Belt for Bullets.

I fancy'd my self now like one of the ancient Giants, which are said to live in Caves, and Holes, in the Rocks, where none could come at them; for I perswaded my self while I was here, if five hundred Savages were to hunt me, they could never find me out; or if they did, they would not venture to attack me here.

The old Goat who I found expiring, dy'd in the Mouth of the Cave, the next Day after I made this Discovery; and I found it much easier to dig a great Hole there, and throw him in, and cover him with Earth, than to drag him out; so I interr'd him there, to prevent the Offence to my Nose.

I was now in my twenty third Year of Residence in this Island, and was so naturaliz'd to the Place, and to the Manner of Living, that could I have but enjoy'd the Certainty that no Savages would come

我的火药库，我的多余的枪械，包括两支鸟枪（我一共有三支），三支短枪（我一共有八支）。在城堡里留下五支短枪架在外墙洞里，像大炮一样，作战中需要时也可以随时拿下来使用。

在这次转移军火时，我也顺便打开了我从海上捞起来的那桶受潮的火药。结果发现，火药四周进了三四寸水，结成了一层坚固的硬壳，可里面部分却完好无损，仿佛壳里的果仁保存得很好。我从桶里弄到了差不多六十磅好火药，这真是一个可喜的收获。不用说，我把全部火药都搬了过去。从此以后，我在城堡里最多只放三磅火药，唯恐发生任何意外。另外，我又把做子弹的铅也全部搬了过去。

我觉得，我现在颇像传说中的那些古代巨人，据说他们住在山穴和岩洞里，谁也没法攻击他们；这里的情况使我相信，只要我待在这儿，哪怕有五百名野人到处搜寻我，也别想找到，就算他们找到了，他们也不敢攻进来。

在我发现这洞穴的第二天，那只奄奄一息的老山羊死在洞口了。我觉得，要把它拖出去比较困难，还是挖个大坑，把它埋起来方便得多，所以就地把它埋进了土中，免得以后臭味熏人。

时光荏苒，我在岛上已滞留了二十三年，已完全适应了这个地方及其生活方式，如果不是野人来此地骚扰的话，我

to the Place to disturb me, I could have been content to have capitulated for spending the rest of my Time there, even to the last Moment, till I had laid me down and dy'd, like the old Goat in the Cave. I had also arriv'd to some little Diversions and Amusements, which made the Time pass more pleasantly with me a great deal, than it did before; as First, I had taught my Poll, as I noted before, to speak; and he did it so familiarly, and talk'd so articulately and plain, that it was very pleasant to me; and he liv'd with me no less than six and twenty Years: How long he might live afterwards, I know not; though I know they have a Notion in the Brasils, that they live a hundred Years; perhaps poor Poll may be alive there still, calling after Poor Robin Crusoe to this Day. I wish no English Man the ill Luck to come there and hear him; but if he did, he would certainly believe it was the Devil. My Dog was a very pleasant and loving Companion to me, for no less than sixteen Years of my Time, and then dy'd, of meer old Age; as for my Cats, they multiply'd as I have observ'd to that Degree, that I was oblig'd to shoot several of them at first, to keep them from devouring me, and all I had; but at length, when the two old Ones I brought with me were gone, and after some time continually driving them from me, and letting them have no Provision with me, they all ran wild into the Woods, except two or three Favourites, which I kept tame; and whose Young when they had any, I always drown'd; and these were part of my Family: Besides these, I always kept two or three houshold Kids about me, who I taught to feed out of my Hand; and I had two more Parrots which talk'd pretty well, and would all call Robin Crusoe; but none like my first; nor indeed did I take the Pains with any of them that I had done with him. I had also several tame Sea-Fowls, whose Names I know not, who I caught upon the Shore, and cut their Wings; and

会怡然自得地在这儿度过余生,直至生命的最后一刻,就像洞里的老山羊那样躺下死去。我还发明了一些消遣玩艺儿,让自己更惬意地打发时光。先是教波儿说话,它讲得流利、清晰而明白,叫我开心极了。它跟我生活了二十六年之多,我不知道后来它又活了多久,在巴西,有人说这种鸟能活一百年,或许至今波尔生活在那儿,呼叫着可怜的鲁滨·克鲁索,我希望没有哪个倒霉的英国人在那儿听到它的呼唤。如果听到了,肯定以为它呼喊的是魔鬼。我的爱犬也是个令我十分开心的伙伴,它跟了我至少十六年,后来老死了。至于我的猫,我已说过,它们繁殖得很多,我在开始时就不得不开枪打死了几只,以免吃完我的一切东西。但到最后,当我带来的两只老猫死掉后,我又不断地驱逐它们,不给它们东西吃,它们都跑到树林里变成野猫了。只有两三只我喜欢的,我把它们驯养起来。而每当它们生出小猫来,我就把小猫都溺死。这就是我家庭中的一部分成员。除了这些,我总是在我身边饲养两三只小山羊,并教它们学会从我的手里叫东西。我另外还有两只鹦鹉,话也学得很好,也都会叫“鲁滨·克鲁索”;但是,这两只都不如前面那一只,况且,我也没有像教前面那一只一样费心去教它们。我还驯了几只海鸟,它们究竟是些什么鸟,我却叫

the little Stakes which I had planted before my Castle Wall being now grown up to a good thick Grove, these Fowls all liv'd among these low Trees, and bred there, which was very agreeable to me; so that as I said above, I began to be very well contented with the Life I led, if it might but have been secur'd from the dread of the Savages.

But it was otherwise directed; and it may not be amiss for all People who shall meet with my Story, to make this just Observation from it, vis. How frequently in the Course of our Lives, the Evil which in it self we seek most to shun, and which when we are fallen into it, is the most dreadful to us, is oftentimes the very Means or Door of our Deliverance, by which alone we can be rais'd again from the Affliction we are fallen into. I cou'd give many Examples of this in the Course of my unaccountable Life; but in nothing was it more particularly remarkable, than in the Circumstances of my last Years of solitary Residence in this Island.

It was now the Month of December, as I said above, in my twenty third Year; and this being the Southern Solstice, for Winter I cannot call it, was the particular Time of my Harvest, and requir'd my being pretty much abroad in the Fields; when going out pretty early in the Morning, even before it was thorow Day-light, I was surpriz'd with seeing a Light of some Fire upon the Shore, at a Distance from me, of about two Mile towards the End of the Island, where I had observ'd some Savages had been as before; but not on the other Side; but to my great Affliction, it was on my Side of the Island.

I was indeed terribly surpriz'd at the Sight, and stepp'd short within my Grove, not daring to go out, least I might be surpriz'd; and yet I had no

不出名字。我把它们从海边捉来后,把它们的翅膀都剪掉了。我在城堡的围墙之外所插的那一片枝条,现在已长成了一片茂密的树林,这些海鸟便栖居在这片低矮的树丛中,并在那里繁殖,看上去真叫人开心。因此,正如我刚才所说,要是无须担心受到了野人的威胁,我对于我现在所过的这种生活当然是心满意足的。

但是现实生活往往与自己的愿望相违背。读过这本书的人大都可以从中得出这么一个正确的结论:在现实生活中,我们因惧怕而竭力躲避的坏事,却往往又是帮助我们脱离苦海、使我们得到解救的唯一途径。这种坏事转变为好事,通过痛苦解脱痛苦的事例,在我一生不可思议的经历中,可以找出许多,而在我独居荒岛的最后几年里,更不少见。

前面已经说过,现在已经是我来到岛上第二十三年的十二月。这时正是冬至前后(其实并不能称之为冬季),正是收获季节,我必须时常出门,到田里去。有一天一清早,天还没有亮,我刚刚出门,忽然看见远处海岸上有一片火光,离开我大约有二英里远,就在我发现野人遗迹的那个方向。然而,令人苦恼的是,并不是在岛的那边,却是在我这边。

我看到这种景象,大大地吃了一惊,便在我的小树林里停住脚步,不敢再往外走,生

more Peace within, from the Apprehensions I had, that if these Savages in rambling over the Island, should find my Corn standing, or cut, or any of my Works and Improvements, they would immediately conclude, that there were People in the Place, and would then never give over till they had found me out: In this Extremity I went back directly to my Castle, pull'd up the Ladder after me, and made all Things without look as wild and natural as I could.

Then I prepar'd my self within, putting my self in a Posture of Defence; I loaded all my Cannon, as I call'd them; that is to say, my Muskets, which were mounted upon my new Fortification, and all my Pistols, and resolv'd to defend my self to the last Gasp, not forgetting seriously to commend my self to the Divine Protection, and earnestly to pray to God to deliver me out of the Hands of the Barbarians; and in this Posture I continu'd about two Hours; but began to be mighty impatient for Intelligence abroad, for I had no Spies to send out.

After sitting a while longer, and musing what I should do in this Case, I was not able to bear sitting in Ignorance any longer; so setting up my Ladder to the Side of the Hill, where there was a flat Place, as I observ'd before, and then pulling the Ladder up after me, I set it up again, and mounted to the Top of the Hill; and pulling out my Perspective Glass, which I had taken on Purpose, I laid me down flat on my Belly, on the Ground, and began to look for the Place; I presently found there was no less than nine naked Savages, sitting round a small Fire, they had made, not to warm them; for they had no need of

怕受到出其不意的袭击。可是,我心里怎么也无法平静了,我怕那些野人万一在岛上走来走去,发现我的庄稼,看到有些已收割了,有些还没有收割,或者发现我其他的一些设施,他们马上会断定岛上有人;那时,他们不把我搜出来是决不会罢休的。在这危险关头,我立即跑回城堡,收起梯子,并把围墙外的一切东西尽量弄成荒芜自然的样子。

然后,我在城堡内做好防御野人袭击的准备。我把手枪和所有的炮全都装好弹药;所谓炮,就是那些架在我的防御工事外墙上的短枪,样子像炮,我就这么叫叫罢了。作好了这些准备,我决心抵抗到最后一息。同时,我也没有忘记把自己交托给上帝,诚心诚意地指望他的保护,恳切地向他祈祷,请他别让我落进那些野人的手中;这样过了两个小时,我开始急于了解外面的情况,因为我没有可以派出去的耳目。

我又继续坐了一会儿,思考着该在这情况下做些什么事,但是想到这样坐下去,对外面的情况仍将一无所知,我就忍不住了;于是我把梯子往小山边一靠,爬上我前面提到过的岩壁上一个平坦的凹处,再把梯子拉上来往那儿一放,登上了小山的顶部,掏出特意带来的望远镜;我趴在那儿,通过望远镜朝那个地方望去,我发现大约有九个野人围坐在一小堆篝火旁,天气这么

that, the Weather being extreme hot; but as I suppos'd, to dress some of their barbarous Diet, of humane Flesh, which they had brought with them, whether alive or dead I could not know.

They had two Canoes with them, which they had haled up upon the Shore; and as it was then Tide of Ebb, they seem'd to me to wait for the Return of the Flood, to go away again; it is not easy to imagine what Confusion this Sight put me into, especially seeing them come on my Side the Island, and so near me too; but when I observ'd their coming must be always with the Current of the Ebb, I began afterwards to be more sedate in my Mind, being satisfy'd that I might go abroad with Safety all the Time of the Tide of Flood, if they were not on Shore before: And having made this Observation, I went abroad about my Harvest Work with the more Composure.

As I expected, so it prov'd; for as soon as the Tide made to the Westward, I saw them all take Boat, and row (or paddle as we call it) all away: I should have observ'd, that for an Hour and more before they went off, they went to dancing, and I could easily discern their Postures, and Gestures, by my Glasses: I could not perceive by my nicest Observation, but that they were stark naked, and had not the least covering upon them; but whether they were Men or Women, that I could not distinguish.

As soon as I saw them shipp'd, and gone, I took two Guns upon my Shoulders, and two Pistols at my Girdle, and my great Sword by my Side, without a Scabbard, and with all the Speed I was able to make, I went away to the Hill, where I had discover'd the first Appearance of all; and as soon as I gat thither, which was not less than two Hours (for I could not go apace, being so loaden with Arms as I was) I perceiv'd there had been three Canoes more of Savages on that Place; and looking out farther, I saw they were all at Sea to-

热,他们显然不是在烤火,而是在用他们带来的俘虏举行人肉宴会,我不知道那些带来的是活人还是死人。

他们带了两个独木舟,均被拖上海滩。此时正是退潮时分,他们好像在等潮水上涨,以便离开。看到野人出现在我这一边,离我这么近,我心里慌乱极了,但当我意识到他们总是在潮水回落的时候来,心里又安定下来。因为当他们不在岸上时,我可以在潮水涨起时安全地出门,观察到这一点后,我以后就可以从容地去收割我的庄稼。

果然如我预料的那样,当潮水向西流去时,他们就全部上了船,摇着桨离去。我可以观察到,在他们离去前一个小时,他们还跳了一阵舞。通过望远镜,我还能很容易地辨出他们的舞姿,再仔细观察,可以看到他们全都赤裸全身一丝不挂。但至于是男是女,我就分辨不出来了。

我一看到他们上船走了,就立即把两支长枪背到肩上,把两把手枪插在腰带上,将一把没有刀鞘的大刀悬在腰间,全速朝海边的那座小山跑去。这段路程用了不到两个钟头的时间,因为我身上背了这么多武器,迈不开步子。我一跑到那里便发现,到这里来的还有另外三只独木舟的野人。再向海面望去,我看到五只独

— 223 —

gether, making over for the Main.

This was a dreadful Sight to me, especially when going down to the Shore, I could see the Marks of Horror, which the dismal Work they had been about had left behind it, viz. The Blood, the Bones, and part of the Flesh of humane Bodies, eaten and devour'd by those Wretches, with Merriment and Sport: I was so fill'd with Indignation at the Sight, that I began now to premeditate the Destruction of the next that I saw there, let them be who, or how many soever.

It seem'd evident to me, that the Visits which they thus make to this Island, are not very frequent; for it was above fifteen Months before any more of them came on Shore there again; that is to say, I neither saw them, or any Footsteps, or Signals of them, in all that Time; for as to the rainy Seasons, then they are sure not to come abroad, at least not so far; yet all this while I liv'd uncomfortably, by reason of the constant Apprehensions I was in of their coming upon me by Surprize; from whence I observe, that the Expectation of Evil is more bitter than the Suffering, especially if there is no room to shake off that Expectation, or those Apprehensions.

During all this Time, I was in the murthering Humour; and took up most of my Hours, which should have been better employ'd, in contriving

木舟已会合在一起,向对面大陆驶去。

我看到这种情况,心里感到十分害怕,而当我来到海边,再一次目睹野人们惨无人道的吃人现场上所留下的斑斑痕迹时,我更加感到难以名状的恐怖。我看着眼前那一滩滩人血、一堆堆人骨和一块块人肉,浑身发抖,毛骨悚然。这一片狼藉足以显示了这帮残忍的家伙是如何一边撕咬着人肉,一边寻欢作乐的。面对眼前的景象,我真是怒不可遏,暗自狠狠地下了决心:如果他们再次上岛来干如此罪恶的勾当而让我碰上的话,无论他们是谁,无论他们有多少人,我非得把他们杀个精光不可。

显然,他们到这岛上来,并不是很经常的,因为,又过了十五个多月,他们才再一次在那里登岸;这就是说,有十五个月之久,我从来没有见过他们,也没有见过他们的任何脚印,任何痕迹。看起来,在雨季里,他们是决不出门的,至少决不到这么远的地方来。然而,在这整段时期,由于我时时担心被他们袭击,我的日子过得非常不舒服。由此可见,一个人时时期待着祸事,比遭遇到祸事还要痛苦,尤其是当一个人无法摆脱这种期待,这种担惊害怕的心情的时候。

在这段期间里,我始终怀着杀人的心情,大部分有用的时间来计划下次看见他们时,

how to circumvent, and fall upon them, the very next Time I should see them; especially if they should be divided, as they were the last Time, into two Parties; nor did I consider at all, that if I kill'd one Party, suppose Ten, or a Dozen, I was still the next Day, or Week, or Month, to kill another, and so another, even ad infinitum, till I should be at length no less a Murtherer than they were in being Man-eaters; and perhaps much more so.

I spent my Days now in great Perplexity, and Anxiety of Mind, expecting that I should one Day or other fall into the Hands of these merciless Creatures; and if I did at any Time venture abroad, it was not without looking round me with the greatest Care and Caution imaginable; and now I found to my great Comfort, how happy it was that I provided for a tame Flock or Herd of Goats; for I durst not upon any account fire my Gun, especially near that Side of the Island where they usually came, least I should alarm the Savages; and if they had fled from me now, I was sure to have them come back again, with perhaps two or three hundred Canoes with them, in a few Days, and then I knew what to expect.

However, I wore out a Year and three Months more, before I ever saw any more of the Savages, and then I found them again, as I shall soon observe. It is true, they might have been there once, or twice; but either they made no stay, or at least I did not hear them; but in the Month of May, as near as I could calculate, and in my four and twentieth Year, I had a very strange Encounter with them, of which in its Place.

The Perturbation of my Mind, during this fifteen or sixteen Months Interval, was very great; I slept unquiet, dream'd always frightful Dreams,

要怎样战胜他们,怎样攻击他们,尤其是当他们如同上次似的,分成两队时。我却没想到,即使我杀光一队,杀死十个人,十二个人,我在第二天,第二个星期,第二个月就得再杀一队,再杀一队,哪怕杀到了无穷数,一直到我变成跟这些吃人族一样残暴,或者更加残暴的杀人者为止。

我现在每天都在疑虑和焦急中过日子,感到自己总有一天会落入那些残忍无情的家伙手中。即使偶然大着胆子外出,也总是东张西望,极端小心谨慎。我现在发现,我老早驯养了一群羊,这真给了我极大的宽慰,因为我无论如何也不敢再开枪,尤其是在他们常来的一带地方,唯恐惊动了那些野人。我知道,即使我暂时把他们吓跑,不出明天他们就会卷土重来,那时,说不定会来两三百只独木舟,我的结果也就可想而知了。

想是这么想,但过了一年三个月我还没见到一个野人,不过随后见到了他们——这是我就要说到的后话。当然,在这期间他们可能已来过一两次,但他们也许是来过就走了,或者我一点也没觉察;不过在我登上这岛的第二十四个年头,据我算来,是在五月份,我又在非常特殊的情况下见到了他们;有关的情况,下面到时候再说。

在这十五六个月里,我心神不宁,夜里觉也睡不好,睡着了也总是做噩梦,还常常从

and often started out of my Sleep in the Night: In the Day great Troubles overwhelm'd my Mind, and in the Night I dream'd often of killing the Savages, and of the Reasons why I might justify the doing of it; but to wave all this for a while; it was in the middle of May, on the sixteenth Day I think, as well as my poor wooden Calendar would reckon; for I markt all upon the Post still; I say, it was the sixteenth of May, that it blew a very great Storm of Wind, all Day, with a great deal of Lightning, and Thunder, and a very foul Night it was after it; I know not what was the particular Occasion of it; but as I was reading in the Bible, and taken up with very serious Thoughts about my present Condition, I was surpriz'd with a Noise of a Gun as I thought fir'd at Sea.

This was to be sure a Surprize of a quite different Nature from any I had met with before; for the Notions this put into my Thoughts, were quite of another kind. I started up in the greatest hast imaginable, and in a trice clapt my Ladder to the middle Place of the Rock, and pull'd it after me, and mounting it the second Time, got to the Top of the Hill, the very Moment, that a Flash of Fire bid me listen for a second Gun, which accordingly, in about half a Minute I heard; and by the sound, knew that it was from that Part of the Sea where I was driven down the Current in my Boat.

I immediately consider'd that this must be some Ship in Distress, and that they had some Comrade, or some other Ship in Company, and fir'd these Guns for Signals of Distress, and to obtain Help: I had this Presence of Mind at that Minute, as to think that though I could not help them, it may be they might help me; so I brought together all the dry Wood I could get at hand, and making a good handsome Pile, I set it on Fire upon the Hill; the Wood was dry, and blaz'd freely; and though the Wind blew very hard, yet it burnt fairly out; that I was certain, if there was any such

梦中吓得惊醒过来。白天里，我心事重重；到了夜里我常常梦到杀野人，并在梦里对自己的行为振振有词。暂时撤下这一切不谈。就我刻在木桩上的日历计算，已是五月中旬的第十六天，暴风雨肆虐了一个白天，狂风大作，电闪雷鸣，到晚上仍未停歇。我不知道这是不是一个特殊机遇。我正在读《圣经》，并对自己的处境沉思遐想，就在这时，从海面传来的一声枪响叫我大吃一惊。

这肯定跟我过去遇到的意外事件的性质完全不同，因为这件事在我头脑里形成的概念完全不一样。我惊跳起来，立刻搭起梯子爬上悬崖上的平台，再拉起梯子往更高处一架，爬上山顶，就在顷刻之间，一道火光划破夜空，我听到第二声枪响，不到半分钟，又是一声。从声音判断，正是从我坐舢板被急流冲走的那一带海面上传来的。

我立即想到，这一定是什么船只遇险了。他们肯定还有其他同伴，有其他结伴的船只，放枪正是他们遇险后求救的信号。我在那一刻反而镇定自若了，我想，虽然我不能援救他们，他们或许能救助我。于是，我把手头上所有的干柴都收起来，堆成一大堆，把它放在山上点起火来。木柴干燥，很快就燃烧起来。虽然风很大，但火还是着得很

Thing as a Ship, they must needs see it, and no doubt they did; for as soon as ever my Fire blaz'd up, I heard another Gun, and after that several others, all from the same Quarter; I ply'd my Fire all Night long, till Day broke; and when it was broad Day, and the Air clear'd up, I saw something at a great Distance at Sea, full East of the Island, whether a Sail, or a Hull, I could not distinguish, no not with my Glasses, the Dna was so great, and the Weather still something haizy also; at least it was so out at Sea.

I look'd frequently at it all that Day, and soon perceiv'd that it did not move; so I presently concluded, that it was a Ship at an Anchor, and being eager, you may be sure, to be satisfy'd, I took my Gun in my Hand, and run toward the South Side of the Island, to the Rocks where I had formerly been carry'd away with the Current, and getting up there, the Weather by this Time being perfectly clear, I could plainly see to my great Sorrow, the Wreck of a Ship cast away in the Night, upon those concealed Rocks which I found, when I was out in my Boat; and which Rocks, as they check'd the Violence of the Stream, and made a kind of Counter-stream, or Eddy, were the Occasion of my recovering from the most desperate hopeless Condition that ever I had been in, in all my Life.

Thus what is one Man's Safety, is another Man's Destruction; for it seems these Men, who-

旺,我确信,如果真有船只之类的话,他们肯定会看到火光。毫无疑问,他们的确是看见了火光的。因为,我点的火刚刚燃起,我又听到了一声枪响,接着又是好几枪,而且都是从一个地方传来的。我给火堆加了一夜的柴,一直加到天亮。天大亮以后,天空晴朗起来。我看见,在岛的正东面,在远处海面上,好像有个什么东西。究竟是一面船帆,还是一具船壳,我看不清楚。它离这里太远了,我用望远镜也看不清。况且,天上还有点雾气,至少说海面上是这样。

那一天,我不时地眺望那个东西,很快就发现它一直停在那里一动不动。我断定那可能是一只抛了锚的大船。我迫不及待地想把事情弄个明白,就拿起枪,急匆匆地向岛的东南角跑去,跑到了那片岩石边上,也就是我上次被急流冲走的那片礁石滩边上。这时,天已完全放晴了。等我接近礁石滩的时候,一眼就看到了一只遇难的大船,而且立刻明白了它肯定是昨晚在这里撞上礁石了。看着这只失事的大船,我心痛不已。我上次驾舢板巡游时,就发现这一带礁石林立,可那一次倒多亏了这些礁石挡住了急流的去路,从而形成了一股逆流,才使我没有被急流冲进外海,才使我得以从生平最绝望的险境中死里逃生。

一个人的安全,往往是另一个人的危险。这些人好像

ever they were, being out of their Knowledge, and the Rocks being wholly under Water, had been driven upon them in the Night, the Wind blowing hard at E. and E. N. E: Had they seen the Island, as I must necessarily suppose they did not, they must, as I thought, have endeavour'd to have sav'd themselves on Shore by the Help of their Boat; but their firing of Guns for Help, especially when they saw, as I imagin'd, my Fire, fill'd me with many Thoughts: First, I imagin'd that upon seeing my Light, they might have put themselves into their Boat, and have endeavour'd to make the Shore; but that the Sea going very high, they might have been cast away; other Times I imagin'd, that they might have lost their Boat before, as might be the Case many Ways; as particularly by the Breaking of the Sea upon their Ship, which many Times obliges Men to stave, or take in Pieces their Boat; and sometimes to throw it over-board with their own Hands: Other Times I imagin'd, they had some other Ship, or Ships in Company, who upon the Signals of Distress they had made, had taken them up, and carry'd them off: Other whiles I fancy'd, they were all gone off to Sea in their Boat, and being hurry'd away by the Current that I had been formerly in, were carry'd out into the great Ocean, where there was nothing but Misery and Perishing; and that perhaps they might by this Time think of starving, and of being in a Condition to eat one another.

As all these were but Conjectures at best; so in the Condition I was in, I could do no more than look on upon the Misery of the poor Men, and pity them, which had still this good Effect on my Side, that it gave me more and more Cause to give Thanks to God who had so happily and comfortably provided for me in my desolate Condition; and that of two Ships Companies who were now cast away upon this part of the World, not one Life should be spar'd but mine: I learn'd here again to

由于不晓得路，并且那些礁石又都在水里隐着，加上昨晚东北风刮得又急，竟然在夜间触了礁。如若他们看见这个岛（如今我必须设定他们并没看见），他们定会竭力以舢板向岸上逃生。他们鸣枪求救，尤其是我的火光被他们看见后，使我有许多感想。我想象我的火光被他们看见以后，他们一定下到舢板里，竭力向岸上摇来，不过当时风浪很大，或许波浪已经卷走了他们。一会儿我又猜想，他们的舢板说不定老早就丢了，因为这种事是屡见不鲜的；尤其碰到惊涛巨浪冲打着船只的时候，人们常常不得不把船上的舢板拆散，甚至把它扔到海里去。一会儿我又猜想，跟他们搭伴同行的，或许还有别的船，见到他们出事的信号，已经把他们救了起来，载走了。一会儿我又猜想，他们说不定已经坐上舢板，下了海，给我上回碰到的那股急流冲到大海里去了；到了大海里，他们就只有受苦和死亡的份儿了，说不定他们这时候已经快要饿死了，到了人吃人的地步。

所有这些想法，仅仅只是我自己的猜测罢了。在我目前的处境下，只能眼睁睁地看着这伙可怜的人遭难，并从心里为他们感到难过；除此之外，我毫无办法。可是，这件事在我思想上产生了很好的影响。从这次事件中，我进一步认识到上帝对自己的恩惠，我是多么感激他对我的关怀啊！

observe, that it is very rare that the Providence of God casts us into any Condition of Life so low, or any Misery so great, but we may see something or other to be thankful for; and may see others in worse Circumstances than our own.

Such certainly was the Case of these Men, of whom I could not so much as see room to suppose any of them were sav'd; nothing could make it rational, so much as to wish, or expect that they did not all perish there; except the Possibility only of their being taken up by another Ship in Company, and this was but meer Possibility indeed; for I saw not the least Signal or Appearance of any such Thing.

I cannot explain by any possible Energy of Words, what a strange longing or hankering of Desires I felt in my Soul upon this Sight; breaking out sometimes thus; O that there had been but one or two; nay, or but one Soul sav'd out of this Ship, to have escap'd to me, that I might but have had one Companion, one Fellow-Creature to have spoken to me, and to have convers'd with! In all the Time of my solitary Life I never felt so earnest, so strong a Desire after the Society of my Fellow-Creatures, or so deep a Regret at the want of it.

尽管我处境悲惨,但我的生活还是过得非常舒适,非常幸福。同时,我也要感谢上帝在船难中仅让我一人死里逃生;到目前为止,我至少已亲自见到两艘船只在海上遇难,这两艘船的全体水手无一幸免,唯我独生。此外,从这件事中,我再一次认识到,不管上帝把我们置于何等不幸的境地或何等恶劣的生活环境,我们总会亲眼看到一些使我们感恩的事,看到有些人的处境比自己更加不幸。

那船上的人们显然就是这个情况了,因为没有任何根据认为他们中有人已经获救;根据所有的情况,只可能得出一个合理的结论,那就是他们已经全都遇难了;他们生还的唯一希望或可能,只在于那条与他们结伴而行的船,但是,他们被那条船搭救的可能性也仅仅是可能性而已,因为我没见到这类事的任何迹象。

看到这一情况,我感到心底里产生了一种莫名其妙的热切想望,这种感觉是无法解释或说明的,任何言词对此都无能为力;有时候我会脱口叫道:"哦,哪怕有一两个人,不,哪怕只有一个人能够死里逃生,从那船上逃到我这里,那该有多好!那样,我也可以有个伙伴,有个同类,跟我说说话,跟我交谈交谈!"在漫长的孤独生活中,我从来不曾有过如此迫切、如此强烈的愿望,需要有个同类跟我交往,也从来没有因为缺少这种交往而

There are some secret moving Springs in the Affections, which when they are set a going by some Object in view, or be it some Object, though not in view, yet rendred present to the Mind by the Power of Imagination, that Motion' carries out the Soul by its Impetuosity to such violent eager embracings of the Object, that the Absence of it is insupportable.

Such were these earnest Wishings, That but one Man had been sav'd! O that it had been but One! I believe I repeated the Words, O that it had been but One! A thousand Times; and the Desires were so mov'd by it, that when I spoke the Words, my Hands would clinch together, and my Fingers press the Palms of my Hands, that if I had had any soft Thing in my Hand, it wou'd have crusht it involuntarily; and my Teeth in my Head wou'd strike together, and set against one another so strong, that for some time I cou'd not part them again.

Let the Naturalists explain these Things, and the Reason and Manner of them; all I can say to them, is, to describe the Fact, which was even surprising to me when I found it; though I knew not from what it should proceed; it was doubtless the effect of ardent Wishes, and of strong Ideas form'd in my Mind, realizing the Comfort, which the Conversation of one of my Fellow-Christians would have been to me.

But it was not to be; either their Fate or mine, or both, forbid it; for till the last Year of my being on this Island, I never knew whether any were saved out of that Ship or no; and had only the Affliction some Days after, to see the Corps of a drownded Boy come on Shore, at the End of the Island which was next the Shipwreck: He had on

感到如此难过。

在我们的感情当中，有一种神秘的力量，这种力量一旦被眼前的目标激发起来，或者不是被眼前的目标，而是被我们想象中的目标激发起来之后，它们就会带着我们的灵魂勇猛向前，以强烈的渴望去寻求这一目标；如果达不到，我们必将痛苦不堪。

我现在最急切的愿望，就是希望哪怕只有一个人逃脱出来。"啊！哪怕只有一个人逃出来！"我不断重复着这句话。"哪怕只有一个人逃出来！"重复了上千遍。我按捺不住心中强烈的渴求，双手紧紧地绞在一起，手指狠命地摁在手掌上，如果我手里有什么软东西，一定会不知不觉地被捏个粉碎。我的牙关咬得紧紧的，一时间难以分开。

让自然学家去解释这种事情，以及其原因和方式吧，我只能进行一些实况描述。我发现了这个情况后，也曾大吃一惊，不知道自己怎么会有这种表现，但毫无疑问，这是我头脑里执拗的念头和热望造成的后果，当我意识到与一个基督教同伴结交将是怎样一件乐事后，我就再也控制不住自己了。

然而，现实却总是与人的愿望背道而驰，我竟连一个生还的人也没见着。看来，这不是他们命该如此，就是我命中注定，要么就是双方的命运都在阻止我们碰到一起，因为，直到我在岛上生活的最后一

no Cloaths, but a Seaman's Wastcoat, a pair of open knee'd Linnen Drawers, and a blew Linnen Shirt; but nothing to direct me so much as to guess what Nation he was of: He had nothing in his Pocket, but two Pieces of Eight, and a Tobacco Pipe; the last was to me of ten times more value than the first.

It was now calm, and I had a great mind to venture out in my Boat, to this Wreck; not doubting but I might find something on board, that might be useful to me; but that did not altogether press me so much, as the Possibility that there might be yet some living Creature on board, whose Life I might not only save, but might by saving that Life, comfort my own to the last Degree; and this Thought clung so to my Heart, that I could not be quiet, Night or Day, but I must venture out in my Boat on board this Wreck; and committing the rest to God's Providence, I thought the Impression was so strong upon my Mind, that it could not be resisted, that it must come from some invisible Direction, and that I should be wanting to my self if I did not go.

Under the Power of this Impression, I hasten'd back to my Castle, prepar'd every Thing for my Voyage, took a Quantity of Bread, a great Pot for fresh Water, a Compass to steer by, a Bottle of

年,我才终于弄清这艘失事船上到底有没有人幸存下来。更让我悲痛万分的是,几天以后,我在岛那头靠近失事船只的海滩上,亲眼看到了一具尸体,是一个被淹死的年轻人。他身上穿的衣服不多,只有一件水手背心,一条齐膝麻纱短裤和一件蓝色的麻纱衬衫。我看不出,也猜不出他是哪国人。他的衣袋里没什么别的东西,只有两块西班牙银币和一支烟斗。这两样东西照我目前来看,后者的价值要大大高于前者,我想,起码高出十倍还不止呢。

这时海上风平浪静,我很想大着胆子坐舢板到那条破船上去,因为我相信一定可以从船上找到一些有用的东西。同时,还有一种动机更有力地推动着我,就是希望船上还会有一两个活着的人,如果有的话,我不仅可以搭救他的性命,而且在搭救他以后,对于我个人也是一种无上的安慰。这种思想时时刻刻盘踞在我的心头,使我昼夜不得安宁,一心想坐舢板到那破船上去。我认为,既然这种念头这样强有力地压迫着我,叫我无法抵抗,那么一定是来自什么看不见的神力的指示,如果我不去,那就是对不起自己。至于其他的事情,我只好委诸天命了。

在这种愿望的驱使下,我匆匆跑回城堡作出航的准备。我拿了不少面包,一大罐淡水,一个驾驶用的罗盘,一罐

Rum; for I had still a great deal of that left; a Basket full of Raisins: And thus loading my self with every Thing necessary, I went down to my Boat, got the Water out of her, and got her afloat, loaded all my Cargo in her, and then went Home again for more; my second Cargo was a great Bag full of Rice, the Umbrella to set up over my Head for Shade; another large Pot full of fresh Water, and about two Dozen of my small Loaves, or Barley Cakes, more than before, with a Bottle of Goats-Milk, and a Cheese; all which, with great Labour and Sweat, I brought to my Boat; and praying to God to direct my Voyage, I put out, and Rowing or Padling the Canoe along the Shore, I came at last to the utmost Point of the Island on that Side, (viz.) N. E. And now I was to launch out into the Ocean, and either to venture, or not to venture. I look'd on the rapid Currents which ran constantly on both Sides of the Island, at a Distance, and which were very terrible to me, from the Remembrance of the Hazard I had been in before, and my Heart began to fail me; for I foresaw that if I was driven into either of those Currents, I should be carry'd a vast Way out to Sea, and perhaps out of my Reach, or Sight of the Island again; and that then, as my Boat was but small, if any little Gale of Wind should rise, I should be inevitably lost.

These Thoughts so oppress'd my Mind, that I began to give over my Enterprize, and having haled my Boat into a little Creek on the Shore, I stept out, and sat me down upon a little rising bit of Ground, very pensive and anxious, between Fear and Desire about my Voyage; when as I was musing, I could perceive that the Tide was turn'd, and the Flood come on, upon which my going was for so many Hours impracticable; upon this

甘蔗酒,这种酒我还剩下不少,以及一满筐葡萄干。我把一切必需品都背在身上,就走到我藏舢板的地方。我先把船里的水淘干,让船浮起来;然后把所有的东西都放进船里。接着,我又跑回家去取些其他东西。这一次我拿了一大口袋米,还有那把挡太阳的伞,又取了一大罐淡水,二十多只小面包,实际上是一些大麦饼,这次拿得比上次还多。另外又拿了一瓶羊奶,一块干酪。我费了不少力气,流了不少汗,才把这些东西通通运到舢板上。然后,我祈祷上帝保佑我一路平安,就驾船出发了。我沿海岸先把独木舟划到小岛的东北角。现在,我得把它驶入大洋中去了;冒险还是不冒险呢?我遥望小岛两边日夜奔腾的急流,想到我上次遇到的危险,心里感到非常害怕,望着大海真想退回去。因为我可以预见,不管我被卷进哪股急流,我都会被冲走卷进大海,也许永远再也看不到,再也回不到这个岛上了。到那时,只要海上起一点点风,我就要同我这一叶孤舟一同葬送到大海里了。

这些想法令我很烦恼,我开始打算放弃我的计划了。于是,我把舢板拖进海岸旁边的一条小溪里,我走下船来,坐到了一块小小的高地上。心里既想出航,又对之怀有恐惧,所以那心情急切而又担忧;就在我冥思苦想之际,我发觉海水的流向有了变化,原

presently it occurr'd to me, that I should go up to the highest Piece of Ground I could find, and observe, if I could, how the Sets of the Tide, or Currents lay, when the Flood came in, that I might judge whether if I was driven one way out, I might not expect to be driven another way home, with the same Rapidness of the Currents: This Thought was no sooner in my Head, but I cast my Eye upon a little Hill, which sufficiently over-look'd the Sea both ways, and from whence I had a clear view of the Currents, or Sets of the Tide, and which way I was to guide my self in my Return; here I found, that as the Current of the Ebb set out close by the South Point of the Island; so the Current of the Flood set in close by the Shore of the North Side, and that I had nothing to do but to keep to the North of the Island in my Return, and I should do well enough.

Encourag'd with this Observation, I resolv'd the next Morning to set out with the first of the Tide; and reposing my self for the Night in the Canoe, under the great Watch-coat, I mention'd, I launched out: I made first a little out to Sea full North, till I began to feel the Benefit of the Current, which set Eastward, and which carry'd me at a great rate, and yet did not so hurry me as the Southern Side Current had done before, and so as to take from me all Government of the Boat; but having a strong Steerage with my Paddle, I went at a great rate, directly for the Wreck, and in less than two Hours I came up to it.

It was a dismal Sight to look at: The Ship,

来这时已开始涨潮,这一来,我在几个小时内是不可能出航了;这时一个念头油然而起,我觉得应该在附近找个最高的地方,尽可能在涨潮时从那儿观察那两股急流的流向变化,以便断定:如果我被一股海流冲走后,是不是有可能被方向相反而同样湍急的海流冲回来。我刚想到这点,眼光便已落在一座小山上;它有足够的高度,完全可以俯瞰两侧的海面,而且从那儿还可以清楚地看到那两股急流,可以判断我回程时该采取什么路线;到了山上一看,我发现那股海流在退潮时贴着岛的南端往外流;而涨潮时却贴着岛的北缘往回流;所以我在回程时唯一要做的,就是朝岛的北面靠,这样就万事大吉了。

这次观察又使我有了信心,我打算第二天一早趁早潮上路。我在独木舟上睡了一夜,身上盖的就是前面提到的那种水手值更时穿的大衣。第二天早上起身后,我就出发了。我先将船向海中开了一点,然后向正北方向开去。不一会儿,一股向东流的急流就帮上了我的忙,将我的舢板向东北推进。不过,这股急流还没有小岛南面的那股强劲,我还不至于像当初那样,控制不住舢板。我把木桨当作舵来使,用力把握住方向,船速很快,一直朝那条破船驶去。用不了两个钟头,我就来到了破船边。

我所看到的是一幅凄凉

which by its building was Spanish, stuck fast, jaum'd in between two Rocks; all the Stern and Quarter of her was beaten to pieces, with the Sea; and as her Forecastle, which stuck in the Rocks, had run on with great Violence, her Mainmast and Foremast were brought by the Board; that is to say, broken short off; but her Boltsprit was found, and the Head and Bow appear'd firm; when I came close to her, a Dog appear'd upon her, who seeing me coming, yelp'd, and cry'd; and as soon as I call'd him, jump'd into the Sea, to come to me, and I took him into the Boat; but found him almost dead for Hunger and Thirst: I gave him a Cake of my Bread, and he eat it like a ravenous Wolf, that had been starving a Fortnight in the Snow: I then gave the poor Creature some fresh Water, with which, if I would have let him, he would have burst himself.

After this I went on board; but the first Sight I met with, was two Men drown'd, in the Cookroom, or Forecastle of the Ship, with their Arms fast about one another: I concluded, as is indeed probable, that when the Ship struck, it being in a Storm, the Sea broke so high, and so continually over her, that the Men were not able to bear it, and were strangled with the constant rushing in of the Water, as much as if they had been under Water. Besides the Dog, there was nothing left in the Ship that had Life; nor any Goods that I could see, but what were spoil'd by the Water. There were some Casks of Liquor, whether Wine or Brandy, I knew not, which lay lower in the Hold; and which, the Water being ebb'd out, I could see; but they were too big to meddle with: I saw several Chests, which I believ'd belong'd to some of the Seamen; and I got two of them into the

的景象。那条船,从建造形式看是只西班牙船,由于撞得很猛,被紧紧地夹在两块岩石之间,船尾和船舱都被海水打碎了,而它的前舱,已撞到岩石中,由于撞得很猛,它的主桅和前杆都倒在了甲板上,折断了。但它的斜樯还算完整,船头看起来也还结实。当我走进船时,突然看到一条狗,它看到我过来,便尖叫起来。看到我在叫它,便跳到海里游了过来,我便把它抱到了舢板里。发现它几乎要饥渴而死。我给了它一块大麦饼,它立即狼吞虎咽地吃了起来,就像一只在雪地里两个星期没吃东西的饿狼。接着我又给这可怜的小东西倒了点水,它又呼噜呼噜地喝了起来,看那样子,如果我尽它喝个够的话,它非要撑破肚皮不可。

随后,我爬上了这只破船。一登上甲板,就看到前舱厨房地上倒着两个淹死的人,他们互相紧紧地抱在一起。看来,船在狂风暴雨中触礁的时候,海面上正是波涛汹涌,不断掀起的巨浪不仅把甲板上的人打得不知所措,不能自持,而且迅速地淹没了甲板,淹死了被浪头打倒的人。所以,船上除了那条狗,没有任何幸存的生命;而且,所有的货物都被海水浸泡坏了,只剩下放在舱底的几大桶酒,可能没有损坏。也不知道里面装的是葡萄酒还是白兰地。这些酒桶因为水已经退了,露在外面;可是桶太大,没法移动。

Boat, without examining what was in them.

Had the Stern of the Ship been fix'd, and the Forepart broken off, I am perswaded I might have made a good Voyage; for by what I found in these two Chests, I had room to suppose, the Ship had a great deal of Wealth on board; and if I may guess by the Course she steer'd, she must have been bound from the Buenos Ayres, or the Rio de la Plata, in the South Part of America, beyond the Brasils, to the Havana, in the Gulph of Mexico, and so perhaps to Spain: She had no doubt a great Treasure in her; but of no use at that time to any body; and what became of the rest of her People, I then knew not.

I found besides these Chests, a little Cask full of Liquor, of about twenty Gallons, which I got into my Boat, with much Difficulty; there were several Muskets in a Cabin, and a great Powder-horn, with about 4 Pounds of Powder in it; as for the Muskets, I had no occasion for them; so I left them, but took the Powder-horn: I took a Fire Shovel and Tongs, which I wanted extremely; as also two little Brass Kettles, a Copper Pot to make Chocolate, and a Gridiron; with this Cargo, and the Dog, I came away, the Tide beginning to make home again; and the same Evening, about an Hour within Night, I reach'd the Island again, weary and fatigu'd to the last Degree.

我又看见几只大箱子,看样子是某些船员的所有物,我搬了两只,运到我的舢板上,至于里面装的是什么,我也没工夫去检查。

假定触礁的是船尾,受伤的是船的前部,我倒不至虚此一行;因为,根据我从这两只大箱子里找到的东西看来,我有充分的理由可以断定船上有很多的财富;同时,根据这只船所走的航线,我不难看出它是从南美巴西附近的布宜诺斯艾利斯或里约拉巴拉他开出来的,准备开到墨西哥海湾的哈瓦那去,再从那里到西班牙去。船上无疑地载着许多财物,但这些财物目前对任何人都成了无用之物。至于船上其余的人都跑到什么地方去了,我完全不清楚。

除了那两只箱子,我还找到了一小桶酒,约有二十加仑。我费了九牛二虎之力,才把酒桶搬到舢板上。船舱里还有几支短枪和一只盛火药的大角筒,里面大约有四磅火药。短枪对我来说已毫无用处。因此我就留下了,只取了盛火药的角筒。另外我又拿了一把火炉铲和一把火钳,这两样正是我十分需要的东西。我还拿了两把小铜壶,一只煮巧克力的铜锅和一只烤东西用的铁耙。我把这些货物通通装进我的舢板,再带上那只狗,就准备回家了。这时正值涨潮,潮水开始向岛上流。天黑后不到一小时,我就回到了岸上,但人已劳累得疲倦不堪

I repos'd that Night in the Boat, and in the Morning I resolved to harbour what I had gotten in my new Cave, not to carry it home to my Castle. After refreshing my self, I got all my Cargo on Shore, and began to examine the Particulars: The Cask of Liquor I found to be a kind of Rum, but not such as we had at the Brasils; and in a Word, not at all good; but when I came to open the Chests, I found several Things, of great use to me: For Example, I found in one, a fine Case of Bottles, of an extraordinary kind, and fill'd with Cordial Waters, fine, and very good; the Bottles held about three Pints each, and were tipp'd with Silver: I found two Pots of very good Succades, or Sweetmeats, so fastned also on top, that the Salt Water had not hurt them; and two more of the same, which the Water had spoil'd: I found some very good Shirts, which were very welcome to me; and about a dozen and half of Linnen white Handkerchiefs, and colour'd Neckcloths; the former were also very welcome, being exceeding refreshing to wipe my Face in a hot Day; besides this, when I came to the Till in the Chest, I found there three great Bags of Pieces of Eight, which held about eleven hundred Pieces in all; and in one of them, wrapt up in a Paper, six Doubloons of Gold, and some small Bars or Wedges of Gold; I suppose they might all weigh near a Pound.

The other Chest I found had some Cloaths in it, but of little Value; but by the Circumstances it must have belong'd to the Gunner's Mate; though there was no Powder in it; but about two Pound of fine glaz'd Powder, in three small Flasks, kept, I suppose, for charging their Fowling-Pieces on oc-

了。

夜里我就睡在舢板上；第二天早晨，我盘算好了，把弄来的东西存放在我那新洞里，不把它们运回我那城堡。吃了些东西之后，我把运来的东西都搬上了岸，开始一一细看。我发现那桶甘蔗酒虽说也是一种甘蔗酒，却不是我们在巴西喝的那种，反正是一点也不好；但打开两个箱子一看，却发现几样对我大有用处的东西。例如，在一个箱子里，我发现一只精巧别致的酒箱，装着几瓶上好的露酒，每个瓶子里都是满满的，约有三品脱左右，瓶盖都是银的。我还发现两罐上等的蜜饯，罐口也封得很好，所以没有被海水毁掉；但另外还有两罐已被海水浸坏了。我找到的还有几件质地很好的衬衫（这是我很需要的东西）和十几条亚麻的白手帕，以及一些彩色的餐巾。手帕也是很受我欢迎的东西，热天用它们擦擦汗是再好不过的了。除此之外，我又在这只箱子里发现一只钱箱，里面有三大袋西班牙银币，一共有一千一百多块。在其中一只口袋里，有一个纸包，里面有六块西班牙金币和一些小块金条。据我估计，这些金子加起来差不多有一磅重。

在另一只箱子里，我找到了一些衣服，但都没有什么用处。从里面的东西来看，这只箱子肯定是属于炮手的。里面虽然没有普通火药，但有两磅左右的细砂火药，分装在三

casion: Upon the whole, I got very little by this Voyage, that was of any use to me; for as to the Money, I had no manner of occasion for it: 'Twas to me as the Dirt under my Feet; and I would have given it all for three or four pair of English Shoes and Stockings, which were Things I greatly wanted, but had not had on my Feet now for many Years: I had indeed gotten two pair of Shoes now, which I took off of the Feet of the two drown'd Men, who I saw in the Wreck; and I found two pair more in one of the Chests, which were very welcome to me; but they were not like our English Shoes, either for Ease, or Service; being rather what we call Pumps, than Shoes: I found in this Seaman's Chest, about fifty Pieces of Eight in Ryals, but no Gold; I suppose this belong'd to a poorer Man than the other, which seem'd to belong to some Officer.

Well, however, I lugg'd this Money home to my Cave, and laid it up, as I had done that before, which I brought from our own Ship; but it was great Pity as I said, that the over Part of this Ship had not come to my Share; for I am satisfy'd I might have loaded my Canoe several Times over with Money, which if I had ever escap'd to England, would have lain here safe enough, till I might have come again and fetch'd it.

Having now brought all my Things on Shore, and secur'd them, I went back to my Boat, and row'd, or paddled her along the Shore, to her old Harbour, where I laid her up, and made the best of my way to my old Habitation, where I found every thing safe and quiet; so I began to repose my

只烧瓶里，我猜测，这大概是随时用来装鸟枪用的。总而言之，我这次出海得到的对我有用的东西很少。至于金钱，我根本无法使用，它对于我来说，就像我脚下的泥土一般，我宁愿用所有的钱币去换三四双英国鞋或袜子，这些东西是我迫切需要的，我已经好多年没有穿在脚上了。事实上，我现在也得到了两双鞋，这是我从船上两个被淹死的人的脚上脱下来的。我在一只箱子里也找到了两双鞋，正是我求之不得的，但却不像我们英国鞋那样，既不舒服又不耐用，只是一种便鞋。我在这位船员的箱子里也发现了五十多枚银币，但却没有金币，我想这只箱子一定属于一位较贫穷的船员，不像那只箱子的主人，像是位高级船员。

不管这些钱有用没用，我还是把它们都带回了城堡，依旧放在帐蓬后面的山洞里，和过去从自己船上弄来的钱币一样，把它们收藏妥当。只可惜我无法进入这艘破船的其余部位，否则的话，我敢肯定，一定能用我的舢板装回好几船的钱币呢。如果有朝一日我能逃回到英国，这些钱币留在岛上也是安全的，等事后有机会时，再回来运走也无妨。

我把全部东西搬到岸上，收藏妥当以后，就回到我的舢板，把它沿着海岸划回它的旧港，把它缆好，然后拖着疲倦的身子回到我的老住处。到了那里，只见一切平安无事。

self, live after my old fashion, and take care of my Family Affairs; and for a while, I liv'd easy enough; only that I was more vigilant than I us'd to be, look'd out oftner, and did not go abroad so much; and if at any time I did stir with any Freedom, it was always to the East Part of the Island, where I was pretty well satisfy'd the Savages never came, and where I could go without so many Precautions, and such a Load of Arms and Ammunition, as I always carry'd with me, if I went the other way.

I liv'd in this Condition near two Years more; but my unlucky Head, that was always to let me know it was born to make my Body miserable, was all this two Years fill'd with Projects and Designs, how, if it were possible, I might get away from this Island; for sometimes I was for making another Voyage to the Wreck, though my Reason told me that there was nothing left there, worth the Hazard of my Voyage: Sometimes for a Ramble one way, sometimes another; and I believe verily, if I had had the Boat that I went from Sallee in, I should have ventur'd to Sea, bound any where, I knew not whither.

I have been in all my Circumstances a Memento to those who are touch'd with the general Plague of Mankind, whence, for ought I know, one half of their Miseries flow; I mean, that of not being satisfy'd with the Station wherein God and Nature has plac'd them; for not to look back upon my primitive Condition, and the excellent Advice of my Father, the Opposition to which, was, as I may call it, my ORIGINAL SIN; my subsequent Mistakes of the same kind had been the Means of my coming into this miserable Condition; for had that Providence, which so happily had seated me at the Brasils, as a Planter, bless'd me with

于是我便开始休息,并且照老样子过日子,照料我的家事。有一段短短的时期,我的日子过得相当优闲自在,仅仅比以前更加警惕一些,时时注意外面的动静,并且也不大出门。即使有时大胆在外面活动,也是在岛的东部,因为我确信那是野人从来不到的地带,因此到那边去用不着处处小心,带那么多的武器和军火,像我到别的地方去时那样。

我在这种情况下又过了将近两年。在这两年里,我头脑里充塞着各种各样的计划,一心设法逃离孤岛,尽管我自己也知道,我那倒霉的头脑似乎生来就是为了折磨我的肉体。有时候,我还想上那条破船去察看一番,尽管我也知道,船上已没有什么东西值得我再次冒险出海了。有时候,我又想乘小舟东逛逛西走走。我毫不怀疑,如果我现在有我从萨利逃出来时坐的那条舢板,早就冒险出海了;至于去什么地方,我也顾不上了。

一般人往往有一种通病,那就是不知足,老是不满足于上帝和大自然对他们的安排。对于这种人来说,我的种种遭遇就是一种警告;因为,当初我毫不考虑自己的家庭背景,不考虑父亲分析得极为透彻的忠告,我认为,违抗这忠告真可谓是我犯下的原罪再加上后来接二连三犯下的同样错误,便铸成了我今日的不幸处境;因为上天当初把我安置在巴西,让我当了事业颇为兴

confin'd Desires, and I could have been contented to have gone on gradually, I might have been by this Time; I mean, in the Time of my being in this Island, one of the most considerable Planters in the Brasils, nay, I am perswaded, that by the Improvements I had made, in that little Time I liv'd there, and the Encrease I should probably have made, if I had stay'd, I might have been worth an hundred thousand Moydors; and what Business had I to leave a settled Fortune, a well stock'd Plantation, improving and encreasing, to turn Supra-Cargo to Guinea, to fetch Negroes; when Patience and Time would have so encreas'd our Stock at Home, that we could have bought them at our own Door, from those whose Business it was to fetch them; and though it had cost us something more, yet the Difference of that Price was by no Means worth saving, at so great a Hazard.

But as this is ordinarily the Fate of young Heads, so Reflection upon the Folly of it, is as ordinarily the Exercise of more years, or of the dear bought Experience of Time; and so it was with me now; and yet so deep had the Mistake taken root in my Temper, that I could not satisfy my self in my Station, but was continually poring upon the Means, and Possibility of my Escape from this Place; and that I may with the greater Pleasure to the Reader, bring on the remaining Part of my Story, it may not be improper, to give some Account of my first Conceptions on the Subject of this foolish Scheme, for my Escape; and how, and upon what Foundation I acted.

I am now to be suppos'd retir'd into my Castle, after my late Voyage to the Wreck, my Frigate

旺的种植园主之后，如果能格外恩典，让我不再心猿意马，那么我就能满足于循序发展，而经过这些年的发展（我是说，如果这些年不是花费在岛上的话），我现在已是巴西举足轻重的种植园主之一了；实际上，根据我在巴西那短短的时间内取得的进展和不断增大的收获，我深信，要是我一直留在那儿，现在我的身价很可能已是十万莫艾多了；我丢下一个颇有实力又日益兴旺发达的好端端的种植园，丢下一个稳稳当当可以发家致富的前程，却到船上当押运员，去几内亚装运黑奴，这算是什么事呢？事实上，只要我们耐心地积累财富，时间一久，不就可以在自个儿门口从黑奴贩子那儿买上几个吗？虽说从黑奴贩子手里购买，价钱要贵得多，但也不值得为了这点差价去冒那么大的风险哪。

这就是一般头脑发热的年轻人的命运。要意识到这么做有多蠢，需要多年的磨砺，并为此付出昂贵的代价；我就是这样一个人，但是这种错误在我的性格中已根深蒂固，所以，直到现在我仍对现状不满，不断盘算着怎样逃出这个地方。为了使我后面讲述的故事让读者更有兴趣，我觉得有必要先讲述一下我那愚蠢的逃跑计划的初步构思，以及后来是怎样实施的，又是在什么基础上实行的。

当我从破船上回来后，我应该隐退到我的城堡了，我的

laid up, and secur'd under Water, as usual, and my Condition restor'd to what it was before: I had more Wealth indeed than I had before, but was not at all the richer; for I had no more use for it, than the Indians of Peru had, before the Spaniards came there.

It was one of the Nights in the rainy Season in March, the four and twentieth Year of my first setting Foot in this Island of Solitariness; I was lying in my Bed, or Hammock, awake, very well in Health, had no Pain, no Distemper, no Uneasiness of Body; no, nor any Uneasiness of Mind, more than ordinary; but could by no means close my Eyes; that is, so as to sleep; no, not a Wink all Night long, otherwise than as follows:

It is as impossible, as needless, to set down the innumerable Crowd of Thoughts that whirl'd through that great thorow-fare of the Brain, the Memory, in this Night's Time: I run over the whole History of my Life in Miniature, or by Abridgment, as I may call it, to my coming to this Island; and also of the Part of my Life, since I came to this Island. In my Reflections upon the State of my Case, since I came on Shore on this Island, I was comparing the happy Posture of my Affairs, in the first Years of my Habitation here, compar'd to the Life of Anxiety, Fear and Care, which I had liv'd ever since I had seen the Print of a Foot in the Sand; not that I did not believe the Savages had frequented the Island even all the while, and might have been several Hundreds of them at Times on Shore there; but I had never known it, and was incapable of any Apprehensions about it; my Satisfaction was perfect, though my Danger was the same; and I was as happy in not knowing my Danger, as if I had never really been

舢板像以往那样被放置好沉在水底下,我的生活恢复到从前的样子。事实上,我比以前有了更多的财富,但并不比以前富裕。因为,这些钱对我毫无用处,就像在西班牙人到达秘鲁之前,当地的印第安人根本不必用钱币一样。

这是我沦落到这座孤岛的第二十四个年头,现在正处于雨季的三月份。且说一天晚上,我躺在我的吊床里,难以入眠。尽管我的身体很好,没有疼痛,没有疾病,也没有肌体上的不适,甚至精神上也很平静,可是,我怎么也合不上眼,怎么也睡不着,整整一夜,一分钟也没睡着,脑子里尽胡思乱想。

在这个不眠之夜里,我的思潮起伏,浮想联翩,许多往事和各种想法在我脑海中不停地闪现出来,实在让我无法,当然也无必要将它们一一叙述出来。我大致回顾了自己一生的经历,从年轻时想到流落这个荒岛时的情景,想到在岛上度过的这些岁月。我想到了最初那些年的愉快生活,也想到了发现沙滩上的野人足迹后那种忧虑不安,担惊受怕的日子。我当然也明白,野人们光顾此岛的事并不是近几年才出现的,他们多年来时常上岛,而且从未间断过,甚至成百上千次地来过。可是俗话说得好:眼不见,心不乱。我以前不知道他们光顾此岛之事,自然不会提心吊胆。尽管那时一样有危险,但

expos'd to it: This furnish'd my Thoughts with many very profitable Reflections, and particularly this one, How infinitely Good that Providence is, which has provided in its Government of Mankind, such narrow bounds to his Sight and Knowledge of Things, and though he walks in the midst of so many thousand Dangers, the Sight of which, if discover'd to him, would distract his Mind, and sink his Spirits; he is kept serene, and calm, by having the Events of Things hid from his Eyes, and knowing nothing of the Dangers which surround him.

After these Thoughts had for some Time entertain'd me, I came to reflect seriously upon the real Danger I had been In, for so many Years, in this very Island; and how I had walk'd about in the greatest Security, and with all possible Tranquillity; even when perhaps nothing but a Brow of a Hill, a great Tree, or the casual Approach of Night, had been between me and the worst kind of Destruction, viz. That of falling into the Hands of Cannibals, and Savages, who would have seiz'd on me with the same View, as I did of a Goat, or a Turtle; and have thought it no more a Crime to kill and devour me, than I did of a Pidgeon, or a Curlieu: I would unjustly slander my self, if I should say I was not sincerely thankful to my great Preserver, to whose singular Protection I acknowledg'd, with great Humility, that all these unknown Deliverances were due; and without which, I must inevitably have fallen into their merciless Hands.

因为不知道,所以照样过得无忧无虑,美满如意。我觉得,不知道危险的存在,就像没有危险一样,可以生活得自由自在,安宁泰然。由此,我悟出不少有益的道理。造物主在统治人类的时候,把人类的认识和知识局限于狭隘的范围,实在是无上的好事。人类虽然有时在千千万万的危险中生活——这些危险如果让他发觉,一定会使他心烦意乱,精神颓唐——但造物主却叫他看不清事情的真相,完全不知道四周的种种危险,从而宁静泰然地过下去。

这种想法在我头脑里盘旋了一段时间后,我就开始郑重其事地想到,这么多年以来,就在这个岛上,我无时无刻不被危机包围着。这种危险是实实在在的,可是,我过去却经常坦然自若地在岛上走来走去。实际上,可能只是一座小山,一棵大树,或是夜正好降临,才使我免遭杀害,而且,将会是以一种最残忍的方式的杀害:那就是落入吃人生番手里。如果落到他们手里,他们就会把我马上抓起来,就像我抓只山羊或海龟一样。同时,在他们看来,把我杀死吃掉,也不是什么犯罪行为,就像把一只鸽子或鹬杀了吃掉在我看来也不是什么犯罪行为一样。我衷心感激我的伟大的救世主,如果我不承认我的感激之情,那我就不诚实了。我必须恭恭敬敬地承认,我之所以在不知不觉中免

When these Thoughts were over, my Head was for some time taken up in considering the Nature of these wretched Creatures; I mean, the Savages; and how it came to pass in the World, that the wise Governour of all Things should give up any of his Creatures to such Inhumanity; nay, to something so much below, even Brutality it self, as to devour its own kind; but as this ended in some (at that Time fruitless) Speculations, it occurr'd to me to enquire, what Part of the World these Wretches liv'd in; how far off the Coast was from whence they came; what they ventur'd over so far from home for; what kind of Boats they had; and why I might not order my self, and my Business so, that I might be as able to go over thither, as they were to come to me.

I never so much as troubl'd my self to consider what I should do with my self, when I came thither; what would become of me, if I fell into the Hands of the Savages; or how I should escape from them, if they attempted me; no, nor so much as how it was possible for me to reach the Coast, and not be attempted by some or other of them, without any Possibility of delivering my self; and if I should not fall into their Hands, what I should do for Provision, or whither I should bend my Course; none of these Thoughts, I say, so much as came in my way; but my Mind was wholly bent upon the Notion of my passing over in my Boat, to the Main Land: I look'd back upon my present Condition, as the most miserable that could possibly be, that I was not able to

于大难,完全是由于救世主的保佑,要是没有他的保佑,我早就落入野人的毒手了。

这样想过之后,我把那些可怜的畜生——我是说,那些野人——想了一阵,考虑了他们的天性问题;我想世上怎么会有这样的事:万物的英明主宰怎么能够容忍,怎么竟听任他所创造的人这么惨无人道——不,简直比一般的畜生还不如——竟听任他们吃掉自己的同类!但这个问题在当时得不出结果,想来想去也只能是各种猜测而已;可我转而又想到了很多问题:这些可怜鬼住在世上的什么地方?从他们那里到我这岛上有多远?他们为什么要冒险出海,到离家这么远的岛上来?他们乘的是怎么样的舢板?既然他们可以上我这儿来,我是不是可以动动脑筋、想想办法,也上他们那儿去?

我懒得费心思考虑我去了那边该干什么;一旦落入野人的手里,我的命运如何;或者如果他们向我进攻,我该如何逃脱。我也没有特别认真地考虑过我怎样做才能有可能不受到攻击地上岸,因为一旦受到攻击,我一点获救的指望都没有,即使我不会被他们捉住,我该从哪儿弄到吃的,又该朝何处去等等,我都没有考虑。总之,这些顾虑一点不碍事,我仍旧津津乐道地设想坐舢板去那边的大陆。我把我现在的处境看作是世界上最悲惨的处境,除了死亡以

— 242 —

throw my self into any thing but Death, that could be call'd worse; that if I reached the Shore of the Main, I might perhaps meet with Relief, or I might coast along, as I did on the Shore of Africk, till I came to some inhabited Country, and where I might find some Relief; and after all perhaps, I might fall in with some Christian Ship, that might take me in; and if the worse came to the worst, I could but die, which would put an end to all these Miseries at once. Pray note, all this was the fruit of a disturb'd Mind, an impatient Temper, made as it were desperate by the long Continuance of my Troubles, and the Disappointments I had met in the Wreck, I had been on board of; and where I had been so near the obtaining what I so earnestly long'd for, viz. Some-body to speak to, and to learn some Knowledge from of the Place where I was, and of the probable Means of my Deliverance; I say, I was agitated wholly by these Thoughts: All my Calm of Mind in my Resignation to Providence, and waiting the Issue of the Dispositions of Heaven, seem'd to be suspended; and I had, as it were, no Power to turn my Thoughts to any thing, but to the Project of a Voyage to the Main, which came upon me with such Force, and such an Impetuosity of Desire, that it was not to be resisted.

When this had agitated my Thoughts for two Hours, or more, with such Violence, that it set my very Blood into a Ferment, and my Pulse beat as high as if I had been in a Feaver, meerly with the extraordinary Fervour of my Mind about it; Nature, as if I had been fatigued and exhausted with the very Thought of it, threw me into a

外,任何遭遇都比它强。如果我到达大陆那边,我也许能够遇救。或者我也可以沿着海岸走,像我以前沿非洲海岸走那样,一直走到有人居住的地方,也许能够得到救援。并且,说不定我能遇到某个基督徒船只,把我收留下来。就是落到最坏的地步,最多也不过一死了之,而且死后这些不幸也就全部了结了。请读者注意,所有这些想法都是我那烦乱不安的心情和焦虑的性情所造成的。一个接一个的打击已使我十分绝望,加之,我上次到那条破船上去又再次失望,没有得到迫切想得到的东西。就是说,我原指望在那条船上能找到一个幸存者,能跟他说说话,并从他那里了解一下,我现在究竟沦落在什么地区,看有没有办法从这里逃出去。总之,我完全被这些因素折磨得心烦意乱。我本想心平气和,一切顺从造物主的意志,一切等待上帝的安排,可现在,我的心境好像根本无法平静。现在,我似乎已无力将我的思想转到别的方面去,只一心想着航行到对面大陆的计划。这一念头以一种巨大的力量和不可阻挡的愿望冲击着我,令我实在无法抗拒。

现在,强烈的欲望又使我激动不已,而且在好长时间内都无法控制住自己。我觉得自己热血沸腾,心跳加速,就像得了热病一样。当然,这只不过是头脑因为冲动而发热罢了。整整一夜,我就这样任

sound Sleep; one would have thought, I should have dream'd of it: But I did not, nor of any Thing relating to it; but I dream'd, that as I was going out in the Morning as usual from my Castle, I saw upon the Shore, two Canoes, and eleven Savages coming to Land, and that they brought with them another Savage, who they were going to kill, in Order to eat him; when on a sudden, the Savage that they were going to kill, jumpt away, and ran for his Life; and I thought in my Sleep, that he came running into my little thick Grove, before my Fortification, to hide himself; and that I seeing him alone, and not perceiving that the other sought him that Way, show'd my self to him, and smiling upon him, encourag'd him; that he kneel'd down to me, seeming to pray me to assist him; upon which I shew'd my Ladder, made him go up, and carry'd him into my Cave, and he became my Servant; and that as soon as I had gotten this Man, I said to my self, now I may certainly venture to the main Land; for this Fellow will serve me as a Pilot, and will tell me what to do, and whether to go for Provisions; and whether not to go for fear of being devoured, what Places to venture into, and what to escape: I wak'd with this Thought, and was under such inexpressible Impressions of Joy, at the Prospect of my Escape in my Dream, that the Disappointments which I felt upon coming to my self, and finding it was no more than a Dream, were equally extravagant the other Way, and threw me into a very great Dejection of Spirit.

Upon this however, I made this Conclusion, that my Only Way to go about an Attempt for an Escape, was, if possible, to get a Savage into my Possession; and if possible, it should be one of

凭思绪像脱缰的野马狂奔乱跑,直到最后精疲力竭,才昏昏睡去。可能有人认为,我在睡觉时也会梦见自己登上了大陆,可我并没有做这样的梦。我梦见的是有一天早晨,我像往常一样走出城堡,忽然发现海边有两只独木舟,载了十个野人登上岸,他们另外还押着一个野人,像是要把他在这里杀死吃掉的样子。突然之间,这个行将被杀的野人猛地一跳,然后就飞跑起来。我在睡梦中恍惚看到,他跑到城堡外那片茂密的小树林里藏了起来。我看到仅他一个人跑过来,其他野人并没有追赶他,便走了过去,向他微笑,叫他不要害怕。他立刻朝我跪下来,仿佛求我援救他。于是我向他指指我的梯子,叫他爬上去,把他带到洞里,他就成了我的仆人。我得到这个人以后,就对我自己说:"我现在真可以冒险向大陆出发了;因为这个人可以作我的向导,告诉我怎么办,到什么地方弄到给养,告诉我什么地方不能去,免得给野人吃掉;告诉我哪些地方可以大胆前去,哪些地方应该躲开。"正这样想着,我就醒了,起初觉得自己有逃走的希望,高兴得无法形容,等清醒过来,发现原来不过是一场梦,我又感到同等地失望,大为懊丧。

可是,从这个梦境,我却明确了一件事:我要想逃走,唯一的办法就是尽可能弄到一个野人,而且,如果可能的

their Prisoners, who they had condemn'd to be eaten, and should bring thither to kill; but these Thoughts still were attended with this Difficulty, that it was impossible to effect this, without attacking a whole Caravan of them, and killing them all; and this was not only a very desperate Attempt, and might miscarry; but on the other Hand, I had greatly scrupled the Lawfulness of it to me; and my Heart trembled at the thoughts of shedding so much Blood, tho' it was for my Deliverance. I need not repeat the Arguments which occurr'd to me against this, they being the same mention'd before; but tho' I had other Reasons to offer now (viz.) that those Men were Enemies to my Life, and would devour me, if they could; that it was Self-preservation in the highest Degree, to deliver my self from this Death of a Life, and was acting in my own Defence, as much as if they were actually assaulting me, and the like. I say, tho' these Things argued for it, yet the Thoughts of shedding Humane Blood for my Deliverance, were very Terrible to me, and such as I could by no Means reconcile my self to, a great while.

However at last, after many secret Disputes with my self, and after great Perplexities about it, for all these Arguments one Way and another struggl'd in my Head a long Time, the eager prevailing Desire of Deliverance at length master'd all the rest; and I resolv'd, if possible, to get one of those Savages into my Hands, cost what it would. My next Thing then was to contrive how to do it, and this indeed was very difficult to resolve on: But as I could pitch upon no probable Means for it, so I resolv'd to put my self upon the Watch, to

话,最好是一个被他们带来准备杀死吃掉的俘虏。但要实现这个计划也有其困难的一面,那就是进攻一大队野人,并把他们杀得一个不留。这种做法可以说是孤注一掷之举,难保不出差错;不仅如此,而且从另一方面来说,这种做法是否合法,也值得怀疑。一想到要杀这么多人,流这么多血,我的心不由得颤抖起来,尽管这样做是为了使自己获救。我前面也已经谈到过我为什么不应该主动去攻击野人的种种理由,所以我不必在此再啰嗦了。另外,我现在还可以举出种种其他理由来证明为什么我应该攻击这些野人。譬如说,这些野人是我的死敌,只要可能,他们就会把我吃掉;再譬如说,我这样做是为了保护自己的生命,是为了拯救自己,这是一种自卫行为。因为,他们若向我进攻,我就不得不还击。如此等等,理由还可以举出一大堆。可是,一想到为了自己获救,非得别人流血,我就感到害怕,好久好久都想不通。

所有这些理由在我脑海中斗来斗去,斗了好长时间,真使我茫然不知所措,但我内心经过了多次较量之后,想要离开这岛的急切愿望终于占了上风,使我下定决心,要尽一切可能,弄到一个野人,哪怕代价再大也在所不惜。接下来,我得做的事便是考虑如何行动了,但要在这个问题上作出决定却十分困难。既然

see them when they came on Shore, and leave the rest to the Event, taking such Measures as the Opportunity should present, let be what would be.

With these Resolutions in my Thoughts, I set my self upon the Scout, as often as possible, and indeed so often till I was heartily tir'd of it, for it was above a Year and Half that I waited, and for great part of that Time went out to the West End, and to the South West Corner of the Island, almost every Day, to see for Canoes, but none appear'd. This was very discouraging, and began to trouble me much, tho' I cannot say that it did in this Case, as it had done some time before that, (viz.) wear off the Edge of my Desire to the Thing. But the longer it seem'd to be delay'd, the more eager I was for it; in a Word, I was not at first so careful to shun the sight of these Savages, and avoid being seen by them, as I was now eager to be upon them.

Besides, I fancied my self able to manage One, nay, Two or Three Savages, if I had them so as to make them entirely Slaves to me, to do whatever I should direct them, and to prevent their being able at any time to do me any Hurt. It was a great while, that I pleas'd my self with this Affair, but nothing still presented; all my Fancies and Schemes came to nothing, for no Savages came near me for a great while.

一时间想不出比较有把握的办法,我决定先仔细观察一番,看看他们什么时候来,其他的事暂时不考虑,以后看情况如何,再见机行事。

这样决定以后,我就开始了外出侦察的工作。只要有空就去等候野人,这一等就等了一年半之久,直等得我又心生厌倦起来。在这期间,我几乎每天都要到岛西边或西南边去,看海面上是否有独木舟出现。可是一年半的时间过去了,竟连一只独木舟的影子也没见到过,这真让我极为扫兴和懊丧。但是在这次等候中,有一点和上次不一样,那就是我没有在日复一日的等待之中,一点一点地放弃自己的希望。相反,我等待的时间越长,渴望的心情就越强烈。一句话,我以前总是小心翼翼地躲避野人,不想看到他们,也不想被他们看到,可我现在却是在急切地盼望着见到他们了。

与此同时,我又打起我的如意算盘来。我认为,假如能弄到一个,不,哪怕两三个野人来,我一定有能力管理好,叫他们服服贴贴地做我的奴隶,吩咐他们去做各种各样的事情,而且,不管在什么时候都能使他们伤害不到我。这一幻想的确让我得意了很久。可是,一切依然没有动静。我所有的幻想和计划一直得不到落实,因为好长一段时间都没有野人到我这里来。

Part 6

About a Year and half after I had entertain'd these Notions, and by long musing, had as it were resolved them all into nothing, for want of an Occasion to put them in Execution, I was surpriz'd one Morning early, with seeing no less than five Canoes all on Shore together on my side the Island; and the People who belong'd to them all landed, and out of my sight: The Number of them broke all my Measures, for seeing so many, and knowing that they always came four or six, or sometimes more in a Boat, I could not tell what to think of it, Or how to take my Measures, to attack Twenty or Thirty Men single handed; so I lay still in my Castle, perplex'd and discomforted: However I put my self into all the same Postures for an Attack that I had formerly provided, and was just ready for Action, if any Thing had presented; having waited a good while, listening to hear if they made any Noise; at length being very impatient, I set my Guns at the Foot of my Ladder, and clamber'd up to the Top of the Hill, by my two Stages as usual; standing so however that my Head did not appear above the Hill, so that they could not perceive me by any Means; here I observ'd by the help of my Perspective Glass, that they were no less than Thirty in Number, that they had a Fire kindled, that they had had Meat dress'd. How they had cook'd it, that I knew not, or what it was; but they were all Dancing in I know not how many barbarous Gestures and Figures, their own Way, round the Fire. While I was thus looking on them, I perceived by my Perspective, two miserable Wretches dragg'd from the Boats, where it seems they were laid by, and were now brought out for the Slaughter. I perceived one of them immediately fell, being knock'd down, I suppose with a Club or Wooden Sword, for that

第 六 部

自从我心里盘算着这个念头以后，又过了一年半，这期间我反复酝酿、斟酌，可就是找不到机会实施我的计划。一天清晨，我吃惊地发现不下五只独木舟停泊在我这边的海岸。船上的人都登了陆，失去踪影。他们的人数打破了我的全盘计划。出现这么多独木舟，并且一般来说每个独木舟上都有五六个甚至更多的人，我不知道该怎么办，该采取什么措施使我能单枪匹马地袭击二三十人。我躺在城堡里，一阵惆怅，一阵难过。不过，我还是立即恢复常态，进入以前布置好的戒备状态，随时准备行动。我等了很长时间，静静地听着他们的动静，最后终于失去了耐心。我把枪放在梯子脚下，像以往那样，分作两步爬到了小山顶上，站在那里，免得把头露出来，让他们看见。在这里我通过望远镜观察到，他们不少于三十个人正点着一堆火，在那里烤肉，至于他们是怎样点燃的，烧的又是什么，我却不知道，只见他们正在那里以他们那种野蛮的舞姿和舞步围着火堆跳舞。当我正这样看他们的时候，通过望远镜，我看到有两个可怜的受害人被从舢板里拖了出来，看起来，他们是事先被放置在舢板里，现在拖出来准备屠杀的。这时，我看见其中有一个被他们用

was their way, and two or three others were at work immediately cutting him open for their Cookery, while the other Victim was left standing by himself, till they should be ready for him. In that very Moment this poor Wretch seeing himself a little at Liberty, Nature inspir'd him with Hopes of Life, and he started away from them, and ran with incredible Swiftness along the Sands directly towards me, I mean towards that part of the Coast, where my Habitation was.

I was dreadfully frighted, (that I must acknowledge) when I perceived him to run my Way; and especially, when as I thought I saw him pursued by the whole Body, and now I expected that part of my Dream was coming to pass, and that he would certainly take shelter in my Grove; but I could not depend by any means upon my Dream for the rest Of it, (viz.) that the other Savages would not pursue him thither, and find him there. However I kept my Station, and my Spirits began to recover, when I found that there was not above three Men that follow'd him, and still more was I encourag'd, when I found that he outstrip'd them exceedingly in running, and gain'd Ground of them, so that if he could but hold it for half an Hour, I saw easily he would fairly get away from them all.

There was between them and my Castle, the Creek which I mention'd often at the first part of my Story, when I landed my Cargoes out of the Ship; and this I saw plainly, he must necessarily swim over, or the poor Wretch would be taken there: But when the Savage escaping came thither, he made nothing of it, tho' the Tide was then up, but plunging in, swam thro' in about Thirty Strokes or thereabouts, landed and ran on with

一根木棍或一把木刀一阵乱打,登时倒了下来,跟着便有两三个野人跑上来,动手把他破腹开膛,准备烹调。至于另外一个受害者,则呆呆地站在一边,等候他们前来动手。这时,这个可怜虫看见自己手脚松了绑,没人照管,不由地起了逃命的希望,突然跳出他们的圈子,用一种令人难以置信的速度沿着海岸往我这边跑,也就是说,朝我所住的这一带跑来。

我一见他朝我这边跑来,尤其是乍一看来,全部的野人都在他后头紧紧追赶,说句老实话,我真吓坏了。我看出我的梦有一部分要实现了,我预料他一定会躲到我的小树林里来。可是,梦境中的其余部分我可不敢相信,那就是那些野人不会来追他,也不会发现他躲在树林里。我仍旧站在原地,一动也不动。后来,我发现追他的只有三个人,胆子就大一点了。尤其是我发现那个野人跑得比追他的三个人快得多,而且把他们愈甩愈远了。只要他能再跑上半小时,就可完全摆脱他们了。这不由使我勇气倍增。

在他们和我的城堡之间,有一条小河。这条小河,我在本书的开头部分曾多次提到过;我把破船上的东西运下来的时候,就是进入小河后搬上岸的。现在情况很明白,他非游过河不可,要不然,这可怜虫就会在那儿被逮住。但那个奔逃的野人一来到河边,尽

exceeding Strength and Swiftness; when the Three Persons came to the Creek, I found that Two of them could Swim, but the Third cou'd not, and that standing on the other Side, he look'd at the other, but went no further; and soon after went softly back again, which as it happen'd, was very well for him in the main.

I observ'd, that the two who swam, were yet more than twice as long swimming over the Creek, as the Fellow was, that fled from them: It came now very warmly upon my Thoughts, and indeed irresistibly, that now was my Time to get me a Servant, and perhaps a Companion, or Assistant; and that I was call'd plainly by Providence to save this poor Creature's Life; I immediately run down the Ladders with all possible Expedition, fetches my two Guns, for they were both but at the Foot of the Ladders, as I observ'd above; and getting up again, with the same haste, to the Top of the Hill, I cross'd toward the Sea; and having a very short Cut, and all down Hill, clapp'd my self in the way, between the Pursuers, and the Pursu'd; hallowing aloud to him that fled, who looking back, was at first perhaps as much frighted at me, as at them; but I beckon'd with my Hand to him, to come back; and in the mean time, I slowly advanc'd towards the two that follow'd; then rushing at once upon the foremost, I knock'd him down with the Stock of my Piece I was loath to fire, because 1 would not have the rest hear; though at that distance, it would not have been easily heard, and being out of Sight of the Smoke too, they wou'd not have easily known what to make of it: Having knock'd this Fellow down, the other who pursu'd with him stopp'd, as if he had been frighted; and I advanc'd a-pace to-

管潮水已经涨起,他却根本不当回事地纵身入水,划了三十来下便上了对岸,照旧是健步如飞;那三个追的人来到河边后,我发现其中两个人会游泳,一个人不会游泳,只得站在岸边,看人家过河,自己却只好到此为止;过了一会儿,他灰溜溜地往回走了;从后来发生的情况看,这对于他来说,真算是一件大好事。

根据我的观察,后面那两人游泳过河所花的时间,比前面那人多一倍还不止。这真叫我激动不已,心想,机会终于来了,现在我又可以弄到个仆人了,或许他还可以做我的伙伴或帮手呢。而我像是得到了上天的召唤,要救这个可怜虫的命。我飞速下了梯子,带上了那两支长枪,我刚才说过,我事先把它们放在梯子下面,然后,又以同样的速度爬了上去,越过了山顶,朝海边奔去。由于我抄了一条很近的路,一路上又都是下山坡,所以,我一下子便插到了追捕者和逃亡者之间。我大声向那个逃跑的野人发出了呼喊。他朝后看了看,起先,他见到我跟见到他们一样害怕。但我向他招招手,示意他回来。与此同时,我又朝那两个前来追捕的野人慢慢走去。忽然,我向前面那个猛地扑了过去,用枪托将他击倒了但我不愿放枪,怕被其余的野人听见。其实距离很远,而且又看不到硝烟,即使听到声音,他们也不容易知道这是在干什么。

wards him; but as I came nearer, I perceiv'd presently, he had a Bow and Arrow, and was fitting it to shoot at me; so I was then necessitated to shoot at him first, which I did, and kill'd him at the first Shoot; the poor Savage who fled, but had stopp'd; though he saw both his Enemies fallen, and kill'd, as he thought; yet was so frighted with the Fire, and Noise of my Piece, that he stood Stock still, and neither came forward or went backward, tho' he seem'd rather enclin'd to fly still, than to come on; I hollow'd again to him, and made Signs to come forward, which he easily understood, and came a little way, then stopp'd again, and then a little further, and stopp'd again, and I cou'd then perceive that he stood trembling, as if he had been taken Prisoner, and had just been to be kill'd, as his two Enemies were; I beckon'd him again to come to me, and gave him all the Signs of Encouragement that I could think of, and he came nearer and nearer, kneeling down every Ten or Twelve steps in token of acknowledgement for my saving his Life: I smil'd at him, and look'd pleasantly, and beckon'd to him to come still nearer; at length he came close to me, and then he kneel'd down again, kiss'd the Ground, and laid his Head upon the Ground, and taking me by the Foot, set my Foot upon his Head; this it seems was in token of swearing to be my Slave for ever; I took him up, and made much of him, and encourag'd him all I could. But there was more work to do yet, for I perceiv'd the Savage who I knock'd down, was not kill'd, but stunn'd with the blow, and began to come to himself; so I pointed to him, and showing him the Savage, that he was not dead; upon this he spoke some Words to me, and though I could not understand them, yet I thought they were pleasant to hear, for they were the first sound of a Man's Voice, that I had heard, my own excepted, for above Twenty Five Years. But there was no time

把第一个野人击倒后，另一个来追赶的野人停住了脚步，好像害怕了。我飞快地向他迎去。但当我走近他时，我立刻发觉他拿了弓和箭，而且正准备向我射箭。这时我必须得先向他开枪了。我向他开两枪，第一枪就把他打死了。那可怜的逃跑的野人这时也停下了脚步，虽然看到他的两个敌人已经倒下或是死了，却又被我的枪声和火光吓坏了，只是呆呆地站在那里，既不敢前进又不敢后退，但看起来他的意思还是倾向于逃跑。我又向他大声呼喊，打着手势叫他过来。他立刻明白了我的意思，开始挪动脚步向我这边走来，可是他走走停停，停停走走。他停下的时候，我看到他浑身颤抖，大概以为自己现在又成了我的俘虏，我也会像杀他两个敌人那样把他杀死的。我一边示意他靠近我，一边做出各种手势叫他不要害怕，他这才一步不停地慢慢向我走了过来。他每走十几步便趴在地上跪拜一下，似乎是在感谢我的搭救之恩。我面带微笑地看着他，用一副和蔼可亲的样子打手势招呼他，让他再靠近一点。最后，他终于走到我跟前，冲着我跪了下来，先是亲吻地面，然后把头贴在地上，把我的一只脚放在他的头上，像是在行跪拜礼，以此宣誓愿做我的终身奴隶。我把他搀扶起来，对他百般抚慰，并尽我所能作出各种手势叫他不要害怕。就在这时，又出

for such Reflections now, the Savage who was knock'd down recover'd himself so far, as to sit up upon the Ground, and I perceived that my Savage began to be afraid; but when I saw that, I presented my other Piece at the Man, as if I would shoot him, upon this my Savage, for so I call him now, made a Motion to me to lend him my Sword, which hung naked in a Belt by my side; so I did: he no sooner had it, but he runs to his Enemy, and at one blow cut off his Head as cleaverly, no Executioner in Germany, could have done it sooner or better; which I thought very strange, for one who 1 had Reason to believe never saw a Sword in his Life before, except their own Wooden Swords; however it seems, as I learn'd afterwards, they make their Wooden Swords so sharp, so heavy, and the Wood is so hard, that they will cut off Heads even with them, ay and Arms, and that at one blow too; when he had done this, he comes laughing to me in Sign of Triumph, and brought me the Sword again, and with abundance of Gestures which I did not understand, laid it down with the Head of the Savage, that he had kill'd just before me.

现了新的情况;因为我看见我用枪杆打倒的那个野人并没有死,只是给我打昏了,现在又开始苏醒过来。于是我把那野人指给他看,表示他没有死。他看见之后,就叽哩咕哝地向我说了几句话。我虽然不明白他的话,可是听起来却非常悦耳,因为除了我自己的声音以外,这是二十五年以来我第一次听见人的声音。可是现在已经没有时间来想这些事情了。那被打倒的野人现在已经完全清醒过来,居然坐了起来。我看见我那野人这时又有点害怕起来,便举起我另外一杆枪,对准那个人,准备开枪。这时候,我那野人(我现在这样叫他了)向我作了一个动作,要求我把腰间挂的那把没有鞘的刀借给他。于是我就把刀借给他。他一拿到刀,就奔向他的敌人,手起刀落,一下子砍下了那个野人的头,其动作干脆利落,胜过德国刽子手。这使我大为惊讶,因为,我完全可以相信,这个人在此之前,除了他们自己的木刀外,一生中从未见过一把真正的刀。但现在看来,他们的木头刀也又快又锋利,砍头杀人照样一刀就能让人头落地。后来我了解到,事实也正是如此。他们的刀是用很硬的木头做成的,做得又沉重又锋利。且说我那野人砍下了敌人的头,带着胜利的笑声回到我跟前,他先把刀还给了我,然后做了许多莫名其妙的手势,把他砍下来的野人头

But that which astonish'd him most, was to know how I had kill'd the other Indian so far off, so pointing to him, he made Signs to me to let him go to him, so I bad him go, as well as I could, when he came to him, he stood like one amaz'd, looking at him, turn'd him first on one side, then on t'other, look'd at the Wound the Bullet had made, which it seems was just in his Breast, where it had made a Hole, and no great Quantity of Blood had follow'd, but he had bled inwardly, for he was quite dead; He took up his Bow, and Arrows, and came back, so I turn'd to go away, and beckon'd to him to follow me, making Signs to him, that more might come after them.

Upon this he sign'd to me, that he should bury them with Sand, that they might not be seen by the rest if they follow'd; and so I made Signs again to him to do so; he fell to Work, and in an instant he had scrap'd a Hole in the Sand, with his Hands, big enough to bury the first in, and then dragg'd him into it, and cover'd him, and did so also by the other; I believe he had bury'd them both in a Quarter of an Hour; then calling him away, I carry'd him not to my Castle, but quite away to my Cave, on the farther Part of the Island; so I did not let my Dream come to pass in that Part, viz. That he came into my Grove for shelter.

Here I gave him Bread, and a Bunch of Raisins to eat, and a Draught of Water, which I found he

放在我脚下。

但是,最使他感到惊讶的,是我怎么能从这么远的距离把另一个野人打死。他用手指了指那个野人的尸体,做着手势要我让他过去看看。我也打着手势,竭力让他懂得我同意他过去。他走到那死人身边,简直惊呆了。他把死者翻过来,翻过去,细看子弹留下的伤口;那伤口在胸前,看上去只是一个小孔,淌出的血并不多,因为这人已经死透,血倒不往外流了。他取了死者的弓箭,走了回来,于是我就离开了,同时向他招招手,要他跟我走,一边还给他打手势,意思是也许还有更多的人会来追他。

这一来,他也就给我打手势,表示要把这两具尸体都埋在沙下,这样,就算后面再有人追来,也见不到了;于是我又给他打手势,表示同意他这么做。于是,他干开了,转眼之间就用手刨了一个坑,大小足以埋下第一个。接着,他便把那个死鬼拖进坑,盖上了土,然后,他又以同样的方式把另一个也埋掉了。我想,他埋那两个家伙前后只不过花了不到一刻钟。完了之后,我便叫他跟我走,但我没有带他去我的城堡,而是把他带到了远在岛的另一部分的我的地洞。我不想完全按照梦里的情形去做,就是说,在梦里,他是跑进我的树林里去藏身的。

到了我的新洞里,我拿了一些面包和一串葡萄干给他

was indeed in great Distress for, by his Running; and having refresh'd him, I made Signs for him to go lie down and sleep; pointing to a Place where I had laid a great Parcel of Rice Straw, and a Blanket upon it, which 1 used to sleep upon my self some times; so the poor Creature laid down, and went to sleep.

He was a comely handsome Fellow, perfectly well made; with straight strong Limbs, not too large; tall and well shap'd, and as I reckon, about twenty six Years of Age. He had a very good Countenance, not a fierce and surly Aspect; but seem'd to have something very manly in his Face, and yet he had all the Sweetness and Softness of an European in his Countenance too, especially when he smil'd. His Hair was long and black, not curl'd like Wool; his Forehead very high, and large, and a great Vivacity and sparkling Sharpness in his Eyes. The Colour of his Skin was not quite black, but very tawny; and yet not of an ugly yellow nauseous tawny, as the Brasilians, and Virginians, and other Natives of America are; but of a bright kind of a dun olive Colour, that had in it something very agreeable; tho' not very easy to describe. His Face was round, and plump; his Nose small, not flat like the Negroes, a very good Mouth, thin Lips, and his line Teeth well set, and white as Ivory. After he had slumber'd, rather than slept, about half an Hour, he wak'd again, and comes out of the Cave to me; for I had been milking my Goats, which I had in the Enclosure just by: When he espy'd me, he came running to me, laying himself down again upon the Ground, with all the possible Signs of an humble thankful Disposition, making a many antick Gestures show it: At last he lays his Head flat upon the Ground, close to my Foot, and sets my other Foot upon his Head, as he had done before; and after this, made all the Signs to me of Subjection,

吃，又弄了点水给他喝。我发现，由于奔跑，他已饥渴万分。让他吃喝完毕后，我表示意着叫他躺下睡觉。我指着一块地方，那地方放着一大堆稻草，还有一条毛毯，以前我自己有时睡在那里。这个可怜虫躺到那儿后，便酣然睡去了。

他是个标致、帅气的小伙子，生就的完美无瑕，四肢修长而强壮，但并不粗大，个子很大而身段匀称。据我估计年龄在二十六岁左右，他有一副好面孔，看上去非但没有狰狞可怖的样子，反而具有一种男人的阳刚气，但又有点欧洲人的和蔼可亲，尤其是他微笑的时候。他的头发又黑又长，但像羊毛似的鬈曲着，他的前额又高又大，一双大眼睛活泼有神。他的皮肤并不很黑，发点黄褐色，但又不是巴西、弗吉尼亚等其他美洲土著人那种丑陋的黄，而是一种灿烂的橄榄色，说不出的赏心悦目。他的脸盘圆润、饱满，鼻子小巧玲珑，不是黑人那种塌鼻子。生就一张漂亮的嘴，嘴唇薄薄的，一排整齐的牙，象牙般地洁白。他最多打了一个盹儿，不超过半小时就醒了过来，跑出地洞来找我。我正在附近的圈地里给羊挤奶。他一眼瞥见我，跑过来，又匍匐在地，打出各种虔诚、感激的手势，作了各种古怪、滑稽的动作来表达自己的心情。最后，他又像上次那样把头贴在靠近我脚边的地上，把我的另一只脚放到他的头上；接着他

Servitude, and Submission imaginable, to let me know, how he would serve me as long as he liv'd; I understood him in many Things, and let him know, I was very well pleas'd with him; in a little Time I began to speak to him, and teach him to speak to me; and first, I made him know his Name should be Friday, which was the Day I sav'd his Life; I call'd him so for the Memory of the Time; I likewise taught him to say Master, and then let him know, that was to be my Name; I likewise taught him to say, YES, and No, and to know the Meaning of them; I gave him some Milk, in an earthen Pot, and let him see me Drink it before him, and sop my Bread in it; and I gave him a Cake of Bread, to do the like, which he quickly comply'd with, and made Signs that it was very good for him.

I kept there with him all that Night; but as soon as it was Day, I beckon'd to him to come with me, and let him know, I would give him some Cloaths, at which he seem'd very glad, for he was stark naked: As we went by the Place where he had bury'd the two Men, he pointed exactly to the Place, and shew'd me the Marks that he had made to find them again, making Signs to me, that we should dig them up again, and eat them; at this I appear'd very angry, express'd my Abhorrence of it, made as if I would vomit at the Thoughts of it, and beckon'd with my Hand to him to come away, which he did immediately, with great Sub mission. I then led him up to the Top of the Hill, to see if his Enemies were gone; and pulling out my Glass, I look'd, and saw plainly the Place where they had been, but no appear-

又作出各种姿势，好像在向我表示他对我的屈从、降服和归顺，表示他愿意终身为我之奴，为我效命。我大致了解他的这些意思后，便告诉他，我对他非常满意。过了一会儿，我开始和他说话，并叫他跟我学着说。我首先告诉他，我给他取名叫"星期五"，因为他是在这一天被我救出了性命，因此取这个名字来纪念这一天。我接着教他说"主人"一词，并叫他以后就这样称呼我。我还教他说"是"和"不是"，也同样告诉了他这两个词的意思。最后我在一个瓦罐里倒了点牛奶，递给他，让他先看着我如何在喝羊奶的时候用面包蘸着奶一块儿吃；然后，我给了他一块面包，让他照我的样子做；他照样子吃下去以后，兴奋地向我作出手势，表示味道好极了。

当天晚上我陪他在地洞里过了一夜，天一亮，我就向他招手，叫他跟着我走，同时让他知道，我要给他一些衣服。他明白了我的意思，仿佛很高兴，因为他这时光着身子，一丝不挂。我们走过他掩埋那两个人的地方的时候，他一下就把那地方指了出来，并且把他所作的记号指给我看，向我作手势，表示我们可以把他们掘出来吃掉！看到这种情况，我就作出发怒的样子，表示我对这种勾当深恶痛绝，并且作样子给他看，表示我一想到这种勾当就要作呕，然后向他招手，叫他走开。他马上

ance of them, or of their Canoes; so that it was plain they were gone, and had left their two Comrades behind them, without any search after them.

But I was not content with this Discovery; but having now more Courage, and consequently more Curiosity, I takes my Man Friday with me, giving him the Sword in his Hand, with the Bow and Arrows at his Back, which I found he could use very dextrously, making him carry one Gun for me, and I two for my self, and away we march'd to the Place, where these Creatures had been; for I had a Mind now to get some fuller Intelligence of them: When I came to the Place, my very Blood ran chill in my Veins, and my Heart sunk within me, at the Horror of the Spectacle: indeed it was a dreadful Sight, at least it was so to me; though Friday made nothing of it: The Place was cover'd with humane Bones, the Ground dy'd with their Blood, great Pieces of Flesh left here and there, half eaten, mangl'd and scorch'd; and in short, all the Tokens of the triumphant Feast they had been making there, after a Victory over their Enemies; I saw three Skulls, five Hands, and the Bones of three or four Legs and Feet, and abundance of other Parts of the Bodies; and Friday, by his Signs, made me under stand, that they brought over four Prisoners to feast upon; that three of them were eaten up, and that he, pointing to himself, was the fourth: That there had been a great Battle between them, and their next King, whose Subjects it seems he had been one of; and that they had taken a great Number of Prisoners, all which were carry'd to several Places by those

十分驯服地走开了。然后我又把他带到那小山顶上,看看他的敌人走了没有。我拉开我的望远镜望过去,一眼就望见他们昨天聚集的地方,可是那起野人和他们的独木舟已经不见了。显然他们已经开船走了,并且已经把他们的两个伙伴丢在脑后,根本不去找他们了。

我对这一发现并不感到满足。现在,我勇气倍增,好奇心也随之增大。因此,我带了我的奴隶星期五,准备到那边看个究竟。我给了他一把刀,让他拿在手里,他自己又把弓箭背在背上;我已经了解到,他是一个出色的弓箭手。另外,我还叫他给我背一支枪,而我自己则背了两支枪。这样武装好之后,我们就向那些野人昨天聚集过的地方出发了,因为我很想获得有关那些野人的充分情报。一到那里,呈现在我面前的是一起惨绝人寰的景象,我血管里的血不由得都冰冷了,连心脏也停止了跳动。那真是一幅可怕的景象,至少对我而言实在惨不忍睹,可是对星期五来说,根本不当一回事。那儿遍地都是死人骨头和人肉,鲜血染红了土地;那大片大片的人肉,有的吃了一半,有的砍烂了,有的烧焦了,东一块西一块的,一片狼藉。总之,一切迹象都表明,他们在战胜敌方后,在那里大开人肉宴,欢庆胜利。我看到了三个头颅,五只手,三四根腿骨和脚骨,还有

that had taken them in the Fight, in order to feast upon them, as was done here by these Wretches upon those they brought hither.

I caus'd Friday to gather all the Skulls, Bones, Flesh, and whatever remain'd, and lay them together on a Heap, and make a great Fire upon it, and burn them all to Ashes: I found Friday had still a hankering Stomach after some of the Flesh, and was still a Cannibal in his Nature; but I discover'd so much Abhorrence at the very Thoughts of it, and at the least Appearance of it, that he durst not discover it; for I had by some Means let him know, that I would kill him if he offer'd it.

When we had done this, we came back to our Castle, and there I fell to work for my Man Friday; and first of all, I gave him a pair of Linnen Drawers, which I had out of the poor Gunners Chest I mention'd, and which I found in the Wreck; and which with a little Alteration fitted him very well; then I made him a Jerkin of Goat's-skin, as well as my Skill would allow; and I was now grown a tollerable good Taylor; and I gave him a Cap, which I had made of a Hare-skin, very convenient, and fashionable enough; and thus he was cloath'd for the present, tollerably well; and was mighty well pleas'd to see himself

许多身体其他部位的残块；我根据星期五的手势得知，他们带来四个供他们大吃一顿的俘虏，其中三个已被吃掉，而他，他指了指他自己，则是第四个。他还让我明白，他们同继位的部落首领大战了一场，而他看来是拥戴这个部落首领的；结果，他们在战斗中抓获了大量的俘虏，把俘虏分别带到几个地点大吃一顿；他们到这儿来吃俘虏的事，同其他几处的这类事情是一样的。

我吩咐星期五把这些骷髅、人骨、人肉，以及所有被野人吃剩的东西，统统收集起来，堆成一堆，然后放一把火把它们全都烧成了灰烬。我看得出，星期五仍然垂涎于这些人肉，在本性上他仍然是个食人者。但我对这种行为表现出深恶痛绝的样子，甚至想都不愿意想，看到这种行为就恶心，他才不敢有所表示。同时，我又想办法让他明白，只要他胆敢吃人肉，我就把他杀掉。

办完这件事后，我们回到城堡。一回到家，我就为星期五忙碌起来。首先，我给了他一条亚麻短裤，这是我从那条失事船上死去的炮手箱子中找来的。我把短裤稍微修改一下后，他穿起来非常合适。然后，我又尽己所能用羊皮给他做了件背心。说句不算吹牛的话，我现在的缝纫手艺已经练得相当不错了。此外，我还给他做了一顶兔皮帽子，戴起来不仅合适，而且相当时

almost as well cloath'd as his Master: It is true, he went awkardly in these Things at first; wearing the Drawers was very awkard to him, and the Sleeves of the Wastcoat gall'd his Shoulders, and the inside of his Arms; but a little easing them where he com plain'd they hurt him, and using himself to them, at length he took to them very well.

The next Day after I came home to my Hutch with him, I began to consider where I should lodge him, and that I might do well for him, and yet be perfectly easy my self; I made a little Tent for him in the vacant Place between my two Fortifications, in the inside of the last, and in the outside of the first; and as there was a Door, or Entrance there into my Cave, I made a formal fram'd Door Case, and a Door to it of Boards, and set it up in the Passage, a little within the Entrance; and causing the Door to open on the inside, I barr'd it up in the Night, taking in my Ladders too; so that Friday could no way come at me in the inside of my innermost Wall, without making so much Noise in getting over, that it must needs waken me; for my first Wall had now a compleat Roof over it of long Poles, covering all my Tent, and leaning up to the side of the Hill, which was again laid cross with smaller Sticks instead of Laths, and then thatch'd over a great Thickness, with the Rice Straw, which was strong like Reeds; and at the Hole or Place which was left to go in or out by the Ladder, I had plac'd a kind of Trap-door, which if it had been attempted on the outside, would not have open'd at all, but would have fallen down, and made a great Noise; and as to Weapons, I took them all to my Side every

髦。就这样,我给他拾掇出一身看上去颇为不错的穿戴。星期五看到自己和主人穿得差不多一样好,心中十分高兴。不过,他起初刚穿上这些衣服的时候,行动起来的确很不习惯,不仅裤子穿起来感到别扭,而且背心的袖口边也磨痛了他的肩膀和胳肢窝。后来我把磨痛他的部位重新加工放宽,加上他也逐渐地习惯了穿着,终于对穿衣戴帽这件事完全适应了。

我带他回到家里后,第二天,我便开始考虑找个地方安顿他。我不仅要使他住着舒服,还要使我自己安全。于是,我在两道围墙之间的空地上给他搭起了一个小帐篷,正处于第一道围墙外边,第二道围墙里边。因为我的山洞原先就有一个小门作入口,我又做了一个正式的门和一个木板门,然后放入洞口里边。我使它朝里开着,每天晚上就上了门,并把梯子也收起来,这样,星期五要想通过我里边的围墙来到我的身边,就必须先弄出一些声音,这样就会把我吵醒。因为第一道围墙我已经用柱子搭起了一层严实的屋顶,和岩壁相接,把我的帐篷全盖了起来。屋顶上又横搭了一些小木棍子代为椽子用,木棍上又盖了一层厚厚的结实如芦苇的稻草。在搭梯子进出的口子上,我做了一个假门,从外面根本打不开,如果有人企图开门,它就会轰地一声坍塌,发出巨大声响。每天

Night.

But I needed none of all this Precaution; for never Man had a more faithful, loving, sincere Servant, than Friday was to me; without Passions, Sullenness or Designs, perfectly oblig'd and engag'd; his very Affections were ty'd to me, like those of a Child to a Father; and I dare say, he would have sacrific'd his Life for the saving mine, upon any occasion whatsoever; the many Testimonies he gave me of this, put it out of doubt, and soon convinc'd me, that I needed to use no Precautions, as to my Safety on his Account.

This frequently gave me occasion to observe, and that with wonder, that however it had pleas'd God, in his Providence, and in the Government of the Works of his Hands, to take from so great a Part of the World of his Creatures, the best uses to which their Faculties, and the Powers of their Souls are adapted; yet that he has bestow'd upon them the same Powers, the same Reason, the same Affections, the same Sentiments of Kindness and Obligation, the same Passions and Resentments of Wrongs, the same Sense of Gratitude, Sincerity, Fidelity, and all the Capacities of doing Good, and receiving Good, that he has given to us; and that when he pleases to offer to them Occasions of exerting these, they are as ready, nay, more ready to apply them to the right Uses for which they were bestow'd, than we are; and this made me very melancholly sometimes, in reflecting as the several Occasions presented, how mean a Use we make of all these, even though we have these Powers enlighten'd by the great Lamp of Instruction, the Spirit of God, and by the Knowledge of his Word, added to our Understanding; and why it has pleas'd God to hide the like saving

晚上,我把所有的武器都收到自己身旁。

其实我用不着采取这么多预防措施,因为星期五对于我实在是一个最忠实、最可爱、最诚恳的仆人,他没有一点脾气,不闹别扭,不怀鬼胎,既听话,又肯干活。他对我一往情深;就像一个孩子对他父亲一样;我敢说,无论在什么场合,他都肯牺牲他的性命来救我。他在这方面给了我许多证明,使我对此毫不怀疑,并且使我深信,我在安全问题上用不着对他采取什么预防措施。

这使我时常注意,并把惊奇之心带着来注意,上帝在他的天命里,在他的统治中,尽管把世界上许多动物使用官能、使用天性的机会夺去,却仍旧把同样的天性,同样的理智,同样的爱,同样的善心和责任感,同样嫉恨恶事的本能,同样感恩、热诚、忠实的观念,同样为善的、知善的能力赋予了他们,与我们没什么两样;并且当上帝给他们机会表现这些才干和良知时,他们和我们一样,立即把上帝赋予他们的才干和良知发挥出来做各种善事,甚至比我们发挥得更充分。对此,我不能不感到惊讶。同时,想到这些,我又感到有些悲哀,因为许多事实证明,我们文明人在发挥这些才干和良知方面,反而显得非常卑劣。尽管我们不仅有能力,而且,我们受到上帝的教诲,上帝的圣灵和上帝的语言的

Knowledge from so many Millions of Souls, who if I might judge by this poor Savage, would make a much better use of it than we did.

From hence, I sometimes was led too far to invade the Soveraignty of Providence, and as it were arraign the Justice of so arbitrary a Disposition of Things, that should hide that Light from some, and reveal it to others, and yet expect a like Duty from both: But I shut it up, and check'd my Thoughts with this Conclusion, (1st.) That we did not know by what Light and Law these should be Condemn'd; but that as God was necessarily, and by the Nature of his Being, infinitely Holy and Just, so it could not be, but that if these Creatures were all sentenc'd to Absence from himself, it was on account of sinning against that Light which, as the Scripture says, was a Law to themselves, and by such Rules as their Consciences would acknowledge to be just, tho' the Foundation was not discover'd to us: And (2d.) that still as we are all the Clay in the Hand of the Potter, no Vessel could say to him, Why hast thou form'd me thus?

But to return to my New Companion; I was greatly delighted with him, and made it my Business to teach him every Thing, that was proper to make him useful, handy, and helpful; but especially to make him speak, and under stand me

启示,这使我们能有更深刻的认识。同时,我也感到奇怪,为什么上帝不给这成千上百万的生灵以同样的教诲和启示,使他们懂得赎罪的道理。我觉得,如果我以这可怜的野人作为判断的依据,那么,他们实在能比我们文明人做得更好。

关于这些问题,我有时甚至会想过头,以至冒犯了上帝的统治权,认为他对世事的安排欠公正,因为他把他的教诲赐予了一部分人,而不赐予另一部分人,但却又要这两部分人负起同样的义务。但是我终于不再对此进行探究了,因为我得出了这样两点结论:首先,我们不知道上帝这样处置他们,凭的是什么依据和律法,然而,既然是上帝,他的本性必然是无限圣洁,无限公正的,所以如果说这些人被判定在他的恩泽之外,那么一定是他们因违背了上帝的教导而犯下了罪孽,因为照《圣经》中的说法,对他们来说,上帝的教导便是律法,而且根据他们良心所承认的标准来看,这样的处置也是公正的,尽管这种标准的基础不为我们所知。其次,既然我们都是这位陶工手中的陶土,那么没有一件陶器能够问他:"你为什么把我做成这样?"

不过,还是让我来继续谈谈我的新伙伴吧。我非常喜欢他,觉得有必要把每件东西都教给他,好使他对我有用,好听我使唤,对我有帮助。当

when I spake, and he was the aptest Schollar that ever was, and particularly was so merry, so constantly diligent, and so pleased, when he cou'd but understand me, or make me understand him, that it was very pleasant to me to talk to him; and now my Life began to be so easy, that I began to say to my self, that could I but have been safe from more Savages, I cared not, if I was never to remove from the place while I lived.

After I had been two or three Days return'd to my Castle, I thought that, in order to bring Friday off from his horrid way of feeding, and from the Relish of a Cannibal's Stomach, I ought to let him taste other Flesh; so I took him out with me one Morning to the Woods: I went indeed intending to kill a Kid out of my own Flock, and bring him home and dress it. But as I was going, I saw a She Goat lying down in the Shade, and two young Kids sitting by her; I catch'd hold of Friday, hold says I, stand still; and made Signs to him not to stir, immediately I presented my Piece, shot and kill'd one of the Kids. The poor Creature who had at a Distance indeed seen me kill the Savage his Enemy, but did not know, or could imagine how it was done, was sensibly surpriz'd, trembled, and shook, and look'd so amaz'd, that I thought he would have sunk down. He did not see the Kid I shot at, or perceive I had kill'd it, but ripp'd up his Wastcoat to feel if he was not wounded, and as I found, presently thought I was resolv'd to kill him; for he came and kneel'd down to me, and embraceing my Knees, said a great many Things I did not understand; but I could easily see that the meaning was to pray me not to kill him.

然，我特别要教他说话，教他听懂我说的话。他比谁都学得快。特别值得一提的是，他总是那么快乐，那么用功。当他听懂了我的话，或者让我明白了他的话的时候，他总是很高兴。所以，对我来说，跟他谈话是件愉快的事。现在，我又生活得从容自在起来。我甚至对自己说，要是不会再有野人来威胁我的安全，就是这辈子不从这里搬走我也不在乎。

回到城堡后两三天的时间里，我一直在想着一定要设法改掉星期五那种可怕的吃相，更重要的是戒掉他那想吃人肉的邪欲。我觉得应该让他尝尝其他肉类的味道，于是一天早晨，我带他到林中圈地去。我原本打算从自己羊圈里找一只子羊，杀死后带回家煮了吃。可是走到半路上远远地看到一只母山羊躺在树荫下歇息，在它身边还趴着两只小山羊。我一把抓住星期五，用手暗示他站住，同时打出手势，叫他千万不要动。然后我端起枪，开枪打死了一只小羊。可怜的小伙子，上次看到我用枪打死他的对手的时候，因为离得太远，没有弄明白是怎么回事，因而也想象不出我是怎样把他的对手打死的。可这一次他就站在我身边看着我开枪，这可真把他给吓坏了。只见他浑身颤抖，愣愣怔怔，几乎要瘫倒在地的样子。他没有看到我射杀小羊，也不相信我已射杀了小羊，只是一个劲地撕扯着他的大衣，

I soon found a way to convince him that I would do him no harm, and taking him up by the Hand laugh'd at him, and pointed to the Kid which I had kill'd, beckoned to him to run and fetch it, which he did; and while he was wondering and looking to see how the Creature was kill'd, I loaded my Gun again, and by and by I saw a great Fowl like a Hawk sit upon a Tree within Shot; so to let Friday understand a little what I would do, I call'd him to me again, pointed at the Fowl which was indeed a Parrot, tho' I thought it had been a Hawk, I say pointing to the Parrot, and to my Gun, and to the Ground under the Parrot, to let him see I would make it fall, I made him understand that I would shoot and kill that Bird; accordingly I fir'd and bad him look, and immediately he saw the Parrot fall, he stood like one frighted again, notwithstanding all I had said to him; and I found he was the more amaz'd, because he did not see me put any Thing into the Gun; but thought that there must be some wonderful Fund of Death and Destruction in that Thing, able to kill Man, Beast, Bird, or any Thing near, or far off; and the Astonishment this created in him was such, as could not wear off for a long Time; and I believe, if I would have let him, he would have worshipp'd me and my Gun: As for the Gun it self, he would not so much as touch it for several Days after; but would speak to it, and talk to it, as if it had answer'd him, when he was by himself; which, as I afterwards learn'd of him, was to desire it not to kill him.

看看他哪儿受伤了没有。我马上便明白他是以为我要杀了他。他跑过来跪在我的面前,抱住我的双腿,说了一大堆我不明白的话,但我不难理解,他的意思是祈求我,不要杀了他。

我想法叫他相信,我绝不会伤害他,我用手把他扶起来,对他大笑不止,并指了指我杀死的那只小羊,示意他跑过去拿过来,他照我的意思做了。但他还是惊奇不已,在那里仔细观察那只小羊是怎么死的,这时,我顺便又装上了我的枪。很快,我发现树上一只像鹰一样的大鸟正好在我的射程内,为了让星期五明白我的意图,我把他叫到身边,指指树上的鸟(其实是只鹦鹉,而我以为是只鹰),又指指我的枪,再指指鹦鹉下面的地,让他亲眼见到我把鹦鹉打落在地,让他明白我将射杀那只鸟。我开枪了,示意他朝那边看,他立刻看到鸟落下来。这一次他又目瞪口呆,尽管我给他作了种种解释。我发现他比以前更加惊异,因为他没见到我往枪里装弹药,以为枪这玩艺儿能源源不断地制造死亡和毁灭,能杀死近处和远处的人、野兽、鸟等任何东西。这件事所给他的惊讶,久久不能消失。我相信,如果我听其自然,他简直可以像崇拜神一样崇拜我和枪,至于那支枪,他一连很长时间都不敢动,然而却整天一个人同枪说话,与枪交谈,就好像枪会回答他一

Well, after his Astonishment was a little over at this, I pointed to him to run and fetch the Bird I had shot, which he did, but stay'd some Time; for the Parrot not being quite dead, was flutter'd away a good way off from the Place where she fell; however, he found her, took her up, and brought her to me; and as I had perceivd his Ignorance about the Gun before, I took this Advantage to charge the Gun again, and not let him see me do it, that I might be ready for any other Mark that might present; but nothing more offer'd at that Time; so I brought home the Kid, and the same Evening I took the Skin off, and cut it out as well as I could; and having a Pot for that purpose, I boil'd, or stew'd some of the Flesh, and made some very good Broth; and after I had begun to eat some, I gave some to my Man, who seem'd very glad of it, and lik'd it very well; but that which was strangest to him, was, to see me eat Salt with it; he made a Sign to me, that the Salt was not good to eat, and putting a little into his own Mouth, he seem'd to nauseate it, and would spit and sputter at it, washing his Mouth with fresh Water after it; on the other hand, I took some Meat in my Mouth without Salt, and I pretended to spit and sputter for want of Salt, as fast as he had done at the Salt; but it would not do, he would never care for Salt with his Meat, or in his Broth; at least not a great while, and then but a very little.

Having thus fed him with boil'd Meat and Broth, I was resolv'd to feast him the next Day with roasting a Piece of the Kid; this I did by

样,后来我听他亲口说,他如此做是求枪不要把他杀死。

且说我等他的惊讶略微缓和过来了一些,就把那鸟指着,叫他去拿来。他跑过去,半天过后才回来,是由于那只鹦鹉中枪之后,并没完全死去,竟鼓着翅膀挣扎了一好段路;然而他最终找到了,捡起来拿给我。我见他对于我的枪完全莫名其妙,就乘这个机会再把它装上弹药,依旧不给他看见我是怎么装的,以便碰到任何其他目标的时候,随时开枪。可是找了半天,什么目标都找不到。于是我就把那只小羊带回家来,当晚把它剥了皮,切得好好的。我本来有一只专门煮肉的罐子,就把一部分肉煮了起来,作成很好的肉汤。我自己先吃了一点,又分了一些给他吃;他吃了以后,仿佛非常满意,非常合他的胃口。最使他感到奇怪的是,我吃肉汤的时候,居然要放盐。他向我做手势,表示盐不好吃,同时又拿了一点放在口里,作出作呕的样子,呸呸地唾了一阵,又赶紧拿清水漱口。另一方面,我也拿了一块没有盐的肉放在嘴里,假装呸呸地唾了一阵,表示我没有盐就吃不下去,正像他有盐就吃不下去一样。但这没有用。他就是不喜欢在肉里或汤里放盐。过了很长一段时间之后,他也只是放很少一点盐。

吃过煮羊肉和羊肉汤之后,我决定第二天请他吃烤羊肉。我按照英国的烤法,在火

hanging it before the Fire, in a String, as I had seen many People do in England, setting two Poles up, one on each side the Fire, and one cross on the Top, and tying the String to the Cross-stick, letting the Meat turn continually: This Friday admir'd very much; but when he came to taste the Flesh, he took so many ways to tell me how well he lik'd it, that I could not but understand him; and at last he told me he would never eat Man's Flesh any more, which I was very glad to hear.

The next Day I set him to work to beating some Corn out, and sifting it in the manner I us'd to do, as I observ'd before and he soon understood how to do it as well as I, especially after he had seen what the Meaning of it was, and that it was to make Bread of; for after that I let him see me make my Bread, and bake it too, and in a little Time Friday was able to do all the Work for me, as well as I could do it my self.

I begun now to consider, that having two Mouths to feed, instead of one, I must provide more Ground for my Harvest, and plant a larger Quantity of Corn, than I us'd to do; so I mark'd out a larger Piece of Land, and began the Fence in the same Manner as before, in which Friday not only work'd very willingly, and very hard; but did it very chearfully, and I told him what it was for; that it was for Corn to make more Bread, because he was now with me, and that I might have e-nough for him, and my self too: He appear'd very sensible of that Part, and let me know, that he thought I had much more Labour upon me on his Account, than I had for my self; and that he would work the harder for me, if I would tell him what to do.

的两边各插一根有叉的木竿，上面再搭上一根横竿，再用绳子把肉吊在横竿上，让它不断转动。星期五对我这种烤肉方法十分惊异。但当他尝了烤羊肉的味道后，用各种方法告诉我他是多么爱吃这种味道；我当然不可能不了解他的意思。最后，他告诉我，他从此之后再也不吃人肉了。听到他讲这句话，我感到非常高兴。

下一天，我叫他干了一阵打谷的活，并用我前面说过的老办法将谷子筛一下。不久以后，他干起这活来已很熟练，同我不相上下，特别是后来他得知这种工作的意义，得知这谷物是用来做面包的，干劲就更大了；因为在他筛好谷子后，我让他看了我做面包、烤面包的全过程，所以没过多久，星期五已包揽下所有这些活，而且干得同我一样好。

现在，我又开始考虑到，目前已不再是一口人吃饭，而是两口人，因此，我的庄稼地的面积必须扩展，播的种也得比过去多。我划出更大的一块地，并按以前的老方法，开始在四周围上篱笆。在干这项工作时，星期五不但很乐意，很卖力，甚至还非常开心。我把这项工作的意义告诉了他，让他明白，这是为了长谷子，为了做更多的面包，因为他现在跟我在一起，我必须有足够的面包够他也够我自己吃。他听了这话，显出很懂事的样子，并让我明白，由于现

This was the pleasantest Year of all the Life I led in this Place; Friday began to talk pretty well, and understand the Names of almost every Thing I had occasion to call for, and of every Place I had to send him to, and talk'd a great deal to me; so that in short I began now to have some Use for my Tongue again, which indeed I had very little occasion for before; that is to say, about Speech; besides the Pleasure of talking to him, I had a singular Satisfaction in the Fellow himself; his simple unfeign'd Honesty, appear'd to me more and more every Day, and I began really to love the Creature; and on his Side, I believe he lov'd me more than it was possible for him ever to love any Thing before.

I had a Mind once to try if he had any hankering Inclination to his own Country again, and having learn'd him English so well that he could answer me almost any Questions, I ask'd him whether the Nation that he belong'd to never conquer'd in Battle, at which he smil'd; and said; yes, yes, we always fight the better; that is, he meant always get the better in Fight; and so we began the following Discourse: You always fight the better said I, How came you to be taken Prisoner then, Friday?

Friday, My Nation beat much, for all that.

Master, How beat; if your Nation beat them,

在多了他一个人,我得干比以前更多的活,所以只要我教他怎么干,他情愿为我多干一点。

这一年是我来孤岛后所过的最愉快的一年。星期五的英语已学得相当不错了,要他拿取的每一种物品,以及差遣他去的每一个地方,他基本上全能明白。他还很喜欢和我交谈,我也非常喜欢和他交谈。他没来之前,我很少有机会使用我的舌头,当然是指用舌头说话啦。现在,我终于又能全面发挥我舌头的功能了,这怎能不是一件值得庆贺的事啊!我不仅喜欢和星期五交谈,还对他的人品更为满意。在和他朝夕相处的过程中,我越来越感受到他的纯朴真诚,真是打心眼里喜欢他。而他对我的那份情感,我相信,也是真爱至极,超过爱世上任何人。

有一次,我有心试试他,看他是不是依旧念念不忘自己的故国。这时候,他的英语已经学得很好,差不多能够回答我的任何问题了。于是我问他,他那个部落是不是从来不打败仗。他听了我的话,微微一笑道:"是的,是的,我们老是打得很好。"他的意思是说,我们老是打胜仗。于是我们开始了下面的谈话:我问他:你们既然老是打胜仗,你怎么会做了俘虏呢,星期五?

星期五:不管怎么样,我的部落打赢的时候很多。

主人:怎么打赢? 如果你

how come you to be taken?

Friday, They more many than my Nation in the Place where me was; they take one, two, three, and me; my Nation over beat them in the yonder Place, where me no was; there my Nation take one, two, great Thousand.

Master, But why did not your Side recover you from the Hands of your Enemies then?

Friday, They run one, two, three, and me, and make go in the Canoe; my Nation have no Canoe that time.

Master, Well, Friday, and What does your Nation do with the Men they take, do they carry them away, and eat them, as these did?

Friday, Yes, my Nation eat Mans too, eat all up.

Master, Where do they carry them?

Friday, Go to other Place where they think.

Master, Do they come hither?

Friday, Yes, yes, they come hither; come other else Place.

Master, Have you been here with them?

Friday, Yes, I been here; [points to the N. W. Side of the Island, which it seems was their Side.]

By this I understood, that my Man Friday had formerly been among the Savages, who us'd to come on Shore on the farther Part of the Island, on the same Man eating Occasions that he was now brought for; and sometime after, when I took the Courage to carry him to that Side, being the same I formerly mention'd, he presently knew the Place, and told me, he was there once when they eat up twenty Men, two Women, and one Child;

的部落打赢了,你怎么会给捉住呢?

星期五:我在的那个地方,他们的人数比我们的多;他们把一个,两个,三个,还有我捉住了。我们在别处打胜了他们;我们在那边把好几千人捉住了。

主人:然而你们部落为什么不从敌人手里抢回你们呢?

星期五:他们用独木舟把一个人,两个人,三个人和我全部带走了,那时我们部落没有独木舟。

主人:那么,星期五,你们部落如何处置捉到的人呢?也带走他们,同样吃掉吗?

星期五:是的,我们部落也吃人,都吃光。

主人:他们把人带到哪里去呢?

星期五:带到其他的地方,带到他们想去的地方。

主人:他们也来这里吗?

星期五:是的,是的,他们来这里,也去别处。

主人:你和他们一起来过这里吗?

星期五:是的,我曾经来过这儿(他指着岛的西北方,那大概是他们常来的地方)。

通过这次谈话,我知道星期五过去也在那群野人中间,常常在岛的另一端上岸,干那种吃人的勾当,就像他这一次被带到岛上来,差一点也给别的野人吃掉一样。过了几天后,我鼓起勇气,把他带到岛的那一头,也就是我前面提到过的那地方。他马上认出了

he could not tell Twenty in English; but he numbred them by laying so many Stones on a Row, and pointing to me to tell them over.

I have told this Passage, because it introduces what follows; that after I had had this Discourse with him, I ask'd him how far it was from our Island to the Shore, and whether the Canoes were not often lost; he told me, there was no Danger, no Canoes ever lost; but that after a little way out to the Sea, there was a Current, and Wind, always one way in the Morning, the other in the Afternoon.

This I understood to be no more than the Sets of the Tide, as going out, or coming in; but I afterwards understood, it was occasion'd by the great Draft and Reflux of the mighty River Oroonooko; in the Mouth, or the Gulph of which River, as I found afterwards, our Island lay; and this Land which I perceiv'd to the W. and N. W. was the great Island Trinidad, on the North Point of the Mouth of the River: I ask'd Friday a thousand Questions about the Country, the Inhabitants, the Sea, the Coast, and what Nation were near; he told me all he knew with the greatest Openness imaginable; I ask'd him the Names of the several Nations of his Sort of People; but could get no other Name than Caribs; from whence I easily understood, that these were the Caribbees, which our Maps place on the Part of America, which reaches from the Mouth of the River Oroonooko to Guiana, and onwards to St. Martha: He told me that up a great way beyond the Moon, that was, beyond the Setting of the Moon, which must be W. from their Country, there dwelt white bearded

那地方。他告诉我,他到过这地方一次,吃了二十个男人、两个女人和一个小孩。他还不会用英国数到二十,所以用了许多石块在地上排成了长长的一行,用手指了指那行石块告诉我这个数字。

我把这一段谈话叙述出来,是因为它与下面的事情有关。那就是,在我与他谈过这次话之后,我就问他,小岛离大陆究竟有多远,独木舟是否经常出事?他告诉我没有任何危险,独木舟也从未出过事。只是出海不远就有一股海流,当然也有风,而且早上是一个方向,下午是另一个方向。

我知道这无非是潮水的涨落而已,但后来才明白,这是奥里诺科那条大河涨潮和退潮时,流量特大而引起的,因为我后来发现,我们的岛正在这大河的出海口上;至于我朝西和朝西北方向望去时见到的那片陆地,则是一个名为特立尼达的大岛,它就位于那河口的正北方。我向星期五提了千百个问题,都是有关那儿的风土人情和河海山川的,还问了那一带有什么部落;他毫无保留地把知道的情况全告诉了我;我问他们那个民族分成多少个部落,都怎么称呼,但是只问出了一个名称——加利布;我一听就明白,这指的是加勒比人;在我们的地图上,他们分布在奥里诺科河口、圭亚那和圣马尔塔一带。这时,他又指着我的胡子

Men, like me; and pointed to my great Whiskers, which I mention'd before; and that they had kill'd much Mans, that was his Word; by all which I under stood he meant the Spaniards, whose Cruelties in America had been spread over the whole Countries, and was remember'd by all the Nations from Father to Son.

I enquir'd if he could tell me how I might come from this Island, and get among those white Men; he told me, yes, yes, I might go in two Canoe; I could not understand what he meant, or make him describe to me what he meant by two Canoe, till at last with great Difficulty, I found he meant it must be in a large great Boat, as big as two Canoes.

This Part of Friday's Discourse began to relish with me very well, and from this Time I entertain'd some Hopes, that one Time or other, I might find an Opportunity to make my Escape from this Place; and that this poor Savage might be a Means to help me to do It.

During the long Time that Friday has now been with me, and that he began to speak to me, and understand me, I was not wanting to lay a Foundation of religious Knowledge in his Mind; particularly I ask'd him one Time who made him? The poor Creature did not understand me at all, but thought I had ask'd who was his Father; but I took it by another handle, and ask'd him who made the Sea, the Ground we walk'd on, and the

告诉我, 在离这里很远很远的地方, 在月亮落下去的那边 (其实, 他是指他们家乡的西面), 住着许多像我一样长着胡子的白人, 他们杀死了许许多多的人 (他用不合文法的英语对我说)。从他的话中, 我一下子明白了, 他指的西班牙人。因为, 他们在美洲的暴行已经远近闻名, 无人不晓, 所有部落的子子孙孙都不会忘记。

我又问他能不能告诉我怎样才能离开这座小岛, 到那些白人中间去。他对我说: "是的, 是的, 可以乘两只独木舟去。" 我弄不懂 "乘两只独木舟去" 是什么意思。一时也无法让他解释 "两只独木舟" 究竟指的是什么。直到最后, 费了半天周折, 比划来比划去, 才明白他是说要乘一只很大的船才行, 大到足有两只独木舟那么大。

星期五的谈话使我感到非常兴奋。从那时起, 潜在心底的希望又开始升腾。我希望迟早有一天, 我会找到机会从这个孤岛上逃出去, 我相信这个可怜的野人会帮助我实现我的愿望。

在星期五和我共同生活的这几年里, 他一点一点学会了英语, 渐渐地能听懂我的话并且和我交谈了。我在教他说话和干活的同时, 一直努力向他传授宗教信仰的基本知识。开始, 我特别提出这么一个问题来问他: 是谁创造了他。可怜的小伙子一点也不

Hills, and Woods; he told me it was one old Bena-muckee, that liv'd beyond all: He could describe nothing of this great Person, but that he was very old; much older he said than the Sea, or the Land; than the Moon, or the Stars: I ask'd him then, if this old Person had made all Things, why did not all Things worship him; he look'd very grave, and with a perfect Look of Innocence, said, All Things do say O to him: I ask'd him if the People who die in his Country went away any where; he said, yes, they all went to Benamuck-ee; then I ask'd him whether these they eat up went thither too, he said yes.

From these Things, I began to instruct him in the Know ledge of the true God: I told him that the great Maker of all Things liv'd up there, pointing up towards Heaven: That he governs the World by the same Power and Providence by which he had made it: That he was omnipotent, could do every Thing for us, give every Thing to us, take every Thing from us; and thus by De-grees I open'd his Eyes. He listned with great At-tention, and receiv'd with Pleasure the Notion of Jesus Christ being sent to redeem us, and of the Manner of making our Prayers to God, and his be-ing able to hear us, even into Heaven; he told me one Day, that if our God could hear us up beyond the Sun, he must needs be a greater God than their Benamuckee, who liv'd but a little way off, and yet could not hear, till they went up to the great Mountains where he dwelt, to speak to him; I ask'd him if ever he went thither, to speak to

明白我问这话的意思，还以为我在问他的父亲是谁呢。我换了一个问法问他，是谁造出了大海、我们脚下的大地，以及山峦和森林？他对我说，那是由一位名叫贝纳木基的老人家创造出来的。他住在极远的地方。他无法告诉我他心目中的大人物是什么样的人，只说他年岁很大，月亮、星宿、大海和陆地都没有他年纪大。我仍问他道："既然这位老人创造了一切，那么万物怎样崇拜他呢？"他表情立刻变得庄严但又纯真地说道："万物都向他说'呵'。"我问他，他们部落里的人死后是否到其他的地方去；他说是的，都到贝纳木基那里去。我又问他，那些被他们吃掉的人是否也到那里去；他说："是的。"

从这些事情着手，我慢慢地给他教导，使他认识真的上帝。我指着天空，告诉他，在那里住着万物的创造者。告诉他，上帝用与创造万物时相同的神力和天命来把世界统治着。告诉他，上帝是万能的；他能为我们做一切事情，他能把一切给我们，能从我们手里夺去一切。就这样，我逐渐使得他睁开了眼睛。他很留心地听我的话，并且很乐于接受我向他灌输的观念：基督是被差来替我们赎罪的；我们应该怎样向上帝祈祷；以及我们的祈祷如何可以让上帝听到。有一天，他对我说：上帝既然能够从比太阳更远的地方听到我们的话，必然是一位比贝纳

him; he said no, they never went that were young Men; none went thither but the old Men, who he call'd their Oowocakee, that is, as I made him explain it to me, their Religious, or Clergy, and that they went to say O, (so he called saying Prayers) and then came back, and told them what Benamuckee said: By this I observ'd, That there is Priestcraft, even amongst the most blinded ignorant Pagans in the World; and the Policy of making a secret Religion, in order to preserve the Veneration of the People to the Clergy, is not only to be found in the Roman, but perhaps among all Religions in the World, even among the most brutish and barbarous Savages.

I endeavour'd to clear up this Fraud, to my Man Friday, and told him, that the Pretence of their old Men going up the Mountains, to say O to their God Benamuckee, was a Cheat, and their bringing Word from thence what he said, was much more so; that if they met with any Answer, or spake with any one there, it must be with an evil Spirit: And then I entred into a long Discourse with him about the Devil, the Original of him, his Rebellion against God, his Enmity to Man, the Reason of it, his setting himself up in the dark Parts of the World to be Worship'd instead of God, and as God; and the many Stratagems he made use of to delude Mankind to his Ruine; how he had a secret access to our Passions, and to our Affections, to adapt his Snares so to our Inclinations, as to cause us even to be our own Tempters, and to run upon our Destruction by our own

木基更伟大的神,因为贝纳木基住的地方不算太远,可是他却听不见他们的话,除非他们到他住的那座山里去,向他谈话。我问他:他可曾到那边去同他谈过话? 他说:没有,年轻人从来不去,只有那些被称为奥乌卡儿的老年人才去。经过他解释,我才知道所谓奥乌卡儿,就是他们的祭司或僧侣。据他说,他们到那边去说了"呵"(这就是他们的祈祷)以后,就回来把贝纳木基的话告诉他们。从星期五的话里,我可以推断,即使是世界上最盲目无知的邪教徒中,也存在着祭司制度;同时,我也发现,把宗教神秘化,从而使人们能敬仰神职人员,这种做法不仅存在于罗马天主教,也存在于世界上一切宗教,甚至也存在于最残忍、最野蛮的野人中间。

我竭力向我的仆人星期五揭发这一骗局。我告诉他,那些老人假装到山里去对贝纳木基说"呵",完全是骗人的把戏。他们说他们把贝纳木基的话带回来,更是骗人的诡计。我对他说,假如他们在那儿真的听到什么,真的在那边同什么人谈过话,那也一定是魔鬼。然后,我用很长的时间跟他谈魔鬼的问题:魔鬼的来历,他对上帝的反叛,他对人类的仇恨及其原因,他怎样统治着世界最黑暗的地方,叫人像礼拜上帝一样礼拜他,以及他怎样用种种阴谋诡计诱惑人类走上绝路,又怎样偷偷潜入我们的情欲和感情,迎合着

Choice.

I found it was not so easie to imprint right Notions in his Mind about the Devil, as it was about the Being of a God. Nature assisted all my Arguments to Evidence to him, even the Necessity Of a great first Cause and over-ruling governing Power; a secret directing Providence, and of the Equity, and Justice, of paying Homage to him that made us, and the like. But there appeared nothing of all this in the Notion of an evil Spirit; of his Original, his Being, his Nature, and above all of his Inclination to do Evil, and to draw us in to do so too; and the poor Creature puzzl'd me once in such a manner, by a Question meerly natural and innocent, that I scarce knew what to say to him. I had been talking a great deal to him of the Power of God, his Omnipotence, his dreadful Nature to Sin, his being a consuming Fire to the Workers of Iniquity; how, as he had made us all, he could destroy us and all the World in a Moment; and he listen'd with great Seriousness to me all the while.

After this, I had been telling him how the Devil was God's Enemy in the Hearts of Men, and used all his Malice and Skill to defeat the good Designs of Providence, and to ruine the Kingdom of Christ in the World; and the like. Well, says Friday, but you say, God is so strong, so great, is he not much strong, much might as the Devil? Yes, yes, says I, Friday, God is stronger than the Devil, God is above the Devil, and therefore we pray to God to tread him down under our Feet, and enable

我们的心理来安排他的陷阱，使我们自己诱惑自己，甘心走上灭亡的道路。

我发现，要让他确信上帝的存在并不难，但要在他心目中确立一种对魔鬼的正确认识，那就不容易了。自然界中，处处都可以为我的论点找到根据，向他证明天地之间必然有个造物主，有个统治一切的神明，有个冥冥中的主宰；我也能够向他证明：上帝既然创造了我们，那么我们崇拜他、赞美他，也是合理而公正的事。但是在有关魔鬼的观念，有关他的形成，他的存在，他的本性，尤其是他一心作恶并引诱我们作恶等问题上，情况就完全不一样了；有一次，这可怜的小伙子提了一个极其自然而天真的问题，却使得我几乎不知怎么回答他才好。在这之前我对他讲了一大堆话，说是上帝神通广大，无所不能，嫉恶如仇，能叫作恶者死无葬身之地；又说上帝既创造了我们和世上的一切，自然也能在顷刻之间使我们和整个世界灰飞烟灭；我说这些话时，他始终都听得非常认真。

在这之后，我又经常跟他讲，在人们的心目中，魔鬼往往是上帝的死对头。魔鬼总是用各种恶毒的诡计跟上帝善良的意旨作对，毁灭基督在这个世界上的王国，等等。星期五听后却对我说："依你的说法，上帝是非常强大的，非常了不起的，可是，他并没有魔鬼那么强大，那么万能，是

us to resist his Temptations and quench his fiery Darts. But, says he again, if God much strong, much might as the Devil, why God no kill the Devil, so make him no more do wicked?

I was strangely surpriz'd at his Question, and after all, tho' I was now an old Man, yet I was but a young Doctor, and ill enough quallified for a Casuist, or a Solver of Difficulties And at first I could not tell what to say, so I pre tended not to hear him, and ask'd him what he said? But he was too earnest for an Answer to forget his Question; so that he repeated it in the very same broken Words, as above. By this time I had recovered my self a little, and I said, God will at last punish him severely; he is reserv'd for the Judgment, and is to be cast into the Bottomless-Pit, to dwell with ever lasting Fire. This did not satisfie Friday, but he returns upon me, repeating my Words, RE-SERVE, AT LAST, me no understand; but, Why not kill the Devil now, not kill great ago? You may as well ask me, said I, Why God does not kill you and I, when we do wicked Things here that offend him? We are preserv'd to repent and be pardon'd: He muses a while at this; mell, All, says he, mighty affectionately, that well; so you, I, Devil, all wicked, all preserve, repent, God pardon all. Here I was run down again by him to the last Degree, and it was a Testimony to me, how the meer Notions of Nature, though they will guide reasonable Creatures to the Know ledge of a God, and of a Worship or Homage due to the supreme Being, of God as the Consequence of our Nature; yet nothing but divine Revelation can form the Knowledge of Jesus Christ, and of a

不是?"我说:"不对,不对,星期五,上帝要比魔鬼强大,上帝在魔鬼之上,所以,我们要祈求上帝把他踩在脚下,帮助我们抗拒他的诱惑,熄灭他向我们射来的火箭。""可是,"他又问,"如果上帝比魔鬼更强大,更有本领,那上帝为什么不把魔鬼杀死呢?为什么不阻止他再作恶呢?"

他突然问了这么一个颇为意外的问题,把我问得瞠目结舌,无言以对。说实在的,我虽然现在已是有些年纪的人了,但是作为向别人布道传教的导师来说,我毕竟还是个新手,资历很浅,水平不高,尚未具备答疑解难的资格。我一时语塞,想不出究竟该如何回答他的问题,便装作没听清楚的样子,问他刚才说的是什么。星期五正在急切地等待着问题的答案,当然不会忘记自己提的是什么问题,于是又结结巴巴地用英语重复了一遍。这时,我已稍稍恢复了镇静,就回答说:"上帝最终一定会严厉地惩罚魔鬼,魔鬼必定会受到审判,他将被投入无底的深渊,在永不熄灭的地狱之火里煎熬。"这个答案并不能使星期五满意,又问我道:"'最终','必定',我不明白,那么,为什么现在不把他杀掉,以前不把他杀死呢?"我说道:"你这就等于问我,在这里,我们做了很多冒犯上帝的坏事,上帝为什么不立刻将我们杀死呢?上帝之所以留着我们,是要给我们机会让我们忏悔,以便有

Redemption purchas'd for us, of a Mediator of the new Covenant, and of an Intercessor, at the Footstool of God's Throne; I say, nothing but a Revelation from Heaven, can form these in the Soul, and that therefore the Gospel of our Lord and Saviour Jesus Christ; I mean, the Word of God, and the Spirit of God promis'd for the Guide and Sanctifier of his People, are the absolutely necessary Instructors of the Souls of Men, in the saving Knowledge of God, and the Means of Salvation.

I therefore diverted the present Discourse between me and my Man, rising up hastily, as upon some sudden Occasion of going out; then sending him for something a good way off, I seriously pray'd to God that he would enable me to instruct savingly this poor Savage, assisting by his Spirit the Heart of the poor ignorant Creature, to receive the Light of the Knowledge of God in Christ, reconciling him to himself, and would guide me to speak so to him from the Word of God, as his Conscience might be convinc'd, hid Eyes open'd, and his Soul sav'd. When he came again to me, I entred into a long Discourse with him upon the Subject of the Redemption of Man by the Saviour of the World, and of the Doctrine of the Gospel preach'd from Heaven, viz. of Repentance towards God, and Faith in our Blessed Lord Jesus. I

机会赦免我们。"对我的话,他体味了半天,才激动地说:"是啊,是啊,你、我和魔鬼都有罪,上帝留着我们,是让我们都忏悔,再都获得赦免!"话说到这里,我却被他弄得尴尬万分。这一切都表明,尽管天赋的观念可令一般有灵性的动物了解上帝,并自然而然地向至尊的上天致敬,然而要想晓得耶稣基督,晓得他曾经替我们赎罪,晓得他是我们同上帝之间所立的新约的中间人,晓得他是把我们引到上帝宝座前的人,那就非要神的启示不可;也就是说,只有神的启示,才能使这些知识存在于我们的灵魂。所以,在关于上帝的知识方面,在获得自救的法门方面,我们的主耶稣基督的福音(也就是说上帝的语言)和将众民引渡的圣灵,是人类灵魂的必要导师。

因此我马上把我和星期五之间的谈话岔到别的事情上去,匆匆忙忙站起来,仿佛突然想到一件要紧的事情,必须出去一下,同时找了一个借口,把他差到一个相当远的地方去。等他走后,我就恳切地祷告上帝,祈求他使我有办法教导这个可怜的野人;祈求他用他的圣灵帮助这可怜无知的人从基督身上接受上帝的真理,和基督结合在一起;同时祈求他指导我用上帝的语言同他谈话,以便使他心悦诚服,睁开眼睛,灵魂得救。当星期五从外面回来时,我又同他进行了长时间的谈话,谈到救

then explain'd to him, as well as I could, why our Blessed Redeemer took not on him the Nature of Angels, but the Seed of Abraham, and how for that Reason the fallen Angels had no Share in the Redemption; that he came only to the lost Sheep of the House of Israel, and the like.

I had, God knows, more Sincerity than Knowledge, in all the Methods I took for this poor Creature's Instruction, and must acknowledge what I believe all that act upon the same Principle will find, That in laying Things open to him, I really inform'd and instructed my self in many Things, that either I did not know, or had not fully consider'd before; but which occurr'd naturally to my Mind, upon my searching into them, for the Information of this poor Savage; and I had more Affection in my Enquiry after Things upon this Occasion, than ever I felt before; so that whether this poor wild Wretch was the better for me, or no, I had great Reason to be thankful that ever he came to me: My Grief set lighter upon me, my Habitation grew comfortable to me beyond Measure; and when I reflected that in this solitary Life which I had been confin'd to, I had not only been moved my self to look up to Heaven, and to seek to the Hand that had brought me there; but was now to be made an Instrument under Providence to save the Life, and for ought I knew, the Soul of a poor Savage, and bring him to the true Knowledge of Religion, and of the Christian Doctrine, that he might know Christ Jesus, to know whom is Life eternal. I say, when I reflected upon all these Things, a secret Joy run through every Part of my Soul, and I frequently rejoyc'd that ever I was brought to this Place, which I had

世主耶稣代人赎罪的事,谈到从天上来的福音的道理,也就是说,谈到向上帝忏悔、信仰救主耶稣这些事情。然后,我又尽可能向他解释,为什么我们的救主不以天使的身份出现,而降世为亚伯拉罕的后代,为什么那些被贬谪的天使不能替人类赎罪,以及耶稣的降生是为了挽救迷途的以色列人等等道理。

事实上,在教导他的时候,我所采用的方法,诚意多于知识。同时,我也必须承认,在向他说明这些道理时,我自己在不少问题上也获得了很多知识;这些问题有的我过去自己也不了解,有的我过去思考得不多,现在因为要教导星期五,自然而然地进行了深入的思考。我想,凡是诚心帮助别人的人,都会有这种边教边学的体会。我感到自己现在探讨这些问题的热情比以前更大了。所以,不管这个可怜的野人将来对我是否有帮助,我也应该感谢他的出现。现在,我不再像以前那样整日愁眉苦脸了,生活也逐渐愉快起来。每当我想到,在我这与世隔绝的孤寂生活中,我不仅自己受到感动而仰慕上苍,寻觅着那只在冥冥中送我到这岛上的巨掌,而且执行了上天的旨意,拯救了一个可怜的野人的性命,还正在尽己所能地拯救他的灵魂,让他认识真正的宗教和基督教的教义,让他认识耶稣基督,而认识他就是获得永生;是啊,每当我想到这

so often thought the most dreadful of all Afflictions that could possibly have befallen me.

In this thankful Frame I continu'd all the Remainder of my Time, and the Conversation which employ'd the Hours between Friday and I, was such, as made the three Years which we liv'd there together perfectly and compleatly happy, if any such Thing as compleat Happiness can be form'd in a sublunary State. The Savage was now a good Christian, a much better than I; though I have reason to hope, and bless God for it, that we were equally penitent, and comforted restor'd Penitents; we had here the Word of God to read, and no farther off from his Spirit to instruct, than if we had been in England.

I always apply'd my self in Reading the Scripture, to let him know, as well as I could, the Meaning of what I read; and he again, by his serious Enquiries, and Questionings, made me, as I said before, a much better Scholar in the Scripture Knowledge, than I should ever have been by my own private meer Reading. Another thing I cannot refrain from observing here also from Experience, in this retir'd Part of my Life, viz. How infinite and inexpressible a Blessing it is, that the Knowledge of God, and of the Doctrine of Salvation by Christ Jesus, is so plainly laid down in the Word of God; so easy to be receiv'd and understood: That as the bare reading the Scripture made me capable of understanding enough of my Duty, to carry me directly on to the great Work of sincere Repentance for my Sins, and laying hold of a Saviour for

一切时,我的整个灵魂里就涌动着一种莫名的喜悦,我甚至常常为自己被送到这里而感到高兴,而在这以前,我却时时认为,我遭到的最倒霉的事,就是来到了这个地方。

我怀着这种感恩的心情度过了我在岛上的最后几年。如果在尘世生活中真有"完美幸福"这一说法的话,那么在我和星期五共同生活的三年中,因为有许多时间同他进行这类交谈,所以日子过得非常完美幸福。野人星期五现在已成了一个比我还要虔诚得多的基督徒。为此,我完全有理由相信,我们两人最终都能成为真正的悔罪人,我们能够在心灵的忏悔中获得安慰,悔过自新。我们在这里就像在英国一样,因为我们手握《圣经》,紧靠圣灵,随时都可以得到上帝的教诲。

我一贯勤于阅读《圣经》,并尽我所能把我所读到的意义讲给他听;而他则认真地追问或提问,这使我对《圣经》的认识更加深刻,这是我以前独自一人研读时所做不到的。有一点我在此不可略去不谈,那就是,从我这段孤寂的生活中,我得出这样的体会:上帝和耶稣基督救人的道理在《圣经》中写得那样清楚明白,那样容易接受,容易读懂,这对我来说,真是一种说不出的、无限的幸福;通过阅读《圣经》,我终于明白了我的职责,并一往无前地承担起忏悔我的罪孽的伟大任务,全心全意地归

Life and Salvation, to a stated Reformation in Practice, and Obedience to all God's Commands, and this without any Teacher or Instructer; I mean, humane; so the same plain Instruction sufficiently serv'd to the enlightning this Savage Creature, and bringing him to be such a Christian, as I have known few equal to him in my Life.

As to all the Disputes, Wranglings, Strife and Contention, which has happen'd in the World about Religion, whether Niceties in Doctrines, or Schemes of Church Government, they were all perfectly useless to us; as for ought I can yet see, they have been to all the rest of the World: We had the sure Guide to Heaven, viz. The Word of God; and we had, blessed be God, comfortable Views of the Spirit of God teaching and instructing us by his Word, leading us into all Truth, and making us both willing and obedient to the Instruction of his Word; and I cannot see the least Use that the greatest Knowledge of the disputed Points in Religion which have made such Confusions in the World would have been to us, if we could have obtain'd it; but I must go on with the Historical Part of Things, and take every Part in its order.

After Friday and I became more intimately acquainted, and that he could understand almost all I said to him, and speak fluently, though in broken English to me; I acquainted him with my own Story, or at least so much of it as related to my coming into the Place, how I had liv'd there, and how long. I let him into the Mystery, for such it was to him, of Gunpowder, and Bullet, and taught him how to shoot: I gave him a Knife, which he was wonderfully delighted with, and I made him a Belt, with a Frog hanging to it, such as in England we wear Hangers in; and in the Frog, instead of a Hanger, I gave him a Hatchet,

顺于救世主,以获得生命的拯救,并修正自己的行为,服从于上帝的指示。这一切都是在没有人指点的情况下,全靠我个人阅读获得的体会。同时,这种浅显的道理也启发了这个野人,使他成了我所见到的为数不多的好基督徒之一。

至于世界上所发生的一切有关宗教的争执、纠缠、斗争和辩论,无论是教义上的微妙,或者是教会行政上的种种计划,对我们来说,大都毫无用处,并且据我看来,对于世界上其他的人也毫无用处。我们有走向天堂的最可靠的指南——上帝的语言;同时上帝的圣灵也在用上帝的言语教导我们,领导我们认识真理,使我们自觉地服从上帝的指示;即使我们对于那些在世界上造成巨大混乱的宗教上的争执获得最高度的知识,我也看不出那对我们有什么用处。不过,现在还是把我的一些重要事件按着先后次序讲下去吧。

当星期五和我更加熟悉之后,等他几乎能全部听明白我向他说的话,而且,他能用断断续续的英语和我能顺利交谈的时候,我给他讲了我的身世,尤其是我是怎么来到这个海岛上的,如何在这里生存,以及在这里生活了多久等等。我又把子弹以及火药的秘密告诉了他(这对他可真是个秘密),又教他学开枪。我又给了他一把刀,他非常喜欢,我还为他做了一条皮腰带,上

which was not only as good a Weapon in some Cases, but much more useful upon other Occasions.

I describ'd to him the Country of Europe, and particularly England, which I came from; how we liv'd, how we worshipp'd God, how we behav'd to one another; and how we traded in Ships to all Parts of the World: I gave him an Account of the Wreck which I had been on board of, and shew'd him as near as I could, the Place where she lay; but she was all beaten in Pieces before, and gone.

I shew'd him the Ruins of our Boat, which we lost when we escap'd, and which I could not stir with my whole Strength then; but was now fallen almost all to Pieces: Upon seeing this Boat, Friday stood musing a great while, and said nothing; I ask'd him what it was he study'd upon, at last says he, me see such Boat like come to Place at my Nation.

I did not understand him a good while; but at last, when I had examin'd farther into it, I understood by him, that a Boat, such as that had been, came on Shore upon the Country where he liv'd; that is, as he explain'd it, was driven thither by Stress of Weather: I presently imagin'd, that some European Ship must have been cast away upon their Coast, and the Boat might get loose, and drive a Shore; but was so dull, that I never once thought of Men making escape from a Wreck thither, much less whence they might come; so I only enquir'd after a Description of the Boat.

边挂了个刀环,类似英国人挂腰刀的玩艺儿,只是在刀环上,我没有让他挂腰刀,只给他挂了一把斧头。因为斧子可说是件极好的武器,有时会比刀更有用处。

我把欧洲的情况,特别是我的故乡英国的情况,说给他听,告诉他我们是怎样生活的,我们怎样崇拜上帝,人与人之间又怎样互相相处,以及怎样乘船到世界各地做生意。我又把我所乘的那条船出事的经过告诉他,并指给他看沉船的大致地方。至于那条船,早已给风浪打得粉碎,现在连影子都没有了。

我又把那只小艇的残骸指给他看,也就是我们逃命时翻掉的那只救生艇。我曾经竭尽全力想把它推到海里去,但怎么使劲小艇都分毫不动。现在,这小艇也已差不多烂成碎片了。看见这只小艇,星期五沉思了许久,也不说一句话,我问他在想什么,最后,他说:"我在我们部落里见过这样的舢板。"

我好久都没弄懂他的意思,后来详细地问了他,总算明白了,原来在他早先待的那个地方,曾有这样的一只船靠岸;据他解释说,这是被风浪打送到那儿去的。我马上就想到,准是有什么欧洲人的船被风吹到他们那沿海一带,而船上的救生艇可能在风浪中掉到了海里,从而漂到了岸边;我的头脑也真是迟钝,竟然完全没有想到也许是大船

Friday describ'd the Boat to me well enough; but brought me better to understand him, when he added with some Warmth, we save the white Mans from drown: Then I presently ask'd him, if there was any white Mans, as he call'd them, in the Boat; yes, he said, the Boat full white Mans: I ask'd him how many; he told upon his Fingers seventeen: I ask'd him then what become of them; he told me, they live, they dwell at my Nation.

This put new Thoughts into my Head; for I presently imagin'd, that these might be the Men belonging to the Ship, that was cast away in Sight of my Island, as I now call it; and who after the Ship was struck on the Rock, and they saw her inevitably lost, had sav'd themselves in their Boat, and were landed upon that wild Shore among the Savages.

Upon this, I enquir'd of him more critically, What was become of them? He assur'd me they lived still there; that they had been there about four Years; that the Savages let them alone, and gave them Victuals to live. I ask'd him, How it came to pass they did not kill them and eat them? He said No, they make Brother with them; that is, as I understood him, a Truce: And then he added, They no eat Mans but when make the War fight; that is to say, they never eat any Men but such as come to fight with them, and are taken in Battle.

失了事,船上的人乘救生艇逃命,才到了那里;当然更不会想到这些人的由来了;所以在当时,我只是追问那救生艇的情况。

星期五把那只舢板描绘得很具体。接着,他又很起劲地加了一句:"我们还从水中救出了一些白人。"这时,我总算明白了几分,便连忙问,是不是从舢板上救出了一些白人。他说:"是的,满满一小船都是白人。"我问他有多少人,他便扳着手指数一遍,一共有十七个。我又问他,那些人后来的情形究竟怎样。他告诉我:"他们都活着,住在我们的部落里。"

听了这话,我忽然想到了另外一件事。我猜想,那些白人一定是我上次在岛上看到的那条失事大船上的船员。大概当时他们发现航船触礁后,知道大船肯定是保不住了,便乘坐救生艇逃命了。结果他们在野人聚居的海岸登了陆。

想到这里,我很不放心,便更加仔细地询问星期五,要他告诉我那些白人到底怎么样了。星期五十分肯定地告诉我,他们现在仍然住在那里,已经住了四年左右了。野人们不去搔扰他们,还给他们粮食吃。我问他,为什么没有把那些白人也杀了吃掉呢?星期五说:"不,我们的人和他们结成了兄弟。"根据我的理解,这就是说,他们中间订了休战协定。接着他又补充说:

It was after this some considerable Time, that being upon the Top of the Hill, at the East Side of the Island, from whence as have said, I had in a clear Day discover'd the Main, or Continent of America; Friday, the Weather being very serene, looks very earnestly towards the Main Land, and in a kind of Surprise, falls a jumping and dancing, and calls out to me, for I was at some Distance from him: I ask'd him, What was the Matter? O joy! Says he, O glad! There see my Country, there my Nation!

I observ'd an extraordinary Sense of Pleasure appear'd in his Face, and his Eyes sparkled, and his Countenance discover'd a strange Eagerness, as if he had a Mind to be in his own Country again; and this Observation of mine, put a great many Thoughts into me, which made me at first not so easy about my new Man Friday as I was before; and I made no doubt, but that if Friday could get back to his own Nation again, he would not only forget all his Religion, but all his Obligation to me; and would be forward enough to give his Countrymen an Account of me, and come back perhaps with a hundred or two of them, and make a Feast upon me, at which he might be as merry as he us'd to be with those of his Enemies, when they were taken in War.

But I wrong'd the poor honest Creature very much, for which I was very sorry afterwards. However as my Jealousy encreased, and held me some Weeks, I was a little more circumspect, and not so familiar and kind to him as before; in which

"他们除了打仗的时候之外，从来不吃人。"这就是说，他们除了吃战争中所俘获的敌人外，不吃别的人。

此后又过了很久，有一天，天气晴朗，我和星期五偶然走上岛东边的那座小山（我从前在一个晴朗的日子里看到美洲大陆，也就是在这座山上），星期五心神贯注地朝大陆那边眺望了一会儿，忽然出乎意料地手舞足蹈起来，把我喊了过去（因为我当时离开他还有几步路）。我问他是怎么回事。他说："真高兴！真快活！我看见我的家乡，我的部落了！"

这时，我见他脸上现出一种异乎寻常的欣喜。他双眼闪闪发光，流露出一种热切兴奋和神往的神色，仿佛想立刻返回他故乡去似的。看到他这种心情，我胡思乱想起来。我对星期五不由起了戒心，因而与他也不像以前那样融洽了。我毫不怀疑，只要星期五能回到自己的部落中去，他不但会忘掉他的宗教信仰，而且也会忘掉他对我的全部义务。他一定会毫不犹豫地把我的情况告诉他部落里的人，说不定还会带上一两百他的同胞到岛上来，拿我来开一次人肉宴。那时，他一定会像吃战争中抓来的俘虏一样兴高采烈。

然而我真是大大地错看了这可怜的老实人，对此，我后来极为懊恼。然而，当时，我的猜疑之心有增无减，在几个星期的时间里都难以排除。

I was certainly in the Wrong too, the honest grateful Creature having no thought about it, but what consisted with the best Principles, both as a religious Christian, and as a grateful Friend, as appeared afterwards to my full Satisfaction.

While my Jealousy of him lasted, you may be sure I was every Day pumping him to see if he would discover any of the new Thoughts, which I suspected were in him; but I found every thing he said was so Honest, and so Innocent, that I could find nothing to nourish my Suspicion; and in spight of all my Uneasiness he made me at last entirely his own again, nor did he in the least perceive that I was Uneasie, and therefore I could not suspect him of Deceit.

One Day walking up the same Hill, but the Weather being haizy at Sea, so that we could not see the Continent, I call'd to him, and said, Friday, do not you wish your self in your own Country, your own Nation? Yes, he said, he be much O glad to be at his own Nation. What would you do there said I, would you turn Wild again, eat Mens Flesh again, and be a Savage as you were before? He lookt full of Concern, and shaking his Head said, No no, Friday tell them to live Good, tell them to pray God, tell them to eat Corn bread, Cattleflesh, Milk, no eat Man again: Why then said I to him, They will kill you. He look'd grave at that, and then said, No, they no kill me, they willing love learn: He meant by this, they would be willing to learn. He added, they learn'd much of the Bearded-Mans that come in the Boat. Then I ask'd him if he would go back to them? He

对于他，我采取了更多的防范措施，对他的态度也明显地不如以前热情友好了。这可真是个天大的错误。实际上，这个忠心诚实的人，从来就没有往这些事情上想过。以后的事实也证明，他的所做所为，完全符合一个充满宗教意识的基督徒的最高准则，或者作为一个知恩图报的朋友的最理想的原则。

对他的猜疑没有消除以前，我每天都用探询的口气同他谈话，希望能发现他的想法来证明我的猜疑。但我发现他说的一切仍是那么天真无邪，我找不出任何使我加深怀疑的地方，尽管我对他存有戒心，他最后还是完全赢得了我的信任。他一点也没感到我的不安，所以他不可能是伪装成无辜的样子。

一天，我们登上原来那座小山，海上水雾迷濛，看不见大陆，我把星期五叫到跟前问："星期五，你想回家乡，回到你的族人那儿去吗？""想，"他说，"要是能够回到自己的部落，我会很高兴的。"我说："你回去做什么呢？你要再变回野人，吃人肉吗？"他很严肃地摇着头说："不，不，星期五会把好好过日子告诉他们，把向上帝祈祷告诉他们，告诉他们吃五谷做的面包，吃牛羊肉，喝牛羊奶，不再吃人肉。"我说："那么，他们一定会杀死你。"他听了这句话，严肃地说："不，他们不会把我杀死的，他们喜欢学习。"他的意思是他们喜欢

smil'd at that, and told me he could not swim so far. I told him I would make a Canoe for him. He told me, he would go, if I would go with him. I go! says I, why they will Eat me if I come there! No, no, says he, me make they no Eat you; me make they much Love you: He meant he would tell them how I had kill'd his Enemies, and sav'd his Life, and so he would make them love me; then he told me as well as he could, how kind they were to seventeen White-men, or Bearded-men, as he call'd them, who came on Shore there in Distress.

From this time I confess I had a Mind to venture over, and see if I could possibly joyn with these Bearded-men, who I made no doubt were Spaniards or Portuguese; not doubting but if I could we might find some Method to Escape from thence, being upon the Continent, and a good Company together, better than I could from an Island 40 Miles off the Shore, and alone without Help. So after some Days I took Friday to work again, by way of Discourse, and told him I would give him a Boat to go back to his own Nation; and accordingly I carry'd him to my Frigate which lay on the other Side of the Island, and having clear'd it of Water, for I always kept it sunk in the Water, I brought it out, shewed it him, and we both went into it.

把知识吸收进来。他接着告诉我,从那些乘救生艇来的大胡子那里,他们已学习到许多东西。我随即问他,他可想回他们那儿。他听后微微一笑说,他游不到那么远。我说,我会给他准备一只独木舟的。他说,如果我同他一起去,他就去。"我一起去?"我说道,"不行;我到了那儿就会被他们吃掉的。""不,不,"他说道,"我要他们不吃你,我要他们大大地爱你。"他的意思是:他要告诉他们,我怎么杀了他的敌人,救了他的性命,这样就能使他们敬爱我;接着他又竭力向我说明,对于遭了难而流落到他们那儿的十七个白人,就是他所说的大胡子,他们是如何友好相待的。

我承认,从这个时候起,我开始想渡过海峡,看能不能跟那些"大胡子"会合在一起。我坚信,他们一定是西班牙或葡萄牙人;同时,我也相信,我们一定可以找到什么办法,从那里逃出去,因为那里是在大陆上,又有很多人结伴同行,总比我一个人势单力薄、孤立无援地从一个离岸四十英里的小岛上出发强得多。几天之后,我又带星期五出去干活。趁跟他谈话的机会我告诉他,我想给他一只舢板,让他回到自己的部落。我把他带到放在岛那边的我的舢板那里。由于我总是将它沉在水里,所以,我先把船里的水排掉,让它浮起来,指给他看,然后我们就一起上了船。

I found he was a most dextrous Fellow at managing it, would make it go almost as swift and fast again as I could; so when he was in, I said to him, Well now, Friday, shall we go to your Nation? He look'd very dull at my saying so, which it seems was, because he thought the Boat too small to go so far. I told him then I had a bigger; so the next Day I went to the Place where the first Boat lay which I had made, but which I could not get into Water: He said that was big enough; but then as I had taken no Care of it, and it had lain two or three and twenty Years there, the Sun had split and dry'd it, that it was in a manner rotten. Friday told me such a Boat would do very well, and would carry much enough Vittle, Drink, Bread, that was his Way of Talking.

Upon the whole, I was by this Time so fix'd upon my Design of going over with him to the Continent, that I told him we would go and make one as big as that, and he should go home in it. He answer'd not one Word, but look'd very grave and sad: I ask'd him what was the matter with him? He ask'd me again thus; Why, you angry mad with Friday, what me done? I ask'd him what he meant; I told him I was not angry with him at all. No angry! No angry! says he, repeating the Words several Times, Why send Friday home away to my Nation? Why, (says I) Friday, did you not say you wish'd you were there? Yes, yes, says he, wish be both there, no wish Friday there, no Master there. In a Word, he would not think of going there without me; I go there! Friday, (says I) what shall I do there? He turn'd

我发现星期五真是一个划船好手,划起船来身手不凡,比我划得要快一倍呢。趁着我们俩都在舢板里,我便对他说:"好啦,星期五,我们现在是不是可以到你们部落那里去啦?"他听了我的话,显出迟疑的神态,看他那样,好像是嫌这船太小,没法完成那么远的航程似的。我就告诉他,我还有一只比这大不少的船呢。于是,第二天我又带他去看了我制造的第一只木船,就是造好之后无法下水的那只。星期五告诉我这只船足够大了。然而可惜的是,舢板由于没有得到很好的保护,在那儿风吹日晒一躺就是二十二、三年,已经四处开裂,全身朽烂了。星期五对我说,如果有这样一只船就完全能够渡海了,可以装上"足够的食物、饮水和面包"。

总之,我现在已经一心一意打算同他一块到大陆上去,因此我就对他说,我们将动手造一只跟这一样大的船,让他坐着回家。他一句话也不回答,脸上显出很庄重、很难过的样子。我问他是怎么回事。他反问我道:"你为什么对星期五生气呢?我做了什么错事吗?"我问他是什么意思,并且告诉他,我一点也没有生他的气。"没有生气!没有生气!"他说,并且把这句话说了一遍又一遍。"那你为什么叫星期五回自己的部落呢?"我说:"星期五,你不是说你想回去吗?""是的,是的,"他说,"我

very quick upon me at this: You do great deal much good, says he, you teach wild Mans be good sober tame Mans; you tell them know God, pray and live new Life. Alas! Friday, (says I) thou knowest not what thou sayest, I am but an ignorant Man my self Yes, yes, says he, you teachee me Good, you teachee them Good. No, no, Friday, (says I) you shall go without me, leave me here to live by my self as I did before. He look'd confus'd again at that Word, and running to one of the Hatchets which he used to wear, he takes it up hastily, comes and gives it me, What must I do with this? says I to him. You take, kill Friday; (says he.) What must I kill you for? said I again. He returns very quick, What you send Friday away for? take, kill Friday, no send Friday away. This he spoke so earnestly, that I saw Tears stand in his Eyes: In a Word, I so plainly discover'd the utmost Affection in him to me, and a firm Resolution in him, that I told him then, and often after, that I would never send him away from me, if he was willing to stay with me.

Upon the whole, as I found by all his Discourse a settled Affection to me, and that nothing should part him from me, so I found all the Foundation of his Desire to go to his own Country, was laid in his ardent Affection to the People, and his Hopes of my doing them good; a Thing which as I had

想两个人都去,不想星期五去,主人不去。"简单一句话,没有我,他是绝不想回去的。我说:"我去!星期五,我到那边去做什么?"他马上回答说:"你可以做很多很多的好事;你可以把野人教导成善良、清醒、温和的人;你教导他们认识上帝,祈祷上帝,并且过一种新的生活。""唉,星期五,"我说,"你简直不知道你在说些什么,我自己也是一个无知的人啊!""你行,你行,"他说,"你能把我教好,也就能把他们大家都教好。""不行,不行,星期五,"我说,"你一个人去吧,让我一个人留在这儿,仍像以前一样过日子吧。"他听了我的话,又给弄糊涂了。他登时跑去把他日常佩带的那把斧头取来交给我。"你给我斧头干什么?"我问他。"拿着它,杀了星期五吧!"他说。"我为什么要杀星期五呢?"我又说。他马上回答说:"你为什么要赶走星期五呢?拿斧头杀了星期五吧,不要赶他走。"他说这几句话的时候,态度十分诚恳,眼睛里噙着眼泪,简言之,我一眼就看出,他对我真是一片真情,不改初衷。于是我当时就告诉他,只要他愿意同我待在一起,我就决不会要他走;这句话,我后来也常对他说。

总之,从他所有的谈话中,我看出他对我的依恋之情始终不变,怎么也不肯离开我,因此我也就明白,他之所以想回故乡,一方面由于他对故乡同胞的热爱,另一方面则

no Notion of my self, so I had not the least Thought or Intention, or Desire of undertaking it. But still I found a strong Inclination to my attempting an Escape as above, founded on the Supposition gather'd from the Discourse, (viz.) That there were seventeen bearded Men there; and therefore, without any more Delay, I went to Work with Friday to find out a great Tree proper to fell, and make a large Periagua or Canoe to undertake the Voyage. There were Trees enough in the Island to have built a little Fleet, not of Periagua's and Canoes, but even of good large Vessels. But the main Thing I look'd at, was to get one so near the Water that we might launch it when it was made, to avoid the Mistake I committed at first.

At last, Friday pitch'd upon a Tree, for I found he knew much better than I what kind of Wood was fittest for it, nor can I tell to this Day what Wood to call the Tree we cut down, except that it was very like the Tree we call Fustic, or between that and the Nicaragua Wood, for it was much of the same Colour and Smell. Friday was for burning the Hollow or Cavity of this Tree out to make it for a Boat. But I shew'd him how rather to cut it out with Tools, which, after I had shew'd him how to use, he did very handily, and in about a Month's hard Labour, we finished it, and made it very handsome, especially when with our Axes, which I shew'd him how to handle, we cut and hew'd the out-side into the true Shape of a Boat; after this, however, it cost us near a Fortnight's Time to get her along as it were Inch by Inch upon great Rowlers into the Water. But when she was in, she would have carry'd twenty Men with great Ease.

是希望我能对他们起开导作用；但我本人完全没这种念头，所以根本就不打算这么做，也不愿这么做。不过我既然从他的话中得到了一个印象，就是那儿有十七个大胡子，也就有了一种强烈的愿望，想要离开本岛；于是我不再耽搁，马上准备做一条担当此次航行任务的独木舟，但首先得找一棵合适的树，砍倒了才行。岛上树木很多，不要说是做几条独木舟，哪怕要建造一支由大船组成的小船队也是足够的。不过我首先考虑的是，这树得长在水边，做成了船就能弄下水去，免得再犯前一回的错误。

最后，星期五先找到一棵树，我知道他比我更了解哪种树更适合造船。至今我还叫不出我们砍下的树的名称，它的样子很像菩提树，或者是菩提树和尼加拉瓜树之间的品种，颜色和气味都很相似。星期五原本打算采取用火烧树木中部的方法制做独木舟，但我告诉他使用工具凿空树木的办法更好。我把工具的使用方法教给他，他很快就掌握了，而且颇为得心应手。凿好船舱后，我又教星期五学会了如何使用斧头砍削，然后我们俩一块用斧头把独木舟外围砍削成真正的船形。就这样，经过一个月左右的辛勤劳动，独木舟终于大功告成，而且制做得非常美观。接着，我们差不多又花了两星期的工夫，用大转木把独木舟一点一点地

When she was in the Water, and tho' she was so big it amazed me to see with what Dexterity and how swift my Man Friday would manage her, turn her, and paddle her along; so. I ask'd him if he would, and if we might venture over in her; Yes, he said, he venture over in her very well, tho' great blow Wind. However, I had a farther Design that he knew nothing of, and that was to make a Mast and Sail and to fit her with an Anchor and Cable: As to a Mast, that was easy enough to get; so I pitch'd upon a strait young Cedar-Tree, which I found near the Place, and which there was great Plenty of in the Island, and I set Friday to Work to cut it down, and gave him Directions how to shape and order it. But as to the Sail, that was my particular Care; I knew I had old Sails, or rather Pieces of old Sails enough; but as I had had them now six and twenty Years by me, and had not been very careful to preserve them, not imagining that I should ever have this kind of Use for them, I did not doubt but they were all rotten, and indeed most of them were so; however, I found two Pieces which appear'd pretty good, and with these I went to Work, and with a great deal of Pains, and awkward tedious stitching (you may be sure) for Want of Needles, I at length made a three Corner'd ugly Thing, like what we call in England, a Shoulder of Mutton Sail, to go with a Boom at bottom, and a little short Sprit at the Top, such as usually our Ships Long Boats sail with, and such as I best knew how to manage; because it was such a one as I had to the Boat, in which I made my Escape from Barbary, as related in the first Part of my Story.

推入水里。等我们把独木舟推下水后，发现它竟能宽宽松松地装载二十个人呢。

独木舟下水后，尽管很大，但我惊奇地发现，我的仆人星期五却能非常灵巧地操纵它，把它开得飞快，转向，划桨，给人以行云流水之感。我问他，我们能不能用它漂过海面。他说："能，就是有大风，我们也能用它漂过海面。"不过，我接下来还有一个打算他就不知道了，就是说，我想做一个桅杆和一面船帆，再配上一副铁锚和缆索。至于桅杆，那很容易办到。我在附近选中了一棵小杉树（这种树岛上很多），又叫星期五动手把它砍倒，教他如何刨削，把它做成桅杆的样子。说到船帆，却颇伤脑筋。我知道，我本来有不少旧船帆，确切地说，有不少旧帆布，但这些东西已经放了二十六年了，我从来就没有仔细保管它们，再也想不到会有这种用场。因此，我毫不怀疑，它们早都烂掉了。而事实上，它们大部分也烂掉了。可是，从这些烂掉的帆布中间，我却找到了两块看起来还不错的，于是便动手用它们来做船帆。因为没有针，缝起来既吃力又不方便；费了不少的劲，才做成一块三角形的丑八怪，就像英国人叫作羊肩帆的那种东西；用的时候，底下装一根横木，顶上再装上一根横杠，就像我们大船上的长艇上面的帆一样。这种帆也是我最会使用的，因为前面讲过，我从

I was near two Months performing this last Work, viz. rigging and fitting my Mast and Sails; for I finish'd them very compleat, making a small Stay, and a Sail, or Foresail to it, to assist, if we should turn to Windward; and which was more than all, I fix'd a Rudder to the Stern of her, to steer with; and though I was but a bungling Shipwright, yet as I knew the Usefulness, and even Necessity of such a Thing, I apply'd my self with so much Pains to do it, that at last I brought it to pass; though considering the many dull Contrivances I had for it that sail'd, I think it cost me almost as much Labour as making the Boat.

After all this was done too, I had my Man Friday to teach as to what belong'd to the Navigation of my Boat; for though he knew very well how to paddle a Canoe, he knew nothing what belong'd to a Sail, and a Rudder; and was the most amaz'd, when he saw me work the Boat too and again in the Sea by the Rudder, and how the Sail gyb'd, and fill'd this way, or that way, as the Course we sail'd chang'd; I say, when he saw this, he stood like one, astonish'd and amaz'd: However, with a little Use, I made all these Things familiar to him; and he became an expert Sailor, except that as to the Compass, I could make him understand very little of that. On the other hand, as there was very little cloudy Weather, and seldom or never any Fogs in those Parts, there was the less occasion for a Compass, seeing the Stars were always to be seen by Night, and the Shore by Day, except in the rainy Seasons, and then no body car'd to stir abroad, either by Land or Sea.

巴尔巴利逃走的时候所坐的那只舢板,也是用的这种帆。

这最后一项工作,差不多花了我两个月左右的功夫,因为我想把制造和装备桅杆和船帆的工作做得尽可能完美无缺。此外,我还配上小小的桅索以帮助支撑桅杆。我在船头还做了个前帆,以便逆风时行船。尤其重要的是,我在船尾还装了一个舵,这样转换方向时就能驾御自如了。我造船的技术当然不能算高明,然而知道这些东西非常有用,而且是必不可少的,也就只好不辞辛劳,尽力去做了。在制造过程中,我当然儿经试验和失败。如果把这些都计算在内,所花费的时间和力气,和造这条船本身相差无几。

这一切全完成以后,我得教星期五驾这船的技术了。因为尽管他能熟练地用桨划船,对于帆和舵却是一无所知的,所以见我操着舵,让船在海面上来来往往,而随着航向的改变,帆一会儿在左舷,一会儿在右舷,反正总是要借足风力,他不禁看得目瞪口呆;没错,他看到这一切时,惊奇得愣在那儿了。但经过短短一段时间的操作,我让他熟悉了这些东西,他成了熟练的驾船人,只是对于罗盘照旧一窍不通,我再怎么讲也很难让他明白。不过话得说回来,那一带的天气以晴好居多,即使不能说从来没有雾天,至少下雾的日子是难得一见的,既然晚上总能见得到星斗,白天总能

I was now entred on the seven and twentieth Year of my Captivity in this Place; though the three last Years that I had this Creature with me, ought rather to be left out of the Account, my Habitation being quite of another kind than in all the rest of the Time. I kept the Anniversary of my Landing here with the same Thankfulness to God for his Mercies, as at first; and if I had such Cause of Acknowledgment at first, I had much more so now, having such additional Testimonies of the Care of Providence over me, and the great Hopes I had of being effectually, and speedily deliver'd; for I had an invincible Impression upon my Thoughts, that my Deliverance was at hand, and that I should not be another Year in this Place: However, I went on with my Husbandry, digging, planting, fencing, as usual; I gather'd and cur'd my Grapes, and did every necessary Thing as before.

The rainy Season was in the mean Time upon me, when I kept more within Doors than at other Times; so I had stow'd our new Vessel as secure as we could, bringing her up into the Creek, where as I said, in the Beginning I landed my Rafts from the Ship, and haling her up to the Shore, at high Water mark, I made my Man Friday dig a little Dock, just big enough to hold her, and just deep enough to give her Water enough to fleet in; and then when the Tide was out, we made a strong Dam cross the End of it, to keep the Water out; and so she lay dry, as to the Tide from the Sea; and to keep the Rain off, we laid a

看得到海岸，所以罗盘倒也不怎么用得到，当然雨季的情况除外，但在那时节，没人愿意出去，不管是走陆路还是走水路。

从我被困在这里到现在，已经是第二十七个年头了，但最后的三年，有星期五在身旁，我的生活和以前绝不相同，这似乎不该计算在内。同过去一样，我怀着极为感动的心情度过了我登上海岛的纪念日。如果过去我有充足的理由感谢上帝，那么今天我就有理由这么做，今天有越来越多的事实可以证明上帝对我的庇护，我也就有希望脱离大难，解脱困境，很久以来我心里一直怀有这种感觉，我觉得我脱离困境的日子已经不远，我感觉我在这里也许不会呆上一年了。尽管如此，我还是继续料理着我的农活，翻地，播种，围篱墙，一切照常，并继续采集葡萄，晒制葡萄干，总之，以前各样必做的事情现在还照常进行。

转眼雨季就要来了，到了雨季，我就不能像平时经常出门了。我尽量把我们的新船藏放妥当，把它拉进了我当初在大船上卸木排的那条小河，然后，趁潮水涨高的时候，再把它拖上了岸。我又叫我的仆人星期五挖了一个舢板坞，其宽度刚好可以容下舢板，其深度可以把海水放进来，让它浮起。等潮水退去之后，我们又在船坞的入口处筑了一道坚固的水坝，再把水排了出

great many Boughs of Trees, so thick, that she was as well thatch'd as a House; and thus we waited for the Month of November and December, in which I design'd to make my Adventure.

When the settled Season began to come in, as the thought of my Design return'd with the fair Weather, I was pre paring daily for the Voyage; and the first Thing I did, was to lay by a certain Quantity of Provisions, being the Stores for our Voyage; and intended in a Week or a Fortnight's Time, to open the Dock, and launch out our Boat. I was busy one Morning upon some Thing of this kind, when I call'd to Friday, and bid him go to the Sea Shore, and see if he could find a Turtle, or Tortoise, a Thing which we generally got once a Week, for the Sake of the Eggs, as well as the Flesh: Friday had not been long gone, when he came running back, and flew over my outer Wall, or Fence, like one that felt not the Ground, or the Steps he set his Feet on; and before I had time to speak to him, he cries out to me, O Master! O Master! O Sorrow! O bad! What's the Matter, Friday? says I; O yonder, there, says he, one, two, three Canoe! one, two, three! By his way of speaking, I concluded there were six; but on en-quiry, I found it was but three: Well, Friday, says I, do not be frighted; so I heartned him up as well as I could: However, I saw the poor Fellow was most terribly scar'd; for nothing ran in his Head but that they were come to look for him, and would cut him in Pieces, and eat him; and the poor Fellow trembled so, that I scarce knew what to do with him: I comforted him as well as I could, and told him I was in as much Danger as

去,这样,既可以使舢板保持干燥,又不让外面的潮水流进来。为了遮挡雨水,我们在舢板上面盖了许多带有茂密树叶的树枝,把船盖了个严严实实,看上去就像个茅草屋顶一样。木船安置妥当后,我们开始静静地等候着十一月和十二月的到来,到那时,我的冒险计划就要付诸实施了。

雨季很快进入尾声,旱季即将来临了。随着天气日渐好转,我也更为忙碌地进行着冒险计划的准备工作。我首先忙着储备足够的粮食以供航行之用,然后打算在一两个星期内挖开船坞,把船放入水里。一天早晨,我由于正忙着这些准备工作,便叫星期五去海边捉几只海龟或者陆龟来。我们每星期总要抓一两只海龟或者陆龟回来,以便享受一番它那蛋和肉的鲜美味道。星期五去了不久,忽然十分迅速地跑了回来,一纵身就跳到围墙里来,好像脚不着地似的;我还没来得及问怎么回事,他就大声说:"主人!主人!大事不好!"我说:"发生了什么事,星期五?"他说:"那边有一只,两只,三只独木舟!一只,两只,三只!"看着他那魂飞魄散的样子,我以为来了六只;详细一问,才知道仅仅三只而已。我说:"不要惊慌,星期五。"我尽量使他摆脱恐惧,但他还是吓得要命;他认为他们是专门为他而来的,他们要把他切成碎块吃掉。他浑身上下抖个不停,我简直不知如何

he, and that they would eat me as well as him; but, says I, Friday, we must resolve to fight them; Can you fight, Friday? Me shoot, says he, but there come many great Number. No matter for that, said I again, our Guns will fright them that we do not kill; so I ask'd him, Whether if I resolv'd to defend him, he would defend me, and stand by me, and do just as I bid him? He said, Me die, when you bid die, Master; so I went and fetch'd a good Dram of Rum, and gave him; for I had been so good a Husband of my Rum, that had a great deal left: When he had drank it, I made him take the two Fowling-Pieces, which we always carry'd, and load them with large Swan-Shot, as big as small Pistol Bullets; then I took four Muskets, and loaded them with two Slugs, and five small Bullets each; and my two Pistols I loaded with a Brace of Bullets each; I hung my great Sword as usual, naked by my Side, and gave Friday his Hatchet.

When I had thus prepar'd my self, I took my Perspective-Glass, and went up to the Side of the Hill, to see what I could discover; and I found quickly, by my Glass, that there were one and twenty Savages, three Prisoners, and three Canoes; and that their whole Business seem'd to be the triumphant Banquet upon these three humane Bodies, (a barbarous Feast indeed) but nothing more than as I had observ'd was usual with them.

I observ'd also, that they were landed not where they had done, when Friday made his Escape; but nearer to my Creek, where the Shore was low,

办好。我极力安慰他，告诉他我跟他一样危险，他们也会像对待他一样把我吃掉。"但是，"我说，"星期五，我们应该下决心与他们斗争。你能打仗吗，星期五？""我会射击，"他说，"但是来了很多人。""没关系，"我又说，"我们的枪声会把没死的人吓跑。"可是，我问他，如果我打算保卫他，他会不会保卫我，站在我这一边，照我说的去做。他说："主人，你叫我死，我就去死。"我拿来一些甘蔗酒给他，我还剩下不少，因为我一直省着喝。他喝完后，我让他拿上两支我们从不离身的鸟枪，里面装上跟手枪子弹一样大的大号鸟枪弹。我拿了四支短枪，每支装有两颗短枪弹丸和五粒小子弹，还有两把手枪，每把装有两粒子弹。最后，我又把我的大刀挂在腰间(跟往常一样，没有刀鞘)，再叫星期五把他的斧子也带上。

我经过了这番武装之后，便拿起望远镜，爬到小山腰上，想看一看海边的情况。通过望远镜，我很快便发现，那里有二十一个野人，三个战俘房和三只独木舟。他们到这里来好像没有别的意图，只是用这三个活人的肉来举行他们的庆功宴；这的确是一种野蛮的宴会，但正如我所说，在他们看来，这是习以为常的事。

我又注意到，他们这次登陆的地点，并不是上回星期五逃走的地方，而是更靠近我那

and where a thick Wood came close almost down to the Sea: This, with the Abhorrence of the inhumane Errand these Wretches came about, fill'd me with such Indignation, that I came down again to Friday, and told him, I was resolv'd to go down to them, and kill them all; and ask'd him, If he would stand by me? He was now gotten over his Fright, and his Spirits being a little rais'd, with the Dram I had given him, he was Cry chearful, and told me, as before, he would die, when I bid die.

In this Fit of Fury, I took first and divided the Arms which I had charg'd, as before, between us; I gave Friday one Pistol to stick in his Girdle, and three Guns upon his Shoulder; and I took one Pistol, and the other three my self; and in this Posture we march'd out: I took a small Bottle of Rum in my Pocket, and gave Friday a large Bag, with more Powder and Bullet; and as to Orders, I charg'd him to keep close behind me, and not to stir, or shoot, or do any Thing, till I bid him; and in the mean Time, not to speak a Word: In this Posture I fetch'd a Compass to my Right-Hand, of near a Mile, as well to get over the Creek, as to get into the Wood; so that I might come within shoot of them, before I should be discover'd, which I had seen by my Glass, it was easy to do.

While I was making this March, my former Thoughts returning, I began to abate my Resolu-

小河旁边,那一带海岸很低,并且有一片厚密的树林一直伸展到海边。我看到这种情形,再加上从心里憎恶这班畜生所要从事的残暴不仁的勾当,不由地怒气冲天,急忙跑下山来,跑到星期五身边,告诉他我已经决心要下去把他们斩尽杀绝,问他肯不肯支持我。他的惊惧心情这时已经消除了,又因为喝了我给他的酒,精神为之一振,听了我的话,大为高兴,便再一次向我表示,就是我叫他死,他也情愿。

我强压着心中的怒火,进行最后的战前准备。我把已装好弹药的武器分作两份,让星期五在腰带上插一支手枪,肩上背三支长枪,我也同样手拿一支手枪,背三支长枪。我们就这样全副武装地出发了。我还在衣袋里放了一小瓶甘蔗酒,又让星期五带上一大袋火药和子弹。我命令星期五紧紧地跟着我,没有我的命令,不许乱动,不许随便开枪,不许任意行动,也不许说话。我们没有朝目的地径直走去,而是向右绕了一个大圈子,多走了约有一英里的样子。我这样做是为了越过小河后能钻进那片靠海岸的小树林里去,能够安全地进入射击的有效位置而不被他们发现。我随身带着望远镜,随时可以观察他们的情况,所以,要做到这一点并不困难。

我们正往前走的时候,以往的想法又萦绕在我的脑际,

tion; I do not mean, that I entertain'd any Fear of their Number; for as they were naked, unarm'd Wretches, 'tis certain I was superior to them; nay, though I had been alone; but it occurr'd to my Thoughts, What Call? What Occasion? much less, What Necessity I was in to go and dip my Hands in Blood, to attack People, who had neither done, or intended me any Wrong? Who as to me were innocent, and whose barbarous Customs were their own Disaster, being in them a Token indeed of God's having left them, with the other Nations of that Part of the World, to such Stupidity, and to such inhumane Courses; but did not call me to take upon me to be a Judge of their Actions, much less an Executioner of his Justice; that whenever he thought fit, he would take the Cause into his own Hands, and by national Vengeance punish them as a People, for national Crimes; but that in the mean time, it was none of my Business; that it was true, Friday might justify it, because he was a declar'd Enemy, and in a State of War with those very particular People; and it was lawful for him to attack them; but I could not say the same with respect to me: These Things were so warmly press'd upon my Thoughts, all the way as I went, that I resolv'd I would only go and place my self near them, that I might observe their barbarous Feast, and that I would act then as God should direct; but that unless something offer'd that was more a Call to me than yet I knew of, I would not meddle with them.

With this Resolution I enter'd the Wood, and with all possible Wariness and Silence, Friday following close at my Heels, I march'd till I came to the Skirt of the Wood, on the Side which was next to them; only that one Corner of the Wood lay between me and them; here I call'd softly to Friday, and shewing him a great Tree, which was just at the Corner of the Wood, I bad him go to

令我冷静下来。当然,并非我担心他们人多势众,毕竟他们赤身露体,手无寸铁,即使我一个人也占绝对优势。然而,我突然想到,我受什么唆使,凭什么,有没有必要去袭击这些人,造成杀人流血?他们从没有侵犯过我,也无意损害我,他们根本就没有罪。他们野蛮的风俗,成为他们自己的难关,这证明上帝有意识地让他们及他们这一带的人处于愚昧无知混沌非人的处境,上帝并没有让我成为他们行动规范的裁决人,更别说是上帝的法律执行者了。无论如何,只要上帝认为适当,他满可以亲自执法,对他们全民族所犯的罪行,进行全民性的惩罚。即使那样,也与我无关。当然,对星期五来说,他倒是名正言顺的,因为他和这群人是公开的敌人,和他们处于交战状态。他要去攻击他们,那倒是合法的。但对我来说,情况就不同了。我一边往前走,一边被这些想法纠缠着。最后,我决定先站在他们附近,观察一下他们野蛮的宴会,然后根据上帝的指示,见机行事。我决定,除非获得上帝的感召,否则决不去干涉他们。

这样决定之后,我就进入了树林。星期五紧随我身后,小心翼翼、悄然无声地往前走。来到最靠近他们的树林尽头,在这里,他们同我们之间只隔着树林的一角;我轻声招呼星期五,向他指了指位于这树林顶端的一棵大树,要他

the Tree, and bring me Word if he could see there plainly what they were doing; he did so, and came immediately back to me, and told me they might be plainly view'd there; that they were all about their Fire, eating the Flesh of one of their Prisoners; and that another lay bound upon the Sand, a little from them, which he said they would kill next, and which fir'd all the very Soul within me; he told me it was not one of their Nation; but one of the bearded Men, who he had told me of, that came to their Country in the Boat: I was fill'd with Horror at the very naming the white-bearded Man, and going to the Tree, I saw plainly by my Glass, a white Man who lay upon the Beach of the Sea, with his Hands and his Feet ty'd, with Flags, or Things like Rushes; and that he was an European, and had Cloaths on.

There was another Tree, and a little Thicket beyond it, about fifty Yards nearer to them than the Place where I was, which by going a little way about, I saw I might come at undiscover'd, and that then I should be within half Shot of them; so I with-held my Passion, though I was indeed enrag'd to the highest Degree, and going back about twenty Paces, I got behind some Bushes, which held all the way, till I came to the other Tree; and then I came to a little rising Ground, which gave me a full View of them, at the Distance of about eighty Yards.

I had now not a Moment to loose; for nineteen of the dreadful Wretches sat upon the Ground, all close huddled together, and had just sent the other two to butcher the poor Christian, and bring him perhaps Limb by Limb to their Fire, and they

去那儿看看他们究竟在做什么,看明白之后就来告诉我;他去了一会儿就回来告诉我说,在那里可以看得很清楚,见到那伙人正围在火边,吃着一个俘虏的肉,而在离他们不远的沙滩上,还躺着一个被捆着的俘虏,他说接下来就轮到杀那个人了;听到这里,我已怒火中烧,而他还告诉我说,那人不是他们部落的,是一个大胡子,也就是他以前说到过的那种乘救生艇到他们那儿的人。他一提到留大胡子的白种人,我觉得毛骨悚然,连忙去树边用望远镜观察,很清楚,是有个白人躺在海滩上,手脚都被菖蒲之类的东西捆着;而且他是个欧洲人,身上穿着衣服。

再往前去还有一棵大树和一小片灌木丛,比我此刻所在的地方离他们要近五十码左右。我觉得,如果再朝前走一点,也不至于被他们发现,到那时,我离他们的距离就不到一半射程了。尽管我此时怒不可遏,但还是压住了火气,朝后走了二十来步,迂回走进了那片灌木丛,又在灌木丛的掩护下,一直潜到最前面的那棵大树的后面。然后,我又来到一片隆起的高地,这里离他们大约八十码,我可以把他们的行动尽收眼底。

这时,我看到十九个野人仍然像刚才那样围挤着坐在地上,却派出另外两个野人去宰杀那个可怜的基督徒。他们很快就要把他大卸八块,一

were stoop'd down to untie the Bands, at his Feet; I turn'd to Friday, now Friday, said I, do as I bid thee; Friday said he would; then Friday, says I, do exactly as you see me do, 'fail in nothing; so I set down one of the Muskets, and the Fowling-Piece, upon the Ground, and·Friday did the like by his; and with the other Musket, I took my aim at the Savages, bidding him do the like; then asking him, If he was ready? He said, yes, then fire at them, said I; and the same Moment I fir'd also.

Friday took his Aim so much better than I, that on the Side that he shot, he kill'd two of them, and wounded three more; and on my Side, I kill'd one, and wounded two: They were, you may be sure, in a dreadful Consternation; and all of them, who were not hurt, jump'd up upon their Feet, but did not immediately know which way to run, or which way to look; for they knew not from whence their Destruction came: Friday kept his Eyes close upon me, that as I had bid him, he might observe what I did; so as soon as the first Shot was made, I threw down the Piece, and took up the Fowling-Piece, and Friday did the like; he see me cock, and present, he did the same again; Are you ready, Friday? said I; yes, says he; let fly then, says I, in the Name of God, and with that I fir'd again among the amaz'd Wretches, and so did Friday; and as our Pieces were now loaden with what I call'd Swan-Shot, or small Pistol Bul-

只胳膊一条腿地拿到火上烤着吃了。情况已到了刻不容缓的危急关头。我看到那两个野人已弯下腰，动手去解绑着白人脚上的菖蒲了。这时我转过头对星期五说："听着，星期五，按我的吩咐行动。"星期五回答说他一定遵命。"这样，星期五，"我快速地对他说，"你看好我的动作，我怎么办，你就怎么办，千万不要误事。"于是，我把一步短枪和一支鸟枪从肩膀上拿下来，放在地上，星期五也照我的样子把他的枪放在地上。我用剩下的那支短枪瞄准野人，并吩咐星期五也一样照办。然后我问星期五是否准备好了，一听他说"好了"，我立刻发出命令："开火!"说时迟，那时快，话音刚落，我们都开了枪。

星期五的枪法比我强的多，他那边的射击结果，打死了两个，又伤了三个。而我这边，只打死了一个，伤了两个。不消说，那群野人顿时吓得魂飞天外，所有没有打死打伤的，都一齐跳了起来。既不知道往哪儿跑好，也不知道往哪儿瞧好，因为他们根本不知道这场灾祸是从哪儿来的。星期五一双眼睛紧紧盯着我，依照我吩咐他的，注意着我的动作。我放完了第一枪，马上把手里的短枪丢在地上，拿起那支鸟枪，星期五也这样作了。他看见我闭着一只眼瞄准，他也照样瞄准。我说："星期五，你预备好了吗?"他说："好了。"我说："凭上帝的名义，开枪!"

lets, we found only two drop; but so many were wounded, that they run about yelling, and skreaming, like mad Creatures, all bloody, and miserably wounded, most of them; whereof three more fell quickly after, though not quite dead.

Now Friday, says I, laying down the discharg'd Pieces, and taking up the Musket, which was yet loaden; follow me, says I, which he did, with a great deal of Courage; upon which I rush'd out of the Wood, and shew'd my self, and Friday close at my Foot; as soon as I perceiv'd they saw me, I shouted as loud as I could, and bad Friday do so too; and running as fast as I could, which by the way, was not very fast, being loaden with Arms as I was, I made directly towards the poor Victim, who was, as I said, lying upon the Beach, or Shore, between the Place where they sat, and the Sea; the two Butchers who were just going to work with him, had left him, at the Suprize of our first Fire, and fled in a terrible Fright, to the Sea Side, and had jump'd into a Canoe, and three more of the rest made the same way; I turn'd to Friday, and bid him step forwards, and fire at them; he understood me immediately, and running about forty Yards, to be near them, he shot at them, and I thought he had kill'd them all; for I see them all fall of a Heap into the Boat; though I saw two of them up again quickly: However, he kill'd two of them, and wounded the third; so that he lay down in the Bottom of the Boat, as if he had been dead.

说着，我就向那群惊惶失措的畜生又开了一枪，星期五也开了枪。这次我们枪里装的都是小铁沙或手枪子弹，所以只有两个倒了下来，但受伤的却很多，只见他们像疯子似地乱跑乱叫，全身是血，多数都受了很重的伤；其中有三个紧跟着又倒了下来，虽然还不曾完全死去。

我把放过了的鸟枪放下来，把那支装好弹药的短枪拿在手里，对星期五说："现在，星期五，你跟我来！"他果然勇敢地跟着我。于是我冲出树林，出现在那些野人面前。星期五紧跟在我后面，寸步不离。当我看到他们已经看得见我们时，我就拼命大声呐喊，同时叫星期五也跟着我大声呐喊。我一面呐喊，一面向前飞跑。其实我根本跑不快，因为身上的枪械实在太重了。我一路向那可怜的俘虏跑去。前面已经说过，那可怜的大胡子这时正躺在野人们所坐的地方和大海之间的沙滩上。那两个正要动手杀他的屠夫，在我们放头一枪时，早已吓得魂不附体。他们丢开了俘虏，拼命向海边跑去，跳上了一只独木船。这时，那群野人中也有三个向同一方面逃跑。我回头吩咐星期五，要他追上去并朝他们开枪；他立即领会了我的意思，朝前跑了四十来码，在离他们较近的地方开了枪；我以为他把五个人都打死了，因为我看到他们都倒在船里了，但很快我就看见其中的

While my Man Friday fir'd at them, I pull'd out my Knife, and cut the Flags that bound the poor Victim, and loosing his Hands, and Feet, I lifted him up, and ask'd him in the Portuguese Tongue, What he was? He answer'd in Latin, Christianus; but was so weak, and faint, that he could scarce stand, or speak; I took my Bottle out of my Pocket, and gave it him, making Signs that he should drink, which he did; and I gave him a Piece of Bread, which he eat; then I ask'd him, What Countryman he was? And he said, Espagniole; and being a little recover'd, let me know by all the Signs he could possibly make, how much he was in my Debt for his Deliverance; Seignior, said I, with as much Spanish as I could make up, we will talk afterwards; but we must fight now; if you have any Strength left, take this Pistol, and Sword, and lay about you; he took them very thankfully, and no sooner had he the Arms in his Hands, but as if they had put new Vigour into him, he flew upon his Murtherers, like a Fury, and had cut two of them in Pieces, in an instant; for the Truth is, as the whole was a Surprize to them; so the poor Creatures were so much frighted with the Noise of our Pieces, that they fell down for meer Amazement, and Fear; and had no more Power to attempt their own Escape, than their Flesh had to resist our Shot; and that was the Case of those Five that Friday shot at in the Boat; for as three of them fell with the Hurt they receiv'd, so the other two fell with the Fright.

两人已坐了起来。不过他毕竟打死了另外的两人,打伤了一人,而那个受伤的也躺在船底,仿佛死了一般。

当我的仆人星期五朝他们开枪的时候,我抽刀把捆着那受害者的菖蒲都割断了;现在这可怜的人手脚都能活动了,我便把他扶了起来,用葡萄牙语问他是什么人。他用拉丁语回答了一声:"基督徒。"看他那样子,既软弱无力,又晕晕糊糊,站都站不住,话也讲不出;我从衣袋里掏出那瓶酒,递给了他,一边给他打手势,要他喝几口;他喝了以后,我又给了他一块面包;待他吃好后,我问他是哪国人。他回答说:"西班牙人。"这时他已有了点精神,便尽量打着手势,让我知道他对我的救命之恩满怀感激之情。我也尽量用西班牙语对他说:"先生,我们以后再谈吧,但现在我们必须战斗。如果你还有力气,就拿着这把手枪和这把刀跟他们干吧。"他非常感激地接了过去。他刚一拿到武器,体内就像注入了新的活力,以不可遏制的狂怒,向他的死敌飞扑过去,顿时把两个家伙剁碎了。说实话,我们袭击实在出乎他们的意料,这些可怜的家伙都给我们的枪声吓慒了,一个个都瘫倒在地无力逃命,只好用皮肉来抵挡我们的枪弹。那五个在船上被星期五射中的家伙也是一样。当然,其中三个是被打后倒下来的,但另外两个却是给吓倒的。

I kept my Piece in my Hand still, without firing, being willing to keep my Charge ready; because I had given the Spaniard my Pistol, and Sword; so I call'd to Friday, and bad him run up to the Tree, from whence we first fir'd, and fetch the Arms which lay there, that had been discharg'd, which he did with great Swiftness; and then giving him my Musket, I sat down my self to load all the rest again, and bad them come to me when they wanted; While I was loading these Pieces, there happen'd a fierce Engagement between the Spaniard, and one of the Savages, who made at him with one of their great wooden Swords, the same Weapon that was to have kill'd him before, if I had not prevented it: The Spaniard, who was as bold, and as brave as could be imagin'd, though weak, had fought this Indian a good while, and had cut him two great Wounds on his Head; but the Savage being a stout lusty Fellow, closing in with him, had thrown him down (being faint) and was wringing my Sword out of his Hand, when the Spaniard, tho' undermost wisely quitting the Sword, drew the Pistol from his Girdle, shot the Savage through the Body, and kill'd him upon the Spot; before I, who was running to help him, could come near him.

Friday being now left to his Liberty, pursu'd the flying Wretches with no Weapon in his Hand, but his Hatchet; and with that he dispatch'd those three, who, as I said before, were wounded at first and fallen, and all the rest he could come up

我把自己的手枪和腰刀给了西班牙人以后,我身边就只有一样武器了。为了留一支装有弹药的枪以防意外,我一直没开枪,只是把枪端在手中。这时,我招呼星期五过去,吩咐他尽快跑到我们刚才放枪的树林里,把那几支用过的枪给拿过来。他很快扛着枪返回我的身边。我把自己的步枪交给他,然后,就坐下来给枪支装弹药,并告诉他需要用枪随时可以来取。就在我给枪支装弹药的时候,忽然发现那个西班牙人和一个野人互相厮打起来,打得难舍难分。那个野人手里挥舞着一把木制大刀攻击西班牙人。这种木头刀,正是他们刚才准备宰杀西班牙人的那种武器,要不是我采用武力袭击野人的话,他早已魂归刀下了。那西班牙人尽管身体虚弱,却表现得勇猛顽强。他已和野人搏杀了好一会儿了,并且把野人的头部砍伤了两处。可那野人也是个极为肥胖异常凶猛强壮的人,他勇敢地往前一扑,把西班牙人放倒在地上,伸过手去夺他手中的刀。西班牙人被他压在底下,赶紧放弃手中的刀,迅速抽出腰中的手枪,对准野人就打了一枪,我还没来得及帮助他,他已把那野人打死了。

这时已无人管星期五,他赶紧放下别的武器,手中握一把斧头,就向那帮逃跑的野人追去。他用斧头砍死了刚才受伤的三个人,又去追杀别的

with, and the Spaniard coming to me for a Gun, I gave him one of the Fowling-Pieces, with which he pursu'd two of the Savages, and wounded them both; but as he was not able to run, they both got from him into the Wood, where Friday pursu'd them, and kill'd one of them; but the other was too nimble for him, and though he was wounded, yet had plunged himself into the Sea, and swam with all his might off to those two who were left in the Canoe, which three in the Canoe, with one wounded, who we know not whether he dy'd or no, were all that escap'd our Hands of one and twenty: The Account of the Rest is as follows;

3 Kill'd at our first Shot from the Tree.

2 Kill'd at the next Shot.

2 Kill'd by Friday in the Boat.

2 Kill'd by Ditto, of those at first wounded.

1 Kill'd by Ditto, in the Wood.

3 Kill'd by the Spaniard.

4 Kill'd, being found dropp'd here and there of their Wounds, or kill'd by Friday in his Chase of them.

4 Escap'd in the Boat, whereof one wounded if not dead.

21 In all.

Those that were in the Canoe, work'd hard to get out of Gun-Shot; and though Friday made two or three Shot at them, I did not find that he hit any of them: Friday would fain have had me took one of their Canoes, and pursu'd them; and indeed I was very anxious about their Escape, least carrying the News home to their People, they should come back perhaps with two or three hundred of their Canoes, and devour us by meer Multitude;

野人,想把他们全部杀光。这时候,那西班牙人也跑过来向我要枪,我就给了他一支鸟枪;他拿着鸟枪追上了两个野人,把他们都打伤了;但因为他跑不动,他们就逃到树林里去了,星期五又追到树林里,把他们砍死了一个;但另外一个却异常敏捷,虽然受了伤,仍旧跳入海内,使出平生之力,向那两个留在独木舟上的野人泅去。这三个人,连同一个受了伤而生死不明的,就是二十一个野人之中从我们手中逃掉的全部的人。全部战果总计如下:

被我们从树后第一枪打死有三人。

第二枪打死的有二人。

被星期五在船上打死的有二人。

因受伤被星期五砍死的有二人。

星期五在林中砍死一人。

西班牙人杀死三人。

星期五追杀或因伤毙命的有四人。

乘独木舟逃走四人,其中一人负伤,生死不明。

总计二十一人。

独木舟里的人拼命划着逃离射程,星期五朝他们开了两三枪,我没发现有人被击中。星期五想乘其中一个独木舟去追他们,我也的确担心他们逃走,万一他们把消息带回家,也许就有两三百个独木舟卷土重来,仅靠着人多势众,就能把我们生吞活剥了。

so I consented to pursue them by Sea, and running to one of their Canoes, I jump'd in, and bad Friday follow me; but when 1 was in the Canoe, I was surpriz'd to find another poor Creature lye there alive, bound Hand and Foot, as the Spaniard was, for the Slaughter, and almost dead with Fear, not knowing what the Matter was; for he had not been able to look up over the Side of the Boat, he was ty'd so hard, Neck and Heels, and had been ty'd so long, that he had really but little Life in him.

I immediately cut the twisted Flags, or Rushes, which they had bound him with, and would have helped him up; but he could not stand, or speak, but groan'd most piteously, believing it seems still that he was only unbound in order to be kill'd.

When Friday came to him, I bad him speak to him, and tell him of his Deliverance, and pulling out my Bottle, made him give the poor Wretch a Dram, which, with the News of his being deliver'd, reviv'd him, and he sat up in the Boat; but when Friday came to hear him speak, and look in his Face, it would have mov'd any one to Tears, to have seen how Friday kiss'd him, embrac'd him, hugg'd him, cry'd, laugh'd, hollow'd, jump'd about, danc'd, sung, then cry'd again, wrung his Hands, beat his own Face, and Head, and then sung, and jump'd about again, like a distracted Creature: It was a good while before I could make him speak to me, or tell me what was the Matter; but when he came a little to himself, he told me, that it was his Father.

所以我也同意星期五到海上去追他们。我立刻跑向一只独木舟跳了上去,并叫星期五也一起上来。可是,我一跳上独木舟,就发现船上还躺着一个俘虏,真是大大出乎我的意外,那俘虏也像那西班牙人一样,手脚都被捆绑着,等着被杀了吃掉。因为他无法抬头看看船外边的情况,所以不知道究竟发生了什么事,人已吓得半死;再加上脖子和脚给绑得太紧,而且也绑得太久,所以只剩一口气了。

我立刻把捆在他身上的菖蒲之类的东西割断,想把他扶起来,但是他连说话的力气都没有了,更不要说站起来了。他只是一个劲儿地哼哼着,样子可怜极了,因为他还以为给他松绑是准备拿他开刀呢。

星期五跑近后,我就叫他来同这人说话,告诉他他已经得救了;同时我掏出酒瓶,叫星期五给这可怜的受难者喝一点。这人一听自己已经获救,又加上喝了酒,就有了精神,在船里坐了起来;星期五一听他开口说话,一看他的脸,顿时就抱住了他,搂得紧紧的,一边吻着他,一边又是哭又是笑又是叫,又是手舞足蹈地高唱,接着又是大哭,扭绞自己的双手,打自己的脸和头,随后又一边唱一边乱跳起来,简直像疯了一般,无论谁看了此情此景,都会感动得流泪。过了好长时间,我也没法让他对我的话作出回答,没法

It is not easy for me to express how it mov'd me to see what Extasy and filial Affection had work'd in this poor Savage, at the Sight of his Father, and of his being deliver'd from Death; nor indeed can I describe half the Extravagancies of his Affection after this; for he went into the Boat and out of the Boat a great many times: When he went in to him, he would sit down by him, open his Breast, and hold his Father's Head close to his Bosom, half an Hour together, to nourish it; then he took his Arms and Ankles, which were numb'd and stiff with the Binding, and chaffed and rubbed them with his Hands; and I perceiving what the Case was, gave him some Rum out of my Bottle, to rub them with, which did them a great deal of Good.

This Action put an End to our Pursuit of the Canoe, with the other Savages, who were now gotten almost out of Sight; and it was happy for us that we did not; for it blew so hard within two Hours after, and before they could be gotten a Quarter of their Way, and continued blowing so hard all Night, and that from the North-west, which was against them, that I could not suppose their Boat could live, or that they ever reach'd to their own Coast.

But to return to Friday, he was so busy about his Father, that I could not find in my Heart to take him off for some time: But after I thought he

叫他告诉我这是怎么回事;后来他略略安静了一些,这才告诉我说:那人是他的父亲。

这个可怜的野人见自己的父亲被从死路上救了下来,真是欣喜若狂,用各种方式表达他对父亲的爱心。这一情景也使我感动得说不出话来。老实说,我怎么夸张也不能把他的这份爱心的一半描述出来;只见他一会儿跑到船上,一会儿跳到岸上,来来回回不知跑了多少趟。当他走到父亲跟前时,便在旁边坐下,解开自己的衣襟,把父亲的头贴在他的胸脯上,一连半个钟头,以便让他恢复知觉。然后,他又握住他父亲那给捆得麻木僵硬的胳膊和双脚,用手揉搓按摩。我见老人的四肢已经麻木,便从瓶子里倒了点甘蔗酒给星期五,叫他用酒来摩擦他父亲的四肢,其效果非常明显。

这件事情的发生,使我们没有能够去追捕乘独木舟逃跑的那几个野人,他们这时已逃得看不见踪影了。不过,我们倒是幸亏没有去追赶他们,因为不到两个小时后,海面上就刮起了狂风,这时,那些野人可能连四分之一的路程都没走到呢。这股与他们航向相逆的西北狂风整整刮了一夜,所以我估计他们要么很难逃出性命,要么很难划回自己的海岸。

再看星期五,这时正手脚不闲地围着他父亲忙个不停,弄得我实在不忍心再派他去

could leave him a little, I call'd him to me, and he came jumping and laughing, and pleas'd to the highest Extream; then I ask'd him, If he had given his Father any Bread? He shook his Head, and said, None: Ugly Dog eat all up self; so I gave him a Cake of Bread out of a little Pouch I carry'd on Purpose; I also gave him a Dram for himself, but he would not taste it, but carry'd it to his Father: I had in my Pocket also two or three Bunches of my Raisins, so I gave him a Handful of them for his Father. He had no sooner given his Father these Raisins, but I saw him come out of the Boat, and run away, as if he had been bewitch'd, he run at such a Rate; for he was the swiftest Fellow of his Foot that ever I saw; I say, he run at such a Rate, that he was out of Sight, as it were, in an instant; and though I call'd, and hollow'd too, after him, it was all one, away he went, and in a Quarter of an Hour, I saw him come back again, though not so fast as he went; and as he came nearer, I found his Pace was slacker, because he had some thing in his Hand.

When he came up to me, I found he had been quite Home for an Earthen Jugg or Pot to bring his Father some fresh Water, and that he had got two more Cakes, or Loaves of Bread: The Bread he gave me, but the Water he carry'd to his Father: However, as I was very thirsty too, I took a little Sup of it. This Water reviv'd his Father more than all the Rum or Spirits I had given him; for he was just fainting with Thirst.

When his Father had drank, I call'd to him to know if there was any Water left; he said, yes; and I bad him give it to the poor Spaniard, who was in as much Want of it as his Father; and I sent one of the Cakes, that Friday brought, to the Spaniard too, who was indeed very weak, and was reposing himself upon a green Place under the Shade of a free; and whose Limbs were also very

干点什么。等我觉得他离开他父亲一会儿不成问题时才把他唤到跟前。他又跳又笑,欣喜若狂地跑来了,我问他是否给他父亲吃了面包,他摇摇头说:"没有。我这头蠢猪把面包吃光了。"我特意带了一只口袋,我从袋里掏出一块面包,还准备给他本人喝一点酒,他尝也不尝,全带去给了父亲。我兜里还有两三串葡萄干,我让他拿一串去给他父亲,他把葡萄干递给父亲,像着了魔似地一溜烟跑了,他是我见过的跑得最快的人,不一会儿就失去踪影,叫都叫不住。不到一刻钟的工夫,他又回来了,不过速度已经没有那样快了。当他走近了,我才发现,他之所以走慢了,是因为他手里正拿着东西呢。

他走到我面前的时候,我才知道,他原来是跑回家去取一只泥罐子,替他父亲弄了一些清水来,并且又带来了两块面包。他把面包交给我,把水送给他父亲。我这时也很口渴,也顺便喝了一口。这点水大大地恢复了他父亲的精神,比我给他的酒还有效,因为他已经渴得要晕过去了。

等他父亲喝过水之后,我把星期五叫过来,问他罐子里还有没有水。他说道:"有。"我命他把水送给西班牙人喝,他同样需要水,我又让他分给西班牙人一块他刚才带来的面包。这时候,西班牙人已经精疲力竭,正在一棵树下的草地

stiff, and very much swell'd with the rude Bandage he had been ty'd with. When I saw that upon Friday's coming to him with the Water, he sat up and drank, and took the Bread, and began to eat, I went to him, and gave him a Handful of Raisins; he look'd up in my Face with all the Tokens of Gratitude and Thankfulness, that could appear in any Countenance; but was so weak, notwithstanding he had so exerted himself in the Fight, that he could not stand up upon his Feet; he try'd to do it two or three times, but was really not able, his Ankles were so swell'd and so painful to him; so I bad him sit still, and caused Friday to rub his Ankles, and bathe them with Rum, as he had done his Father's.

I observ'd the poor affectionate Creature every two Minutes, or perhaps less, all the while he was here, turn'd his Head about, to see if his Father was in the same Place, and Posture, as he left him sitting; and at last he found he was not to be seen; at which he started up, and without speaking a Word, flew with that Swiftness to him, that one could scarce perceive his Feet to touch the Ground, as he went: But when he came, he only found he had laid himself down to ease his Limbs; so Friday came back to me presently, and I then spoke to the Spaniard to let Friday help him up if he could, and lead him to the Boat, and then he should carry him to our Dwelling, where I would take Care of him: But Friday, a lusty strong Fellow, took the Spaniard quite up upon his Back, and carry'd him away to the Boat, and set him down softly upon the Side or Gunnel of the Canoe, with his Feet in the inside of it, and then lifted him quite in, and set him close to his Father, and presently stepping out again, launched the Boat off, and paddled it along the Shore faster than I could walk, tho' the Wind blew pretty hard too; so he brought them both safe into our Creek; and leaving them in the Boat, runs away to fetch the

上躺着休息,他的手脚又肿又僵,显然是被捆绑的缘故。星期五把水送给他,他坐起来,喝着水,又接过面包吃起来,我来到他跟前,抓一把葡萄干给他。他抬头望着我,目光里显出万分感激的样子。但是由于十分虚弱,虽然他在厮杀时勇敢拼命,现在却怎么也站不起来了。他试了几次,但由于脚部痛疼,只好作罢。我让他坐着别动,命星期五替他按摩脚,并同他父亲一样,再用甘蔗酒擦洗。

我发现,星期五真是个心地诚挚的孝子。他一边为西班牙人搓擦,一边频频回头看他的父亲是否还坐在原来的地方。有一次,他忽然发觉他父亲不见了,就立刻跳起来,一句话也不说,飞跑到他父亲那边,他跑得飞快,简直脚不点地。他过去一看,原来他父亲为了舒舒手脚的筋骨,躺了下去。他这才放心,又赶紧跑回来。这时我对西班牙人说,让星期五扶他走到舢板上去,然后坐船到我们的住所,这样我可以照顾他。不料星期五力大无比,一下子把那西班牙人背在身上,向舢板那边走去。到了船边,星期五把西班牙人朝里轻轻放到船沿上,又把他拖起来往里一挪,安置在他父亲身旁。然后,星期五立即跳出舢板,把船推到水里,划着它沿岸驶去。尽管这时风已刮得很大了,可他划得比我走还快。他把船安安稳稳

other Canoe. As he pass'd me, I spoke to him, and ask'd him, whither he went, he told me, Go fetch more Boat; so away he went like the Wind; for sure never Man or Horse run like him, and he had the other Canoe in the Creek, almost as soon as I got to it by Land; so he wafted me over, and then went to help our new Guests out of the Boat, which he did; but they were neither of them able to walk; so that poor Friday knew not what to do.

划到了我们那小河后，便让那两人留在船里，自己奔去找另一条独木舟。他经过我旁边时，我问他上哪儿去；他说了声"去再拿船"，便一阵风似地跑了过去；他那种速度，无论是人还是马，都是比不上的；不一会儿，他已把另一只独木舟驾到这小河里，而我这时也只不过刚在岸上走到这处河边；他把我划到对岸后，就去帮助两位新来的客人，把他们背出了船；但他们两人都已走不动路了，弄得可怜的星期五不知道该怎么办才好。

Part 7

To remedy this, I went to Work in my Thought, and calling to Friday to bid them sit down on the Bank while he came to me, I soon made a Kind of Hand-Barrow to lay them on, and Friday and I carry'd them up both together upon it between us: But when we got them to the outside of our Wall or Fortification, we were at a worse Loss than before; for it was impossible to get them over; and I was resolv'd not to break it down: So I set to Work again; and Friday and I, in about 2 Hours time, made a very handsom Tent, cover'd with old Sails, and above that with Boughs of Trees, being in the Space without our outward Fence, and between that and the Grove of young Wood which I had planted: And here we made them two Beds of such things as I had (viz.) of good Rice-Straw, with Blankets laid upon it to lye on, and another to cover them on each Bed. My Island was now peopled, and I thought my self very rich in Subjects; and it was a merry Reflection which I frequently made, How like a King I look'd. First of all, the whole Country was my own meer Property; so that I had an undoubted Right of Dominion. 2dly, My People were perfectly subjected: I was absolute Lord and Law-giver; they all owed their Lives to me, and were ready to lay down their Lives, if there had been Occasion of it, for me. It was remarkable too, we had but three Subjects, and they were of three different Religions. My Man Friday was a Protestant, his Father was a Pagan and a Cannibal, and the Spaniard was a Papist: However, I allow'd Liberty of Conscience throughout my Dominions: But this is by the Way.

第七部

为了解决这个问题,我沉思良久,吩咐星期五叫他们在岸上坐下,一个人过来。我做了一个担架模样的东西,让他们坐在上面,我和星期五一边一个抬着他们走。我们来到围墙角下后,更加不知所措,因为我们没法把他们抬过围墙,我又不愿意把这道墙毁掉。为此,我又忙开了,星期五和我用两个小时的时间搭成一个非常漂亮的帐篷,帐篷用旧帆布做成,顶上铺满树枝,就搭在我们外墙的外面空地上,也就是我们外墙与我种的小树林之间的那块地上。然后,我们用手头能找到的东西给他们铺了两张床,就是说,床是用干净的稻草铺的,每张床上各放两条毯子,一条作垫的,一条作盖的。现在,我的小岛终于人丁兴旺起来,我觉得自己俨然是个君主,并拥有不少属于自己的国民。每当想起这些,我便感到十分开心。首先,整个这片土地都是我个人的财产,我对它有无可争议的统治权。其次,我的国民都对我服服帖帖。我是绝对的君主和立法者。他们能活下来,多亏了我的搭救,所以,在关键时刻,他们都乐于为我献出他们的生命。非常有趣的是,我虽然只有三个国民,但他们都信仰不同的宗教。我的仆人星期五是个新教徒,他的父亲是异教徒,来

As soon as I had secur'd my two weak rescued Prisoners, and given them Shelter, and a Place to rest them upon, I began to think of making some Provision for them: And the first thing I did, I order'd Friday to take a yearling Goat, betwixt a Kid and a Goat, out of my particular Flock, to be kill'd, when I cut off the hinder Quarter, and chopping it into small Pieces, I set Friday to Work to boiling and stewing, and made them a very good Dish, I assure you, of Flesh and Broth, having put some Barley and Rice also into the Broth; and as I cook'd it without Doors, for I made no Fire within my inner Wall, so I carry'd it all into the new Tent; and having set a Table there for them, I sat down and eat my own Dinner also with them, and, as well as I could, chear'd them and encourag'd them; Friday being my Interpreter, especially to his Father, and indeed to the Spaniard too; for the Spaniard spoke the Language of the Savages pretty well.

After we had dined, or rather supped, I order'd Friday to take one of the Canoes, and go and fetch our Muskets and other Fire-Arms, which for Want of time we had left upon the Place of Battle, and the next Day I order'd him to go and bury the dead Bodies of the Savages, which lay open to the Sun, and would presently be offensive; and I also order'd him to bury the horrid Remains of their barbarous Feast, which I knew were pretty much, and which I could not think of doing my self; nay, I could not bear to see them, if I went that Way: All which he punctually performed, and defaced

自吃人的部落,而那个西班牙人则是个天主教徒。尽管如此,在我的领土上,我却让他们有自己的精神自由。当然,这只是顺便提一提。

我从野人手里救下性命的两个人都已虚弱不堪,所以等我给他们安顿好遮风挡雨的栖身之所后,我就想着该给他们弄点吃的东西了。星期五从羊圈里挑出一只刚够一年的山羊宰杀洗净,我剁下山羊的后半部,切成小块,让星期五加水熬煮,再往这羊肉汤里加点大麦和大米,熬制成味道鲜美的羊肉粥。由于没在内墙里生火,因此我们这顿饭是在外墙外的空地上做的。我把烧好的羊肉粥端进新帐篷,坐在已摆放于帐篷内的桌子边,和他们一块进餐。同时,我尽我所能安抚他们,给他们打气壮胆,好让他们尽快高兴起来。谈话时,星期五就作我的翻译,不仅把我的话翻译给他父亲听,还翻译给那西班牙人听,那西班牙人已经很会说野人部落的话了。

吃完了中饭,或者不如说吃完了晚饭,我就命令星期五驾一只独木舟,把我们的短枪和其他枪枝搬回来,因为当时时间仓促,这些武器仍留在战场上。第二天,我又命令他把那几个野人的尸体埋掉,因为尸体在太阳下暴晒,不久就会发臭。我也叫他把他们那场野蛮的人肉宴所剩下的残骨剩肉也一齐顺便埋掉。我知道那些残骸还剩有不少,可

the very Appearance of the Savages being there; so that when I went again, I could scarce know where it was, otherwise than by the Corner of the Wood pointing to the Place.

I then began to enter into a little Conversation with my two new Subjects; and first I set Friday to enquire of his Father, what he thought of the Escape of the Savages in that Canoe, and whether we might expect a Return of them with a Power too great for us to resist: His first Opinion was, that the Savages in the Boat never could live out the Storm which blew that Night they went off, but must of Necessity be drowned or driven South to those other Shores where they were as sure to be devoured as they were to be drowned if they were cast away; but as to what they would do if they came safe on Shore, he said he knew not; but it was his Opinion that they were so dreadfully frighted with the Manner of their being attack'd, the Noise and the Fire, that he believed they would tell their People, they were all kill'd by Thunder and Lightning, not by the Hand of Man, and that the two which appear'd, (viz.) Friday and me, were two Heavenly Spirits or Furies, come down to destroy them, and not Men with Weapons: This he said he knew, because he heard them all cry out so in their Language to one another, for it was impossible to them to conceive that a Man could dart Fire, and speak Thunder, and kill at a Distance without lifting up the Hand, as was done now: And this old Savage was in the right; for, as I understood since by other Hands, the Savages never attempted to go over to the Island afterwards; they were so terrified with the Accounts given by those four Men, (for it seems they

我实在不想自己亲自动手去埋掉,不要说埋,就是路过都不忍看一眼。所有这些工作,星期五都很快就完成了,而且,他把那群野人留在那一带的痕迹都消灭得干干净净。后来我再到那边去时,要不是靠了那片树林的一角辨别方向,简直认不出那个地方了。

我和我的两个新国民进行了一次简短的谈话。首先,我叫星期五问他父亲对于那几个坐独木舟跑掉的野人有什么感想,并且问他,照他看来,他们会不会带着我们所不能抵抗的兵力卷土重来。他的初步意见是,那条舢板上的野人必然逃不过那天晚上的大风,不是淹死在海里,就是给大风刮到南方其他海岸上去;假如被刮到那边去,他们必然会给当地的野人吃掉,正如万一他们的舢板出了事,他们必然会给淹死一样。至于说,万一他们平平安安回到自己的海岸,他们可能采取什么行动,那就难说了。不过,依他看来,他们已经被我们突如其来的进攻方式、被我们的枪声和火光吓得半死,他相信他们回去以后,一定会告诉他们的人说,其余的人不是给人打死的,是给霹雳和闪电殛死的;而且尽管他们明明看到了两个人,就是星期五和我,也当我们是从天而降的复仇之神,专门来消灭他们的,决不会知道我们只是使用武器的人。他说他是清楚地知道这一点的,因为他听见他们彼此

did escape the Sea) that they believ'd whoever went to that enchanted Island would be destroy'd with Fire from the Gods.

This however I knew not, and therefore was under continual Apprehensions for a good while, and kept always upon my Guard, me and all my Army; for as we were now four of us, I would have ventur'd upon a hundred of them fairly in the open Field at any Time.

In a little Time, however, no more Canoes appearing, the Fear of their Coming wore off, and I began to take my former Thoughts of a Voyage to the Main into Consideration, being likewise assur'd by Friday's Father, that I might depend upon good Usage from their Nation on his Account, if I would go.

But my Thoughts were a little suspended, when I had a serious Discourse with the Spaniard, and when I understood that there were sixteen more of his Countrymen and Portuguese, who having been cast away, and made their Escape to that Side, liv'd there at Peace indeed with the Savages, but were very sore put to it for Necessaries, and indeed for Life: I ask'd him all the Particulars of their Voyage, and found they were a Spanish Ship

间用土话这么乱嚷嚷的。在他们说来,实在也不可能想象有人能喷火,能发出雷电般的声响,能这样连手也不举一下就远远地置人于死地。这个老野人讲得对;因为后来我从别人那里听说,野人们从此就再也不敢渡海来这岛上了;看来那四个家伙居然没在海里淹死,回去后把经过情况一讲,那些野人大为恐慌,深信这个魔岛是来不得的,谁来谁就会被天神的火活烧死。

不过这些情况我开始并不知道,所以我又担忧了好长时间,并且一直带着我的全部军队严加警戒。但我同时又想,我们现在一共有四个人了,也用不着过于害怕他们。只要在平坦空旷的地方,他们就是来上一百个人,我也是敢跟他们较量一下的。

短期内再也不曾有独木舟出现,我担心他们会卷土重来的恐惧心理也渐渐消除了。我又考虑起前段时间航行到对面大陆去的计划。星期五的父亲向我保证,假如我愿意去他们部落,他们的人一定会看在他的份上,给我很好的照顾。

然而,跟那个西班牙人进行过一次深入的交谈后,我又暂时改变了想法。通过交谈我得知,那里还有他的十六个西班牙同胞和一些葡萄牙人,他们是失事后逃到那里去的;他们跟当地的野人的确相安无事,但生活用品奇缺,生计异常艰难。我详细询问了他

bound from the Rio de la Plata to the Havana, being directed to leave their Loading there, which was chiefly Hides and Silver, and to bring back what European Goods they could meet with there; that they had five Portuguese Seamen on Board, who they took out of another Wreck; that five of their own Men were drowned when the first Ship was lost, and that these escaped thro' infinite Dangers and Hazards, and arriv'd almost starv'd on the Cannibal Coast, where they expected to have been devour'd every Moment.

He told me, they had some Arms with them, but they were perfectly useless, for that they had neither Powder or Ball, the Washing of the Sea having spoil'd all their Powder but a little, which they used at their first Landing to provide themselves some Food.

I ask'd him what he thought would become of them there, and if they had form'd no Design of making any Escape? He said, They had many Consultations about it, but that having neither Vessel, or Tools to build one, or Provisions of any kind, their Councils always ended in Tears and Despair.

I ask'd him how he thought they would receive a Proposal from me, which might tend towards an Escape? And whether, if they were all here, it might not be done? I told him with Freedom, I fear'd mostly their Treachery and ill Usage of me, if I put my Life in their Hands; for that Gratitude was no inherent Virtue in the Nature of Man; nor

们贸易航行的情况，得知他们的船是一条西班牙船，从拉普拉塔河出发，前往哈瓦那。船上主要装载的是皮货和银子，准备在哈瓦那卸下这些货后，再看看那里有什么需要运往欧洲的货物，以便在返程时带回。他们船上那五个葡萄牙水手，是从另一条遇难船上救下来的，而他们自己的商船遇难时，也失去了五名西班牙船员。船只遇难后，他们这十七个人经历了重重危难才逃出性命，当他们在食人族的海岸登陆的时候，几乎都快饿死了；他们上岸后也是战战兢兢，时刻担心着会被野人吃掉。

他又告诉我，他们本来也随身带了一些枪械，但毫无用处，因为既没有火药，又没有子弹，海水把他们所有的火药都泡坏了，只剩下一点点，在他们初上岸的时候，打猎充饥用了。

我问他，据他看来，那些人结果会怎么样，有没有什么逃走的打算。他说，他们对这件事也曾商量过不少次，但既没有船只，又没有造船的工具，又没有什么粮食，所以他们的商讨往往是以眼泪和失望为收场的。

我问他，根据他的判断，要是我给他们一个逃跑建议，他们能接受吗？如果让他们全到这里来，是否可行？我坦率地告诉他，若是我把我的生命交给他们手中，我最担心的是他们的背叛和恩将仇报。

did Men always square their Dealings by the Obligations they had receiv'd, So much as they did by the Advantages they expected. I told him it would be very hard, that I should be the Instrument of their Deliverance, and that they should afterwards make me their Prisoner in New Spain, where an English Man was certain to be made a Sacrifice, what Necessity, or what Accident soever, brought him thither: And that I had rather be deliver'd up to the Savages, and be devour'd alive, than fall into the merciless Claws of the Priests, and be carry'd into the Inquisition. I added, That otherwise I was perswaded, if they were all here, we might, with so many Hands, build a Bark large enough to carry us all away, either to the Brasils South-ward, or to the Islands or Spanish Coast North-ward: But that if in Requital they should, when I had put Weapons into their Hands, catty me by Force among their own People, I might be ill used for my Kindness to them, and make my Case worse than it was before.

He answer'd with a great deal of Candor and Ingenuity, That their Condition was so miserable, and they were so sensible of it, that he believed they would abhor the Thought of using any Man unkindly that should contribute to their Deliverance; and that, if I pleased, he would go to them with the old Man, and discourse with them about it, and return again, and bring me their Answer: That he would make Conditions with them upon their solemn Oath, That they should be absolutely under my Leading, as their Commander and Captain; and that they should swear upon the Holy Sacraments and the Gospel, to be true to me, and to go to such Christian Country, as that I should agree to, and no other; and to be directed wholly

因为感恩在人的本性之中并不是可靠的美德。而且,人们并不总是根据他们所受的恩惠来制约自己的行动,相反,很多时候他们根据希望得到的利益来决定自己的行动。我告诉他,如果我使他们脱离险境,可随后他们却把我当作他们的囚犯送到西班牙,那可是太糟糕了。因为在那里,不管是迫于无奈的原因还是偶然,到那里的英国人,都定要受到宗教迫害。我情愿把自己交给那些野人,让他们吃掉,也不想落到那些西班牙僧侣手中而受到宗教审判。我又进一步说,除了这些情况,我敢相信,如果那些野人全部到这边来,我们集中人力,一定可以制造一艘足够大的船,我们可以乘着到南方的巴西,或北方的诸岛,或西班牙殖民地去。可如果交给他们武器,他们如果把我给劫走,我岂不是自己给自己惹麻烦吗?

听了我的话,他回答说,他们当前处境非常悲惨,而且吃足了苦头,所以,他深信,他们对任何能帮助他们脱险的人,绝不会有忘恩负义的念头。他说这些话时,态度极为诚恳坦率。同时,他又说,如果我愿意的话,他可以同那老野人一齐去见他们,同他们谈谈这件事,然后把他们的答复带回来告诉我。他说他一定会跟他们订好条件,叫他们郑重宣誓,绝对服从我的领导,把我看作他们的司令和船长;同时,还要让他们用《圣经》和《福

and absolutely by my Orders, 'till they were landed safely in such Country, as I intended; and that he would bring a Contract from them under their Hands for that Purpose.

Then he told me, he would first swear to me himself, That he would never stir from me as long as he liv'd, 'till I gave him Orders; and that he would take my Side to the last Drop of his Blood, if there should happen the least Breach of Faith among his Country-men.

He told me, they were all of them very civil honest Men, and they were under the greatest Distress imaginable, having neither Weapons or Cloaths, nor any Food, but at the Mercy and Discretion of the Savages; out of all Hopes of ever returning to their own Country; and that he was sure, if I would undertake their Relief, they would live and die by me.

Upon these Assurances, I resolv'd to venture to relieve them, if possible, and to send the old Savage and this Spaniard over to them to treat: But when we had gotten all things in a Readiness to go, the Spaniard himself started an Objection, which had so much Prudence in it on one hand, and so much Sincerity on the other hand, that I could not but be very well satisfy'd in it; and by his Advice, put off the Deliverance of his Comerades, for at least half a Year. The Case was thus:

He had been with us now about a Month; dur-

音书》宣誓对我效忠到底,不管我叫他们到哪一个基督教国家去,都要毫无异议地跟我去,并绝对服从我的命令,直到他们把我送到我所指定的地方平安登陆为止。最后,他又说,他一定要叫他们亲手签订盟约,并把签约带回来见我。

讲到这里,他对我说道,他本人愿意第一个向我起誓,保证一辈子不离开我,除非我要他走;并保证永远站在我这边,万一他那些同胞干出任何背信弃义的事,那么他宁可为我流尽最后一滴血。

他告诉我说,他们都是很文明的正派人,现在生活在难以想象的困苦之中,不仅没有武器,而且衣食不周,就连性命也全在那些野人手里,哪里还能指望回到本乡本土;所以他可以肯定,如果我肯帮他们脱离苦海,他们准会死活都跟着我。

他的一番保证,让我最终下了决心,决定冒险去拯救他们,先派他和那老野人渡海去和他们商谈此事,并随即着手他俩出行的准备工作。可就在我们把一切准备妥当,即将送他俩上路时,那西班牙人自己倒忽然提出了反对意见。不过,我认为他的意见提得不仅谨慎明智,而且非常真诚,所以我欣然接受。就这样,这个提议把搭救他同伴的计划推迟了至少一年半的时间。详细情况且听我慢慢道来。

这西班牙人已在这里和

ing which time, I had let him see in what Manner I had provided, with the Assistance of Providence, for my Support; and he saw evidently what Stock of Corn and Rice I had laid up; which as it was more than sufficient for my self, so it was not sufficient, at least without good Husbandry, for my Family; now it was encreas'd to Number four: But much less would it be sufficient, if his Country-men, who were, as he said, fourteen' still alive, should Come over. And least of all should it be sufficient to victual our Vessel, if we should build one, for a Voyage to any of the Christian Colonies of America. So he told me, he thought it would be more advisable, to let him and the two other, dig and.cultivate some more Land, as much as I could spare Seed to sow; and that we should wait another Harvest, that we might have a Supply of Corn for his Country-men when they should come; for Want might be a Temptation to them to disagree, or not to think themselves deliver'd, otherwise than out of one Difficulty into another. You know, says he, the Children of Israel, though they rejoyc'd at first for their being deliver'd out of Egypt, yet rebell'd even against God himself that deliver'd them, when they came to want Bread in the Wilderness.

His Caution was so seasonable, and his Advice so good, that I could not but be very well pleased with his Proposal, as well as I was satisfy'd with his Fidelity. So we fell to digging all four of us, as well as the Wooden Tools we were furnish'd with permitted; and in about a Month's time, by the

我们共同生活了近一个月了。在这段时间里,他亲眼看到了我是如何在上苍的帮助下,以自力更生的方式维持着自己的生计。我所储存囤集的大麦和稻子他也看得清清楚楚,这些粮食,让我一个人吃是绰绰有余的。可是,供我们现在这一家人吃(现在我们已经增长到了四口人),如果不精打细算就不够了。然而,如果他的那些同胞(据他说,还有十六人活着)都到这里来,那就更不够吃了。再说,如果我们造一条船,用它航行到美洲哪个信仰基督教的殖民地去,这点粮食怎么也不够这么多人在路上吃。因此,他对我说,他认为现在最可取的办法是,让他和另外那两个人再开垦一些耕地,并从我的储粮中尽可能多拿出一些来,做种子播下去。这样,到下一个收获季节,如果他的同胞到这里来,就有足够的粮食吃了。因为,如果缺少吃的,他们就会意见不和,认为自己并没有真的获救,而是从一个困境到了另一个困境。"你当然知道,"他说,"起初那些以色列人被救出埃及后,虽然一个个都欢欣鼓舞,可是,在荒野之中没有面包吃的时候,他们居然公开背叛拯救他们的上帝。"

他的顾虑实在合情合理,他的意见也实在很好,所以我对他的建议感到非常欣悦,对于他的忠诚感到非常满意。于是我们四个人便尽量发挥我们那些木头工具的效力,一

End of which it was Seed time, we had gotten as much Land cur'd and trim'd up, as we sowed 22 Bushels of Barley on, and 16 Jarrs of Rice, which was in short all the Seed we had to spare; nor indeed did we leave our selves Barley sufficient for our own Food, for the six Months that we had to expect our Crop, that is to say, reckoning from the time we set our Seed aside for sowing; for it is not to be supposed it is six Months in the Ground in the Country.

Having now Society enough, and our Number being sufficient to put us out of Fear of the Savages, if they had come, unless their Number had been very great, we went freely all over the Island, where-ever we found Occasion; and as here we had our Escape or Deliverance upon our Thoughts, it was impossible, at least for me, to have the Means of it out of mine; to this Purpose, I mark'd out several Trees which I thought fit for our Work, and I set Friday and his Father to cutting them down; and then I caused the Spaniard, to whom I imparted my Thought on that Affair, to oversee and direct their Work. I shewed them with what indefatigable Pains I had hewed a large Tree into single Planks, and I caused them to do the like, till they had made about a Dozen large Planks of good Oak, near 2 Foot road, 35 Foot long, and from 2 Inches to 4 Inches thick: hat prodigious Labour it took up, any one may imagine. At the same time I contriv'd to encrease my little Flock of tame Goats as much as I could; and to this Purpose, I made Friday and the Spaniard go out one Day, and my self with Friday the next Day; for we took our Turns: And by is Means we got above 20 young Kids to breed up with the rest; for when-ever we shot the Dam, we saved

齐动手开掘土地。不到一个月的工夫，恰好在播种季节的前夕，就开垦整顿好了大片的土地，足够播下二十二蒲式耳大麦，十六罐稻谷；简单一句话，足够播下我们所能省下来的全部种子。老实说，在收获以前的六个月中间，我们所保留下来的大麦甚至还不够我们自己吃的。这里所谓六个月，是从我们把种子搁在一边、准备播种的时候算起，不要认为庄稼在这地方要长六个月。

现在，我们已有不少居民，即使那些野人再来，也不用害怕了，除非他们来的人数特别多。所以，我们只要有机会，就可在全岛到处自由来往。由于我们的脑子里都想着逃走和脱险的事情，所以大家都无时无刻不在想办法，至少我自己是如此。为了这个目的，我把几棵适于造船的树做了记号，叫星期五父子把它们砍倒。然后，我又把自己的意图告诉那西班牙人，叫他监督和指挥星期五父子工作。我把自己以前削好的一些木板给他们看，告诉他们我是怎样不辞辛劳地把一棵大树削成木板的，并叫他们照着去做。最后，他们居然用橡树做成了十二块很大的木板，每块约二英尺宽，三十五英尺长，二至四英寸厚。至于这项工作究竟花费了多么艰巨的劳动，那就可想而知了。与此同时，我又想方设法，尽量使我那小小的羊群增大起来，为了

the Kids, and added them to our Flock: But above all, the Season for curing the Grapes coming on, I caused such a prodigious Quantity to be hung up in the Sun, that I believe, had we been at Alicant where the Raisins of the Sun are cur'd, we could have fill'd 60 or 80 Barrels; and these with our Bread was a great Part of our Food, and very good living too, I assure you; for it is an exceeding nourishing Food.

It was now Harvest, and our Crop in good Order; it was not the most plentiful Encrease I had seen in the Island, but however it was enough to answer our End; for from our 22 Bushels of Barley, we brought in and thrashed out above 220 Bushels; and the like in Proportion of the Rice, which was Store enough for our Food to the next Harvest, tho' all the 16 Spaniards had been on Shore with me; or if we had been ready for a Voyage, it would very plentifully have victualled our Ship, to have carry'd us to any Part of the World, that is to say, of America.

When we had thus hous'd and secur'd our Magazine of Corn, we fell to Work to make more Wicker Work, (viz.) great Baskets in which we kept it; and the Spaniard was very handy and dexterous at this Part, and often blam'd me that I did not make some things, for Defence, of this Kind of Work; but I saw no Need of it.

达到这个目的,我采取轮流的办法,一天让他星期五同西班牙人出去,一天让他跟我出去,一共捉来了二十多只小羊,同我们的家羊养在一起;因为我们每次打死了母羊,总把小羊留下,添进我们的羊群。特别值得一提的是,晒制葡萄干的时节一到,我让他们采了不知其数的葡萄,一串串地挂在阳光下;我深信,如果是在晒制葡萄干的阿利坎特,我们晒的这些定可装满七八十桶;而葡萄干同面包一样,是我们的主食;我还可以肯定地说,这是日常生活中的一件好东西,因为它营养特别丰富。

如今,又是收割季节,我们的收成很不错。虽说这次算不上我上岛以来的最大丰收,但对于我们的所需已是足够了。我们播种的大麦只有二十二蒲式耳,可现在我们竟然收获了二百二十多蒲式耳,稻谷的情形与这大致相同。有了这些粮食,即使是那十六个西班牙人都到我们这里来,吃到下次收获是足够的了。而且,如果我们准备去航海,只要把充足的粮食搬到船上,我们就可以航行到世界的任何地方,当然这只是说,能到达美洲的任何地方。

我们把打下的粮食收藏贮存好以后,又动手编制了许多用于存放粮食的大筐子。那西班牙人对于编制藤器很内行,编起东西来又快又好,是把好手。他时常怪我以前没有编更多的藤器作防御用,

And now having a full Supply of Food for all the Guests I expected, I gave the Spaniard Leave to go over to the Main, to see what he could do with those he had left behind him there. I gave him a strict Charge in Writing, Not to bring any Man with him, who would not first swear in the Presence of himself and of the old Savage, That he would no way injure, fight with, or attack the Person he should find in the Island, who was so kind to send for them in order to their Deliverance; but that they would stand by and defend him against all such Attempts, and wherever they went, would be entirely under and subjected to his Commands; and that this should be put in Writing, and signed with their Hands: How we were to have this done, when I knew they had neither Pen or Ink; that indeed was a Question which we never asked.

Under these Instructions, the Spaniard, and the old Savage the Father of Friday, went away in one of the Canoes, which they might be said to come in, or rather were brought in, when they came as Prisoners to be devour'd by the Savages.

I gave each of them a Musket with a Firelock on it, and about eight Charges of Powder and Ball, charging them to be very good Husbands of both, and not to use either of them but upon urgent Occasion.

This was a chearful Work, being the first Measures used by me in View of my Deliverance for now 27 Years and some Days. I gave them Provisions of Bread, and of dry'd Grapes, sufficient for themselves for many Days, and sufficient for all

可我却始终看不出这究竟有多大的必要。

既然现在的粮食足够我所期盼的客人们吃，我便打发那个西班牙人到对面大陆上去，看他有没有办法说服还留在那边的那些人过来。在他上路之前，我先跟他签订了一份严格的委托书，告诉他，谁要是想来，就必须先在他和那个年老的野人面前发誓，保证到了这里之后不伤害我们，不跟我们争斗，不袭击我们，因为我们是好心好意要救他们出海的；而且，如果碰到这种情况，他们必须站出来支持我，保卫我，不管到哪里，都必须绝对服从我的指挥；这些条件都必须写下来，要他们在上面签字。然而，他们既没有笔，也没有墨水，该如何执行呢？这个问题我们根本没有想过。

在接受了我的这些指令后，那西班牙人和老野人，也就是星期五的父亲，便准备乘坐一只独木舟出发了。他们乘坐的独木舟正是他们来岛时乘坐的，不同的是，他们来岛时是被野人押来的，是被当作俘虏押来准备杀食的。

我给了他们每人一支带有燧发机的步枪和八份弹药，并叮嘱他们务必节省使用，不到万不得已决不随意放枪。

这是一件令人愉快的工作，因为这是我二十七年以来为了解救自己而采取的第一个步骤。我给了他们许多面包和葡萄干，够他们吃好多天

their Country-men for about eight Days time; and wishing them a good Voyage, I see them go, agreeing with them about a Signal they should hang out at their Return, by which I should know them again, when they came back, at a Distance, before they came on Shore.

They went away with a fair Gale on the Day that the Moon was at Full by my Account, in the Month of October: But as for an exact Reckoning of Days, after I had once lost it I could never recover it again; nor had I kept even the Number of Years so punctually, as to be sure that I was right, tho' as it prov'd, when I afterwards examin'd my Account, I found I had kept a true Reckoning of Years.

It was no less than eight Days I had waited for them, when a Strange and unforeseen Accident interveen'd, of which the like has not perhaps been heard of in History: I was fast asleep in my Hutch one Morning, when my Man Friday came running in to me, and call'd aloud, Master, Master, they are come, they are come.

I jump'd up, and regardless of Danger, I went out, as soon as I could get my Cloaths on, thro' my little Grove, which by the Way was by this time grown to be a very thick Wood; I say, regardless of Danger, I went without my Arms, which was not my Custom to do: But I was surpriz'd, when turning my Eyes to the Sea, I presently saw a Boat at about a League and half's Distance, standing in for the Shore, with a Shoulder of Mutton Sail, as they call it; and the Wind blowing pretty fair to bring them in; also I observ'd presently, that they did not come from that Side which the Shore lay on, but from the Southermost End of the Island: Upon this I call'd Friday in, and bid him lie close, for these were not the People we look'd for, and that we might not know yet whether they were Friends or Ene-

的,也够那批西班牙人吃七八天的。于是我祝他们一路平安,送他们动身,一方面同他们约定好回来时悬挂的信号,好叫我在他们回来的时候,不等他们靠岸,老远老远就把他们认出来。

他们走的时候是顺风,也正是月圆之日;据我计算,那天该是在十月里。但是我记的日子曾经出过一次错,后来就再也纠正不过来了,因此对所记日子的是否准确甚至对所记的年份是否准确,我不敢肯定;不过后来经过检查,我发现自己在年份上没有弄错。

我等他们回来,整整等了八天,却发生了一件完全意想不到的怪事,这样的怪事也许在过去是闻所未闻的。那天早晨,我正在小屋里睡觉,星期五奔了进来,高声叫道:"主人,主人! 他们来,他们来!"

我立即从床上跳起来,不顾一切危险,急忙披上衣服,穿过小树林(现在它已长成一片浓密的树林了),跑了出去。我说不顾一切危险,意思是我连武器都没有带就跑出去了。这完全违反了我平时的习惯。当我放眼向海上望去时,不觉大吃一惊。只见大约四英里半之外,有一只舢板,正挂着一副所谓"羊肩帆"向岸上驶来。当时正好顺风,把舢板直往岸上送。接着我就注意到,那舢板不是从大陆方向来的,而是从岛的最南端驶过来的。于是我把星期五叫到身边,叫他不要离开我。因为,这些人

mies.

In the next Place, I went in to fetch my Perspective Glass, to see what I could make of them; and having taken the Ladder out, I climb'd up to the Top of the Hill, as I used to do when I was apprehensive of any thing, and to take my View the plainer without being discover'd.

I had scarce Set my Foot on the Hill, when my Eye plainly discover'd a Ship lying at an Anchor, at about two Leagues and an half's Distance from me South-south-east, but not above a League and an half from the Shore. By my Observation it appear'd plainly to be an English Ship, and the Boat appear'd to be an English Long-Boat.

I cannot express the Confusion I was in, tho' the Joy of seeing a Ship, and one who I had Reason to believe was Mann'd by my own Countrymen, and consequently Friends, was such as I cannot describe; but yet I had some secret Doubts hung about me, I cannot tell from whence they came, bidding me keep upon my Guard. In the first Place, it occurr'd to me to consider what Business an English Ship could have in that Part of the World, since it was not the Way to or from any Part of the World, where the English had any Traffick; and I knew there had been no Storms to drive them in there, as in Distress; and that if they were English really, it was most probable that they were here upon no good Design; and that I had better continue as I was, than fall into the Hands of Thieves and Murtherers.

Let no Man despise the secret Hints and Notices of Danger, which sometimes are given him, when he may think there is no Possibility of its being real. That such Hints and Notices are given us, I

不是我们所期待的人,现在还不清楚他们是敌是友。

紧接着,我便跑回去取我的望远镜,想把情况看个究竟;我又把梯子拿了出来,爬上了小山顶,往常我是遇到可疑的情况也都是这样做的,因为这样既可以看清目标,又不会被对方发现。

我刚刚爬上小山顶,一眼便看到,在东南偏南方向,有一条大船正停泊在离我这里约七八英里的海上,但离岸最多不过四英里半。根据我的观察,那条船看上去显然是条英国船,而那只舢板看上去也像是只英式小划子。

当时,我心中的那种慌乱简直无法描述。尽管我看到了一艘大船,而且有理由相信会被自己的同胞所救,取得他们的同情,而且那种喜悦是难以形容的。然而,我的内心仍被不知从哪里冒出来的疑虑所充斥,促使我保持戒备。首先,这使我想到,一艘英国船有什么事情要到这里来呢?这里又不是英国人与世界上有贸易交往的地区的往来通道。并且我知道,因为没有任何风暴把他们吹到这里来或是在那里失事。如果他们果真是英国人,他们来这里,极有可能是没有好意,我宁可继续在这里呆下去也比落到那些强盗和杀人犯手里强得多。

千万不要对危险的信号和预兆掉以轻心,往往在你没感觉到危险的可能性时出现这些信号。我们一旦接受这

believe few that have made any Observations of things, can deny; that they are certain Discoveries' of an invisible World, and a Converse of Spirits, we cannot doubt; and if the Tendency of them seems to be to warn us of Danger, why should we not suppose they are from some friendly Agent, whether supreme, or inferior, and subordinate, is not the Question; and that they are given for our Good?

The present Question abundantly confirms me in the Justice of this Reasoning; for had I not been made cautious by this secret Admonition, come it from whence it will, I had been undone inevitably, and in a far worse Condition than before, as you will see presently.

I had not kept my self long in this Posture, but I saw the Boat draw near the Shore, as if they look'd for a Creek to thrust in at for the Convenience of Landing; however, as they did not come quite far enough, they did not see the little Inlet where I formerly landed my Rafts; but run their Boat on Shore upon the Beach, at about half a Mile from me, which was very happy for me; for otherwise they would have landed just as I may say at my Door, and would soon have beaten me out of my Castle, and perhaps have plunder'd me of all I had.

When they were on Shore, I was fully satisfy'd that they were English Men; at least, most of them; one or two I thought were Dutch; but it did not prove so: There were in all eleven Men, whereof three of them I found were unarm'd, and as I thought, bound; and when the first four or five of them were jump'd on Shore, they took those three out of the Boat as Prisoners: One of the three I could perceive using the most passion-

种信号，只要你是个有心观察事物的人，你就不会忽略它们。这些信号和预兆是某种无法怀疑的隐形世界的显现，一种心灵交流，如果它们是向我们示警，为什么就不能认为这是一种对我们友善的力量呢？这种力量无论是高贵的，还是低贱的，都无关紧要。

后来发生的情况，就充分证明了我的感觉是完全正确的。要是没有这种神秘的不知从何而来的警示让我谨慎从事，那我可就又要陷入灾难，陷入更糟更可怕的境地了。往下看，你就会知道，我这并不是危言耸听。

我在小山上观望了没多会儿，就看到那只舢板驶近了岸边。然后，我发现他们好像是在沿着海岸寻找便于登岸的河湾。不过他们并没走太远，所以，没有发现我从前卸木排的那条小河，只好把舢板停在离我半英里以外的沙滩上。这真让我感到万分地幸运。因为不然的话，他们一定会紧对着我的门口上岸，而且一定会把我从我的城堡里赶走，并且说不定还会把我所有的东西抢个精光。

他们上岸之后，我看出他们果然都是英国人，至少大部分是英国人。有一两个看样子像荷兰人，后来证明并不是。他们一共有十一个人，其中有三个看样子没有带武器，而且仿佛是被绑起来的样子。船一靠岸，就有四五个人首先跳上岸来，把这三个人押下船

ate Gestures of Entreaty, Affliction and Despair, even to a kind of Extravagance; the other two I could perceive lifted up their Hands sometimes, and appear'd concern'd indeed, but not to such a Degree as the first.

I was perfectly confounded at the Sight, and knew not what the Meaning of it should be. Friday call'd out to me in English, as well as he could, O Master! You see English Mans eat Prisoner as well as Savage Mans. Why, says I, Friday, Do you think they are a going to eat them then? Yes, says Friday, They mill eat them: No, no, says I, Friday, I am afraid they mill murther them indeed, but you may be sure they will not eat them.

All this while I had no thought of what the Matter really was; but Stood trembling with the Horror of the Sight, expecting every Moment when the three Prisoners should be kill'd; nay, Once I saw one of the Villains lift up his Arm with a great Cutlash, as the Seamen call it, or Sword, to spike one of the poor Men; and I expected to see him fall every Moment, at which all the Blood in my Body seem'd to run chill in my Veins.

I wish'd heartily now for my Spaniard, and the Savage that was gone with him; or that I had any way to have come undiscover'd within shot of them, that I might have rescu'd the three Men; for I saw no Fire Arms they had among them; but it fell out to my Mind another way.

After I had Observ'd the outragious Usage of the three Men, by the insolent Seamen, I observ'd the Fellows run scattering about the Land, as if

来。我看见其中的一个正在那里指手画脚，作出种种恳求、悲痛和失望的姿势，甚至作得有点过火；同时我又见那另外的两个人，有时也举起双手，作出很苦恼的样子，但没有第一个人那样激动。

看到这幅情景，我真有点莫名其妙，不知他们究竟在搞什么名堂。星期五在旁边一直用英语对我喊道："啊，主人，你看英国人也吃俘虏，同野人一样！""怎么，星期五，"我说，"你以为他们会吃那几个人吗？""是的，"星期五说，"他们一定会吃的。""不会，不会，"我说，"星期五，我看他们会杀死他们，但决不会吃他们，这我敢担保！"

这时，我不知道眼前发生的一切究竟是怎么回事，只是站在那里，看着这可怕的情景发抖，并一直担心那三个俘虏会给他们杀掉。有一次，我看到一个坏蛋甚至举起一把水手们称为腰刀的那种长刀，向其中一个可怜的人砍去，眼看他就要倒下来了，把我吓得不寒而栗。

现在我真是巴不得那西班牙人和星期五的父亲没走，也巴不得能找个办法，逼近他们这帮人而不被他们发现，只要他们在我的射程之内，我就能把这三个人救出来了，因为据我观察，那帮坏蛋没带火器；但这时我另有了主意。

那些气焰嚣张的水手把那三人作践了一番之后，我看到他们都四散跑开了，似乎要

they wanted to see the Country: I observ'd that the three other Men had Liberty to go also where they pleas'd; but they Sat down all three upon the Ground, very pensive, and look'd like Men in Despair.

This put me in Mind of the first Time when I came on Shore, and began to look about me; How I gave my self over for lost: How wildly I look'd round me: What dreadful Apprehensions I had: And how I lodg'd in the Tree all Night for fear of being devour'd by wild Beasts.

As I knew nothing that Night of the Supply I was to receive by the providential Driving of the Ship nearer the Land, by the Storms and Tide, by which I have since been so long nourish'd and Supported; so these three poor desolate Men knew nothing how certain of Deliverance and Supply they were, how near it was to them, and how effectually and really they were in a Condition of Safety, at the same Time that they thought themselves lost, and their Case desperate.

So little do we see before us in the World, and so much reason have we to depend chearfully upon the great Maker of the World, that he does not leave his Creatures so absolutely destitute, but that in the worst Circumstances they have always something to be thankful for, and sometimes are nearer their Deliverance than they imagine; nay, are even brought to their Deliverance by the Means by which they seem to be brought to their Destruction.

It was just at the Top of High-Water when these People came on Shore, and while partly they stood parlying with the Prisoners they brought, and partly while they rambled about to see what kind of a Place they were in; they had carelessly staid till the Tide was spent, and the Water was ebb'd considerably away, leaving their Boat a-

看看这个岛上的情况。我再注意一瞧，见那三个人倒也可以自由走动了；可他们三人却忧心忡忡地朝地上一坐，脸上满是绝望的神情。

这使我想起了初次上岸时的情景，我举目四顾，怎样认为自己已经没命了，四周是多么地荒凉，心里是怎样地惶恐不安；由于怕被野兽吞吃怎样藏在树上过了整整一夜。

我没有想到那天晚上，风暴和海浪把大船冲到海岸附近，使我得到物品供给，靠这些财物维持了我相当长的生活。同样，这三个可怜的苦命人也没有想到他们一定会获得援助和救济，而且离他们是这样地近。同时他们也没想到，他们本以为已经没命没有活路的时候，他们却真正处于安全之中了。

在这个世界上，我们没有几个人能料事如神，这就是为什么我们有充分的理由依赖伟大的造物主，他从来不把他的子民逼上绝路，他使子民们在最差的处境里总能找到值得感谢的东西，有时候得到的救援可能来得比他们想象的快得多，常常看似毁灭他们的途径其实就是拯救他们的渠道。

那些人是在满潮的时候上的岸。在这段时间里，他们当中一些人站在那里跟那三个他们带来的俘虏谈判，另一些人则四处走动，想看看他们究竟到了一个什么地方。在这期间，他们根本没有留心潮

ground.

They had left two Men in the Boat, who as I found afterwards, having drank a little too much Brandy, fell a-sleep; however, one of them waking Sooner than the other, and finding the Boat too fast a-ground for him to stir it, hollow'd for the rest who were straggling about, upon which they all Soon came to the Boat; but it was past all their Strength to launch her, the Boat being very heavy, and the Shore on that Side being a soft ousy Sand, almost like a Quick-Sand.

In this Condition, like true Seamen who are perhaps the and least of all Mankind given to lore-thought, they gave it over, and away they stroll'd about the Country again; and I heard one of them say aloud to another, calling them off from the Boat, Why let her alone, Jack, can't ye, she will float next Tide; by which I was fully confirm'd in the main Enquiry, of what Countrymen they were.

All this while I kept my self very close, not once daring to stir out of my Castle, any farther than to my Place of Observation, near the Top of the Hill; and very glad I was, to think how well it was fortify'd: I knew it was no less than ten Hours before the Boat could be on float again, and by that Time it would be dark, and I might be at more Liberty to see their Motions, and to hear their Discourse, if they had any.

水已经退得差不多了,他们的舢板已经搁浅在沙滩上了。

他们在舢板上本来留了两个人,但我后来发现,那两个人由于多喝了一点白兰地,竟然都睡着了。尽管其中一个比另一个较早睡醒,可是,他发现舢板已经牢牢地搁住了,他一个人已经推不动了。他连忙招呼其余那些四散在岸上闲逛的人。他们见此情景,便一下子都跑到了舢板这里。可是,他们就是使足了劲也推不动它了,因为舢板很重,更何况小岛这一边的沙滩都是松软的淤沙,跟流沙差不多。

水手大概是世界上最无所顾忌的一种人了,所以在这种情况下,他们干脆停下手来,又四处散开,东游西逛去了。这时,我还听见一个人大声叫喊着另一个人离开舢板,只听他说:"杰克,随他去吧,别白费力气了。等到涨潮时,它自然会浮起来的。"听到他的说话声,我彻底证实了自己的判断,他们的确是英国人。

到目前为止,我一直都躲在暗中,把自己隐蔽得严严实实,除了小山顶上的瞭望点外,一步也不敢离开自己的城堡范围。想到自己的城堡有这么坚固的防御工事,我感到非常欣慰。我知道那舢板至少十个时辰之后才能浮起来。到那时,天也接近黑了,我就能够更加便利地观察他们的行动,窃听他们之间的谈话了。

In the mean Time, I fitted my self up for a Battle, as before; though with more Caution, knowing I had to do with another kind of Enemy than I had at first: I order'd Friday also, who I had made an excellent Marks-Man with his Gun, to load himself with Arms: I took my self two Fowling-Pieces, and I gave him three Muskets; my Figure indeed was very fierce; I had my formidable Goat-Skin Coat on, with the great Cap I have mention'd, a naked Sword by my Side, two Pistols in my Belt, and a Gun upon each Shoulder.

It was my Design, as I said above, not to have made any Attempt till it was Dark: But about Two a Clock, being the Heat of the Day, I found that in short they were all gone straggling into the Woods, and as I thought were laid down to Sleep. The three poor distressed Men, too Anxious for their Condition to get any Sleep, were however set down under the Shelter of a great Tree, at about a quarter of a Mile from me, and as I thought out of sight of any of the rest.

Upon this I resolv'd to discover my self to them, and learn something of their Condition: Immediately I march'd in the Figure as above, my Man Friday at a good Distance behind me, as formidable for his Arms as I, but not making quite so staring a Spectre-like Figure as I did.

I came as near them undiscover'd as I could, and then before any of them saw me, I call'd aloud to them in Spanish, What are ye Gentlemen?

与此同时，我时刻准备着战斗，如同先前一样。这一次，我比过去更加谨慎，因为我十分清楚，我要对付的敌人与从前是完全不一样的。现在，星期五在我的训练之下，射技大增，简直高明极了。我本人也全副武装起来。我自己拿了两支鸟枪，让星期五拿三支短枪。我现在的样子，真是十分恐怖：身上穿件羊皮袄，模样已够可怕，头上戴顶大帽子，那古怪的样子我前面也曾讲过。腰间和往日一样挂着一把没有刀鞘的刀，两支手枪插在腰间，两支枪拎在肩上。

上面已经说过，我的计划是在黄昏到来以前不采取任何行动。可是，到了下午两点钟前后，天气正热的时候，我发现他们都三三两两地跑到树林里去，大概都躺着睡觉去了。可是那三个可怜的遭难者，却因为焦虑着自己的处境，睡也睡不着，只好在一棵大树的荫凉底下呆呆地坐着，离我大约有四分之一英里远，而且，依我猜想，是在其余那些人的视线之外。

看到这种情况，我决定走过去对他们的状况进行一下了解。我想到这儿立刻向他们走过去。我上面说了，我的样子十分吓人，后面远远地跟着仆人星期五，也是全副武装，样子像我一样狰狞可怖，但比我稍好一些。

我蹑手蹑脚地走近他们，还没等到他们发现我，我就抢先用西班牙语向他们大声喊

They started up at the Noise, but were ten times more confounded when they saw me, and the uncouth Figure that I made. They made no Answer at all, but I thought I perceiv'd them just going to fly from me, when I spoke to them in English, Gentlemen, said I, do not be surpriz'd at me; perhaps you may have a Friend near you when you did not expect it. He must be sent directly from Heaven then, said one of them very gravely to me, and pulling off his Hat at the same time to me, for our Condition is past the Help of Man. All Help is from Heaven, Sir, said I. But can you put a Stranger in the way how to help you, for you seem to me to be in some great Distress? I saw you when you landed, and when you Seem'd to make Applications to the Brutes that came with you, I saw one of them lift up his Sword to kill you.

The poor Man with Tears running down his Face, and trembling, looking like one astonish'd, return'd, Am I talking to God, or Man! Is it a real Man, or an Angel! Be in no fear about that, Sir, said I, if God had sent an Angel to relieve you, he would have come better Cloath'd, and Arm'd after another manner than you see me in; pray lay aside your Fears, I am a Man, an English-man, and dispos'd to assist you, you see; I have one Servant only; we have Arms and Ammunition; tell us freely, Can we serve you? - What is your Case?

Our Case, said he, Sir, is too long to tell you, while our Murtherers are so near; but in Short, Sir, I was Commander of that Ship, my Men have Mutinied against me; they have been hardly

道:"先生们,你们从哪里来?"

他们听见响动,马上跳了起来,及至看到我本人,看到我那副奇形怪状,就更加十倍地惊惶起来。他们一句话也回答不出来;我见他们仿佛要跑开,就和他们说英国话。"诸位先生,不要怕我,"我说,"说不定近在你们眼前的正是你们料想不到的朋友呢。""那他一定是天国派来的。"其中一个一本正经地说,一边脱帽向我致意,"因为凡人是救不了我们的。""所有的救助都是来自天国,先生,"我说,"不过,你们愿意不愿意一个陌生人来帮助你们呢?你们看上去很不幸。你们一上岸,我就看见了你们。我看到当你们向那些跟你们来的坏蛋求饶的时候,有一个举起刀要杀你们。"

那可怜的人泪流满面,浑身发抖,显得十分惊异。他回答说:"我是在对上帝说话呢,还是在对人说话?你是人,还是天使?""这你不用担心,先生,"我说,"如果上帝真的派一位天使来拯救你们,他的穿戴一定会比我好得多,他的武器也一定完全不一样。请你们放心吧。我是人,而且是英国人。你们看,我是来救你们的。我只有一个仆人。我们都有武器。请你们大胆告诉我们,我们能为你们效劳吗?你们到底发生了什么事?"

"我们的事,先生,"他说,"说来话长,而我们的凶手又近在咫尺。现在,就长话短说吧,先生。我是那条船的船长,

prevail'd on not to Murther me, and at last have set me on Shore in this desolate Place, with these two Men with me; one my Mate, the other a Passenger, where we expected to Perish, believing the Place to be uninhabited, and know not yet what to think of it.

Where are those Brutes, your Enemies, said I, do you know where they are gone? There they lye, Sir, Said he, pointing to a Thicket of Trees; my Heart trembles, for fear they have seen us, and heard you speak, if they have, they will certainly Murther us all.

Have they any Fire-Arms, said I, He answered they had only two Pieces, and one which they left in the Boat. Well then, Said I, leave the rest to me; I see they are all asleep, it is an easie thing to kill them all; but shall we rather take them Prisoners? He told me there were two desperate Villains among them, that it was scarce safe to shew any Mercy to; but if they were secur'd, he believ'd all the rest would return to their Duty. I ask'd him, which they were? He told me he could not at that distance describe them; but he would obey my Orders in any thing I would direct. Well, says I, let us retreat out of their View or Hearing, least they awake, and we will resolve further; so they willingly went back with me, till the Woods cover'd us from them.

我手下的人反叛了。我好不容易才说服他们不杀我。最后,他们把我和这两个人一起押送到这个岛上来。他们一个是我的大副,一个是旅客。我们想,在这个荒岛上,我们一定会饿死的。我们相信,这是一个没有人烟的荒岛,真不知道该怎么办呢!"

"你们的敌人,那些暴徒,现在在什么地方?"我问,"你们知道他们到哪儿去啦?""他们正在那边躺着呢,先生。"他指着一个灌木林说。"我现在心里吓得直发抖,怕他们看到我们,听到你说话。要是那样的话,我们就通通没命了!"

"他们有没有枪?"我问。他回答说:他们只带了两支枪,一支留在那舢板上了。"好吧,"我说道,"别的事情都由我去办了;我看,他们现在都睡着了,要把他们杀个精光也是件轻而易举的事;不过,是不是抓活的为好?"他告诉我说,那帮家伙里有两个穷凶极恶的坏蛋,如果饶了他们,那就相当危险;他相信,只要把他们解决了,其他人都会回到各自的岗位上去。我问他是哪两个人。他说现在同他们隔着那么段距离,很难把他们指认出来;但他说他愿意听命于我,叫他干什么就干什么。"行,"我说道,"现在我们后撤,别让我们的说话声惊醒了他们,撤到他们看不见的地方之后再作计较。"于是他们自觉自愿地跟我后撤,撤到一片树林里之后,那帮家伙就没法看

Look you, Sir, said I, if I venture upon your Deliverance, are you willing to make two Conditions with me? he anticipated my Proposals, by telling me, that both he and the Ship, if recover'd, should be wholly Directed and Commanded by me in every thing; and if the Ship was not recover'd, he would live and dye with me in what Part of the World soever I would send him; and the two other Men said the same.

Well, says I, my Conditions are but two. 1. That while you stay on this Island with me, you will not pretend to any Authority here; and if I put Arms into your Hands, you will upon all Occasions give them up to me, and do no Prejudice to me or mine, upon this Island, and in the mean time be govern'd by my Orders.

2. That if the Ship is, or may be recover'd, you will carry me and my Man to England Passage free.

He gave me all the Assurances that the Invention and Faith of Man could devise, that he would comply with these most reasonable Demands, and besides would owe his Life to me, and acknowledge it upon all Occasions as long as he liv'd.

Well then, said I, here are three Muskets for you, with Powder and Ball; tell me next what you think is proper to be done. He shew'd all the Testimony of his Gratitude that he was able; but offer'd to be wholly guided by me. I told him I thought it was hard venturing any thing; but the best Method I could think of was to fire upon them

见我们了。

"请注意听着,先生,"我说,"假如我冒险把你们救出来,你们愿意跟我订两个条件吗?"我还没有把条件说出口,他便抢先对我说,假如大船能够收复,那么,他和他的船一定完全听从我的指挥,处处听从我的命令;万一不能收复,不论我把他派到什么地方去,他都愿意与我同存亡,共生死。另外那两个人也都是这么说的。

"好吧,我只有两个条件,"我对他们说,"第一条,在你们逗留本岛期间,决不允许僭越我的主权,同我争权夺势;在我发给你们武器之后,你们必须随时按我的命令交回武器;你们必须完全服从我的管理,不得反对和伤害我和我的手下人。

"第二条,如果大船能够收复回来,你们必须免费把我和我的仆人送回英国。"

船长对我提出的条件满口应允,并向我作出了种种保证,简直可以说把世上所有能想到的和令人信服的保证都说尽了。他保证一定遵守我这些最合理的要求,同时他还要感谢我的救命之恩,终身不忘。

"那么好吧,"我说,"现在我交给你们三支短枪,外带火药和子弹;现在就请你们告诉我,下一步应该怎么办。"他极力向我表示感谢,说他情愿完全听从我的指挥。我告诉他,现在事情很棘手;不过照我

at once, as they lay; and if any was not kill'd at the first Volley, and offered to submit, we might save them, and so put it wholly upon God's Providence to direct the Shot.

He said very modestly, that he was loath to kill them, if he could help it, but that those two were incorrigible Villains, and had been the Authors of all the Mutiny in the Ship, and if they escaped, we should be undone still; for they would go on Board, and bring the whole Ship's Company, and destroy us all. Well then, says I, Necessity legitimates my Advice; for it is the only Way to save our Lives. However, seeing him still cautious of shedding Blood, I told him they should go themselves, and manage as they found convenient.

In the Middle of this Discourse, we heard some of them awake, and soon after, we saw two of them on their Feet, I ask'd him, if either of them were of the Men who he had said were the Heads of the Mutiny? He said, No: Well then, said I, you may let them escape, and Providence seems to have wakned them on Purpose to save themselves. Now, says I, if the rest escape you, it is your Fault.

Animated with this, he took the Musket, I had given him, in his Hand, and a Pistol in his Belt, and his two Comerades with him, with each Man a Piece in his Hand. The two Men who were with him, going first, made some Noise, at which one of the Seamen who was awake, turn'd about, and seeing them coming, cry'd out to the rest; but it was too late then; for the Moment he cry'd out, they fir'd; I mean the two Men, the Captain wisely reserving his own Piece: They had so well aim'd their Shot at the Men they knew, that one

看,最好的办法就是趁他们睡着的时候立刻向他们开火,如果第一排枪开出以后还有没有死的,情愿投降,我们可以饶他们的性命;至于开枪以后的情况怎么样,那就全看上帝的安排了。

他非常谦恭地说,如果他能办到的话,他不愿意杀他们,但那两人是无可救药的坏蛋,叛敌的头儿,要让他们逃脱,我们还是会完蛋。他们会到大船上把全体人马拉过来,把我们全部消灭掉。"这么说我的建议也是出于无奈,因为这是唯一叫我们免于一死的办法。"但我看得出,他仍旧不愿意流血,我告诉他们,一切由他们裁决,他们认为怎么方便就怎么行动。

正在谈话间,我们看到有两个人醒了,不久站了起来。我问他那两个人中间有没有他说的叛敌的头儿。他说:"没有!""那么,好吧!"我说,"你可以让他们逃走。上帝似乎是有意叫醒他们,让他们自己逃命的。如今,"我说,"如果其余的人都逃掉,就是你的过错。"

受我的话的鼓动,他拿起我交给他的短枪,在腰带上又插了一支手枪。他的两个同伴跟着他,每人手持一支长枪。走在前边的他的两个同伴,弄出了一点响声,其中一个醒过来的水手,转身看见他们走过来,大声呼叫其他的人。但是为时已晚,就在他刚开始呼叫的时候,他们开火了,我说的是另外两个人,而

of them was kill'd on the Spot, and the other very much wounded; but not being dead, he started up upon his Feet, and call'd eagerly for help to the other; but the Captain stepping to him, told him, 'twas too late to cry for help, he should call upon God to forgive his Villany, and with that Word knock'd him down with the Stock of his Musket, so that he never spoke more: There were three more in the Company, and one of them was also slightly wounded: By this Time I was come, and when they saw their Danger, and that it was in vain to resist, they begg'd for Mercy: The Captain told them, he would spare their Lives, if they would give him any Assurance of their Abhorrence of the Treachery they had been guilty of, and would swear to be faithful to him in recovering the Ship, and afterwards in carrying her back to Jamaica, from whence they came: They gave him all the Protestations of their Sincerity that could be desir'd, and he was willing to believe them, and spare their Lives, which I was not against, only that I oblig'd him to keep them bound Hand and Foot while they were upon the Island.

While this was doing, I sent Friday with the Captain's Mate to the Boat, with Orders to secure her, and bring away the Oars, and Sail, which they did; and by and by, three straggling Men that were (happily for them) parted from the rest, came back upon hearing the Guns fir'd, and seeing their Captain, who before was their Prisoner, now their Conqueror, they submitted to be bound also; and so our Victory was compleat.

It now remain'd, that the Captain and I should

船长仍然自在地端着枪。他们都瞄得很准,当场打死了一个,另一个也受了重伤,但还没死。他一头爬起来,急忙向其余的人呼救。这时船长已一步跳到他跟前,对他说,现在呼救已太晚了,他应该祈求上帝宽恕他的罪恶。说着,船长用枪把一下子把他打倒在地,叫他再也开不了口。跟那两个水手在一起的还有其余三个人,其中有一个已经受了轻伤。就在这时,我也到了。他们看到了危险临头,知道抵抗已没有用了,就只好哀求饶命。船长告诉他们,他可以饶他们的命,但他们得向他保证,表示痛恨自己所犯的反叛的罪行,并宣誓效忠船长,帮他把大船夺回来,然后再把他们开回牙买加去,因为他们正是从牙买加来的。他们竭力向船长表示他们的诚意,船长也愿意相信他们,并饶他们的命。对此我也并不反对,只是要求船长在他们留在岛上期间,应把他们的手脚捆绑起来。

我一边招呼着这儿的事,一边叫星期五同那大副去把舢板看住,把舢板上的桨和帆拿走。他们照办以后不久,三个在别处转悠的人听到枪声都赶了回来,也算是他们运气,没同别的人在一起,但一看见原先在他们手中的船长不但自由了,而且打败了他们,也就束手就擒;我们由此大获全胜。

现在船长和我也该彼此

enquire into one another's Circumstances: I began first, and told him my whole History, which he heard with an Attention even to Amazement; and particularly, at the wonderful Manner of my being furnish'd with Provisions and Ammunition; and indeed, as my Story is a whole Collection of Wonders, it affected him deeply; but when he reflected from thence upon himself, and how I seem'd to have been preserv'd there, on purpose to save his Life, the Tears ran down his Face, and he could not speak a Word more.

After this Communication was at an End, I carry'd him and his two Men into my Apartment, leading them in, just where I came out, viz. At the Top of the House, where I refresh'd them with such Provisions as I had, and shew'd them all the Contrivances I had made, during my long, long, inhabiting that Place.

All I shew'd them, all I Said to them, was perfectly amazing; but above all, the Captain admir'd my Fortification, and how perfectly I had conceal'd my Retreat with a Grove of Trees, which having been now planted near twenty Years, and the Trees growing much faster than in England, was become a little Wood, and so thick, that it was unpassable in any Part of it, but at that one Side, where I had reserv'd my little winding Passage into it: I told him, this was my Castle, and my Residence; but that I had a Seat in the Country, as most Princes have, whither I could retreat upon Occasion, and I would shew him that too another Time; but at present, our Business was to consider how to recover the Ship: He agreed with me as to that; but told me, he was perfectly at a Loss what Measures to take; for that there were still six and twenty Hands on board, who having entred into a cursed Conspiracy, by which they had all forfeited their Lives to the Law, would be harden'd in it now by Desperation; and would carry it on, knowing that if they were

了解一下了。我先向他谈了我的全部经历，他全神贯注地听着，特别是听到我生产粮食和得到火药的出奇经过，简直都快听呆了；事实上，我的经历是一连串奇迹的组合，这使他深受感动；从我的故事，他联想到他自己，觉得上天安排我活了下来，就是为了救他的性命，不由得流下了眼泪，一句话也说不出来。

随后，我又带他和他的两个人来到我的住处，我怎么出来的，也就教他们怎么进去；也就是，从房顶爬进去。我用食品款待他们，指给他们看我在这漫长的岁月中制造的各种设施。

我指给他们看的一切东西都叫他们啧啧称奇。船长特别欣赏我的防卫措施，就是把我的住宅隐蔽在树林后面。这些树种了二十年，这里的树比英国生长得快，因此这片树林已成为无法通行的茂密森林，只在旁边留下一条弯弯曲曲的小道通向住处。我告诉他，这是我的城堡和家宅，此外，我还跟大多数王公诸侯一样，有一处乡间别墅，作为我必要的退隐之所，打算改日再带他们去看看。我们眼下的任务是，得好好筹划一下，该如何收复大船。他同意我的这一想法。但他告诉我，至于该采取怎样的办法，他却一筹莫展。因为大船上还有二十六个人，都参与了这一可诅咒的阴谋，为此，他们都因触犯了法律而难逃死罪。他们必

reduc'd, they should be brought to the Gallows, as soon as they came to England, or to any of the English Colonies; and that therefore there would be no attacking them, with so small a Number as we were.

I mus'd for some Time upon what he had said; and found it was a very rational Conclusion; and that therefore something was to be resolv'd on very speedily, as well to draw the Men on board into some Snare for their Surprize, as to prevent their Landing upon us, and destroying us; upon this it presently occurr'd to me, that in a little while the Ship's Crew wondring what was become of their Comrades, and of the Boat, would certainly come on Shore in their other Boat, to see for them, and that then perhaps they might come arm'd, and be too strong for us; this he allow'd was rational.

Upon this, I told him the first Thing we had to do, was to stave the Boat, which lay upon the Beach, so that they might not carry her off; and taking every Thing out of her, leave her so far useless as not to be fit to swim; accordingly we went on board, took the Arms which were left on board, out of her, and whatever else we found there, which was a Bottle of Brandy, and another of Rum, a few Bisket Cakes, a Horn of Powder, and a great Lump of Sugar, in a Piece of Canvas; the Sugar was five or six Pounds; all which was very welcome to me, especially the Brandy, and Sugar, of which I had had none left for many Years.

When we had carry'd all these Things on Shore (the Oars, Mast, Sail, and Rudder of the Boat, were carry'd away before, as above) we knock'd a great Hole in her Bottom, that if they had come strong enough to master us, yet they could not carry off the Boat.

定会孤注一掷,硬着头皮顽抗到底,继续干下去。因为他们明白,一旦他们被降服了,回到英国或英国殖民地去,很快就会被送上绞刑架。再说,我们一共就这几个人,跟他们硬拼总不是个办法。

我捉摸了一下他的话,发现很有道理。所以有些事需要迅速作出决定。一方面,出其不意地将他们引入某些圈套,另一方面,要阻止他们上岸攻击我们,消灭我们。因此,有一点提醒了我。一会儿之后,大船上的人一定会纳闷他们的同伴和舢板究竟出了什么事,一定会乘坐船上另外的舢板前来寻找他们,或许他们带着武器,实力大大超过我们。他认为我说的合乎情理。

因此,我对他说,我们首先把海滩上的舢板凿破,免得他们把它开走,并把船上所有的东西都取下来,使它不再具有航行能力。于是,我们上了舢板,把里面的那支枪和其它东西全部拿了下来。这些东西里面有一瓶白兰地、一瓶甘蔗酒和几块饼干,还有一大包用帆布包着的白糖,大约有五六磅重。这些东西对我来说可真是求之不得的好东西,特别是白兰地和白糖,我已有好多年没尝过它们的味道了。

舢板上的船桨、桅杆、船帆以及船舵等等东西,早已由星期五他们拿走了。所以我们把剩下的这些东西搬上岸以后,就在船底凿了个大洞。这样,即使他们的兵力再强

Indeed, it was not much in my Thoughts, that we could be able to recover the Ship; but my View was that if they went away without the Boat, I did not much question to make her fit again, to carry us away to the Leeward Islands, and call upon our Friends, the Spaniards, in my Way, for I had them still in my Thoughts.

While we were thus preparing our Designs, and had first, by main Strength heav'd the Boat up upon the Beach, so high that the Tide would not fleet her off at High-Water-Mark; and besides, had broke a Hole in her Bottom, too big to be quickly stopp'd, and were sat down musing what we should do; we heard the Ship fire a Gun, and saw her make a Waft with her Antient, as a Signal for the Boat to come on board; but no Boat stirr'd; and they fir'd several Times, making other Signals for the Boat.

At last, when all their Signals and Firings prov'd fruitless, and they found the Boat did not stir, we saw them by the Help of my Glasses, hoist another Boat out, and row towards the Shore; and we found as they approach'd, that there was no less than ten Men in her, and that they had Fire-Arms with them.

As the Ship lay almost two Leagues from the Shore, we had a full View of them as they came, and a plain Sight of the Men even of their Faces, because the Tide having set them a little to the

大,他们也无法把舢板给带走。

说句心里话,我觉得收复大船的可能性实在不大。我的看法是,只要他们不把这只舢板带走,我就一定可以把它重新修好,把我们载到利华群岛去,顺便把那些西班牙朋友带走;因为我心里还时刻记着他们。

我们正依照计划进行,首先用全部力量把舢板推到沙滩的高处,使潮水在高潮时不至于把它漂起来,然后又把船底凿了一个大洞,大得短时间内没法堵住。我们正坐在地上,寻思着下一步该怎么办,只听见大船上放了一枪,并且摇动旗帜作为信号,叫舢板回去。可是他们看不见舢板的动静。于是他们接着又放了几枪,并且对舢板发出一些别的信号。后来,他们见信号和放枪都没有结果,舢板还是没有动静,我们就从我的望远镜里看见他们把另外一只舢板放下来,向岸上摇过来。于是,接着又放了几枪,并向舢板又发出了一些别的信号。

最后,他们见信号和放枪都没有用处,舢板还是没有任何动静。我们在望远镜里看见他们把另一只舢板放下来,向岸上摇来。当他们逐渐靠近时,我们看出舢板上载着不下十来人,而且都带着枪支。

那条大船停泊在离岸大约六英里的地方。他们坐舢板划过来时,我们看得清清楚楚,连他们的脸也认得出来。

East of the other Boat, they row'd up under Shore, to come to the same Place, where the other had landed, and where the Boat lay.

By this Means, I say, we had a full View of them, and the Captain knew the Persons and Characters of all the Men in the Boat, of whom he said, that there were three very honest Fellows, who he was sure were led into this Conspiracy by the rest, being over-power'd and frighted.

But that as for the Boatswain, who it seems was the chief Officer among them, and all the rest, they were as outragious as any of the Ship's Crew, and were no doubt made desperate in their new Enterprize, and terribly apprehensive he was, that they would be too powerful for us.

I smil'd at him, and told him, that Men in our Circumstances were past the Operation of Fear: That seeing almost every Condition that could be, was better than that which we were suppos'd to be in, we ought to expect that the Consequence, whether Death or Life, would be sure to be a Deliverance: I ask'd him, What he thought of the Circumstances of my Life? And, Whether a Deliverance were not worth venturing for? And where, Sir, said I, is your Belief of my being preserv'd here on purpose to save your Life, which elevated you a little while ago? For my Part, said I, there seems to be but one Thing amiss in all the Prospect of it; What's that? Says he; why, said I, 'Tis, that as you say, there are three or four honest Fellows among them, which should be spar'd; had they been all of the wicked Part of the Crew, I should have thought God's Providence had singled them out to deliver them into your Hands; for depend upon it, every Man of them that comes a-shore are our own, and shall die, or live, as they

他们向岸上划来时，潮水把他们冲到第一只舢板的东边去了。于是他们又沿着海岸往西划，直奔第一只舢板靠岸和停泊的地方。

这就是说，我们把他们看得一清二楚，船长说得出船上的人谁是谁，以及他们的性格品行。他说，其中有三个人非常老实；他相信，他们之所以参与谋反，是因为受到其他人的威吓，而他们又势单力薄，因而是被迫的。

看来，水手长是他们中的头子，他和其他几个人都是船员中穷凶极恶的家伙，这回过来，肯定也是狗急跳墙之举；船长显得非常担心，觉得他们人多势众，我们难以对付。

我朝他微微一笑，告诉他说，处于我们这种境况的人，已过了担惊受怕的阶段了。可以说，不管发生什么情况，都比束手就擒好，所以无论结果是死是活，我们应该把这结果看作是一种解脱。我问他，对我的生活境况有什么想法，是不是值得为寻求解脱冒冒险。"先生，"我说道，"你刚才不是还认为，上天让我在这儿生存下来，就是为了搭救你们，并因此而感到很受鼓舞，很有信心吗？现在这信心到哪儿去了呢？而就我来说，在整个这件事情里，到头来恐怕只有一点会使我感到遗憾。"他问道："是什么？"我说："你说里面有三四个老实人，可以饶他们不死，亏得他们跟那帮邪恶的家伙不是一伙的，不然的

behave to us.

As I spoke this with a rais'd Voice and chearful Countenance, I found it greatly encourag'd him; so we set vigorously to our Business: We had upon the first Appearance of the Boat's coming from the Ship, consider'd of separating our Prisoners, and had indeed secur'd them effectually.

Two of them, of whom the Captain was less assur'd than ordinary, I sent with Friday, and one of the three (deliver'd Men) to my Cave, where they were remote enough, and out of Danger of being heard or discover'd, or of finding their way out of the Woods, if they could have deliver'd themselves: Here they left them bound, but gave them Provisions, They promis'd them if they continu'd there quietly, to give them their Liberty in a Day or two; but that if they attempted their Escape, they should be put to Death without Mercy: They promis'd faithfully to bear their Confinement with Patience, and were very thankful that they had such good Usage, as to have Provisions, and a Light left them; for Friday gave them Candles (such as we made our selves) for their Comfort; and they did not know but that he stood Sentinel over them at the Entrance.

The other Prisoners had better Usage; two of them were kept pinion'd indeed, because the Captain was not free to trust them; but the other two were taken into my Service upon their Captain's Recommendation, and upon their solemnly engaging to live and die with us; so with them and the three honest Men, we were seven Men, well arm'd; and I made no doubt we shou'd be able to deal well enough with the Ten that were a coming, considering that the Captain had said, there

话，我会认为这是天意安排，把他们交到你手中。相信我，上岸的每个人都逃不出我们的手心，是死是活就看他们的表现了。"

我提高嗓门，快活地说出这一席话，发现他很受鼓舞，于是，我们干劲十足地忙乎起来。当舢板从大船上下来时，我们就开始考虑疏散俘虏，这一点我们毫不费力地做到了。

其中有两个船长认为不太老实的，我派星期五和三个获救的人中的一个押送他们到山洞，那儿很远，他们的动静不会被人发现，如果他们挣脱逃走，也会在森林里迷路。他们把那两个人捆起来，供给他们食物，而且答应他们，如果他们安静耐心地呆在里边，一两天之内他们就可以获得自由；如果他们试图逃跑，他们就会被毫不客气地处死。他们都老实地答应耐心忍受禁闭，并对我们给予的供给表示十分感激。星期五还给了他们一些我们自制的蜡烛，好让他们舒适一些。他们根本不知道星期五正在洞口看守他们。

其余的俘虏受到了比较好的待遇，虽然船长不确信的那两个家伙始终没有松绑，另外两个人我却录用了。当然，这是由于船长的举荐，加上他们曾郑重宣誓，要和我们同生共死，所以，加上这两个，再加上船长等三个诚实的落难者，我们现在一共有七个人，而且都有武器。因此我一点

were three or four honest Men among them also.

As soon as they got to the Place where their other Boat lay, they run their Boat in to the Beach, and came all on Shore, haling the Boat up after them, which I was glad to see; for I was afraid they would rather have left the Boat at an Anchor, some Distance from the Shore, with some Hands in her, to guard her; and so we should not be able to seize the Boat.

Being on Shore, the first Thing they did, they ran all to their other Boat, and it was easy to see that they were under a great Surprize, to find her stripp'd as above, of all that was in her, and a great hole in her Bottom.

After they had mus'd a while upon this, they set up two or three great Shouts, hollowing with all their might, to try if they could make their Companions hear; but all was to no purpose: Then they came all close in a Ring, and fir'd a Volley of their small Arms, which indeed we heard, and the Ecchos made the Woods ring; but it was all One, those in the Cave we were sure could not hear, and those in our keeping, though they heard it well enough, yet durst give no Answer to them.

They were so astonish'd at the Surprize of this, that as they told us afterwards, they resolv'd to go all on board again to their Ship, and let them know, that the Men were all murther'd, and the Long-Boat stav'd; accordingly they immediately launch'd their Boat again, and gat all of them on

也不怀疑,我们有足够的实力去对付从大船上划来的那十个人,况且船长已经说过,那十个人当中还有三四个老实人呢。

且说那伙人刚划到前一只舢板停靠的地方,便把他们的舢板靠到沙滩上,一窝蜂般地上了岸,又把身后的舢板拉上了岸。见此情景,我心中暗喜。因为,我担心的是,他们会把舢板停泊在离岸远一点的水中,并留下人手看着。若是那样,我们就没法把舢板逮住了。

他们上岸后的第一件事情就是跑去看第一只舢板。显而易见,当他们看到舢板的所有设备已被拆卸一空,船底还有一个大洞时,他们全都惊呆了。

他们在那儿想了一会儿后,便一齐扯开嗓子大喊了两三声,拼命呼唤他们的同伴,可是没有任何回应。于是他们又围成一圈,朝天放了一排枪。这阵枪声我们当然听见了,而且枪声的回音在树林中产生了一连串的共鸣声,可是仍然没有任何回应。关在洞里的那两个,肯定是听不见这阵枪声的;而关在我们这里的两个俘虏,虽然听得很清楚,却自然不敢发出任何声音。

他们对于这桩出乎意料的事真是万分惊讶,据他们后来告诉我们,他们当时曾经决定回到大船上,告诉大家,那批人都给杀光了,长艇也给凿沉了。于是,他们马上把舢板

board.

The Captain was terribly amaz'd, and even confounded at this, believing they would go on board the Ship again, and set Sail, giving their Comrades for lost, and so he should still lose the Ship, which he was in Hopes we should have recover'd; but he was quickly as much frighted the other way.

They had not been long put off with the Boat, but we perceiv'd them all coming on Shore again; but with this new Measure in their Conduct, which it seems they consulted together upon, viz. To leave three Men in the Boat, and the rest to go on Shore, and go up into the Country to look for their Fellows.

This was a great Disappointment to us; for now we were at a Loss what to do; for our Seizing those Seven Men on Shore would be no Advantage to us, if we let the Boat escape; because they would then row away to the Ship, and then the rest of them would be sure to weigh and set Sail, and so our recovering the Ship would be lost.

However, we had no Remedy, but to wait and see what the Issue of Things might present; the seven Men came on Shore, and the three who remain'd in the Boat, put her off to a good Distance from the Shore, and came to an Anchor to wait for them; so that it was impossible for us to come at them in the Boat.

Those that came on Shore, kept close together, marching towards the Top of the little Hill, under which my Habitation lay; and we could see them plainly, though they could not perceive us: We could have been very glad they would have come nearer to us, so that we might have fir'd at them, or that they would have gone farther off, that we

推到水里，一齐上了船。

船长看到这种情形，非常吃惊，简直不知道怎么办才好。他相信他们一定会回到大船上去，把船开走，把他们那群伙伴丢在脑后，认为他们已经没有命了，而那样一来，他一心指望我们能够收复的大船，也就靠不住了。可是，很快地，他又同样地为另外一桩事情惊惶起来。

我们看到他们把船划出不远，又一起重新回到岸上。这次行动他们采取了新的措施。看来，他们刚才已商量好了。那就是，留三个人在舢板上，其余的人一齐上岸，深入小岛去寻找他们的伙伴。

这使我们大失所望，简直不知怎么办才好。因为如果我们让舢板开跑，即使我们把岸上的七个人通通抓住，那也毫无用处。那三个人必然会把舢板划回大船，大船上的人必然会起锚扬帆而去，那我们收复大船的希望同样会落空。

可是，我们除了静候事情的发展，别无良策。那七个人上岸了。留下的三个人把船划离了岸，远远地下锚泊定，等着接回那七个人；所以对我们而言，要进攻舢板上的人是绝无可能的。

上岸的那些人凑得很近，一起向小山头走来，而我的住处正是在这小山下；他们看不见我们，我们却可以把他们看得很清楚，可惜他们离我们还不够近，即使开枪也打不到他们；而如果他们向远一些的地

might have come abroad.

But when they were come to the Brow of the Hill, where they could see a great way into the Valleys and Woods, which lay towards the North-East Part, and where the Island lay lowest, they shouted, and hollow'd, till they were weary; and not caring it seems to venture far from the Shore, nor far from one another, they sat down together under a Tree, to consider of it: Had they thought fit to have gone to sleep there, as the other Party of them had done, they had done the Jobb for us; but they were too full of Apprehensions of Danger, to venture to go to sleep, though they could not tell what the Danger was they had to fear neither.

The Captain made a very just Proposal to me, upon this Consultation of theirs, viz. That perhaps they would all fire a Volley again, to endeavour to make their Fellows hear, and that we should all Sally upon them, just at the Juncture when their Pieces were all discharg'd, and they would certainly yield, and we should have them without Bloodshed: I lik'd the Proposal, provided it was done while we were near enough to come up to them, before they could load their Pieces again.

But this Event did not happen, and we lay still a long Time, very irresolute what Course to take; at length I told them, there would be mothing to be done in my Opinion till Night, and then if they did not return to the Boat, perhaps we might find a way to get between them, and the Shore, and so might use some Strangem with them in the Boat, to get them on Shore.

We waited a great while, though very impatient for their removing; and were very uneasy, when

方走倒也不错,因为那样的话,我们可以出击了。

他们登上了山脊,往东北面一看,见到的是一个宽阔的山谷和密密的树林——这里是岛上最低的部分——便大声叫唤起来,直叫到声嘶力竭;看来他们既不敢走得离海岸太远,也不敢彼此相距太远,只见他们在一棵树下往地上一坐,考虑该怎么办。要是他们像前面那帮人一样倒头睡觉就好了,那他们可就帮了我们的大忙。可是,他们惴惴不安,根本不敢睡觉,尽管他们搞不清面临的是什么样的危险。

船长对他们的商量结果进行了一个合理的推测,他猜他们也许会再打一排枪,努力让同伴听到,趁他们射空子弹后,我们一古脑冲上前去,他们肯定会投降,我们无需流血就能拿住他们。我很赞成这个提议,只是我们要靠近一些才能办到,要不等他们重新装上弹药就发动袭击。

然而,他们并没有放排枪。我们静静地等了很久,踌躇不定,不知该采取什么办法才好。后来,我对他们几位说,依我的看法,不到晚上,我们都无法采取行动。只有到了晚上,假使他们还没有回到舢板上去的话,我们或许能找一条路穿插到他们和沙滩之间,略施巧计,把舢板上的那三个家伙骗到岸上来。

我们等了老半天,心里非常焦急,巴不得他们尽快走

after long Consultations, we saw them start all up, and march down toward the Sea: It seems they had such dreadful Apprehensions upon them, of the Danger of the Place, that they resolv'd to go on board the Ship again, give their Companions over for lost, and so go on with their intended Voyage with the Ship.

As soon as I perceiv'd then go towards the Shore, I imagin'd it to be as it really was, That they had given over their Search, and were fot going back again; and the Captain, as soon as I told him my Thoughts, was ready to sink at the Apprehensions of it; but I presently thought of a Stratagem to fetch them back again, and which answer'd my End to a Tittle.

I order'd Friday, and the Captain's Mate, to go over the little Creek Westward, towards the Place where the Savages came to Shore, when Friday was rescu'd; and as soon as they came to a little rising Ground, at about half a Mile Distance, I bad them hollow, as loud as they could, and wait till they found the Seamen heard them; that as soon as ever they heard the Seamen answer them, they should return it again, and then keeping out of Sight, take a round, always answering when the other hollow'd, to draw them as far into the Island, and among the Woods, as possible, and then wheel about again to me, by such ways as I directed them.

They were just going into the Boat, when Friday and the Mate hollow'd, and they presently heard them, and answering run along the Shore Westward, towards the Voice they heard , when they were presently stopp'd by the Creek, where the Water being up, they could not get over, and call'd for the Boat to come up, and Set them over,

开。忽然,他们商量过一番之后,就站了起来,朝海边走去,这又使我们不安起来。看情形,他们非常担心这个地方对他们有危险,所以决定回到大船上去(以为他们那些同伴全完蛋了),按他们既定的航行计划,把大船开走。

一见他们向海边走去,我立刻就意识到他们这一回绝对是要放弃搜寻了,而且事实也正如我所料。我连忙把情况告诉了船长。他为此感到万分的忧愁和沮丧。不过,我这时倒是急中生智,想出了一个巧妙的计谋,把这些正要离岛的人又给引了回来。正是这条妙计,使我最终实现了梦寐以求的愿望。

我吩咐星期五和那位大副往西越过小河,走到那次野人们押解星期五上岸的地方,再走上半英里以外的那个小山坡上,然后尽量放声大喊,直到喊声被那些水手们听见为止;在听到那些水手们的回答之后,一定要大声回应他们;然后,以绝对隐蔽的方式,一边叫喊,一边回应,尽可能地引着他们绕上一个大圈子,把他们从海边往岛内的树林里带;目的达到后,再按照我指定的路线返回到我这边来。

那些人刚要上舢板,星期五和大副就大声喊叫起来。他们马上就听见了,于是他们一面回答着,一面沿海岸往西跑,冲着他们听见的声音跑去,跑了一程,他们就被小河挡住去路;这时河水已经涨了

as indeed I expected.

When they had Set themselves over, I observ'd, that the Boat being gone up a good way into the Creek, and as it were, in a Harbour within the Land, they took one of the three Men out of her to go along with them, and left only two in the Boat, having fastned her to the Stump of a little Tree on the Shore.

This was what I wish'd for, and immediately leaving Friday and the Captain's Mate to their Business, I took the rest with me, and crossing the Creek out of their Sight, we surpriz'd the two Men before they were aware; one of them lying on Shore, and the other being in the Boat; the Fellow on Shore, was between sleeping and waking, and going to start up, the Captain who was foremost, ran in upon him, and knock'd him down, and then call'd out to him in the Boat, to yield, or he was a dead Man.

There needed very few Arguments to perswade a single Man to yield, when he Saw five Men upon him, and his Comrade knock'd down; besides, this was it seems one of the three who were not so hearty in the Mutiny as the rest of the Crew, and therefore was easily perswaded, not only to yield, but afterwards to joyn very sincere with us.

In the mean time, Friday and the Captain's Mate so well manag'd their Business with the rest, that they drew them by hollowing and answering, from one Hill to another, and from one Wood to another, till they not only heartily tyr'd them but left them, where they were very Sure they could not reach back to the Boat, before it was dark; and indeed they were heartily tyr'd themselves also by the Time they came back to us.

起来，他们没法过河，只好把那舢板叫过来，把他们渡过去，一切都如我所料。

那舢板沿着小河往上驶了一段路程，开到一个好像内河港口的地方。他们渡过小河之后，就把船拴在一根小树桩上，又从船上三个人中间叫了一个下来跟他们一块走，只留下两个人看船。

这一切正合我的心愿。我让星期五和大副继续干他们的事，自己马上带其余的人偷偷渡过小河，出其不意地向那两个人扑过去。当时，一个人正躺在岸上，一个人还在船里呆着。那岸上的人半睡半醒，正想爬起来，走在头里的船长一下冲到他跟前，把他打倒在地。然后，船长又向船上的人大喝一声，叫他赶快投降，否则就要他的命。

当一个人看到五个人向他扑来，而他的同伴又已被打倒，叫他投降是用不着多费什么口舌的。而且，他又是被迫参加叛乱的三个水手之一，所以，他不但一下子就被我们降服了，而且后来还忠心耿耿地参加到我们这边来。

与此同时，星期五和大副那边的事进行得也很顺利，他们的叫唤和回应把那帮人从一座小山引到另一座小山，从一片树林引到另一片树林，不但使他们累得筋疲力尽，而且最后把他们撂在一个地方，使他们在天黑以前绝对回不到舢板上；事实上，星期五和大副回来时，他们自己也是累得

We had nothing now to do, but to watch for them, in the Dark, and to fall upon them, so as to make sure work with them.

It was several Hours after Friday came back to me, before they came back to their Boat; and we could hear the foremost of them long before they came quite up, calling to those behind to come along, and could also hear them answer and complain, how lame and tyr'd they were, and not able to -come any faster, which was very welcome News to us.

At length they came up to the Boat; but 'tis impossible to express their Confusion, when they found the Boat fast a-Ground in the Creek, the Tide ebb'd out, and their two Men gone We could hear them call to one another in a most lamentable Manner, telling one another, they were gotten into an inchanted Island; that either there were Inhabitants in it, and they should all be murther'd, or else there were Devils and Spirits in it, and they should be all carry'd away, and devour'd.

They hallow'd again, and call'd their two Comerades by their Names, a great many times, but no Answer. After some time, we could see them, by the little Light there was, run about wringing their Hands like Men in Despair; and that sometimes they would go and sit down in the Boat to rest themselves, then come ashore again, and walk about again, and so over the same thing again.

够呛的。

现在,我们已没有别的事可做,只需在黑暗中守候他们,给他们以出其不意的打击,把他们彻底消灭掉。

星期五回到我这里后,又过了好几个钟头,那伙人才回到他们的舢板这里。我们听见走在前面的几个对远远地落在后面的几个大声叫唤,叫他们快点赶上来,又听见后面那几个一边答应,一边抱怨,说他们腿都走瘸了,精疲力竭,再也走不动了。对我们来说,这实在是个好消息。

最后,他们终于走到了舢板旁。可是,他们发现舢板已牢牢地搁在河床上(因为潮水此刻已经退去),留下看船的两个人也已无影无踪。他们那种惊惶的样子真不知道该怎么形容才好。我们听到他们用一种凄凉悲惨的声音互相呼唤着彼此的名字,然后唉声叹气地抱怨自己误上了一个魔岛,说这岛上不是有什么栖居者会把他们杀死,就是有什么鬼怪会把他们抓走或吞食。

接着,他们开始放声呼喊起来,一遍一遍地叫着那两个守船同伴的名字,可是他们始终听不到任何回音。过了一会儿,我们借着黄昏暗淡的光线,看到他们在不知所措地来回走动,不由自主地扭动着双手,一副万分绝望无法自持的样子。他们一会儿跑到舢板上坐下来休息,一会儿又回到岸上继续狂走乱跑,就这么来

My Men would fain have me given them Leave to fall upon them at once in the Dark; but I was willing to take them at some Advantage, so to spare them, and kill as few of them as I could; and especially I was unwilling to hazard the killing any of our own Men, knowing the other were very well armed. I resolved to wait to see if they did not separate; and therefore to make sure of them, I drew my Ambuscade nearer, and order'd Friday and the Captain, to creep upon their Hands and Feet as close to the Ground as they could, that they might not be discover'd, and get as near them as they could possibly, before they offered to fire.

They had not been long in that Posture, but that the Boatswain, who was the principal Ringleader of the Mutiny, and had now shewn himself the most dejected and dispirited of all the rest, came walking towards them with two more of their Crew; the Captain was so eager, as having this principal Rogue so much in his Power, that he could hardly have Patience to let him come so near, as to be sure of him; for they only heard his Tongue before: But when they came nearer, the Captain and Friday starting up on their Feet, let fly at them.

The Boatswain was kill'd upon the Spot, the next Man was Shot into the Body, and fell just by him, tho' he did not die 'till an Hour or two after; and the third run for it.

At the Noise of the Fire, I immediately advanc'd with my whole Army, which was now 8 Men, viz. my self Generalissimo, Friday my Lieutenant-General, the Captain and his two Men, and the three Prisoners of War, who we had trusted with Arms.

来回回,反复不停。

这时候,我手下的人恨不得我允许他们趁着夜色立即攻上去;可是我的意思是找一个更有利的机会向他们进攻,给他们留一条生路,尽可能少杀死几个。我尤其不愿意我们中间有人受到伤亡,因为我知道对方都是全副武装的。我决定等待着,看他们是不是会散开。因此,为了更有把握制服他们,我把我的埋伏向前推进了一段距离,命令星期五和船长尽可能贴着地面向前爬进,不让他们看见,并且在他们动手开枪以前,爬得离他们越近越好。

他们在那儿埋伏了没多长时间,就看见水手长同另外两个人走近了他们;这个叛变中的首恶分子现在是众人里头最垂头丧气、情绪低落的;船长一心要打得这罪魁祸首措手不及,所以只是听见他说话声音,没等他走近后认准是他,就急不可待地同星期五一跃而起,向已经走近的他们开了枪。

水手长当场就被击毙,另一个人身上中了弹,跌倒在水手长的尸体旁,过了一两个小时才断气;第三个人撒腿就跑。

我一听见枪响,立即带领全军前进。我这支军队现在一共有八个人,那就是:我,总司令;星期五,我的副司令。另外是船长和他的两个部下。还有三个我们信得过的俘虏,

We came upon them indeed in the Dark, so that they could not see our Number; and I made the Man we had left in the Boat, who was now one of us, call to them by Name, to try if I could bring them to a Parley, and so might perhaps reduce them to Terms, which fell out just as we desir'd: for deed it was easy to think, as their Condition then was, they would be very willing to capitulate; so he calls out as loud as he could, to one of them, Tom Smith, Tom Smith; Tom Smith answered immediately, Who's that, Robinson? for it seems he knew his Voice: T'other answered, Ay, ay; for God's Sake, Tom Smith, throw down your Arms, and yield, or, you are all dead Men this Moment.

Who must me yield to? where are they? (says Smith again;) Here they are: says he, here's our Captain, and fifty Men with him, have been hunting you this two Hours; the Boatswain is kill'd, Will Frye is wounded, and I am a Prisoner; and if you do not yield, you are all lost.

Will they give us. Quarter then, (says Tom Smith) and we will yield? I'll go and ask, if you promise to yield, says Robinson; So he ass:'d the Captain, and the Captain then calls himself out, You Smith, you know my Voice, if you lay down your Arms immediately, and submit, you shall have your Lives all but Will. Atkins.

我们也发给了他们枪。

趁着漆黑的夜色，我们向他们发动了猛攻。他们根本看不清我们究竟有多少人。那个被他们留在舢板上的人，现在已是我们的人了。我命令他喊那些水手的名字，看看能否促使他们和我们谈判，强其他们投降。结果我们如愿以偿。因为不难理解，他们处在当前的情况下是十分愿意投降的。于是，他尽量提高嗓门，喊出他们中间一个人的名字："汤姆·史密斯！汤姆·史密斯！"汤姆·史密斯似乎听出了他的声音，立即回答说："是鲁滨逊吗？"那个人恰好也叫鲁滨逊。他回答说："是啊，是我！看在上帝的份上，汤姆·史密斯，快放下武器投降吧！要不然你们马上就都没命了。"

"我们向谁投降？他们在哪儿？"史密斯随即问道。"他们就在这儿，"鲁滨逊答道，"我们的船长就在这儿，有五十个人同他在一起，跟踪你们已有两个小时啦！水手长已被打死，威尔·弗赖依也被打伤了，我已经成了俘虏。要是你们不投降，你们就全完了。"

"要是我们投降了，他们会饶我们性命吗？"汤姆·史密斯又问道。"如果你们答应投降，我就去问。"鲁滨逊说后，就问船长，于是船长亲自发话道："听着，史密斯，你是听得出我的声音的。只要你立刻放下武器，我保证缴枪不杀，别人也一样，只除了威尔·阿特金斯。"

Upon this, Will Atkins cry'd out, For God's Sake, Captain, give me Quarter, what have I done? They have been all as bad as I, which by the Way was not true neither; for it seems this Will. Atkins was the first Man that laid hold of the Captain, when they first mutiny'd, and used him barbarously, in tying his Hands, and giving him injurious Language. However, the Captain told him he must lay down his Arms at Discretion, and trust to the Governour's Mercy, by which he meant me; for they all call'd me Governour.

In a Word, they all laid down their Arms, and begg'd their Lives; and I sent the Man that had parley'd with them, and two more, who bound them all; and then my great Army of 50 Men, which particularly with those three, were all but eight, came up and seiz'd upon them all, and upon their Boat, only that I kept my self and one more out of Sight, for Reasons of State.

Our next Work was to repair the Boat, and think of seizing the Ship; and as for the Captain, now he had Leisure to parley with them: He expostulated with them upon the Villany of their Practices with him, and at length upon the farther Wickedness of their Design, and how certainly it must bring them to Misery and Distress in the End, and perhaps to the Gallows.

They all appear'd very penitent, and begg'd hard for their Lives; as for that, he told them, they were none of his Prisoners, but the Commander of the Island; that they thought they had set

威尔·阿特金斯听了这话,便叫道:"看在上帝的份上,船长,饶了我吧。我究竟干了什么坏事呀?他们都跟我一样呢。"顺便提一句,他这是睁着眼睛撒谎。据说,在叛乱开始的时候,就是这个威尔·阿特金斯首先拿住了船长,而且非常残暴地虐待他,用绳子捆住他的手,又用污言秽语辱骂他。尽管如此,船长还是叫他自动放下武器,向总督大人求情。他所谓的总督便是指我,因为他们都称我是总督。

总而言之,他们全都放下了武器,纷纷请求饶命。我随即指派刚才向他们喊话劝降的鲁滨逊和另外两个人去把他们统统捆起来。然后,我的五十人大军——其实连同鲁滨逊他们三人,我们总共才只有八个人——蜂拥而上,把他们和舢板全部扣押了起来。由于身份的关系,我和另外一个人没有露面。

我们下一步的工作就是要修复那只舢板,并且考虑夺回大船的具体事宜。船长这时也趁空闲时间与他们进行谈判。他首先谴责了他们对待他的恶劣态度,继而痛斥了他们发动叛乱的邪恶居心,最后告诫他们,他们的罪恶行径最终必将导致自己的不幸与灾难,也许还会被送上绞刑架。

他们一个个表示悔罪,苦苦地哀求饶命。关于这一点,他告诉他们,他们并不是他的俘虏,而是岛上主管长官的俘

him on Shore in a barren uninhabited Island, but it had pleased God so to direct them, that the Island was inhabited, and that the Governour was an English Man; that he might hang them all there, if he pleased; but as he had given them all Quarter, he supposed he would send them to England to be dealt with there, as Justice requir'd, except Atkins, who he was commanded by the Governour to advise to prepare for Death; for that he would be hang'd in the Morning.

Though this was all a Fiction of his own, yet it had its desired Effect; Atkins fell upon his Knees to beg the Captain to interceed with the Governour for his Life; and all the rest beg'd of him for God's Sake, that they might not be sent to England.

It now occurr'd to me, that the time of our Deliverance was come, and that it would be a most easy thing to bring these Fellows in, to be hearty in getting Possession of the Ship; so I retir'd in the Dark from them, that they might not see what Kind of a Governour they had, and call'd the Captain to me; when I call'd, as at a good Distance, one of the Men was order'd to speak again, and say to the Captain, Captain, the Commander calls for you; and presently the Captain reply'd, Tell his Excellency, I am just a coming: This more perfectly amused' them; and they all believed that the Commander was just by with his fifty Men.

Upon the Captain's coming to me, I told him my Project for seizing the Ship, which he lik'd of wonderfully well, and resolv'd to put it in Execution the next Morning.

But in Order to execute it with more Art, and secure of Success, I told him, we must divide the

房。他说，他们满以为把他送上了一个无人的荒岛，可是上帝却指示他们把他送上一个有居民的岛，而且岛上的总督还是一个英国人。他说如果总督高兴，他很可以把他们通通吊死在岛上；可是，他现在既然饶恕了他们，大概要把他们送英国，秉公治罪，只有阿特金斯一个，他已经奉到总督的命令，通知他准备受死，因为明天一清早就要吊死他。

这些话虽然都是船长杜撰出来的，然而却达到了预期的效果。阿特金斯跪下来哀求船长向总督求情，饶他一命。其余的人也一起向船长哀求，要他看在上帝的份上，不要把他们送回英国。

这时我忽然想到，我们获救的时刻到了。现在把这些人争取过来，让他们全心全意去夺取那只大船，已非难事。于是我在夜色中离开了他们，免得他们看见我是怎样的一个总督。然后，我把船长叫到身边。当我叫他的时候，因为已有相当的距离，就派了一个人去传话，对船长说："船长，司令叫你。"船长马上回答说："回去告诉阁下，我就来。"这样一来，就使他们更加深信不疑了。他们都相信，司令和他手下的五十名士兵就在附近。

船长走过来后，我就把夺船的计划告诉了他。他认为非常好，并决定在第二天早晨进行。

为了使计划进行得更巧妙，成功的系数更大，我建议

Prisoners, and that he should go and take Atkins and two more of the worst of them, and send them pinion'd to the Cave where the others lay: This was committed to Friday and the two Men who came on Shore with the Captain.

They convey'd them to the Cave, as to a Prison; and it was indeed a dismal Place, especially to Men in their Condition.

The other I order'd to my Bower, as I call'd it, of which I have given a full Description; and as it was fenc'd in, and they pinion'd, the Place was secure enough, considering they were upon their Behaviour.

To these in the Morning I sent the Captain, who was to enter into a Parley with them, in a Word to try them, and tell me, whether he thought they might be trusted or no, to on Board and surprize the Ship. He talk'd to them of the Injury done him, of the Condition they were brought to; and that though the Governour had given them Quarter for their Lives, as to the present Action, yet that if they were sent to England, they would all be hang'd in Chains, to be sure; but that if they would join in so just an Attempt, as to recover the Ship, he would have the Governour's Engagement for their Pardon.

Any one may guess how readily such a Proposal would be accepted by Men in their Condition; they fell down on their Knees to the Captain, and promised with the deepest Imprecations, that they would be faithful to him to the last Drop, and that they should owe their Lives to him, and would go with him all over the World, that they would own

我们必须把俘虏分开,他应该去把阿特金斯和另外两名他们中最坏的家伙带走,把他们捆送到关闭另外几个人的岩洞里,我们把这件事交给了星期五和另两个跟船长上岸的人去办。

他们把那几个家伙遣送到岩洞里,像到了监狱一般。那儿确实是个不幸的地方,尤其是对他们这种处境的人而言。

其余的人我命令把他们送到我的别墅,这座别墅,我在前面已作过详细描述,那里有篱墙围着,而这些人又被捆绑着,所以那地方还是很安全的。他们也清楚,他们的命运取决于他们的表现。

第二天早上,我要船长去对他们讲话,其实也就是去试探他们,看看他们能不能信任,能不能派他们去夺大船;我要他在讲话后把他的想法告诉我。他对他们讲了一番,指责了他们对他造成的伤害,指明了他们目前的处境,同时也指出,尽管总督眼下饶了他们性命,但只要被押回英国,就肯定全要被铁链吊死;然而,如果他们参加夺船的行动,将功赎罪,那么他愿意去求情,请总督答应赦免他们。

不难想象,这样一个建议,对于他们这种处境的人来说,是非常乐于接受的。他们便跪倒在船长面前,又是保证,又是发誓,表示要对他效忠,直到流尽最后一滴血;同时,又是感激他救了他们的

him for a Father to them as long as they liv'd.

Well, says the Captain, I must go and tell the Governour what you say, and see what I can do to bring him to consent to it: So he brought me an Account of the Temper he found them in; and that he verily believ'd they would be faithful.

However, that we might be very secure, I told him he should go back again, and choose out five of them, and tell them, they might see that he did not want Men, that he would take out those five to be his Assistants, and that the Governour would keep the other two, and the three that were sent Prisoners to the Castle, (my Cave) as Hostages, for the Fidelity of those five; and that if they prov'd unfaithful in the Execution, the five Hostages should be hang'd in Chains alive upon the Shore.

This look'd severe, and convinc'd them that the Governour was in Earnest; however they had no Way left them, but to accept it; and it was now the Business of the Prisoners, as much as of the Captain, to perswade the other five to do their Duty.

Our Strength was now thus ordered for the Expedition: 1. The Captain, his Mate, and Passenger. 2. Then the two Prisoners of the first Gang, to whom having their Characters from the Captain, I had given their Liberty, and trusted them with Arms. 3. The other two who I had kept till now, in my Bower, pinion'd; but upon the Captain's Motion, had now releas'd. These five

命,愿意跟随他到天涯海角,并且今生今世都把他当作父亲对待。

"很好,"船长说,"我得去把你们的话禀报总督,并尽我所能,求他同意你们的请求。"他便把他们的想法原原本本地告诉了我。他坚信,他们都忠诚可靠。

不过,为了确保万无一失,我让船长再去一趟,从他们当中挑选五个人出来。我叫船长告诉他们,现在并不缺少人手,所以只需要挑选五个人做他的助手;另外,总督要把这里剩下的两个人和已经送往城堡(其实是地洞)中关押的三个人留下作为人质,以保证参加行动的那五个人的忠诚。如果被挑出的五个人在收复大船的过程中有半点不忠的表现,留在这里的五个人质就要在岸边被铁链活活绞死。

这个办法不仅看起来非常严厉,而且使他们确信这位总督办事极其严谨认真,所以他们除了接受之外,别无他法。而且,这样一来,留下的人质反而像船长那样,竭尽全力地告诫那五个人要尽忠职守,不得疏忽。

我们出征的兵力是这样安排的:一,船长、大副、旅客。二,第一批水手中的两个俘虏,我从船长口里了解了他们的品行,业已恢复他们的自由,并且发给他们武器;三,另外两个水手,这两个人直到现在为止都被捆起来关在我的

releas'd at last: So that they were twelve in all, besides five we kept Prisoners in the Cave, for Hostages.

I ask'd the Captain, if he was willing to venture with these Hands on Board the Ship; for as for me and my Man Friday, I did not think it was proper for us to stir, having seven Men left behind; and it was Employment enough for us to keep them assunder, and supply them with Victuals.

As to the five in the Cave, I resolv'd to keep them fast, but Friday went in twice a Day to them, to supply them with Necessaries; and I made the other two carry Provisions to a certain Distance, where Friday was to take it.

When I shew'd my self to the two Hostages, it was with the Captain, who told them, I was the Person the Governour had order'd to look after them, and that it was the Governour's Pleasure they should not stir any where, but by my Direction; that if they did, they should be fetch'd into the Castle, and be lay'd in Irons; so that as we never suffered them to see me as Governour, so I now appear'd as another Person, and Spoke of the Governour, the Garrison, the Castle, and the like, upon all Occasions.

The Captain now had no Difficulty before him, but to furnish his two Boats, Stop the Breach of one, and Man them. He made his Passenger Captain of one, with four other Men; and himself, and his Mate, and five more, went in the other: And they contriv'd their Business very well; for they came up to the Ship about Midnight: As soon as they came within Call of the Ship, he made Robinson hale them, and tell them they had

茅屋里,现在经船长建议,也把他们释放了;四,那五个最后被释放的人。因此,除了我们关在地洞的五个俘虏和两个还没有关起来的人质以外,一共有十二个人。

我问船长,他是否愿意冒险带领这些人去收复大船。我认为,我和星期五不宜出动,因为岛上还有七个俘虏,而且他们又都被分散看守着,还得供给他们饮食,也够我们忙的了。

我决定牢牢看守好关在洞里的那五个人。我让星期五一天去两次,给他们送些食品去。我要其他两个人先把东西送到一个指定的地点,然后再由星期五送去。

当我在那两个人质面前露面时,我是同船长一起去的。船长向他们介绍,我是由总督派来监视他们的。总督的命令是,没有我的指示,不允许他们到处乱动,否则,就会被押回城堡用铁链吊死。就这样,我们从不让他们把我看作总督。在许多时候,我都以另外一个人的身份出现,同他们谈到总督、城堡、驻兵等等。

现在船长除了安置好他的两只舢板,修补好其中一只的漏洞,并派齐人员之外,已没有什么困难了。他那名乘客做了其中一只船的船长,并派了其他四个人,他和大副以及其他五个人则上了另一只舢板。他们的事情进展很顺利,到半夜时分已接近大船,

— 342 —

brought off the Men and the Boat, but that it was a long time before they had found them, and the like holding them in a Chat 'till they came to the Ship's Side when the Captain and the Mate entring first with their Arms, immediately knock'd down the second Mate and Carpenter, with the But-end of their Muskets, being very faithfully seconded by their Men, they secur'd all the rest that were upon the Main and Quarter Decks, and began to fasten the Hatches to keep them down who were below, when the other Boat and their Men entring at the fore Chains, secur'd the Fore-Castle of the Ship, and the Scuttle which went down into the Cook Room, making three Men they found there, Prisoners.

When this was done, and all safe upon Deck, the Captain order'd the Mate with three Men to break into the Round-House where the new Rebel Captain lay, and having taken the Alarm, was gotten up, and with two Men and a Boy had gotten Fire Arms in their Hands, and when the Mate with a Crow split open the Door, the new Captain and his Men fir'd boldly among them, and wounded the Mate with a Musket Ball which broke his Arm, and wounded two more of the but kill'd no Body.

The Mate calling for Help, rush'd however into the Round-House, wounded as he was, and with his Pistol shot the new Captain thro' the Head, the Bullet entring at his Mouth, and came out again behind one of his Ears; so that he never spoke a Word; upon which the rest yielded, and the Ship was taken effectually, without any more Lives lost.

As soon as the Ship was thus secur'd, the Cap-

当他们靠近大船能够喊话时，他便让鲁滨逊喊话，告诉对方他们已经把人和舢板都带回来了，但找他们却花了很长时间，还有些诸如此类的话，一边谈着，一边靠近了大船，与此同时，船长、大副首先带枪上了大船，一下子就用枪托把二副和船上的木匠打倒在地。在手下的人密切配合下，他们制服了前后甲板上的人，接着便把舱口盖关上，使舱下的人上不来；这时另一条舢板上的人已从船头的锚链攀援而上，占领了前舱和通向厨房的舱口，活捉了他们在那里发现的三个人。

做到这一步之后，他们已牢牢地控制了甲板；船长随即命令大副带三个人去攻打艉楼的甲板室。叛变后担任船长的家伙正睡在里面，这时已情知有变，立刻起了床，带着两个部下和跟班都取枪在手；大副用起货钩刚把门撬开，这新船长和他的死党竟悍然开火，一颗火枪的子弹打伤了大副，使他手臂骨折，他的两个伙伴也受了伤，幸好没有打死人。

大副一面呼救，一面冲进舱室。尽管身上带伤，但他还是用手枪击中了新船长的脑袋，子弹从那家伙的嘴里进去，从他的耳朵里出来，这样，他便永远说不出话来了。其余的人见此情景，便都投了降。至此，大船已完全收复，没有再死更多的人。

大船刚一收复，船长便下

tain order'd seven Guns to be fir'd, which was the Signal agreed upon with me, to give me Notice of his Success, which you may be sure I was very glad to hear, having sat watching upon the Shore for it till near two of the Clock in the Morning.

令鸣放七枪(这是我们事先订好的信号),通知我行动已经成功。你一定想象得出,听到这枪声我心里多么高兴,因为我坐在沙滩上等待鸣枪,一直等到将近凌晨两点。

Part 8

Having thus heard the Signal plainly, I laid me down; and it having been a Day of great Fatigue to me, I slept very sound, 'till I was something surpriz'd with the Noise of a Gun; and presently starting up, I heard a Man call me by the Name of Governour, Governour, and presently I knew the Captain's Voice, when climbing up to the Top of the Hill, there he stood, and pointing to the Ship, he embrac'd me in Arms, My dear Friend and Deliverer, says he, there's your Ship, for she is all yours, and so are we and all that belong to her. I cast my Eyes to the Ship, and there she rode within little more than half a Mile of the Shore; for they had weighed for as soon as they were Masters of her; and the Weather being fair, had brought her to an Anchor just against the Mouth of the little Creek; and the Tide being up, the Captain had brought the Pinnace in near the Place where I at first landed my Rafts, and so landed just at my Door. I was at first ready to sink down with the Surprize. For I saw my Deliverance indeed visibly put into my Hands, all things easy, and a large Ship just ready to carry me away whither I pleased to go. At first, for some time, I was not able to answer him one Word; but as he had taken me in his Arms, I held fast by him, or I should have fallen to the Ground.

He perceived the Surprize, and immediately pulls a Bottle out of his Pocket, and gave me a Dram of Cordial, which he had brought on Purpose for me; after I had drank it, I sat down upon the Ground; and though it brought me to my self, yet it was a good while before I could speak a

第 八 部

我听清了信号，便放心地睡觉了。忙碌劳累了一整天，我已疲乏至极，所以，睡得十分香甜。突然，在睡梦之中听到一声枪响，我立刻惊醒过来。这时，听到有人在大声喊："总督！总督！"我听出是船长的声音，就走上小山的山顶，果真见到船长站在那里，他指了指大船，然后把我拥抱在怀里，对我说："我亲爱的朋友，我亲爱的救命恩人，这是你的船！这船是你的，我们这些人和船上的一切都是你的！"我朝他指的方向望去，只见大船就停泊在离岸半英里之处。原来，船长他们收复大船后，看天气晴朗，就起锚开船来到我的小河口上。由于正值涨潮，船长便划着舢板来到我当初停泊木筏卸货的地方，正好在我的家门口上了岸。起初，这个突如其来的喜讯，几乎使我晕倒在地，因为我亲眼看见我脱险的事情已经十拿九稳，百事顺利，而且还有一条大船准备把我载到我愿意去的地方。有好半天，我一句话也回答不上来，要不是他用手臂把我紧紧地抱住，我早已倒在地上了。

他看见我那么震动，马上从袋子里取出一个瓶子来，把他特别为我带来的提神酒给我喝了几口。喝完之后，我就坐在地上；虽然这几口酒使我恢复了知觉，可是又过了好半

Word to him.

All this while the poor Man was in as great an Extasy as I, only not under any Surprize, as I was; and he said a thousand kind tender things to me, to compose me and bring me to my self; but such was the Flood of Joy in my Breast, that it put all my Spirits into Confusion, at last it broke out into Tears, and in a little while after, I recovered my Speech.

Then I took my Turn, and embrac'd him as my Deliverer; and we rejoyc'd together. I told him, I look upon him as a Man sent from Heaven to deliver me, and that the whole Transaction seemed to be a Chain of Wonders; that such things as these were the Testimonies we had of a secret Hand of Providence governing the World, and an Evidence, that the Eyes of an infinite Power could search into the remotest Corner of the World, and send Help to the Miserable whenever he pleased.

I forgot not to lift up my Heart in Thankfulness to Heaven, and what Heart could forbear to bless him, who had not only in a miraculous Manner provided for one in such a Wilderness, and in such a desolate Condition, but from whom every Deliverance must always be acknowledged to proceed.

When we had talk'd a while, the Captain told me, he had brought me some little Refreshment, such as the Ship afforded, and such as the Wretches that had been so long his Master had not plunder'd him of: Upon this he call'd aloud to the Boat, and bid his Men bring the things ashore that were for the Governour; and indeed it was a Present, as if I had been one not that was to be carry'd away along with them, but as if I had been to dwell upon the Island still, and they were to go without me.

First he had brought me a Case of Bottles full of

天我才说得出话。

这时候,船长也和我一样欣喜若狂,只是不像我那么激动罢了。于是,他对我说了无数亲切温暖的话,让我安定下来,清醒过来。但我心中惊喜交加,不能自已,最后,我失声大哭。又过了一会儿,我才能开口说话。

这时,我拥抱了船长,把他当作我的救命恩人。我们两个人都喜不自胜。我告诉他,在我看来,他是上天特意派来救我脱险的;又说这件事的经过简直是一连串的奇迹。这类事情证明,有一种天意在冥冥中支配着世界,证明上帝无所不在,并能看清天涯海角发生的一切,只要他愿意,任何时候都可以救助不幸的人。

我心里并没有忘记感谢上帝。我又怎能不感谢上帝呢?他不仅在这种荒野的地方,在这种孤苦伶仃的处境中,用一种神奇的方式使我自给自足,就是我的每次脱险,也都应该归功于他的恩典。

当我们谈了一会儿后,船长便告诉我他给我带来了一些面食,这是船上所能够拿出的,也是那帮坏蛋控制大船以后没有掠取的东西。这时,船长向舢板大喊了一声,吩咐他的手下把带给总督的东西送上岸,实际上,这是一份丰厚的礼物,初看起来,似乎我将不被他们带走,而是要留在这个岛上继续居住下去,不同他们一块离开。

首先,他送了我一箱上等

excellent Cordial Waters, six large Bottles of Madera Wine; the Bottles held two Quarts apiece; two Pound of excellent good Tobacco, twelve good Pieces of the Ship's Beef, and six Pieces of Pork, with a Bag of Pease, and about a hundred Weight of Bisket.

He brought me also a Box of Sugar, a Box of Flower, a Bag full of Lemons, and two Bottles of Lime-Juice, and Abundance of other things: But besides these, and what was a thousand times more useful to me, he brought me six clean new Shirts, six very good Neckcloaths, two Pair of Gloves, one Pair of Shoes, a Hat, and one Pair of Stockings, and a very good Suit of Cloaths of his own, which had been worn but very little: In a Word, he cloathed me from Head to Foot.

It was a very kind and agreeable Present, as any one may imagine to one in my Circumstances: But never was any thing in the World of that Kind so unpleasant, awkard, and uneasy, as it was to me to wear such Cloaths at their first putting on.

After these Ceremonies past, and after all his good things were brought into my little Apartment, we began to consult what was to be done with the Prisoners we had; for it was worth considering, whether we might venture to take them away with us or no, especially two of them, who we knew to be incorrigible and refractory to the last Degree; and the Captain said, he knew they were such Rogues, that there was no obliging them, and if he did carry them away, it must be in Irons, as Malefactors to be delivered over to Justice at the first English Colony he could come at; and I found that the Captain himself was very anxious about it.

露酒,六大瓶马德拉白葡萄酒,每瓶容量为半加仑;两磅上好的烟草,十二大块船上食用的牛肉,六大块猪肉,一袋豌豆,一百磅饼干。

他还送给我一箱糖,一桶面粉,满满一袋柠檬,两瓶酸橙汁和许多其他的东西。除了这些,他还为我带来了六件干净的新衬衫,六条高质量的领巾,两副手套,一双皮鞋,一顶帽子,一双长筒袜和一套他自己没怎么穿过的上好衣服。对我而言,这些东西的用处真是不知有多大;千句并一句,他让我从头到脚穿戴得焕然一新。

谁都可以想象得出,对于处在我这种境地的人,这份礼物包含着多少爱心,又多么受我欢迎。可是,当我刚刚穿上这些衣服的时候,又觉得天底下没有什么东西比这些衣服更使我感到难受、别扭和不自然。

行过这些仪式,把他的所有这些好东西搬进我的住处后,我们便开始讨论,该如何处置我们所抓的这些俘虏。我们得慎重考虑一下,是否能冒险把他们随船带走,特别是那两个恶棍,我们知道,这两个人简直不可救药,顽固不化到了极点。船长说,他知道他们是两个无赖,对他们不留情,假如带他们走,就得把他们当作罪犯,用铁链子锁住,等我们途中行到一个英国殖民地,就将他们移交当局法

Upon this, I told him, that if he desir'd it, I durst undertake to bring the two Men he spoke of, to make it their own Request that he should leave them upon the Island: I should be very glad of that, says the Captain, with all my Heart.

Well, says I, I will send for them up, and talk with them for you; so I caused Friday and the two Hostages, for they were now discharg'd, their Comrades having perform'd their Promise; I say, I caused them to go to the Cave, and bring up the five Men pinion'd, as they were, to the Bower, and keep them there 'till I came.

After some time, I came thither dress'd in my new Habit, and now I was call'd Governour again; being all met, and the Captain with me, I caused the Men to be brought before me, and I told them, I had had a full Account of their villanous Behaviour to the Captain, and how they had run away with the Ship, and were preparing to commit farther Robberies, but that Providence had ensnar'd them in their own Ways, and that they were fallen into the Pit which they had digged for others.

I let them know, that by my Direction the Ship had been seiz'd, that she lay now in the Road; and they might see by and by, that their new Captain had receiv'd the Reward of his Villany; for that they might see him hanging at the Yard-Arm.

办。看得出来,船长对于带走这两个人,心存忧虑,十分担心。

见此情形,我告诉他,如果他同意,我可以负责让这两个人自己提出请求留在岛上。"你要是能这么做,那我可就太高兴了!"船长说,"我完全同意!"

"那好,"我说,"我现在就派人把他们带来,跟他谈一谈。"我派星期五和那两个原来留在岛上监外看管的人质一起去执行这个任务。这两个人质在他们的同伴履行了收复大船的诺言后就被彻底解除了监管。星期五带着他俩按照我的吩咐把关在地洞中的五个人质依然捆绑着带到了我的茅屋,暂时关在那里等候我的到来。

过了一会儿,我就穿着我的新衣服到那边去了。现在,我又以总督的身份出现了。我和船长到了那边,跟我们的人碰了头,我就叫人把他们带到我面前来,对他们说,关于他们对待船长的罪恶行为,我已经获得了详细的报告,我已经知道他们怎样把船夺走,并且还准备去干别的强盗勾当,但上帝却使他们自投罗网,跌进了他们替别人掘的陷阱里。

我让他们知道,在我的指挥下,大船已经夺了回来,现在正停泊在海口里;他们等一会儿就可以看见他们的新船长已经受到了他的作恶多端的报应,被吊在桅杆顶上示众。

That as to them, I wanted to know what they had to say, why I should not execute them as Pirates taken in the Fact, as by my Commission they could not doubt I had Authority to do.

One of them answer'd in the Name of the rest, That they had nothing to say but this, That when they were taken, the Captain promis'd them their Lives, and they humbly implor'd my Mercy; But I told them, I knew not what Mercy to shew them; for as for my self, I had resolv'd to quit the Island with all my Men, and had taken Passage with the Captain to go for England: And as for the Captain, he could not carry them to England, other than as Prisoners in Irons to be try'd for Mutiny, and running away with the Ship; the Consequence of which, they must needs know, would be the Gallows; so that I could not tell which was best for them, unless they had a Mind to take their Fate in the Island; if they desir'd, that I did not care, as I had Liberty to leave it, I had some Inclination to give them their Lives, if they thought they could shift on Shore.

They seem'd very thankful for it, said they would much rather venture to stay there, than to be carry'd to England to be hang'd; so I left it on that Issue.

However, the Captain seem'd to make some Difficulty of it, as if he durst not leave them there: Upon this I seem'd a little angry with the Captain, and told him, That they were my Prisoners, not his; and that seeing I had offered them so much Favour, I would be as good as my Word; and that if he did not think fit to consent to it, I would set them at Liberty, as I found them; and

至于他们，我倒想知道他们还有什么话可说。事实上，我完全可以把他们以海盗论处。当然，他们绝不会怀疑，我完全有权把他们处死。

这时，他们中间有一个人出来代表大家说话了。他说，他们没有什么话可说。只是他们被俘时，船长曾答应饶他们不死的。他们现在只有低头恳求我的宽恕。可是，我告诉他们，因为我自己已决定带着手下的人离开本岛，跟船长一起搭船回英国去，所以我不知道该如何宽恕他们。至于船长，他只能把他们当作囚犯关起来带回英国，并以谋反和劫船的罪名送交当局审判。其结果他们应该都知道，那必定是上绞刑架。所以，我实在也为他们想不出更好的办法，除非他们决定留在岛上，听任命运的安排。如果他们同意这个办法，我本人没有意见，因为我反正要离开本岛了。只要他们愿意留在岛上自谋生计，我可以饶他们不死。

他们对这个办法颇为感激，表示他们宁愿冒险留在岛上，也不愿被带回英国送上绞刑架。于是，我便同意这么做了。

尽管如此，船长似乎还不太满意，仿佛是不敢把他们留在这里似的。我对船长这种态度颇为生气，就告诉他，这些人是我的俘虏，并不是他的，既然已经看到我对他们许下特权我就该尽量去履行。如果他认为这样做不合适不

if he did not like it, he might take them again if he could catch them.

Upon this they appear'd very thankful, and I accordingly set them at Liberty, and bad them retire into the Woods to the Place whence they came, and I would leave them some Fire Arms, some Ammunition, and some Directions how they should live very well, if they thought fit.

Upon this I prepar'd to go on Board the Ship, but told the Captain, that I would stay that Night to prepare my things, and desir'd him to go on Board in the mean time, and keep all right in the Ship, and send the Boat on Shore the next Day for me; ordering him in the mean time to cause the new Captain who was kill'd, to be hang'd at the Yard-Arm that these Men might see him.

When the Captain was gone, I sent for the Men up to me to my Apartment, and entred seriously into Discourse with them of their Circumstances, I told them, I thought they had made a right Choice; that if the Captain carry'd them away, they would certainly be hang'd. I shewed them the new Captain, hanging at the Yard-Arm of the Ship, and told them they had nothing less to expect.

When they had all declar'd their Willingness to stay, I then told them, I would let them into the Story of my living there, and put them into the Way of making it easy to them: Accordingly I gave them the whole History of the Place, and of my coming to it; shew'd them my Fortifications, the Way I made my Bread, planted my Corn, cured my Grapes; and in a Word, all that was

赞同，我将像我发现他们时那样，全放了他们。如果他不愿意这样，他可以把他们再抓回来，只要他能够抓到他们。

看到这情形，他们显出感激万分的样子，我随即也就放了他们，要他们先回树林中他们原先待的地方；我还答应他们，将给他们留些武器弹药，而且如果他们需要的话，还可以给他们一些指导，让他们在这儿能过得舒坦些。

办好这事之后，我要为上船作准备了；我对船长说，我还得在岸上待一夜，收拾收拾东西，要他去船上过夜，第二天再派舢板到岸边接我；同时我又要他吩咐下去，把那个已被打死的新船长吊在桅杆顶上，让那批人看看这下场。

船长走后，我派人把那几个留岛的俘虏带到了我的住所里，就他们当前的处境，给他们作了一次极为严肃的谈话。我说，他们选择留在岛上，这是非常明智的决定。如果让船长把他们带走，他们肯定逃脱不了被绞死的下场。我让他们看了吊在大船桅杆顶上的新船长的尸体，告诉他们，他们本来也只能是这种下场而别无其他的指望。

等他们都表示愿意呆在这里之后，我便告诉他们，我愿意把我在这里生活的种种经历讲给他们听，让他们知道怎样把日子过好。因此，我把这个地方以及我来这里之后的历史原原本本地告诉了他们，并把我的防御工事指点给

necessary to make them easy: I told them the Story also of the sixteen Spaniards that were to be expected; for whom I left a Letter, and made them promise to treat them in common with themselves.

I left them my Fire Arms, viz. Five Muskets, three Fowling Pieces, and three Swords. I had above a Barrel and half of Powder left; for after the first Year or two, I used but little, and wasted none. I gave them a Description of the Way I manag'd the Goats, and Directions to milk and fatten them, and to make both Butter and Cheese.

In a Word, I gave them every Part of my own Story; and I told them, I would prevail with the Captain to leave them two Barrels of Gun-Powder more, and some Garden-Seeds, which I told them I would have been very glad of; also I gave them the Bag of Pease which the Captain had brought me to eat, and bad them be sure to sow and encrease them.

Having done all this, I left them the next Day, and went an Board the Ship: We prepared immediately to sail, but did not weigh that Night: The next Morning early, two of the five Men came swimming to the Ship's Side, and making a most lamentable Complaint of the other three, begged to be taken into the Ship, for God's Sake, for they should be murthered, and begg'd the Captain to take them on Board, tho' he hang'd them immediately.

他们。告诉他们,我是怎样做面包的,怎样种庄稼的,怎样晒葡萄干的。一句话,这些改善他们的生活所必需的知识,我都教给了他们。我把那十七个西班牙人将要到这里来的事也告诉了他们。同时,我还给那些西班牙人留了一封信,叫他们保证不歧视这五个人。

我给这几个人留下了五支步枪,三支猎枪,还有三把腰刀,并把剩下的一桶半火药也给了他们。这些火药我用得十分节省,只是在上岛的头两年里用了一些,以后几乎没怎么用过,更不敢浪费一丁点儿。为了让他们也节省火药,我给他们讲述了驯养山羊的方法,教他们如何挤奶和脱脂,如何制造奶油和奶酪。

总之,我把我的个人的历史详详细细地告诉了他们,又说我一定要劝船长再给他们留下两桶火药和一些我所求之不得的菜种。我又把船长给我送来的一口袋豆子送给他们,叮嘱他们一定要拿来下种,把它们繁殖起来。

这些事办完之后,第二天,我就离开他们上船去了。我们本来准备即刻开船;可是当晚却不曾起锚,第二天一大早,那五个人里面,忽然有两个泅水到船边来,哀哀地诉说另外三个人怎样歧视他们,请求我们看在上帝的份上收留他们,不然的话,他们准会被他们害死,他们请求船长收留他们,就是马上把他们吊死,

Upon this the Captain pretended to have no Power without me; But after some Difficulty, and after their solemn Promises off Amendment, they were taken on Board, and were some time after soundly whipp'd and pickl'd; after which, they prov'd very honest and quiet Fellows.

Some time after this, the Boat was order'd on Shore, the Tide being up, with the things promised to the Men, to which the Captain at my Intercession caused their Chests and Cloaths to be added, which they took, and were very thankful for; I also encourag'd them, by telling them, that if it lay in my Way to send any Vessel to take them in, I would not forget them.

When I took leave of this Island, I carry'd on board for Reliques, the great Goat's-Skin-Cap I had made, my Umbrella, and my Parrot; also I forgot not to take the Money I formerly mention'd, which had lain by me so long useless, that it was grown rusty, or tarnish'd, and could hardly pass for Silver, till it had been a little rubb'd, and handled; as also the Money I found in the Wreck of the Spanish Ship.

And thus I left the Island, the Nineteenth of December, as I found by the Ship's Account, in the Year 1686, after I had been upon it eight and twenty Years, two Months, and 19 Days; being deliver'd from this second Captivity, the same Day of the Month, that I first made my Escape in the Barco-Longo, from among the Moors of Sallee.

In this Vessel, after a long Voyage, I arriv'd in

他们也甘心情愿。

船长看到这种情形，就假装自己无权决定，要征得我的同意才行。后来，经过种种留难，他们也发誓痛改前非，才把他们收容上船。上船后，每人结结实实地挨了一顿鞭子，打完后再用盐和醋擦伤处。从那以后，他们果然成了安分守己的人了。

过了一会儿，潮水上涨了。我就命令把我答应给那三个人的东西，用舢板运到岸上去。我又向船长说情，把他们三人的箱子和衣服一起送去。他们收到后，都千恩万谢，感激不尽；我又鼓励他们说，如果将来我有机会派船来接他们，我一定不会忘记他们。

当我离开这个小岛时，我把我做的那顶羊皮帽子、伞，以及我的鹦鹉都带到船上，作为纪念。同时，我也没有忘记带上我前面提到的那笔钱，这笔钱因为多年放在身边不用，已经生了锈，不经过摩擦使用，都难以认出这是银币了。在那只失事的西班牙船上找到的钱币，情形也大致如此。

我就这样离开了这个岛。根据船上的航海日志，这天是一六八六年十二月十九日，也就是我在这岛上度过了二十八年两个月零十九天。凑巧的是，我离开这岛的日子，同我当初从萨利的摩尔人那里乘长艇出逃的日子，月份和日期竟然相同。

我在这船上经过了长途

England, the Eleventh of June, in the Year 1687, having been thirty and five Years absent.

When I came to England, I was as perfect a Stranger to all the World, as if I had never been known there. My Benefactor and faithful Steward, who I had left in Trust with my Money, was alive; but had had great Misfortunes in the World; was become a Widow the second Time, and very low in the World: I made her easy as to what she ow'd me, assuring her, I would give her no Trouble; but on the contrary, in Gratitude to her former Care and Faithfulness to me, I reliev'd her as my little Stock would afford, which at that Time would indeed allow me to do but little for her; abut I assur'd her, I would never forget her former Kindness to me; nor did I forget her, when I had sufficient to help her, as shall be observ'd in its Place.

I went down afterwards into Yorkshire; but my Father was dead, and my Mother, and all the Family extinct, except that I found two Sisters, and two of the Children of one of my Brothers; and as I had been long ago given over for dead, there had been no Provision made for me; so that in a Word, I found nothing to relieve, or assist me; and that little Money I had, would not do much for me, as to settling in the World.

I met with one Piece of Gratitude indeed, which I did not expect; and this was, That the Master of the Ship, who I had so happily deliver'd, and by the same Means sav'd the Ship and Cargo, having given a very handsome Account to the Owners, of the Manner how I had sav'd the Lives of the Men,

航行,于一六八七年六月十一日抵达英国,回到我阔别了三十五年的故土。

我回到英国时,没有一个人认识我,就仿佛我是个外乡人一样。我的恩人与忠诚的管家,即那位替我保管钱的夫人,还活在世上。可是,她的命运极其不幸,竟第二次做了寡妇,生计特别艰难。至于她欠我的钱,我叫她不要感到不安,并向她保证,我一定不会找她的麻烦。恰恰相反,尽管我现在的资本微乎其微,但为了报答她当初对我的关怀与忠心,我还是尽我所能接济了她。当然,这一点救助根本不能帮她摆脱困境。不过,我向她保证,我永远不会忘记她当初对我的好心。后来,当我真的有足够的资本接济她的时候,我也确实没有忘记她。关于这一点,下次再谈。

接着,我去了故乡约克城。我的父母亲已经过世,其他家人也大都故去了。我只找到了两个妹妹和一位哥哥的两个孩子。因为大家都以为我早已不在人世,所以没有给我留下任何遗产。总之,我在这里找不到任何一点接济和资助,而我身上仅有的一点钱,又实在难以让我安身立命。

就在这时,我碰到了一件知恩图报的善举,真让我感到意外地惊喜。那位带我回英国的船长先生,因为我幸运地救了他,也使他的船和货物幸免于难,就把我怎样救下大船

and the Ship, they invited me to meet them, and some other Merchants concern'd, and altogether made me a very handsome Compliment upon the Subject, and a Present of almost two hundred Pounds Sterling.

But after making several Reflections upon the Circumstances of my Life, and how little way this would go towards settling me in the World, I resolv'd to go to Lisbon, and see if I might not come by some Information of the State of my Plantation in the Brasils, and of what was become of my Partner, who I had reason to suppose had some Years now given me Over for dead.

With this View I took Shipping for Lisbon, where I arriv'd in April following; my Man Friday accompanying me very honestly in all these Ramblings, and proving a most faithful Servant upon all Occasions.

When I came to Lisbon, I found out by Enquiry, and to my particular Satisfaction, my old Friend the Captain of the Ship, who first took me up at Sea, off of the Shore of Africk: He was now grown old, and had left off the Sea, having put his Son, who was far from a young Man, into his Ship; and who still used the Brasil Trade. The old Man did not know me, and indeed, I hardly knew him; but I soon brought him to my Remembrance, and as soon brought my self to his Remembrance, when I told him who I was.

After some passionate Expressions of the old Acquaintance, I enquir'd, you may be sure, after my Plantation and my Partner: The old Man told me he had not been in the Brasils for about nine Years; but that he could assure me, that when he came away, my Partner was living, but the Trustees, who I had join'd with him to take Cog-

和船上人的事情，原原本本地向他的船主们作了汇报。于是，船主们邀请我去和他们以及有关的商人会面，不仅对我的行为大加赞扬，还送了我二百英镑作为酬谢。

但是我详细考虑了一下我的生活环境，考虑到这一点钱实在很难使我安身立命，就决定到里斯本去一趟，看看能不能打听到我在巴西的种植园的情形和我那合伙人的情形；我猜想我那合伙人一定以为我死去多年了。

抱着这个希望，我搭上了开往里斯本的船，于四月间抵达该城。当我这样东奔西跑的时候，星期五一直很忠实地跟着我，无时无刻不是我的最忠心的仆人。

到了里斯本，我几经打听，找到了我的老朋友，也就是把我从非洲海面上救起来的那位船长。这真使我高兴极了。船长现在年事已高，早就不再出海了；他让儿子当了船长，而儿子也已近中年了，仍旧做巴西生意。那老人家已经不认得我了；说实在话，我也一样认不出他了。但不久我就记起了他的面貌。当我告诉他我是谁之后，他也记起了我的面貌。

老友重逢，交谈之际，言词热切。不用说，我接着就询问了我的种植园和合伙人的情况。老人家告诉我，他已经有九年没有去巴西了。但他可以向我保证，当他离开那里的时候，我的合伙人还在人

nizance of my Part, were both dead; that however, he believ'd that I would have a very good Account of the Improvement of the Plantation; for
that upon the general Belief of my being cast
away, and drown'd, my Trustees had given in the
Account of the Produce of my Part of the Plantation, to the Procurator Fiscal, who had appropri-
ated it, in Case I never came to claim it; one
Third to the King, and two Thirds to the
Monastery of St. Augustine, to be expended for
the Benefit of the Poor, and for the Conversion of
the Indians to the Catholick Faith; but that if I
appear'd, or any one for me, to claim the Inheritance, it should be restor'd; only that the Improvement, or Annual Production, being distributed to charitable Uses, could not be restor'd; but
he assur'd me, that the Steward of the King's
Revenue (from Lands) and the Proviedore, or
Steward of the Monastery, had taken great Care
all along, that the Incumbent, that is to say my
Partner, gave every Year a faithful Account of the
Produce, of which they receiv'd duly my Moiety.

I ask'd him if he knew to what height of Improvement he had brought the Plantation? And,
Whether he thought it might be worth looking after? Or, Whether on my going thither, I should
meet with no Obstruction to my Possessing my just
Right in the Moiety?

He told me, he could not tell exactly, to what
Degree the Plantation was improv'd; but this he
knew, that my Partner was grown exceeding Rich
upon the enjoying but one half of it; and that to
the best of his Remembrance, he had heard, that
the King's Third of my Part, which was it seems
granted away to some other Monastery, or Religious House, amounted to above two hundred
Moidores a Year; that as to my being restor'd to a
quiet Possession of it, there was no question to be

世。我曾委托的那两个同他
一起的我的代理人都已经去
世了。不过,他相信我可以得
到一份关于种植园收益的详
细账目。因为大家都认为我
已经出了事淹死了,于是我的
几位代理人便把我那部分种
植园收入报告给了税收官,税
收官已经预先作了安排,如果
我不再回来申请的话,我的财
产三分之一划归国库,三分之
二给圣奥古斯汀修道院,用来
救济穷人和向印第安人传教,
但如果我回来,或是任何我的
遗产继承人申请的话,财产就
可以归还,只是年年上缴作慈
善用的那一部分不能返还。
但他向我保证,政府征管田税
的官员和修道院的管家一直
都监督着种植园的收益。我
的合伙人,每年都要交一份详
细的收入报告,并把我应得的
那一部分上缴。

我问他是否知道,我那种
植园已发展到了什么地步;又
问他,照他的看法,是不是值
得我亲自去料理一下;而到了
那儿之后,要是我提出恢复我
的合法权益,会不会遇到什么
阻碍。

他说,有关那种植园究竟
发展到什么程度,他没法提供
确切的数字,只知道我那合伙
人仅凭他那一半产权,已经成
了巨富;而且就他回忆所及,
他当年曾听说,我那划归国库
的三分之一的年收入,似乎是
拨给了另一个修道院或某一
个宗教团体,数额应当在每年
二百块葡萄牙金币以上。至

made of that, my Partner being alive to witness my Title, and my Name being also enrolled in the Register of the Country; also he told me, That the Survivors of my two Trustees, were very fair honest People, and very Wealthy; and he believ'd I would not only have their Assistance for putting me in Possession, but would find a very considerable Sum of Money in their Hands, for my Account; being the Produce of the Farm while their Fathers held the Trust, and before it was given up as above, which as he remember'd, was for about twelve Years.

I shew'd my self a little concern'd, and uneasy at this Account, and enquir'd of the old Captain, How it came to pass, that the Trustees should thus dispose my Effects, when he knew that I had made my Will, and had made him, the Portuguese Captain, my universal Heir, & c.

He told me, that was true; but that as there was no Proof of my being dead, he could not act as Executor, until some certain Account should come of my Death, and that besides, he was not willing to intermeddle with a thing so remote; that it was true he had registred my Will, and put in his Claim; and could he have given any Account of my being dead or alive, he would have acted by Procuration, and taken Possession of the Ingenio, so they call'd the Sugar-House, and had' given his Son, who was now at the Brasils, Order to do it.

But, says the old Man, I have one Piece of News to tell you, which perhaps may not be so acceptable to you as the rest, and that is, That be-

于要顺利地收回这产权,这是不成问题的,因为我的合伙人还活着,能够证明我的身份;我的名字已经注册在国家的登记册里。他还告诉我,我那两个代理人的后人都是特别正直的人,并且都特别富有,所以,他相信,他们不仅会帮助我收回这份每年的收入,并且还会给我可观的一笔现款,作为我的资产在他们父辈管理期间的利润,或作为我的收入权充公之前的收入。因为,根据他的记忆,我的收入归公是最近十二年的事。

听了这番陈述,我有点担心与不安。我问老船长,开始我既然立了遗嘱,立他为我财产的终身继承人(他自己也知道),可是,我的两个受托人为什么要这样处理我的财产呢?

老船长说,他是我的财产继承人,这的确是事实,但是他一直得不到任何能证明我已经死亡的证据。在没有获悉我死亡的确切消息之前,他是不能行使作为我遗嘱执行人的权力的。此外,由于相隔太远,对这种鞭长莫及的事,他不也愿意过多地干预。不过他确实已经将我的遗嘱注册登记过,也提出了他的产权要求。如果他能提交有关我生死的证明,那他早就会行使他的财产委托权,接管我的糖厂,让他目前在巴西的儿子去经营了。

"我还有件事情要告诉你,"老人家接着对我说:"你听了这事也许会不大高兴。那

lieving you were lost, and all the World believing so also, your Partner and Trustees did offer to accompt to me in your Name, for six or eight of the first Years of Profits, which I receiv'd; but there being at that time, says he, great Disbursements for encreasing the Works, building an Ingenio, and buying Slaves, it did not amount to near so much as afterwards it produced: However, says she old Man, I shall give you a true Account of what I have received in all, and how I have disposed of it.

After a few Days farther Conference with this ancient Friend, he brought me an Account of the six first Years Income of my Plantation, sign'd by my Partner and the Merchants Trustees, being always deliver'd in Goods, viz. Tobacco in Roll, and Sugar in Chests, besides Rum, Molossus, &c. which is the Consequence of a Sugar Work; and I found by this Account, that every Year the Income considerably encreased; but as above, the Disbursement being large, the Sum at first was small: However, the old Man let me see, that he was Debtor to me 470 Moidores of Gold, besides 60 Chests of Sugar, and 15 double Rolls of Tobacco which were lost in his Ship; he having been Ship-wreck'd coming Home to Lisbon about 11 Years after my leaving the Place.

The good Man then began to complain of his Misfortunes, and how he had been obliged to make Use of my Money to recover his Losses, and buy him a Share in a new Ship: However, my old Friend, says he, you shall not want a Supply in your Necessity; and as soon as my Son returns, you shall be fully satisfy'd.

Upon this, he pulls out an old Pouch, and gives me 160 Portugal Moidores in Gold; and giving me

就是，当我们相信你已经死了，别的人也这样相信的时候，你的合伙人和代理人曾经把你的头六七年的利息交给我，我都收下了；不过那时候种植园正需要扩充设备，建立糖厂，又要买奴隶，所以数目没有后来那么大。不过，我一定要把我一共收了多少，以及我怎么处理它们，开一份可靠的账目给你。"

我和这位老朋友又连续商谈了几天，他就把我的种植园最初六年的收入开了一笔细账给我，上面有我的合伙人和两位代理人的签字。交出来的都是现货，例如成卷的烟叶、成箱的糖，还有糖厂其他副产品，像甘蔗、酒、糖浆等等。从这笔账上，我可以看到，收入每年都有增加，但正如上面所提到的，由于开头几年开支较大，实际上收入不大。尽管如此，老人家还是告诉我，他欠我四百七十块葡萄牙金币，另外还有六十箱糖和十五大捆烟叶。那些货物在船只开往里斯本的航行中因失事而全部损失了。那是我离开巴西十一年以后发生的事。

这位善良的人开始向我诉说了他的不幸遭遇，说他万不得已，才拿我的钱去弥补损失，在一条新船上搭了一股。"不过，我的老朋友，"他说，"你要是用钱的话，钱是有的。等我儿子回来，就可以把钱都还给你。"

说着，老人又拿出一条旧布包，给了我一百六十块葡萄

the Writing of his Title to the Ship, which his Son was gone to the Brasils in, of which he was a Quarter Part Owner, and his Son another, he puts them both into my Hands for Security of the rest.

I was too much mov'd with the Honesty and Kindness of the poor Man, to be able to bear this; and remembering what he had done for me, how he had taken me up at Sea, and how generously he had used me on all Occasions, and particularly, how sincere a Friend he was now to me, I could hardly refrain Weeping at what he said to me: Therefore, first I asked him, if his Circumstances admitted him to spare so much Money at that time, and if it would not straiten him? He told me, he could not say but it might straiten him a little; but however it was my Money, and I might want it more than he.

Every thing the good Man said was full of Affection, and I could hardly refrain from Tears while he spoke: In short, I took 100 of the Moidores, and call'd for a Pen and Ink to give him a Receipt for them; then I returned him the rest, and told him, If ever I had Possession of the Plantation, I would return the other to him also, as indeed I afterwards did; and that as to the Bill of Sale of his Part in his Son's Ship, I would not take it by any Means; but that if I wanted the Money, I found he was honest enough to pay me; and if I did not, but came to receive what he gave me reason to expect, I would never have a Penny more from him.

牙金币,并把他儿子开到巴西去的那只船上的股权开列出来,他在船上有四分之一股权,他儿子也有四分之一股权。

我对老人的善良诚实大受感动,不能自已,我想起了他曾为我做过的事情,想起他怎样把我从海上救起,而且他不论何时总是对我那样慷慨大度,尤其是他现在还是我真挚的朋友,我听了他的话,忍不住抽泣起来。于是,我开始问他,以他目前的处境,能否在当时拿出这么多钱来,这样是否会把他搞得很紧张,他说当然会紧张一些,但这毕竟是我的钱,而我比他更需要钱。

这位好人说的话全都出自真心实意,我听着听着,差一点情不自禁地流下泪来。总之,我收下了一百块葡萄牙金币,同时向他要了笔和墨水,写了一张收据给他,说是收到了一百块葡萄牙金币;随即就把余下的那些金币退还给他,对他说道,如果我要回了种植园,连这一百个金币我也退还给他——这一点以后也确实做到了。至于他写的那张字据,说是准备出让他在他儿子船上的那部分投资,我是无论如何也不肯收的;事实上,如果今后我需要这笔钱,他的诚实就足以保证他会把钱给我;而如果今后我不需要这笔钱,倒是能收回他认为我有理由收回的产业,那么我永远也不会再要他的一个铜子了。

When this was pass'd, the old Man began to ask me, If he should put me into a Method to make my Claim to my Plantation? I told him, I thought to go over to it my self: He said, I might do so if I pleas'd; but that if I did not, there were Ways enough to secure my Right, and immediately to appropriate the Profits to my Use; and as there were Ships in the River of Lisbon, just ready to go away to Brasil, he made me enter my Name in a Publick Register, with his Affidavit, affirming upon Oath that I was alive, and that I was the same Person who took up the Land for the Planting the said Plantation at first.

This being regularly attested by a Notary, and a Procuration affix'd, he directed me to send it with a Letter of his Writing, to a Merchant of his Acquaintance at the Place, and then propos'd my staying with him till an Account came of the Return.

Never any Thing was more honourable, than the Proceedings upon this Procuration; for in less than seven Months, I receiv'd a large Packet from the Survivors of my Trustees the Merchants, for whose Account I went to Sea, in which were the following particular Letters and Papers enclos'd.

First, There was the Account Current of the Produce of my Farms or Plantation, from the Year when their Fathers had ballanc'd with my old Portugal Captain, being for six Years; the Ballance appear'd to be 1174 Moidores in my Favour.

Secondly, There was the Account of four Years more while they kept the Effects in their Hands,

谈完之后，老人又问我，要不要他帮我想想办法，去把我的种植园收回。我告诉他，我计划自己亲自去处理。他说，如果我愿意这样做，那就亲自去。不过，如果我不愿意，也有许多办法来收回我的产权，而且可以很快使属于我的利润归我使用。因为里斯本正有一批商船准备开往巴西，所以，他叫我到官方登记处去把我的名字登记入册，并加上他的证明书，宣誓证明我还活着，证明我跟当初征用土地开辟种植园的那个人是同一个人。

我把老人的宣誓书连同我附上的一份委托书按常规进行了公证。老人让我把这两份文件和他替我写的一封信一并寄给了他在巴西的一位商人朋友，然后建议我住在他家里等候回音。

结果，我的财产委托手续办得极为顺利，真可谓最公道体面不过了。信寄出不到七个月，我就收到了那两位代理人(当年正是为了他们两人我才离开种植园出海航行的)的财产继承人寄给我的一大包邮件，里面全是有关我财产委托方面的文件和信函。

第一，是我的土地或种植园的收入的流水账，从他们父亲和我这位葡萄牙老船长结算的那一年算起，一共是六年，应该找给我一千一百七十四块葡萄牙金币。

第二，是在政府接管以前，由他们当作一个失踪的人

before the Government claim'd the Administration, as being the Effects of a Person not to be found, which they call'd Civil Death; and the Ballance of this, the Value of the Plantation encreasing, amounted to [38,892] Cruisadoes, which made 3241 Moidores.

Thirdly, There was the Prior of the Augustin's Account, who had receiv'd the Profits for above fourteen Years; but not being to account for what was dispos'd to the Hospital, very honestly declar'd he had 872 Moidores not distributed, which he acknowledged to my Account; as to the King's Part, that refunded nothing.

·There was a Letter of my Partner's, congratulating me very affectionately upon my being alive, giving me an Account how the Estate was improv'd, and what it produced a Year, with a Particular of the Number of Squares or Acres that it contained; how planted, how many Slaves there were upon it, and making two and twenty Crosses for Blessings, told me he had said so many Ave Marias to thank the Blessed Virgin that I was alive; inviting me very passionately to come over and take Possession of my own; and in the mean time to give him Orders to whom he should deliver my Effects, if I did not come my self; concluding with a hearty Tender of his Friendship, and that of his Family, and sent me, as a Present, seven fine Leopard's Skins, which he had it seems received from Africa, by some other Ship which he had sent thither, and who it seems had made a better Voyage than I: He sent me also five Chests of excellent Sweet-meats, and an hundred Pieces of Gold uncoin'd, not quite so large as Moidores.

（法律上叫做"民事死亡"）的产业来保管的四年里面的账目，这笔尾数，由于种植园的价值逐年提高，一共值三千二百四十一块葡萄牙金币。

第三，是圣奥古斯汀修道院院长的账单。他已经获得十四年的收益。他十分诚实，告诉我说，除了医院方面用去的钱以外，还存有八百七十二块葡萄牙金币。他现在把这笔钱记在我的账上。至于划归国库的那部分，则不能再偿还了。

另外，还有一封我的合伙人写给我的信。他祝贺我还活在人世，言词十分诚挚亲切。他向我报告了我们产业发展的情况以及每年的生产情况，并详细谈到了我们的种植园现在一共有多少英亩土地，怎样种植，有多少奴隶等等。他在信纸上画了二十二个十字架，为我祝福。他还说，他念了无数遍以"万福玛丽亚"开头的祷词，为我活在人间感谢圣母玛丽亚，并热情地邀请我过去收回我自己的产业，同时请示我，如果我自己不过去应该把我的种植园交给谁，最后，又表达出他及家人对我的深厚友情，并把七张精美的豹皮作为礼物送给我。这些豹皮可能是从他派往非洲去的其他船只那儿得来的，而他们的航行，显然比我要好得多，他还送给了我五箱上等的蜜饯，及一百块比葡萄牙金币略小没有铸造过的金块。

By the same Fleet, my two Merchant Trustees shipp'd me 1 200 Chests of Sugar, 800 Rolls of Tobacco, and the rest of the whole Accompt in Gold.

I might well say, now indeed, That the latter End of Job was better than the Beginning. It is impossible to express pere the Flutterings of my very Heart, when I look'd over these Letters, and especially when I found all my Wealth about me; for as the Brasil Ships come all in Fleets, the same Ships which brought my Letters, brought my Goods; and the Effects were safe in the River before the Letters came to my Hand. In a Word, I turned pale, and grew sick; and had not the old Man run and fetch'd me a Cordial, I believe the sudden Surprize of Joy had overset Nature, and I had dy'd upon the Spot.

Nay after that, I continu'd very ill, and was so some Hours, 'till a Physician being sent for, and something of the real Cause of my illness being known, he order'd me to be let Blood; after which, I had Relief, and grew well: But I verily believe, if it had not been eas'd by a Vent given in that Manner, to the Spirits, I should have dy'd.

I was now Master, all on a Sudden, of above 5000 l. Sterling in Money, and had an Estate, as I might well call it, in the Brasils, of above a thousand Pounds a Year, as sure as an Estate of Lands in England: And in a Word, I was in a Condition which I scarce knew how to understand, or how to compose my self, for the Enjoyment of it.

The first thing I did, was to recompense my original Benefactor, my good old Captain, who had been first charitable to me in my Distress, kind to

在同一批船队上,我的两位代理人的后代还给我运来了一千二百箱糖,八百捆烟叶及账上剩余的全部金币。

现在我倒真是可以说自己同约伯一样,晚景好于当初了。我读着这些信,特别是得知自己身边有这么多财富,因为从巴西来的船,都是成群结队的,凡是带信给我的那些船上,都有带给我的货物,信还没交到我手里时,那些货已安全抵达里斯本的河道了,我内心的激动简直难以言表。总之,我当时脸色惨白,感到头晕目眩,要不是老船长奔去给我拿来一些露酒,我相信,这突如其来的惊喜一定会使我身心失常,当时就一命呜呼。

即使喝了露酒之后,一连几个小时我还是特别难受。后来,老船长把医生请来了,终于诊出了我的病因。医生要我马上放血。放完血之后,我感到舒服多了,身体也就好了。不过,我敢肯定,要不是以这种方式缓解我的情绪,平定我的精神,我真的已经死了。

转眼之间,我竟得到了五千英镑的现款,还有一处在巴西的田产,这处田产每年的收入也在一千英镑以上,和英国境内的田产一样可靠。总而言之,我莫明其妙地荣华富贵起来了,我简直不知道该怎样让自己的激动情绪平息下来,去享受这一切。

财产到手后我所做的第一件事情,就是报答我的恩人,那位好心的老船长。当年

me in my Beginning, and honest to me at the End: I shew'd him all that was sent me, I told him, that next to the Providence of Heaven, which disposes all things, it was Owing to him; and that it now lay on me to reward him, which I would do a hundred fold: So I first return'd to him the hundred Moidores I had receiv'd of him, then I sent for a Notary, and caused him to draw up a general Release or Discharge for the 470 Moidores, which he had acknowledg'd he ow'd me in the fullest and firmest Manner possible; after which, I caused a Procuration to be drawn, impowering him to be my Receiver of the annual Profits of my Plantation, and appointing my Partner to accompt to him, and make the Returns by the usual Fleets to him in my Name; and a Clause in the End, being a Grant of 100 Moidores a Year to him, during his Life, out of the Effects, and 50 Moidores a Year to his Son after him, for his Life: And thus I requited my old Man.

I was now to consider which Way to steer my Course next, and what to do with the Estate that Providence had thus put into my Hands; and indeed I had more Care upon my Head now, than I had in my silent State of Life in the Island, where I wanted nothing but what I had, and had nothing but what I wanted: Whereas I had now a great Charge upon me, and my Business was how to secure it. I had ne'er a Cave now to hide my Money in, or a Place where it might lye without Lock or Key, 'till it grew mouldy and tarnish'd before any Body would meddle with it: On the contrary, I

正是老船长无限仁慈地把我从茫茫大海中救助出来,而且,以善良待我为始,以真诚对我为终。我把收到的东西全都拿给他看了,并对他说,我今天获得的这一切,除了主宰世事的天意外,都应归功于他的帮助;所以,现在该是我回报他的时候了,我一定要百倍地报答他才行。我先把他给我的一百块葡萄牙金币退还给他;然后请来了一位公证人,让他起草了一份解除债务证明书,以最彻底、最可靠的方式全部免除了老船长自认欠我的四百七十块葡萄牙金币。我又让他起草了一份委托书,委托老船长作为我种植园年收入的收管人,并让我的合伙人按期向他报告收支账目,把我应得的收入交给固定的船队带给他。委托书最后一项条款是,老船长在世之时,每年从我的收入中拨给他一百块葡萄牙金币;过世之后,每年拨给他儿子五十块葡萄牙金币。就这样,我如愿以偿,报答了我的老船长。

现在我必须考虑我今后的动向,考虑怎样处置上天赐给我的这份产业了。老实说,比起我在岛上过那种孤寂生活的时候,我现在需要更多的慎重。在岛上,我除了我所有的,什么都不需要,除了我所需要的,什么都没有;可是现在,我却肩负着一副很沉重的担子,必须把它妥为安排。我现在没有山洞可以藏我的钱,也没有这样一个地方,把钱放

knew not where to put it, or who to trust with it. My old Patron, the Captain, indeed was honest, and that was the only Refuge I had.

In the next Place, my Interest in the Brasils seem'd to summon me thither, but now I could not tell, how to think of going thither, 'till I had settled my Affairs, and left my Effects in some safe Hands behind me. At first I thought of my old Friend the Widow, who I knew was honest, and would be just to me; but then she was in Years, and but poor, and for ought I knew, might be in Debt; so that in a Word, I had no Way but to go back to England my self, and take my Effects with me.

It was some Months however before I resolved upon this; and therefore, as I had rewarded the old Captain fully, and to his Satisfaction, who had been my former Benefactor, so I began to think of my poor Widow, whose Husband had been my first Benefactor, and she, while it was in her Power, my faithful Steward and Instructor. So the first thing I did, I got a Merchant in Lisbon to write to his Correspondent in London, not only to pay a Bill, but to go find her out, and carry her in Money, an hundred Pounds from me, and to talk with her, and comfort her in her Poverty, by telling her she should, if I liv'd, have a further Supply: At the same time I sent my two Sisters in the Country, each of them an Hundred Pounds, they being, though not in Want, yet not in very good Circumstances; one having been marry'd, and left a Widow; and the other having a Husband not so kind to her as he should be.

在那里，锁都不用锁，就是长了霉，生了锈，也没有人动它。相反地，我现在真不知道把它放在什么地方，交给谁才好，只有我的老东家船长是个诚实正直的人，是我唯一可以托付的人。

其次，我在巴西的利益似乎也得要我自己去一趟。可是现在，我无法处理好我的财产，不能把它交付给妥善的人，我又怎样能去那里呢？首先，我想到我的老朋友，那位寡妇，她很诚实，又很正直，她年纪已大，还很穷困，而且据我所知还欠着债，因此，我别无他法，只有自己带上财产，回英国去一趟。

然而，过了好几个月，才把这件事情决定下来。我现在已充分报答了我从前的恩人老船长，他也感到心满意足。所以，我开始想到那位可怜的寡妇了。她的丈夫是我的第一位恩人，而且，她本人在有能力时，一直是我忠实的管家，并尽长辈之责经常开导我。因此，我做的第一件事情就是，让一位在里斯本的商人写信给他在伦敦的关系人，除了请他替我把汇票兑成现款外，还请他亲自找到她，替我把一百英镑的现款亲自交给她。我还要此人当面和她谈一下，因为她目前非常贫困，境况不佳，所以我要此人好好安慰她，并告诉她，只要我活在人世，以后还会接济她。另外，我又给我那两个住在乡下的妹妹每人寄了一百英镑。

But among all my Relations, or Acquaintances, I could not yet pitch upon one, to whom I durst commit the Gross of my Stock, that I might go away to the Brasils, and leave things safe behind me; and this greatly perplex'd me.

I had once a Mind to have gone to the Brasils, and have settled my self there; for I was, as it were, naturaliz'd to the Place; but I had some little Scruple in my Mind about Religion, which insensibly drew me back, of which I shall say more presently. However, it was not Religion that kept me rom going there for the present; and as I had made no Scruple of being openly of the Religion of the Country, all the while I was among them, so neither did I yet; only that now and then having of late thought more of it, (than formerly) when I began to think of living and dying among them, I began to regret my having profess'd my self a Papist, and thought it might not be the best Religion to die with.

But, as I have said, this was not the main thing that kept me from going to the Brasils, but that really I did not know with whom to leave my Effects behind me; so I resolv'd at last to go to England with it, where, if I arrived, I concluded I should make some Acquaintance, or find some Relations that would be faithful to me; and according I prepar'd to go for England with all my Wealth.

In order to prepare things for my going Home, I first, the Brasil Fleet being just going away, resolved to give Answers suitable to the just and

她们虽然并不贫困，但境况也不太好，一个妹妹结了婚，后来成了寡妇；另一个妹妹的丈夫对她很不好。

然而，在我的全部亲友中间，我想不出一个完全合适的人，在我去巴西的时候，可以放心地把我的大宗资财托交给他，让我没有后顾之忧；这个情况使我感到非常难办。

我曾经一度下决心到巴西去，决定在那里安家，因为我以前曾加入过巴西国籍。但是，我头脑中对宗教还有点顾虑，这一点使我没有动身，我将在下边详谈这个问题。但是我没有立刻动身去巴西，却不是由于宗教的缘故，因为我以前已经毫无顾忌地加入了那里的宗教，一直是其中的一员，现在当然更不顾忌什么了。只是近来我比以前多考虑了一下这个问题。当我想到不论生死都是他们中的一员时，我不禁有些后悔自己做了一名天主教徒，觉得不应该以这种教徒的身份死去。

我已经说过，我没有去巴西的主要原因并不是因为这一点，而是我不知道把我的资财留下来托谁经管；所以最后决定还是带着钱回英国，我想到了那儿以后，自会结交到一些朋友，或者亲属里也有可以信托的人；于是我开始准备起来，打算带上全部钱财回英国去。

为了在回国之前把有些事情料理好，而且去巴西的船队出发在即，我决定先根据巴

faithful Account of things I had from thence; and first to the Prior of St. Augustine I wrote a Letter full of Thanks for their just Dealings, and the Offer of the 872 Moidores, which was indisposed of, which I desir'd might be given 500 to the Monastery, and 372 to the Poor, as the Prior should direct, desiring the good Padres Prayers for me, and the like.

I wrote next a Letter of Thanks to my two Trustees, with all the Acknowledgment that so much Justice and Honesty call'd for; as for sending them any Present, they were far above having any Occasion of it.

Lastly, I wrote to my Partner, acknowledging his Industry in the Improving the Plantation, and his Integrity in encreasing the Stock of the Works, giving him Instructions for his future Government of my Part, according to the Powers I had left with my old Patron, to whom I desir'd him to send whatever became due to me, 'till he should hear me more particularly; assuring him that it was my Intention, not only to come to him, but to settle my self there for the Remainder of my Life: To this I added a very handsom Present of some Italian Silks for his Wife, and two Daughters, for such the Captain's Son inform'd me he had; with two Pieces of fine English broad Cloath, the best I could get in Lisbon, five Pieces of black Bays, and some Flanders Lace of a good Value.

Having thus settled my Affairs, sold my Car-

西寄来的公正而可靠的报告，作出相应的回答；首先，我给圣奥古斯汀修道院院长写了一封热情洋溢的信，衷心感谢他们的公正处理。同时，我把那没有安排出去的八百七十二块葡萄牙金币全部捐给他们。根据我的同愿，其中五百块捐给修道院，三百七十二块用于接济穷人（由院长本人具体施舍），并请求这位善良的神父为我祈祷。

其次，我给我那两个代理人的后代写了封感激信，感谢他们把事情办得这样公正，对我这么诚实。至于送礼物给他们，我想，他们根本不需要。

最后，我又给我的合伙人写了一封信，感谢他在经营发展种植园方面所付出的辛勤劳动，以及他在扩大生产和财产积累方面表现出的公平正直的态度。在信中，我还对今后如何管理我那部分产业作了指示，请按我赋予老船长的权利，把我应得的收益寄给他。如果以后有什么变更，我再详细告知之。我还在信中告诉他，我不仅会亲自去巴西看他，还打算在那里定居，度过我的余生。我听老船长的儿子说他已有了家室，所以又随这封信给他的太太和两个女儿送了一份厚礼，其中包括一些意大利丝绸，两匹里斯本市面上所能买到的最好的英国细平纹布，还有五匹黑粗呢以及一些价格昂贵的佛兰德斯花边等等。

我把事情料理清楚，把货

goe, and turn'd all my Effects into good Bills of Exchange, my next Difficulty was, which Way to go to England: I had been accustom'd enough to the Sea, and yet I had a strange Aversion to going to England by Sea at that time; and though I could give no Reason for it, yet the Difficulty encreas'd upon me so much, that though I had once shipp'd my Baggage, in order to go, yet I alter'd my Mind, and that not once, but two or three times.

It is true, I had been very unfortunate by Sea, and this might be some of the Reason: But let no Man slight the strong Impulses of his own Thoughts in Cases of such Moment: Two of the Ships which I had singl'd out to go in, I mean, more particularly singl'd out than any other, that is to say, so as in one of them to put my things on Board, and in the other to have agreed with the Captain; I say, two of these Ships miscarry'd, viz. One was taken by the Algerines, and the other was cast away on the Start near Torbay, and all the People drown'd except three; so that in either of those Vessels I had been made miserable; and in which most, it was hard to say.

Having been thus harass'd in my Thoughts, my old Pilot, to whom I communicated every thing, press'd me earnestly not to go by Sea, but either to go by Land to the Groyne, and cross over the Bay of Biscay to Rochell, from whence it was but an easy and safe Journey by Land to Paris, and so to Calais and Dover; or to go up to Madrid, and so all the Way by Land thro' France.

In a Word, I was so prepossess'd against my go-

卖出去，又把我的动产换成可靠的汇票之后，下一步的难题是走哪一条路回英国去。我走海路本来是走熟了的，可是这时我心里却对走海路产生了一种奇怪的反感，不愿意走海路到英国去；虽然说不出什么理由来，可是这种阻力在我心里却不断加强，有一次，甚至把行李都搬上船去了，临时又改了主意，而且一连两三次都是这样。

不错，我这一辈子在海上碰到的倒霉事儿实在太多了，这可能是一部分的理由；但是，在这种事情上，一个人也不能完全忽视自己内心的冲动。我曾特别挑选过两条船，本来我是决定要搭乘的。其中有一条，我把行李都搬上去了；另一条，我也都和船长讲定了。可是，最后我两条船都没有上。后来，那两条船果然都出事了。一条给阿尔及利亚人掳了去；另一条在托贝湾的斯塔特岬角沉没了，除了三个人生还外，其他人都淹死了。反正不管我上哪条船，都得倒霉；至于上哪条船更倒霉，那就很难说了。

我为这事心里烦透了，就去与老船长商量。他坚决反对我走海路，而劝我最好走陆路到拉科鲁尼亚，渡过比斯开湾到罗谢尔，再从罗谢尔走陆路到巴黎，既安全又舒适，然后再从巴黎到加来和多佛尔；或先到马德里，然后由陆路穿过法国。

总之，除了从加来到多佛

ing by Sea at all, except from Calais to Dover, that I resolv'd to travel all the Way by Land; which as I was not in Haste, and did not value the Charge, was by much the pleasanter Way; and to make it more so, my old Captain brought an English Gentleman, the Son of a Merchant in Lisbon, who was willing to travel with me: After which, we pick'd up two more English Merchants also, and two young Portuguese Gentlemen, the last going to Paris only; so that we were in all six of us, and five Servants; the two Merchants and the two Portuguese, contenting themselves with one Servant, between two, to save the Charge; and as for me, I got an English Sailor to travel with me as a Servant, besides my Man Friday, who was too much a Stranger to be capable of supplying the Place of a Servant on the Road.

In this Manner I set out from Lisbon; and our Company being all very well mounted and armed, we made a little Troop, whereof they did me the Honour to call me Captain, as well because I was the oldest Man, as because I had two Servants, and indeed was the Original' of the whole Journey.

As I have troubled you with none of my Sea-Journals, so I shall trouble you now with none of my Land-Journal: But some Adventures that happen'd to us in this tedious and difficult Journey, I must not omit.

When we came to Madrid, we being all of us Strangers to Spain, were willing to stay some time to see the Court of Spain, and to see what was worth observing; but it being the latter Part of the Summer, we hasten'd away, and set out from Madrid about the Middle of October: But when

尔这一段海路我不反对外,我对走海路已经厌倦,于是,我下决心所有的路程都全走陆路。因为我并不着急,又不在乎花钱,走陆路倒是愉快得多。为了使旅程更愉快,老船长给我带来了一位英国绅士,是里斯本一位商人的儿子,他很乐意同我一块旅行。之后,我们又选择了两位英国商人,两名年轻的葡萄牙绅士,后者只到巴黎,这样我们一共是六个人,还有五个仆人。那两位商人和两位葡萄牙绅士,为了节省开支,每两个人只用一个仆人,至于我,除了星期五之外,我又找了一名英国水手做我旅程的仆人。因为星期五作为一个异乡人,做不了我旅行中的仆人。

我就这样从里斯本出发了;我们这一行人个个骑着骏马,带着好枪,倒也成了一支小小的部队;承他们的情,称我为队长;这不仅因为我在其中年纪最大,而且还因为我带有两名仆人,再说,这次旅行也是我发起的。

既然先前我没有用航海日记叫你们看得心烦,现在也决不会用陆行日记这么做。但是在这次累人而艰难的跋涉中,我们也遇上了几件惊险的事,这可不能撇下不提。

由于我们都是头一次到西班牙,所以,来到马德里后,都愿意游玩几天,想参观一下西班牙宫廷,或者看看别的值得一看的景点名胜。可是,由于现在已是夏末,我们还是匆

we came to the Edge of Navarre, we were alarm'd at several Towns on the Way, with an Account, that so much Snow was fallen on the French Side of the Mountains, that several Travellers were obliged to come back to Pampeluna, after having attempted, at an extream Hazard, to pass on.

When we came to Pampeluna it self, we found it so indeed; and to me that had been always used to a hot Climate, and indeed to Countries where we could scarce bear any Cloaths on, the Cold was insufferable; nor indeed was it more painful than it was surprising, to come but ten Days before out of the old Castile where the Weather was not only warm but very hot, and immediately to feel a Wind from the Pyrenean Mountains, so very keen, so severely cold, as to be intollerable, and to endanger benumbing and perishing of our Fingers and Toes.

Poor Friday was really frighted when he saw the Mountains all cover'd with Snow, and felt cold Weather, which he had never seen or felt before in his Life.

To mend the Matter, when we came to Pampeluna, it continued snowing with so much Violence, and so long, that the People said, Winter was come before its time, and the Roads which were difficult before, were now quite impassable: For in a Word, the Snow lay in some Places too thick for us to travel; and being not hard frozen, as is the Case in Northern Countries: There was no going without being in Danger of being bury'd alive every Step. We stay'd no less than twenty Days at Pampeluna; when seeing the Winter coming on, and no Likelihood of its being better; for it was the severest Winter all over Europe that had

匆地上了路,于十月中旬从马德里出发了。当我们行到纳瓦拉的边境地带时,沿途几个小镇上的人们都纷纷议论,说法国那边的山里下起了大雪,有几个旅客本想不顾一切地冒险穿过山区,但都没有成功,被迫折回了潘普洛纳。这让我们不安起来。

当我们到达潘普洛纳时,发现情况正如人们所说。许多年来,我已完全习惯了热带气候,在那里所到之处都是热得连衣服也穿不住,可现在忽然遇上这么寒冷的天气,真让我不堪忍受。特别是我们十天前才离开气候温暖甚至略感炎热的旧卡斯蒂尔,而现在却要面对从比利牛斯山脉刮过来的刺骨寒风,大家都感到冷得承受不了。我们的手和脚都被冻得僵硬,手指和脚指甚至快要被冻掉了。

可怜的星期五一辈子没有见过雪,受过冻,现在忽然看见满山大雪,碰到这么寒冷的天气,简直把他吓坏了。

更糟糕的是,我们到了潘普洛纳以后,雪还是那么猛烈地、不停地下着,人们都说,今年的冬天比往年来得特别早。路本来已经很难走,现在简直是无法通行了,因为有些地方雪积得太厚,寸步难行,而且这一带的雪又不像北方那样,冻得结结实实的,假如再往前走,到处都有被活埋的危险,我们在潘普洛纳耽搁了不下二十天,眼看冬季已经到来,天气已经没有好转的可能了

been known in the Memory of Man. I propos'd that we should all go away to Fonterabia, and there take Shipping for Bourdeaux, which was a very little Voyage.

But while we were considering this, there came in four French Gentlemen, who having been stopp'd on the French Side of the Passes, as we were on the Spanish, had found out a Guide, who traversing the Country near the Head of Languedoc, had brought them over the Mountains by such Ways, that they were not much incommoded with the Snow; and where they met with Snow in any Quantity, they said it was frozen hard enough to bear them and their Horses.

We sent for this Guide, who told us, he would undertake to carry us the same Way with no Hazard from the Snow, provided we were armed sufficiently to protect our selves from wild Beasts; for he said, upon these great Snows, it was frequent for some Wolves to show themselves at the Foot of the Mountains, being made ravenous for Want of Food, the Ground being covered with Snow: We told him, we were well enough prepar'd for such Creatures as they were, if he would ensure us from a Kind of two-legged Wolves, which we were told, we were in most Danger from, especially on the French Side of the Mountains.

He satisfy'd us there was no Danger of that kind in the Way that we were to go; so we readily agreed to follow him, as did also twelve other Gentlemen, with their Servants, some French, some Spanish; who, as I said, had attempted to go, and were obliged to come back again.

（因为这一次是全欧洲多年以来最寒冷的冬天）。于是我提议，我们不妨先到封塔拉比亚，再从那里坐船到波尔多，那段海路没有多远。

正当我们在考虑另寻出路时，忽然来了四位法国绅士。他们曾经在法国境内的山路上被雪所阻，正像我们在这儿西班牙境内的山路上被雪所阻一样。但是，他们后来找到了一个向导，带他们绕过朗格多克附近的山区，一路上没碰到什么大雪；即使在雪最多的地方，据他们说也冻得很硬，人和马通行是不成问题的。

于是我们就把那位向导找了来。他对我们说，他愿意从原路把我们带过去，不会遇到大雪的阻碍，但我们必须多带武器，防备野兽的袭击，因为，他说，大雪过后，经常有些狼在山脚下出没。因为遍地大雪，它们找不到食物，已经饿慌了。我们告诉他，我们对狼这一类野兽已有充分的准备；不过他是否能保证我们不会遇到两条腿的狼，因为，我们听说，这一地区十分危险，经常会受到强人的抢劫，尤其是在法国境内。

他答复我们说，走这条路绝没有这种危险。于是，我们马上同意跟他走。和我们一起赞同跟他走的还有十二位其他绅士带着他们的仆人，他们有的是法国人，也有西班牙人。这些人，就是我曾说过，那些试图过去但又被迫返回来

Accordingly, we all set Out from Pampeluna, with our Guide, on the fifteenth of November; and indeed, I was surpriz'd, when instead of going forward, he came directly back with us, on the same Road that we came from Madrid, above twenty Miles; when being pass'd two Rivers, and come into the plain Country, we found our selves in a warm Climate again, where the Country was pleasant, and no Snow to be seen; but on a sudden, turning to his left, he approach'd the Mountains another Way; and though it is true, the Hills and Precipices look'd dreadful, yet he made so many Tours, such Meanders, and led us by such winding Ways, that we were insensibly pass'd the Height of the Mountains, without being much incumbred with the Snow; and all on a sudden, he shew'd us the pleasant fruitful Provinces of Languedoc and Gascoign, all green and flourishing; tho' indeed it was at a great Distance, and we had some rough Way to pass yet.

We were a little uneasy however, when we found it snow'd one whole Day, and a Night, so fast, that we could not travel; but he bid us be easy, we should soon be past it all: We found indeed, that we began to descend every Day, and to come more North than before; and so depending upon our Guide, we went on.

It was about two Hours before Night, when our Guide being something before us, and not just in Sight, out rushed three monstrous Wolves, and after them a Bear, out of a hollow Way, adjoyning to a thick Wood; two of the Wolves flew upon the Guide, and had he been half a Mile before us, he

的一帮人。

于是,我们便一起跟着向导,于十一月五日从潘普洛纳出发了。使我吃惊的是,向导并没有带着我们向前走,而是带着我们径直返回了从马德里出来的那条路上,一直走了有二十英里。穿越两条河后,我们进入了一个平原地带,天气也温和起来。这儿非但看不到雪,而且完全是一派风和日暖的田野风光;但突然他往左一拐,从另一条路线进了山;这一路上虽说山势高峻,峭壁陡立,看来地形险恶,但是他左转右转、绕来绕去地盘旋而行,我们竟然在不知不觉中过了山脊,而且也没有碰到大雪封路的情况;突然他把手向远处一指,叫我们看那明媚又丰饶的朗格多克和加斯科涅地区,只见那是一片葱绿茂盛的景象,只是距离还远,得走好一程崎岖难行的路才能到达。

但我们开始有些不安了,因为我们碰上了坏天气,纷飞的大雪整整下了一天一夜,又不能上路了;然而他叫我们别急,说是坏天气很快就会过去的。我们果然一天一天地往平地走,并且向北开进了许多。就这样,我们在向导的带领下,继续前进。

一天,离天黑还有两个小时的时候,我们的向导正好走到我们前面去了。他时隐时现地在前面走着。突然,从密林后面的空谷里冲出三只硕大的饿狼,紧跟着的是一只黑

— 370 —

had been devour'd indeed, before we could have help'd him: One of them fastned upon his Horse, and the other attack'd the Man with that Violence, that he had not Time, or not Presence of Mind enough to draw his Pistol, but hollow'd and cry'd out to us most lustily; my Man Friday being next me, I bid him ride up, and see what was the Matter; as soon as Friday came in Sight of the Man, he hollow'd as loud as t'other, O Master! O Master! But like a bold Fellow, rode directly up to the poor Man, and with his Pistol shot the Wolf that attack'd him into the Head.

It was happy for the poor Man, that it was my Man Friday; for he having been us'd to that kind of Creature in his Country, had no Fear upon him; but went close up to him, and shot him as above; whereas any of us, would have fir'd at a farther Distance, and have perhaps either miss'd the Wolf, or endanger'd shooting the Man.

But it was enough to have terrify'd a bolder Man than I, and indeed it alarm'd all our Company, when with the Noise of Friday's Pistol, we heard on both Sides the dismallest Howling of Wolves, and the Noise redoubled by the Eccho of the Mountains, that it was to us as if there had been a prodigious Multitude of them; and perhaps indeed there was not such a Few, as that we had

熊。其中两只狼朝我们的向导飞扑过去。要是他离我们有半英里的路程,我们就来不及救他,他就会被狼吃掉。且说其中一只狼已经死死咬住了他的马,另一只已向他猛扑过去。他一方面因为来不及,另一方面因为慌了手脚,竟没有拔出手枪,而是向我们这边拼命地喊。这时,我的仆人星期五正走在我的旁边,我便叫他赶快骑到前面去看看到底发生了什么事。他一见到向导的危急情况,也立刻高喊起来:"主人!主人!"不过,星期五到底是条勇敢的汉子,立即毫不犹豫地拍马冲到可怜的向导那儿,举起枪对准狼的脑门,一枪就要了那畜牲的性命。

可怜的向导能得到星期五的救助,真是运气不坏。早在家乡时,星期五他们与野兽打交道就已是习以为常的事,所以一点也不胆怯。他能够泰然自若地走到狼的眼皮子底下,对准狼的脑门再开枪。如果换了我们,肯定谁也不敢靠狼那么近才开枪。而在远处开枪,那就难免会出现要么打不中狼,要么击中自己人的可怕后果。

就是叫一个胆子比我大的人碰到这种情形,也要给吓得魂不附体。老实说,我们整个旅行团都吓坏了,因为紧跟着星期五的枪声一响,我们就听见两边的狼群发出一片最凄惨的嚎叫,这种声音又被山里的回声加以扩大,就仿佛有

no cause of Apprehensions.

However, as Friday had kill'd this Wolf, the other that had fastned upon the Horse, left him immediately, and fled; having happily fastned upon his Head, where the Bosses of the Bridle had stuck in his Teeth; so that he had not done him much Hurt: The Man indeed was most Hurt; for the raging Creature had bit him twice, once on the Arm, and the other Time a little above his Knee; and he was just as it were tumbling down by the Disorder of his Horse, when Friday came up and shot the Wolf.

It is easy to suppose, that at the Noise of Friday's Pistol, we all mended our Pace, and rid up as fast as the Way (which was very difficult) would give us leave, to see what was the Matter; as soon as we came clear of the Trees, which blinded us before, we saw clearly what had been the Case, and how Friday had disengag'd the poor Guide; though we did not presently discern what kind of Creature it was he had kill'd.

But never was a Fight manag'd so hardily, and in such a surprizing Manner, as that which follow'd between Friday and the Bear, which gave us all (though at first we were surpriz'd and afraid for him) the greatest Diversion imaginable: As the Bear is a heavy, clumsey Creature, and does not gallop as the Wolf does, who is swift, and light; so he has two particular Qualities, which generally are the Rule of his Actions; First, As to Men, who are not his proper Prey; I say, not his proper Prey; because tho' I cannot say what excessive Hunger might do, which was now their Case, the Ground being all cover'd with Snow; but as to Men, he does not usually attempt them, unless

成千上万只狼似的,说不定真的不止来了这么微不足道的几只呢。

星期五把这一只打死之后,另外一只本来正紧紧地咬住马不放,登时也松了嘴逃走了。幸亏它咬住的是马头,马勒头上的铁圈刚好卡住了它的牙,马没有受什么大伤。可是向导受的伤可不轻,因为那只激怒的野兽一共咬了他两口,一口咬在他的膀子上,一口咬在他的膝盖上,而且,当星期五跑过去把狼打死的时候,他那匹受惊的马几乎把他摔下马来。

不用说,一听到星期五的枪声,我们立即催马向前。尽管道路很难走,我们还是快马加鞭,想看看前面到底发生了什么情况。我们一转出挡住视线的小树林,就把情况看得一清二楚,并亲眼看到星期五怎样救了那位可怜的向导,但当时我们还看不清楚他打死的究竟是只什么野兽。

紧接着,星期五和那只大熊之间展开了一场最大胆、最惊人的大战。这场大战起初确实使我们胆战心惊,最后却使大家开怀大笑。熊的身体笨重,行动蹒跚,跑起来当然没有狼那样轻快。因此,他的行动有两个特点。第一,对人来说,他一般不把人当作猎食的对象;当然,像现在这样大雪遍地,极端饥饿的时候,这笨拙的大家伙是否也会吃人,那就很难说了。但一般情况下,除非人们先向它进攻,它

— 372 —

they first attack him: On the contrary, if you meet him in the Woods, if you don't meddle with him, he won't meddle with you; but then you must take Care to be very Civil to him, and give him the Road; for he is a very nice Gentleman, he won't go a Step out of his Way for a Prince; nay, if you are really afraid, your best way is to look another Way, and keep going on; for sometimes if you stop, and stand still, and look steadily at him, he takes it for an Affront; but if you throw or toss any Thing at him, and it hits him, though it were but a bit of a Stick, as big as your Finger, he takes it for an Affront, and sets all his other Business aside to pursue his Revenge; for he will have Satisfaction in Point of Honour; that is his first Quality: The next is, That if he be once affronted, he will never leave you, Night or Day, till he has his Revenge; but follows at a good round rate, till he overtakes you.

My Man Friday had deliver'd our Guide, and when we came up to him, he was helping him off from his Horse; for the Man was both hurt and frighted, and indeed, the last more than the first; when on the sudden, we spy'd the Bear come Out Of the Wood, and a vast monstrous One it was, the biggest by far that ever I saw: We were all a little surpriz'd, when we saw him; but when Friday saw him, it was easy to see Joy and Courage in the Fellow's Countenance; O! O! O! Says Friday, three Times, pointing to him; O Master, You give me te Leave! Me shakee te Hand mith him: Me make you good laugh.

I was surpriz'd to see the Fellow so pleas'd; You Fool you, says I, he mill eat you up: Eatee me up! Eatee me up! Says Friday, twice over again; Me eatee him up: Me make you good laugh: You

是不会先攻击人们的。相反，如果你在树林里遇到它，如果你不去招惹它，它是不会惹你的。但这时你必须注意要对它谦恭有礼，给它让路。因为它是一位很挑剔的绅士，就是王子过来，它也不会让开一步的。不仅如此，如果你真的害怕，最好的办法就是眼望别处，继续走你的路。因为如果你有时停住，站在原地，盯着它看，它会认为这是一种侮辱，并把别的一切置之不理，来达到它报仇的目的，只有挽回了面子，它才会满意。这是它的第一个特点。它的第二个特点是，一旦受到侮辱，它就会不分白天黑夜地跟着你。即使你绕上许多路，它也要抓住你，直到报仇为止。

我的仆人星期五使向导脱了险；我们来到他们跟前时，他正在扶向导上马，因为向导受了伤又受了惊，而且受惊的程度比受伤的程度还要重些；正在这时，我们忽然看见那只熊走出树林，真是好一个庞然大物，我一辈子还没见过这么大的熊呢。一见到它，我们大家都不免有些吃惊，但星期五上脸上露出兴高采烈和精神抖擞的样子。"哦！哦！哦！"星期五指着熊，连叫了三声，"哦，主人！你给我个答应！我要同它握握手。我要叫你们笑个够。"

看到这家伙这么高兴，我感到奇怪。"你呀，你这个傻瓜，"我说道，"他会把你吃掉的。""吃掉我？吃掉我？"星期

all stay here, me show you good laugh; so down he sits, and gets his Boots off in a Moment, and put on a Pair of Pumps (as we call the flat Shoes they wear) and which he had in his Pocket, gives my other Servant his Horse, and with his Gun away he flew swift like the Wind.

The Bear was walking softly on, and offer'd to meddle with no Body, till Friday coming pretty near, calls to him, as if the Bear could understand him; Hark ye, hark ye, says Friday, me speakee wit your: We follow'd at a Distance; for now being come down on the Gascoign side of the Mountains, we were entred a vast great Forest, where the Country was plain, and pretty open, though many Trees in it scatter'd here and there.

Friday, who had as we say, the Heels of the Bear, came up with him quickly, and takes up a great Stone, and throws at him, and hit him just on the Head; but did him no more harm, than if he had thrown it against a Wall; but it answer'd Friday's End; for the Rogue was so void of Fear, that he did it purely to make the Bear follow him, and show us some Laugh as he call'd it.

As soon as the Bear felt the Stone, and saw him, he turns about, and comes after him, taking Devilish long Strides, and shuffling along at a strange Rate, so as would have put a Horse to a midling Gallop; away runs Friday, and takes his Course, as if he run towards us for Help; so we all resolv'd to fire at once upon the Bear, and deliver

五连说了两遍。"我吃掉它。我要让大家笑个够。你们都呆在这里别动,我要让诸位看个笑话!"说完,他便往地上一坐,转眼就把靴子脱了下来,从口袋里拿出一双便鞋,(就是我们所说的那种平底鞋)穿上,又把它的马交给我的另一个仆人,然后便拿着他的枪,一阵风似地飞快地跑了过去。

那头熊正悠哉悠哉地向前走着,并不想搭理任何人。星期五却走上前去,对它叫喊,就好像黑熊能听明白他的话似的。"你给我听着,你给我听着,"星期五说,"我正和你说话呢。"我们都远远地跟着。这时,我们已经来到了加斯科涅这一边的山区,已经进了一座浩翰的森林,这里的地势既平坦又开阔,树木却长得遍地都是。

星期五快速地靠近了大熊,拾起一块大石头朝它扔过去,刚好打中熊的脑袋。其实,对于熊来说,这石块打在它身上跟打在一堵墙上没什么两样,一点皮毛也伤不着,可是星期五却达到了自己的目的。这小子真是天不怕地不怕,摆明了是要挑逗熊来追赶他,好让我们像他说的那样"笑个够"。

大熊感觉到有石头打它,同时又看见了星期五,便立刻调转身向星期五追来。它甩着大步,摇摇摆摆,竟然走得飞快,快得差不多和马的碎步小跑一样。星期五见状也撒腿跑了起来,好像是向我们这

my Man; though I was angry at him heartily, for bringing the Bear back upon us, when he was going about his own Business another Way; and especially I was angry that he had turn'd the Bear upon us, and then run away; and I call'd out, You Dog, said I, is this your making us laugh? Come away, and take your Horse, that me may shoot the Creature; he hears me, and crys Out, No shoot, no shoot, stand still, you get much Laugh. And as the nimble Creature run two Foot for the Beast's one, he turn'd on a sudden, on one side of us, and seeing a great Oak-Tree, fit for his Purpose, he beckon'd to us to follow, and doubling his Pace, he gets nimbly up the Tree laying his Gun down upon the Ground, at about five or six Yards from the Bottom of the Tree.

The Bear soon came to the Tree, and we follow'd at a Distance; the first Thing he did, he stopp'd at the Gun, smelt to it, but let it lye, and up he scrambles into the Tree, climbing like a Cat, though so monstrously heavy: I was amazed at the Folly, as I thought it, of my Man, and could not for my Life see any Thing to laugh at yet, till seeing the Bear get up the Tree, we all rod nearer to him.

When we came to the Tree, there was Friday got out to the small End of a large Limb of the Tree, and the Bear got about half way to him; as soon as the Bear got out to that part where the Limb of the Tree was weaker, Ha, says he to us, now you see me teachee the Bear dance; so he falls

边跑来求援似的。于是大家准备立刻开枪,好救助我的仆人。我这时对星期五感到十分气恼,熊原本好端端地走它自己的路,可这小子却偏偏要去惹它;更让我来火的是,他把熊引到了我们这边,自己却跑掉了。于是我高声叫道:"你这狗东西,你是这样叫我们笑吗?赶快走开,把你的马牵过去,好让我们把这东西打死。"他听见我的声音,就大声叫道:"别开枪!别开枪!站住不要动,你们有笑话看。"他生就一双飞毛腿,他跑两步熊才能跑一步,突然之间,他掉转身子,从我们旁边跑开了,看见那边有一棵大橡树正合他的需要,就向我们招手,叫我们跟上去,一面把脚步加速,把他的枪放在离树根大约五六码的地上,很敏捷地爬上了树。

那只熊转眼之间也来到树下,我们远远地跟了上去。它首先在那杆枪前面停下来,把它闻了闻,并不去动它,跟着就往树上爬,爬得像猫一样敏捷,虽然它的身子又大又重。我对星期五的这种愚蠢行为深为惊愕,一点也看不出有什么好笑的地方。我们看到熊已经上了树,就一起策马向前。

当我们来到大树跟前时,星期五已爬到一根树枝的枝梢上,那根树枝长长地向外伸展着。这时,大熊也上了那树枝。它沿着树枝向外爬,越向外爬,树枝就越细越软。"哈,"

a jumping and shaking the Bough, at which the Bear began to totter, but stood still, and begun to look behind him, to see how he should get back; then indeed we did laugh heartily: But Friday had not done with him by a great deal; when he sees him stand still, he calls out to him again, as if he had suppos'd the Bear could speak English; What you no come farther, pray you come farther; so he left jumping and shaking the Tree; and the Bear, just as if he had understood what he said, did come a little further, then he fell a jumping again, and the Bear stopp'd again.

We thought now was a good time to knock him on the Head, and I call'd to Friday to stand still, and we would shoot the Bear; but he cry'd out earnestly, O pray! O pray! No shoot, me shoot, by and then; he would have said, By and by: However, to shorten the Story, Friday danc'd so much, and the Bear Stood so ticklish, that we had laughing enough indeed, but still could not imagine what the Fellow would do; for first we thought he depended upon shaking the Bear off; and we found the Bear was too cunning for that too; for he would not go out far enough to be thrown down, but clings fast with his great broad Claws and Feet, so that we could not imagine what would be the End of it, and where the Jest would be at last.

But Friday put us out of doubt quickly; for seeing the Bear cling fast to the Bough, and that he would not be persuaded to come any farther;

星期五对我们说,"现在你们看我教熊跳舞。"于是他在那树枝上大跳大摇,弄得那熊摇摇欲坠,只好站住不动,并开始往后回顾,看看怎样才能爬回去。我们看到这样子,果然都开怀大笑起来。但星期五玩熊才刚刚开个头呢。他看到那熊站着不动了,就又去招呼它,仿佛相信熊也能讲英语似的。"嗨,怎么啦! 你不过来了? 请你再朝前走吧!"于是,他不再摇摆树枝了。那只大熊仿佛听懂了他的话似的,果真又向前靠了一点。然后星期五又开始跳动,那只熊又站住了。

我们都认为这是个好机会,可以往它的头上开一枪。于是,我便喊星期五,让他站住,说我们要向大熊开枪了。不料,星期五却着急地喊道:"噢,求求你们,求求你们,不要开枪,等一会儿我来打死它。"简言之,星期五在树上跳够了,那只熊在上面东摇西晃的,让我们笑了个够,但我们却猜不出星期五究竟要怎么办。开始,我们都以为星期五要把熊摇下来,但我们又发现,这只熊也很狡猾,它生怕自己被摇晃下来,便再也不肯往前走,而且用它那又宽又大的爪子把树枝牢牢抓住。因此,我们想象不出这件事该怎样结束,这场玩笑最后结局如何。

但星期五很快就给我们解开了这个谜;他一看熊紧紧地抓着树枝不动,不管怎么

Well, well, says Friday, you no come farther, me go, me go; you no come to me, me go come to you; and upon this, he goes out to the smallest End of the Bough, where it would bend with his Weight, and gently lets himself down by it, sliding down the Bough, till he came near enough to jump down on his Feet, and away he run to his Gun, takes it up, and stands still.

Well, said I to him Friday, What will you do now? Why don't you shoot him? No shoot, says Friday, no yet, me shoot nom, me no kill; me stay, give you one more laugh; and indeed so he did, as you will see presently; for when the Bear see his Enemy gone, he comes back from the Bough where he stood; but did it mighty leisurely, looking behind him every Step, and coming backward till he got into the Body of the Tree; then with the same hinder End foremost, he came down the Tree, grasping it with his Claws, and moving one Foot at a Time, very leisurely; at this Juncture, and just before he could set his hind Feet upon the Ground, Friday stept up close to him, clapt the Muzzle of his Piece into his Ear, and shot him dead as a Stone.

Then the Rogue turn'd about, to see if we did not laugh, and when he saw we were pleas'd by our Looks, he falls a laughing himself very loud; so me kill Bear in my Country, says Friday; so you kill them, says I, Why you have no Guns:

No, says he, no Gun, but shoot, great much long Arrow.

This was indeed a good Diversion to us; but we were still in a wild Place, and our Guide very

哄，再也不肯往前挪动一步，便开口说道："好吧，好吧，你不过来，我过去，我过去；你不来找我，我去找你。"此话说罢，他便来到那树枝的顶尖上，让树枝因他的体重而慢慢弯下，他趁势滑落到离地很近时便往地上一跳，接着就跑去拿起他的枪，站在那儿不动。

"喂，"我对他叫道，"星期五，你现在要干什么？为什么不开枪打它？""不开枪，"星期五答道，"还不开；我现在要开，我不杀它；我等等，给你们再笑。"不一会儿，他果然这么做了，这一点你们马上就会看到；因为熊一看敌人已经离开，也就从它待着的树枝上往后退，不过每退一步都回头望望，退得不慌不忙，等退到了树干部分，还是照样把爪子紧紧地抓着树，屁股朝下一点一点地退下树来；就在它慢条斯理地刚让后脚着地时，星期五走到它边上，把枪口往它耳朵里一顶便开了枪，打得它像一块岩石似地倒毙在地。

然后，这个捣蛋鬼便转过身来，看看我们有没有笑。他从我们的表情看得出来，我们都很高兴。他自己也放声大笑起来。"我们那里的人就是这样打熊的。"星期五说。"你们就是这样打的吗？"我说，"你们不是没有枪吗？"

"是的"，他说，"是没有枪，我们用箭射，用很大很大的箭射。"

这确实让我们很开心。可是，我们仍处在荒野之中，

much hurt, and what to do we hardly knew; the Howling of Wolves run much in my Head; and indeed, except the Noise I once heard on the Shore of Africa, of which I have said something already, I never heard any thing that filled me with so much Horrour.

These things, and the Approach of Night, called us off, or else, as Friday would have had us, we should certainly have taken the Skin of this monstrous Creature off, which was which saving; but we had three Leagues to go, and our Guide hasten'd us, so we left him, and went forward on our Journey.

The Ground was still cover'd with Snow, tho' not so deep and dangerous as on the Mountains, and the ravenous Creatures, as we heard afterwards, were come down into the Forest and plain Country, press'd by Hunger to seek for Food; and had done a great deal of Mischief in the Villages, where they surpriz'd the Country People, kill'd a great many of their Sheep and Horses, and some People too.

We had one dangerous Place to pass, which our Guide told us, if there were any more Wolves in the Country, we should find them there; and this was in a small Plain, surrounded with Woods on every Side, and a long narrow Defile or Lane, which we were to pass to get through the Wood, and then we should come to the Village where we were to lodge.

It was within half an Hour of Sun-set when we entred the first Wood; and a little after Sun-set, when we came into the Plain. We met with nothing in the first Wood, except, that in a little Plain

而向导又受了重伤，我们简直不知道如何是好。刚才那阵饿狼的嗥叫仍在我的脑际回荡，老实说，除了我在非洲海岸听到的那种吼声，再没有什么声音比这狼嗥更让我感到害怕的了。

由于以上这些情况，再加上天也快黑了，我们不得不匆匆离开了此地。要不然，我们一定会按星期五的主张把那大熊的皮给剥下来，那张皮可是相当值钱的。但是我们前面还有九英里的路要赶，向导也一个劲地催着我们速速上路，我们只得丢下大熊，继续朝前赶路。

这里的地面上仍有积雪，却已远不如山里的雪那么深，那么危险了。我们后来听说，那些凶猛的野兽由于大雪天在山里找不到吃的，都饿急了，纷纷窜到山脚下的树林里和平原上来寻找食物。附近的村子都遭到了它们的袭击，被它们咬死叼走许多羊只和马匹，甚至还伤了一些人，弄得居民们都惊恐不安。

我们还要经过一个危险的地方。向导告诉我们，如果这一带还有狼的话，我们一定会在那里遇见。那地方是一片小小的平川，四面都是树林，要想穿过树林，必须穿过一条又长又窄的小路，然后才能到我们要宿夜的村子。

我们走进第一片树林时，离太阳落下去只有半个小时了；等到我们进入那片平川，太阳已经下去了。在第一片

within the Wood, which was not above two Fur-
longs over, we saw five great Wolves cross the
Road, full Speed one after another, as if they had
been in Chase of some Prey, and had it in View;
they took no Notice of us, and were gone, and out
of our Sight in a few Moments.

Upon this our Guide, who by the Way was a
wretched faint-hearted Fellow, bid us keep in a
ready Posture; for he believed there were more
Wolves a coming.

We kept our Arms ready, and our Eyes about
us, but we saw no more Wolves, 'till we came
thro' that Wood, which was near half a League,
and entred the Plain; as soon as we came into the
Plain, we had Occasion enough to look about us:
The first Object we met with, was a dead Horse;
that is to say, a poor Horse which the Wolves had
kill'd, and at least a Dozen of them at Work; we
could not say eating of him, but picking of his
Bones rather; for they had eaten up all the Flesh
before.

We did not think fit to disturb them at their
Feast, neither did they take much Notice of us:
Friday would have let fly at them, but I would not
suffer him by any Means; for I found we were like
to have more Business upon our Hands than we
were aware of. We were not gone half over the
Plain, but we began to hear the Wolves howl in
the Wood on our Left, in a frightful Manner, and
presently after we saw about a hundred coming on
directly towards us, all in a Body, and most of
them in a Line, as regularly as an Army drawn up
by experienc'd Officers. I scarce knew in what
Manner to receive them; but found to draw our
selves in a close Line was the only Way: so we

树林里,我们什么都没碰见,
只有在树林里一块二百来码
见方的空地上,看见有五条大
狼,一条跟一条,飞快地在路
上越过去,大概是在追赶一个
什么小动物,而那小动物就在
它们前面。它们根本没有理
会我们,不到一会儿工夫,就
不见踪影了。

我们的向导本来就是一
个胆小如鼠的人,他看到这情
景,就嘱咐我们早作准备,因
为他相信,一定会来更多的
狼。

我们手里紧握着枪,眼睛
紧盯着四面八方。可是在我
们穿过那座一英里多长的树
林,进入平川地以前,再也没
有看见过别的狼。等我们一
进入平川,向四下一望,头一
眼就见到一匹死马。这是一
匹被狼群咬死的马,同时见到
至少有十二条狼在那里大吃
特吃;其实,马肉早就给它们
吃光了,现在它们正在啃马骨
头呢。

我们感到不应该去打扰
它们的盛宴,何况它们也没有
注意我们。星期五本来想向
它们开枪,可是我怎么也不同
意。因为我感到,我们的麻烦
还在后面呢,尽管我们现在还
不知道。我们在那片平地里
还没有走出一半的路,便听到
我们左侧的树林里狼群的嗥
叫声,声音十分骇人。只一会
儿,我们便看到约有上百只狼
向我们蜂拥扑来。大多数狼
都排成一行,十分整齐,就像
是一位有经验的指挥官所带

form'd in a Moment: But that we might not have too much Interval, I order'd, that only every other Man should fire, and that the others who had not fir'd should stand ready to give them a second Volley immediately, if they continued to advance upon us, and that then those who had fir'd at first, should not pretend to load their Fusees again, but stand ready with every one a Pistol; for we were all arm'd with a Fusee, and a Pair of Pistols each Man; so we were by this Method able to fire six Volleys, half of us at a Time; however, at present we had no Necessity; for upon firing the first Volley, the Enemy made a full Stop, being terrify'd as well with the Noise, as with the Fire; four of them being shot into the Head, dropp'd, several others were wounded, and went bleeding off, as we could see by the Snow: I found they stopp'd, but did not immediately retreat; whereupon remembring that I had been told, that the fiercest Creatures were terrify'd at the Voice of a Man, I caus'd all our Company to hollow as loud as we could; and I found the Notion not altogether mistaken; for upon our Shout, they began to retire, and turn about; then I order'd a second Volley to be fir'd, in their Rear, which put them to the Gallop, and away they went to the Woods.

This gave us leisure to charge our Pieces again, and that we might loose no Time, we kept going; but we had but little more than loaded our Fusees,

领的部队。我真不知该怎样去对付它们。但终究觉得我们自己也应该聚拢起来排成一行才是唯一的办法。于是,我们立刻这样做了。为了使火力不致于中断太久,我下令只许一半的人开枪,另一半不开枪的人则站在那里做好准备,如果它们继续向我们冲过来,就立刻给它们第二排枪。同时,那些第一排开枪的人,不要急于去装他们的长枪,而是拿好各自的手枪,站在那里做好准备。因为我们每个人身上都带了一杆长枪,两把手枪。用这种办法,我们可以连续开六排枪,每次有一半的人开枪。其实,目前我们还没有这样做的必要。因为第一排枪放出以后,狼群便停下了,因为他们被枪声和火光吓坏了。其中四只狼脑袋中弹后倒毙在地,另几只狼受了伤,淌着血跑掉了,这在雪地上可以看得很清楚。我看到它们都收住了脚步,却没有立即后退,就想起了人家告诉过我的一句话:哪怕是最凶猛的野兽,听见人的声音也会害怕的;于是我叫大家一起尽量大声喊叫;我发现那说法并非无稽之谈,因为我们这么一叫,那些狼便开始后退并转身就跑;这时我下令朝它们后面放第二排枪,这下子打得它们狂奔起来,转眼都钻进树林里去了。

这刚好让我们有时间给枪支装火药。为了不耽误时间,我们又继续前进。可是,我

and put our selves into a Readiness, when we heard a terrible Noise in the same Wood, on our Left, only that it was farther onward the same Way we were to go.

The Night was coming on, and the Light began to be dusky, which made it worse on our Side; but the Noise encreasing, we could easily perceive that it was the Howling and Yelling of those hellish Creatures; and on a sudden, we perceiv'd 2 or 3 Troops of Wolves, one on our Left, one behind us, and one on our Front; so that we seem'd to be surrounded with 'em; however, as they did not fall upon us, we kept our Way forward, as fast as we could make Our Horses go, which the Way being very rough, was only a good large Trot; and in this Manner we came in View of the Entrance of a Wood, through which we were to pass, at the farther Side of the Plain; but we were greatly surpriz'd, when coming nearer the Lane, or Pass, we saw a confus'd Number of Wolves standing just at the Entrance.

On a sudden, at another opening of the Wood, we heard the Noise of a Gun; and looking that Way, out rush'd a Horse, with a Saddle, and a Bridle on him, flying like the Wind, and sixteen or seventeen Wolves after him, full Speed; indeed, the Horse had the Heels of them; but as we suppos'd that he could not hold it at that rate, we doubted not but they would get up with him at last, and no question but they did.

们刚把长枪装好,作好了准备,就听见一阵恐惧的嗥叫又从我们左边的那片树林里传了出来,所不一样的是,这叫声是在我们所走的这条路的更前方。

夜晚就要降临了,周围渐渐暗了下来,这使我们的处境更加艰难。嗥叫声却越来越响,不难听出,这就是那样魔鬼般的野兽发出的嗥叫与狂吼。就在这时,在我们的周围突然出现了三群狼。一群在我们左边,一群在我们后边,还有一群在我们前面,我们好像是被它们包围了。不过,很侥幸,狼群并没有向我们发起进攻,我们便赶紧扬鞭策马尽快地向前跑去。可是崎岖的山路实在太难走了,马只能碎步小跑地朝前行进。我们就这样来到了一片树林的入口处。现在只要穿过这片树林,我们就能走出这片平川到达村庄了。可就在我们走近那条林间小道时,我们全都大吃一惊,只见路边站满了恶狼,黑压压的一片,数都数不清。

突然之间,在树林的另外一个口子上,我们听见一声枪响。我们向那边一看,只见一匹鞍勒俱全的马从里面冲了出来,一阵风似地朝前急驰,同时有十六七只狼,飞快地在后面追着。看起来,那匹马比它们跑得快得多,把它们远远地抛在后面,可是据我们估计,那匹马是支持不了多么久的,最后毫无疑问会被它们追上。

But here we had a most horrible Sight; for riding up to the Entrance where the Horse came out, we found the Carcass of another Horse, and of two Men, devour'd by the ravenous Creatures, and one of the Men was no doubt the same who we heard fir'd the Gun; for there lay a Gun just by him, fir'd off; but as to the Man, his Head, and the upper Part of his Body was eaten up.

This fill'd us with Horror, and we knew not what Course to take, but the Creatures resolv'd us' soon; for they gather'd about us presently, in hopes of Prey; and I verily believe there were three hundred of them: It happen'd very much to our Advantage, that at the Entrance into the Wood, but a little Way from it, there lay some large Timber Trees, which had been cut down the Summer before, and I Suppose lay there for Carriage; I drew my little Troop in among those Trees, and placing our selves in a Line, behind one long Tree, I advis'd them all to light, and keeping that Tree before us, for a Breast Work, to stand in a Triangle, or three Fronts, enclosing Our Horses in the Center.

We did so, and it was well we did; for never was a more furious Charge than the Creatures made upon us in the Place; they came on us with a growling kind of a Noise (and mounted the Piece of Timber, which as I said, was our Breast Work) as if they were only rushing upon their Prey; and this Fury of theirs, it seems, was principally occasion'd by their seeing our Horses behind us, which was the Prey they aim'd at: I order'd our Men to fire as before, every other Man; and they took their Aim so sure, that indeed they kill'd several of the Wolves at the first Volley; but there was a Necessity to keep a continual Firing; for they came on like Devils, those behind pushing on those before.

正当此时,我们又看到了一幅可怕的景象。当我们催马走近那匹马奔出来的路口时,见到了一匹马和两个人的尸骸,毫无疑问是被狼咬死吃掉的。其中一个人身边还丢着一支枪,枪是放过的,所以一定就是刚才开枪的人。现在,他的头和上半身都已被狼吃掉了。

看到这副惨状,我们都不禁心惊肉跳,不知如何是好。但那群野兽不久就逼得我们不得不采取行动。这时,狼群已把我们包围,想以我们一行人马果腹。我相信,一共有三百来只。所幸的是,在距树林入口不远处,堆放着一大批木料,我猜测是夏天砍伐下来准备运走的。我把我的小部队带到那堆木料后边,我们在一根长木后边排成一行,都身在明处,用木料当作胸墙,站成三角形或三面环绕的阵线,把我们的马围在中间。

我们这样做了,也幸好这么做了。因为这一带的狼从未像这一次一样如此不顾死活地往上冲。它们嗷嗷乱叫地跃上我们当作胸墙的木料,扑向自己的猎物。它们之所以这样疯狂,大概主要是因为看到了我们身后的马,马是它们捕猎的对象。我命令我的人照以前那样每隔一人开枪,他们瞄得很准,每一排枪就杀死好几只狼。但是,只有连续开枪才有用,这些狼像魔鬼似地前仆后继,后面的推着前面的往前冲。

When we had fir'd our second Volley of our Fusees, we thought they stopp'd a little, and hop'd they would have gone off; but it was but a Moment; for others came forward again; so we fir'd two Volleys of our Pistols, and I believe in these four Firings, we had kill'd seventeen or eighteen of them, and lam'd twice as many; yet they came on again.

I was loath to spend our last Shot too hastily; so I call'd my Servant, not my Man Friday, for he was better employ'd; for with the greatest Dexterity imaginable, he had charg'd my Fusee, and his own, while we were engag'd; but as I said, I call'd my other Man, and giving him a Horn of Powder, I bad him lay a Train, all along the Piece of Timber, and let it be a large Train; he did so, and had but just Time to get away, when the Wolves came up to it, and some were got up upon it; when I snapping an uncharg'd Pistol, close to the Powder, set it on fire; those that were upon the Timber were scorcht with it, and six or seven of them fell, or rather jump'd in among us, with the Force and Fright of the Fire; we dispatch'd these in an Instant, and the rest were so frighted with the Light, which the Night, for it was now very near Dark, made more terrible, that they drew back a little.

Upon which I order'd our last Pistol to be fir'd off in one Volley, and after that we gave a Shout; upon this, the Wolves turn'd Tail, and we sally'd immediately upon near twenty lame Ones, who we

我们用长枪作了第二次齐射以后，觉得它们略略停了一下，这时我希望它们会就此跑开；但只是转眼的工夫，别的狼又冲来了，于是我们用手枪作了两次齐射；我相信，在这四次齐射中，我们击毙了十七八只狼，打伤的数目则是此数目的两倍；但它们还是在冲过来。

我们只能再打一次排枪了，我不愿让这一枪很快就打掉，便叫来我的仆人，不是星期五，他得做更要紧的事，因为他极其灵活，可以在我们忙着打狼的同时，抽空给我和给他自己的长枪重装弹药；我叫来另一名仆人后，把装在空牛角里的火药给了他一筒，要他沿那根大树撒上一道火药，而且要撒得宽一些、多一些；他便奉命做了。他刚完成任务返回，那些狼便扑到了火药带跟前，其中有些已经踩上了火药。这时，我用一支没有装药的手枪凑上去一扣，就把火药带打着了。那些爬上木材的家伙，身上都着了火。由于爆炸的冲击力，再加上它们对火光的害怕，其中有六七个倒下了，有几只跳到了我们当中，这几只很快就被我们解决了。而其余那些都被火光吓得魂飞魄散，朝后退了一段，因为这时天几乎黑了，它们看到火光便更加害怕。

我一鼓作气，命令所有的人用最后一支还没放过的手枪一齐开火。放完枪，我们又齐声呐喊起来，这才使狼群掉

found struggling on the Ground, and fell a cutting them with our Swords, which answer'd our Expectation; for the Crying and Howling they made, was better understood by their Fellows, so that they all fled and left us.

We had, first and last, kill'd about three Score of them; and had it been Day-Light, we had kill'd many more: The Field of Battle being thus clear'd, we made forward again; for we had still near a League to go. We heard the ravenous Creatures houl and yell in the Woods as we went, several Times; and sometimes we fancy'd we saw some of them, but the Snow dazling our Eyes, we were not certain; so in about an Hour more, we came to the Town, where we were to lodge, which we found in a terrible Fright, and all in Arms; for it seems, that the Night before, the Wolves and some Bears had broke into the Village in the Night, and put them in a terrible Fright, and they were oblig'd to keep Guard Night and Day, but especially in the Night, to preserve their Cattle, and indeed their People.

The next Morning our Guide was so ill, and his Limbs swell'd with the rankling of his two Wounds, that he could go no farther; so we were oblig'd to take a new Guide there, and go to Tholouse, where we found a warm Climate, a fruitful pleasant Country, and no Snow, no Wolves, or any Thing like them; but when we told our Story at Tholouse, they told us it was nothing but what was ordinary in the great Forest at the Foot of the Mountains, especially when the Snow lay on the Ground: But they enquir'd much what kind of a Guide we had gotten, that would

转了尾巴。我们抓住时机,立刻冲到还在地上挣扎着的二十多条受伤的狼跟前,举起刀一阵砍杀。这个做法果真达到了我们预想的效果。被我们砍杀的伤狼发出了一阵阵凄惨的哀嚎声,使得它们的同伴情知不妙,统统逃之夭夭了。

我们从头至尾打死了六十多条狼;如果是在白天,我们打死的一定还要多。我们肃清了敌人,就继续前进;因为我们还要赶三英里的路。我们一边走着,有好几次听见它们在森林里嚎叫咆哮,有时仿佛还看到几只,不过因为我们的眼睛被雪光照花了,所以不敢十分肯定。又过了半个小时,我们才到了我们要过夜的那个城镇;只见全镇恐惧异常,人人手中都拿着枪械;因为,据说,头天晚上曾经有不少的狼和少数的熊,侵入了村子,把人们吓坏了,只好昼夜不停地(特别是在夜间)严加把守,不仅为了保全牲畜,也为了保全居民。

到了第二天早晨,我们那向导的两处伤口溃烂得很厉害,四肢也肿了起来,病得很重,根本无法上路。于是,我们只好从当地又找了一位新向导,带我们到达土鲁斯。那里气候温暖,物产丰饶,没有积雪,也没有狼之类的野兽。当我们把我们的经历讲给土鲁斯当地人听的时候,他们告诉我们,这在山脚下的大森林里,尤其是积雪覆盖地面时,

venture to bring us that Way in such a severe Season; and told us, it was very much' we were not all devour'd. When we told them how we plac'd our selves, and the Horses in the Middle, they blam'd us exceedingly, and told us it was fifty to one but we had been all destroy'd; for it was the Sight of the Horses which made the Wolves so furious, Seeing their Prey; and that at other Times they are really afraid of a Gun; but the being excessive Hungry, and raging on that Account, the Eagerness to come at the Horses had made them sensless of Danger; and that if we had not by the continu'd Fire, and at last by the Stratagem of the Train of Powder, master'd them, it had been great Odds but that we had been torn to Pieces; whereas had we been content to have sat still on Horseback, and fir'd as Horsemen, they would not have taken the Horses for so much their own, when Men were on their Backs, as otherwise; and withal they told us, that at last, if we had stood altogether, and left our Horses, they would have been so eager to have devour'd them, that we might have come off safe, especially having our Fire Arms in our Hands, and being so many in Number.

For my Part, I was never so sensible of Danger in my Life; for seeing above three hundred Devils come roaring and open mouth'd to devour us, and having nothing to shelter us, or retreat to, I gave my self over for lost; and as was, I believe, I shall never care to cross those Mountains again; I think I would much rather go a thousand Leagues by Sea, though I were sure to meet with a Storm once a Week.

这种情况是很平常的。他们多次询问我们究竟找了一位什么样的向导,敢在这样严寒的季节带我们冒险走这条路。还说我们总算幸运,没有被狼吞掉。当我们告诉他们我们怎样布阵,怎样把马匹挡在中间时,他们对我们大大责备了一番,说我们没有被狼吃掉,真是万幸。因为那些狼是由于看到了马匹,看见了它们的口中美餐,所以才那样凶狠的,而一般情况下,它们是很怕开枪的。它们一方面饿极了,饿得发狂,另一方面又急于捉马,以致于不顾危险地往前冲,要不是我们连续开火,后来又布置了一圈火网把它们压住,我们很有可能已被撕成碎片;如果我们坐在马背上不动,像骑兵那样朝它们开火,那么,它们看到马上有人,就不会把这些马看得同没人骑着的马一样,看作是它们的当然猎物;此外,他们还告诉我们说,到了最后关头,如果我们人都聚在一起,不再管我们的马,那么它们就会忙着去吃马,而我们就能安全地撤离,何况我们手里都有枪,人数又这么多。

对于我来说,我是第一次这么深切地感受到危险究竟是什么滋味。想想看:有三百多个魔鬼怒吼着向我们扑来,张着血盆大嘴要把我们吃掉,而我们既没处躲藏,又没有退路。当时,我真的以为完蛋了。我相信,我今后再也不想从那里的山区经过了;我宁可在海

I have nothing uncommon to take Notice of, in my Passage through France; nothing but what other Travellers have given an Account of, with much more Advantage than I can. I travell'd from Tholouse to Paris, and without any considerable Stay, came to Callais, and landed safe at Dover, the fourteenth of January, after having had a severely cold Season to travel in.

I was now come to the Center of my Travels, and had in a little Time all my new discover'd Estate safe about me, the Bills of Exchange which I brought with me having been very currently paid.

My principal Guide, and Privy Councellor, was my good antient Widow, who in Gratitude for the Money I had sent her, thought no Pains too much, or Care too great, to employ for me; and I trusted her so entirely with every Thing, that I was perfectly easy as to the Security of my Effects; and indeed, I was very happy from my Beginning, and now to the End, in the unspotted Integrity of this good Gentle-woman.

And now I began to think of leaving my Effects with this Woman, and setting out for Lisbon, and so to the Brasils; but now another Scruple came in my Way, and that was Religion; for as I had entertain'd some Doubts about the Roman Religion, even while I was abroad, especially in my State of Solitude; so I knew there was no going to the Brasils for me, much less going to settle there, unless I resolv'd to embrace the Roman Catholick Religion, without any Reserve; unless on the other hand, I resolv'd to be a Sacrifice to my Princi-

上走三千英里路,哪怕每礼拜都碰到一次大风暴,也不愿走这种陆路。

在法国境内的旅程,没有什么特别的事情可记,所遇之事,与其他旅行家已记载过的事大同小异,更何况他们记得要比我的好得多呢。我从土鲁斯到达巴黎后,一路上没有耽搁,直抵加来。在经历了一个最严寒冬季的旅行之后,于一月十四日平安渡过海峡到达了多佛尔。

现在我来到了我各次旅行的出发点或目的地;没花多少时间,我就把带在身边的那些汇票兑成了现款,这样我新近找回来的财产已实实在在地掌握在我手中。

那位年高德劭的孀妇是我最重要的导师,给我出过不少好主意;对于我送她的那笔钱,她深为感谢,觉得再怎么为我尽心尽力也是义不容辞的;而我也把自己的一切全都托付给她,一点也不为这些财产担心;对于这位一丝不苟、人品极好的老太太,我自始至终都感到非常满意。

我现在的打算是,把财产托付给这位太太保管以后,就出发去里斯本,再从那里去巴西。可是一想到去巴西,我就又产生了宗教方面的顾虑。在国外时,特别是荒岛上孤独生活的时候,我就对罗马天主教产生了怀疑,因此,我现在如果要去巴西,甚至要在那里定居的话,那我首先必须做出决定,是毫无保留地信奉天主

ples, be a Martyr for Religion, and die in the Inquisition; so I resolv'd to stay at Home, and if I could find Means for it, to dispose of my Plantation.

To this Purpose I wrote to my old Friend at Lisbon, who in Return gave me Notice, that he could easily dispose of it there: But that if I thought fit to give him Leave to offer it In my Name to the two Merchants, the Survivors of my Trustees, who liv'd in the Brasils, who must fully under + stand the Value of it, who liv'd just upon the Spot, and who I knew were very rich; so that he believ'd they would be fond of buying it; he did not doubt, but I should make 4 or 5000 Pieces Of Eight, the more of it.

Accordingly I agreed, gave him Order to offer it to them, and he did so; and in about 8 Months more, the Ship being then return'd, he sent me Account, that they had accepted the Offer, and had remitted 33000 Pieces Of Eight, to a Correspondent of theirs at Lisbon, to pay for it.

In Return, I sign'd the Instrument of Sale in the Form which they sent from Lisbon, and sent it to my old Man, who sent me Bills of Exchange for 32800 Pieces of Eight to me, for the Estate; reserving the Payment of 100 Moidores a Year to him, the old Man, during his Life, and 50 Moidores afterwards to his Son for his Life, which I had promised them, which the Plantation was to make good as a Rent-Charge. And thus I have given the first Part of a Life of Fortune and Adventure, a Life of Providence's Checquer-Work,

教呢，还是为自己的宗教思想作出牺牲，作一个殉教者，在宗教法庭上被判处死刑。因此，我决定住在本国，并且，如果有办法的话，把我的种植园卖掉。

抱定了这个宗旨，我写了一封信给我那位里斯本的老朋友。他回信通知我，他可以很容易地把它卖掉。但如果我同意让他把我卖产的意思通知那两位住在巴西的商人，也就是我那两位代理人的后代，他相信他们一定愿意买，并且毫无疑问可以多出四五千块葡萄牙金币，因为他们住在当地，必然知道我那份产业值多少钱，而且他们也有钱。

所以，他相信，他们一定会乐意买下来。他也毫不怀疑，我至少可以多卖四五千块葡萄牙金币。我同意让他通知他们。他也照办了。大约八个月之后，去巴西的那艘船又回到了里斯本。他写信告诉我，他们接受了我的卖价，并已经汇了三万三千块葡萄牙金币给他们在里斯本的代理人，嘱咐他照付。

我在他们从里斯本寄给我的卖契上签了字，并把契约寄回给在里斯本的我那位老朋友。接着，他便给我寄来了三万二千八百块葡币的汇票作为我产业的卖价。我便在老人家有生之年每年付给他一百块葡币，他死后，每年付给他儿子五十块葡币，作为种植园产业对他们的津贴。这都是我以前许诺他们的。这

and of a Variety which the World will seldom be able to show the like of: Beginning foolishly, but closing much more happily than any Part of it ever gave me Leave so much as to hope for.

Any one would think, that in this State of complicated good Fortune, I was past running any more Hazards; and so indeed I had been, if other Circumstances had concurr'd, but I was inur'd to a wandring Life, had no Family, not many Relations, nor however rich had I contracted much Acquaintance; and though I had sold my Estate in the Brasils, yet I could not keep the Country out of my Head, and had a great Mind to be upon the Wing again, especially I could not resist the strong Inclination I had to see my Island, and to' know if the poor Spaniards were in Being there, and how the Rogues I left there had used them.

My true Friend, the Widow, earnestly diswaded me from it, and so far prevail'd with me, that for almost seven Years she prevented my running Abroad; during which time, I took my two Nephews, the Children of one of my Brothers into my Care: The eldest having something of his own, I bred up as a Gentleman, and gave him a Settlement of some Addition to his Estate, after my Decease; the other I put out to a Captain of a Ship; and after five Years, finding him a sensible bold enterprising young Fellow, I put him into a good Ship, and sent him to Sea: And this young Fellow afterwards drew me in, as old as I was, to farther Adventures my self.

样,我便把我遭遇和冒险的第一部分讲完了。我的生活犹如上帝盛衰无常的杰作,变化万千,世间少有,虽然起初愚昧无知,但结局却比我所希望的要好许多。

人们会想,现在我鸿运高照,好事一齐来,我总不会再冒着危险出去闯荡了;是啊,要是换了一种情况,我确实会如此,但我已经闯荡惯了,既没有家室又没有几个亲属,而且虽说已很富裕,却也没结交很多朋友;再说,尽管我卖掉了巴西的产业,但心中还念念不忘那片地方,很想再去走一趟;尤其是我还有个无法抑制的强烈愿望,想去看看我的那个岛,看看那些可怜的西班牙人是否已来到岛上,看看我们留在那儿的恶棍们怎样对待他们。

我那真诚的朋友,那个寡妇,真心实意地劝我不要去,并真的把我劝住了。到现在为止,她已经一连七年劝阻我出门远游。在这段时间里,我把我的两个侄子(我的一个哥哥的孩子)带到我身边监护。大侄子自己本来有点财产,我把他培养成了一个上流社会的绅士。除了他本身有一份田产外,我又拨给他一些财产,等我死后再由他继承。另一个侄子,我把他送到一个船长那里去见习。五年之后,我发现他成长为一个懂道理、有胆量、有雄心的好青年。我又送他上了一条好船,让他去独立航海。后来,虽然我已经老

In the mean time, I in Part settled my self here; for first of all I marry'd, and that not either to my Disadvantage or Dissatisfaction, and had three Children, two Sons and one Daughter: But my Wife dying, and my Nephew coming Home with good Success from a Voyage to Spain, my Inclination to go Abroad, and his Importunity prevailed and engag'd me to go in his Ship, as a private Trader to the East Indies: This was in the Year 1694.

In this Voyage I visited my new Collony in the Island, saw my Successors the Spaniards, had the whole Story of their Lives, and of the Villains I left there; how at first they insulted the poor Spaniards, how they afterwards agreed, disagreed, united, separated, and how at last the Spaniards were oblig'd to use Violence with them, how they were subjected to the Spaniards, how honestly the Spaniards used them; a History, if it were entred into, as full of Variety and wonderful Accidents, as my own Part, particularly also as to their Battles with the Carribeans, who landed several times upon the Island, and as to the Improvement they made upon the Island it self, and how five of them made an Attempt upon the main Land, and brought away eleven Men and five Women Prisoners, by which, at my coming, I found about twenty young Children on the Island.

了,但这个年轻人却又把我拉上了新的冒险历程。

在英国居住的这几年里,我基本上算是安了家。我娶了妻,生了子。我的婚姻还算不错,没什么让我觉得特别不满意的地方。我有三个孩子,两个儿子和一个女儿。可是,妻子后来去世了。这时,恰逢我的侄子刚刚航海归来,他的西班牙之行非常成功,赚了一大笔钱。这又勾起了我对出海航游的强烈渴望,加上我的侄子也竭力劝我和他一起走,我就以一个私家客商的身份,乘他的船去了东印度群岛。这是一六九四年的事。

这次航行中,我回到了我那岛上的新殖民地,看到了我那些承继人,那批西班牙人,了解了他们的生活情况以及我留在那里的恶棍们的情况;知道他们起初怎样侮辱那批可怜的西班牙人;后来又怎样时而和好,时而不合,时而联合,时而分开;最后那批西班牙人怎样被迫用武力对付他们;以及他们怎样被那些西班牙人制服,那批西班牙人怎样公正地待他们。他们的这段经历如果写出来,也会像我自己的经历一样光怪陆离,变化多端,尤其是他们同加勒比人打仗的故事,更是惊险异常。那些加勒比土人曾三番五次地登上海岛。他们也谈到了岛上生产发展和生活改善情况,以及他们怎样派了五个人攻到大陆上去,掳来了十一个男人和五个女人。所以,当我

Here I stay'd about 20 Days, left them Supplies of all necessary things, and particularly of Arms, Powder, Shot, Cloaths, Tools, and two Work-men, which I brought from England with me, viz. a Carpenter and a Smith.

Besides this, I shar'd the Island into Parts with 'em, reserv'd to my self the Property of the whole, but gave them such Parts respectively as they agreed on; and having settled all things with them, and engaged them not to leave the Place, I left them there.

From thence I touch'd at the Brasils, from whence I sent a Bark, which I bought there, with more People to the Island, and in it, besides other Supplies, I sent seven Women, being such as I found proper for Service, or for Wives to such as would take them: As to the English Men, I promis'd them to send them some Women from England, with a good Cargoe of Necessaries, if they would apply themselves to Planting, which I afterwards perform'd. And the Fellows prov'd very honest and diligent after they were master'd, and had their Properties set apart for them. I sent them also from the Brasils five Cows, three of them being big with Calf, some Sheep, and some Hogs, which, when I came again, were consider-ably encreas'd.

But all these things, with an Account how 300 Caribbees came and invaded them, and ruin'd their Plantations, and how they fought with that whole

这次重访小岛时,那儿已经有了二十来个孩子。

我在岛上停留了二十来天,给他们留下了一些必需品,尤其是武器、火药、子弹、衣服、工具,以及我从英国带来的两个工人、一个木匠和一个铁匠。

另外,我把全岛的领土划分了一下,按照他们各自的意愿,把划分后的土地一一分配给他们,我自己则保留全岛的主权。我替他们把岛上的事情安置妥当之后,又再三叮嘱他们不要丢弃小岛,然后,我就离开了那里。

我从那里去了巴西,又从巴西给岛上送去了一条帆船。在那条船上,除了一些急用物资以外,又给他们送去了一些人,其中包括七个妇女。我想这些妇女到了岛上,可以替男人们洗衣做饭,操持家务。假如他们愿意的话,也可以娶她们做老婆。至于那三个英国人,我向他们作了保证,只要他们勤于耕种,就给他们从英国送几个女的来,并给他们运一大船生活必需品,我后来真的做到了。这三个家伙,在我把他们制服又给他们把财产分开后,日后都成了非常诚实勤勉的人。此外,我又从巴西给他们送去了五头母牛(其中三头已怀小牛)、一些小羊、一些猪。等我再到那里去的时候,它们已繁殖了很多。

除了这些事之外,还有这么件事:三百个加勒比土著来进犯他们,毁了他们的庄稼,

Number twice, and were at first defeated, and three of them kill'd; but at last a Storm destroying their Enemies Cannoes, they famish'd or destroy'd almost all the rest, and renew'd and recover'd the Possession of their Plantation, and still liv'd upon the Island.

All these things, with some very surprizing Incidents in some new Adventures of my own, for ten Years more, I may perhaps give a farther Account of hereafter.

他们两次同那大帮野人血战，起先是打败了，死了三个人；但后来一场风暴摧毁了这些敌人的独木舟，他们设法让其余的野人几乎全都饿死，从而收复并恢复了他们的庄园，至今还生活在那座小岛上。

所有这些事情，以及我个人以后十年间的惊人遭遇，我以后可能会再作记述。